KV-277-009

the ultimate gay guide

the
ultimate
GAY
guide

John Szponarski

First published in Great Britain in 1999 by
Absolute Press, Scarborough House, 29 James Street West,
Bath, BA1 2BT, England
T: 44 (0) 1225 316013 F: 44 (0) 1225 445836
E-mail: sales@absolutepress.demon.co.uk

Copyright © John Szponarski/Absolute Press 1999

All rights reserved. No part of this publication may be
reproduced, stored in a retrieval system or transmitted in
any form or by any means, electronic or otherwise,
without the prior permission of the copyright owner.

A catalogue record of this book is
available from the British Library

ISBN 1 899791 86 8

Photoset by Tradespools Ltd, Frome, Somerset
Cover printed by Devenish & Co., Bath, Somerset
Text printed by The Bath Press, Bath, Somerset

Typographic design by Philip Lewis
Maps by Map Creation Ltd
Cover design by Christine Leech

Acknowledgments

This book is dedicated to the thousands of people who devote their time and energy in order to make the lives of gay men and women more tolerable in a world of bias, ignorance and misunderstanding.

I would like to thank the following people and organisations for their invaluable help and grateful contribution towards the compilation of this book:

Mark Gavin, Manchester Gay Switchboard
Brenda Oakes, FFLAG
Mike Le Nell, Lifeline
Jamie Taylor, GMFA
Fen Coles, GALOP
David Hall (for research material)
Pamela Sexton
The Beaumont Society
The Northern Concord
Cross Talk
Terrence Higgins Trust
Healthy Gay Manchester
Health Education Authority
Millivres/Zipperstore (for book descriptions)
National Drugs Helpline
Manchester Law Centre

And a special and heartfelt thanks to Matthew Inwood (Absolute Press) for turning what was essentially a sow's ear into a glittering pink silk purse.

Contents

About This Guide

So why is this The *Ultimate* Gay Guide?
Perhaps because it includes the most extensive, detailed British gay scene listings ever published – both vast and groundbreaking in their content. Perhaps because it offers the most valuable resource directory there is – everything from who to talk to if you are unsure about coming out to where your nearest local HIV support group is based. From which gay-empathetic solicitor to contact to which shops cater for transvestite customers. From which hotelier might accommodate you and your gay partner to the most up-to-date gay press available (. . . I could go on). Perhaps, because it is unique, in that it offers *you*, the reader, the opportunity to contribute and update the next, bigger, more definitive edition.

But the simple answer? This is the most comprehensive gay guide ever published.

And it's extremely user-friendly. Great emphasis has been placed upon the user finding each of the venues listed – more than beneficial to the tourist and for those wishing to avoid the embarrassment/trepidation factor of asking for directions.

- A-Z references have been taken from either street plans or city guides and are included for many of the listings (many cruising grounds and locations fall outside the boundaries of most A-Z guides, thus, their locations have been further clarified by road names, numbers and/or landmarks). A complete listing of all the towns and cities with A-Z reference points and the guides that they have come from are listed within the 'Maps' section at the back of this book.

- Nearest landmarks are cited for most listings in order that you can ask anyone the whereabouts of the landmark and then be within walking distance of the gay venue.

- The nearest train station serves two purposes: the obvious one (should you be travelling by rail) and to act also as a location point for the car driver (many listings indicate how far you can further expect to travel from the station).

- The nearest tube references should enable you to network your way around London and Glasgow with relative ease.

- Each section of listings is broken down into London, England, Scotland and Wales, with each city/town listed alphabetically therein.

To enable you to source venues, there are two indexes at the back of this book. Index 1 lists all establishments (from the pubs/clubs, saunas and accommodation sections of this guide) by establishment or organiser/event name, directing you to the relevant page for each venue. If you do not know the name of the establishment or organiser, or, if you are wishing to explore a particular town or city at your leisure, then Index 2 lists all the cities and towns alphabetically, with every attributable venue and event listed under the city/town headings.

Maps are provided for the major cities (that is those with the greatest density of gay goings-on) and should help you to find your bearings before setting off on any cross-country jaunt. The key gay village areas are detailed with venues dotted onto the maps indicating where everything is.

And perhaps the most *user-friendly* aspect: the facilities and entertainment of and for each venue have, where they apply, been described in *full*, thus dispensing with the picture-icon format that other guides favour and the laborious task of cross-referencing to the back of the book to decipher every other paragraph.

This is a lucid and detailed (have I already mentioned unique?) guide which will enlighten, entertain and encourage almost everyone: man or woman; in or out of the closet; on this side or that side of the fence: scene queen or shrinking violet.

Should you have any suggestions on how to make future editions of *The Ultimate Gay Guide* more comprehensive and/or reader-friendly then please forward your thoughts using the contact details listed in the Introduction.

Foreword

Welcome to the first edition of The Ultimate Gay Guide, the main aim of which is to bring to you the most detailed resource directory of gay life in Britain . . . ever produced. It is written specifically with the assumption that you may have limited, or indeed no knowledge of the gay lifestyle. It aims to answer all your *initial* questions and doubts, although even the longest serving 'scene queen' will see something within these pages that they will find interesting.

As a first edition it does contain some other 'firsts'. More notably, it is the first guide ever published to list known 'gay cruising areas' in detail. It is also the first guidebook to detail *all* of the gay saunas throughout Britain (at the time of going to press), which in all probability could have warranted a separate edition in themselves. It is also the first gay guide to go beyond a concise information format and explain the venues in *extreme* detail. This should help reassure the person embarking out onto the gay scene for the first time. We've all been there, sitting in our car or walking up and down outside a gay venue wondering what lay behind those doors . . . trying to pluck up the courage to venture through those 'secret' portals for the first time (aahh! Memories . . .). Hopefully, this guide will enable you to realise that there is no real, significant difference between gay and straight venues, except that in a gay venue you can be who you are and meet the people you want to meet, without the constrictions of 'putting on a show' just to keep up appearances.

Throughout the guide I have tried to differentiate between 'exclusively gay' and 'gay-friendly' venues. There is still much debate amongst members of our community as to whether or not a 'mixed' venue works, and no doubt the debate will rage on for many years yet. In some places – more notably cities and the larger towns – the integration of gay and straight works very well, providing a unique atmosphere of tolerance and acceptance. 'Trade' in London is only one fine example of this. However, there are still some venues that 'jump on the bandwagon' and see the gay community as an extra source of revenue and thus – without the absolute enthusiasm and positive approach towards this clientele – fail miserably. At the end of the day the choice of patronage is yours. There is such a huge variety of venues nowadays that we as gay people do not have to put up with bad service, arrogant attitude and over-inflated prices just to meet up in a venue that identifies as being gay. I know of someone who complained to a manager of a well-known London 'gay-friendly' venue about the state of the toilets and was instantly asked (told!) not to return. Needless to say, he never returned and neither did his friends, resulting in a modest, but significant loss of income for the proprietor.

User feedback will play the most important part in producing the next edition. Every gay person has at least one small snippet of information that other readers would find interesting. It is with this in mind that I encourage you to be a part of the next edition. I'm inviting you to update the existing text and add your own individual comments on the venues listed (good and bad). I also want you to add new venues and to suggest new groups that would be of interest to other gay members of our community and indeed anything else that YOU feel would make for extremely interesting and informative reading. See the following 'Introduction' for details of how to impart your worldly pearls of wisdom.

Have fun and always remember: if you play safe, you play for longer!

John Szponarski
June 1999

Introduction

The main aim of writing this guide was to produce a book foremost and specifically for the person venturing out onto the gay scence for the first time, yet also for the seasoned clubber looking for venues further afield from their home town. The information it contained had to be detailed and essentially up-to-date and complete. It is in no way meant to be a critique of the venues listed; it is left for you to make up your own mind whether to revisit.

Every proprietor of gay and gay-friendly venues throughout England, Scotland and Wales was contacted. They were sent a questionnaire, which requested opening times, admission charges, membership arrangements and numerous other questions such as the availability of food, nearest car parking facilities, etc. The vast majority responded with copious amounts of information, enabling a listing to be truly reflective of their venue.

Most gay venues known to be in existence have been included whether the owner responded or not, although where they didn't, it is the essential information, i.e. admission charges, specialist nights, etc. that is unfortunately excluded. With this in mind, it is worth remembering that not the publishers, contributors nor myself can be held in any way responsible for misrepresentation or possible errors included in the subsequent text.

The introductory texts at the beginning of each section are just that, 'an introduction'. They are written with a thought for the reader who may not have had any previous experience with the subjects covered and they aim to answer all the *initial* questions and doubts. Wherever possible, or indeed, where available, there will always be contact sources listed, should you have further questions of a more individual nature. It would have been virtually impossible to cover every single aspect of *each* field due to the enormity and complexities of the subject matter.

Information about cruising areas has been taken from reputation as well as from word of mouth. Additional information, on cruising grounds either incorrectly referenced or not listed, would be gratefully received in writing (to the address at the end of this Introduction). As cruising grounds are ever-changing and because the areas listed are outside the control of anyone in particular, no liability whatsoever can be accepted by myself or anyone else associated with the publication of this guide. The upkeep of information regarding cruising grounds will be ongoing and all additional information will be verified prior to inclusion in the next volume. All cruising grounds are to be visited 'at your own risk'. It is impossible to guarantee the safety of any such area and this is not implied, nor should it be inferred, for any listing herein.

The sections with legal implications are not to be taken as the final word of the law, as it stands at the current time. They are offered only as *guidelines*. Should you find yourself in situations requiring legal assistance or involved in matters regarding the police or legal authorities, then contact your local gay switchboard. They will be able to refer you to a solicitor, who specialises in gay matters, for initial advice.

For a guide like this to succeed, it is essential that I receive your feedback. Perhaps there are chapters that you would like to see in the next edition (e.g. a chapter and listings on leather, S&M and fetish bars/clubs). The lesbian scene in particular is growing considerably – furnish me with the information so as I can level out the gay-lesbian balance for the next edition. Maybe you have just 'come out' and have a case history on how you were treated on the gay scene, and a story on how this guide helped you to find the scene that interested you. In addition to this, I would be interested to receive personal accounts (or reviews) of your experiences in the venues listed (good or bad), particularly ones detailing the facets of the establishment that would not normally be included in a guide book. For example, where in a particular establishment you would go for an intimate encounter or perhaps how friendly the venue was for the first-time visitor.

Mention the guide to other people. Tell the venues that you visit that you found them in the guide. Tell the venues that aren't in the guide that they should be in the guide! This circuit of information should result in feedback from users and readers of the guide plus updated and correct listings from and for the venues featured within.

There are forms to be found at the back of this guide which you can fill in and return to me. Alternatively, you may wish to expand upon this format. Forms, letters – however large or small – are more than welcome. You can also e-mail me or visit The Ultimate Gay Guide website, which will be operational from September 1999 onwards and deposit your information there. All information received will be treated in the strictest of confidence and under no circumstances will any personal details be held on any kind of retrieval system. Please contact me via one of the following:

Write to

Ultimate Guides
PO Box 64
Manchester
M7 4NZ

E-mail **ugg@ic24.net**
Website **http://www.absolutepress.demon.co.uk**

Finally, the gay pub and club scene is ever-changing, especially the one-nighters and specialist evenings. In addition to this, new venues are springing up all of the time. It is worth bearing in mind that if you are planning to travel a fair distance to a venue then you should first phone the club/pub/sauna to ensure that the details listed are still correct.

With all of this said, I leave you to enjoy this guide and hope that the contents will spur you on and into trying out pastures new.

John Szponarski

the ultimate guide to
Help, Advice and Support

Coming Out

The hardest thing for a gay man or woman to do is to declare their sexuality to their parents. It is equally hard for parents to accept, whether right or wrong, that their child is in fact gay. The consequences of such revelations are impossible to foretell since each family unit is different from the next. There are of course several points that you should always remember:

1. The hardest part of coming out is to accept your sexuality yourself. Once you have done this then the rest is so much easier. If you choose to ignore it, thinking that you may be able to change the way you feel by getting married, then you are in for a very big shock. Consider what will happen when you realise at a later date that you have made a mistake and that you should not have married. How are you going to tell your wife/husband? How are they going to react? Are you going to carry on the relationship based on a web of lies? Are you going to have relationships with same-sex partners with the risk of passing on sexually transmitted diseases to your spouse? Don't think for one minute that marriage will solve all of your problems, it will not. There are numerous testimonials to that fact. However, on the same note, if you are truly not sure what your sexuality is, then experiment without hurting anyone. It may be that you are bisexual and able to carry on a relationship with either sex. You may at an early age have an infatuation with someone of the same sex even though your sexuality is heterosexual.

    The bottom line is, if you know, deep down, that you *are* gay, then you will have to come to terms with it. If this seems impossible at the moment then the best advice anyone can give you is to talk it through with someone that understands what it is that you are going through. If you do not have anyone close enough to talk it through with, consider calling your local gay switchboard or nearest youth group helpline. These organisations have had years of experience with these matters and are willing, and able, to help you through it.

2. You are not alone. Every gay person has to decide whether or not to tell someone about their sexuality. This may be their parents,

their siblings, their work colleagues, their doctor or their closest friends. The reactions will vary greatly, some people will already have guessed and be waiting for you to tell them. Others will be shocked but will accept it by saying that you are still 'the same person'. The minority will not be able to accept it and it is these that have the problem, *not you*. You will have to decide whether or not the friendship or relationship is worth carrying on with.

3. When you feel that the time is right for you to come out, prepare a strategy. Your best friend should probably be one of the first people that you tell. If he or she is a true friend then there should be no problem: they will accept you for who you are, not what you are. If you are fortunate enough to have a parent whom you can talk to then consider telling him or her. I believe mothers instinctively know whether or not their child is gay, so it may not be a complete shock to them, although they will have to come to terms with the reality of actually knowing it for a fact. Back your self up with allies in your family, if you are close to your siblings then tell them, they will usually come to your defence when you are confronted with a misinformed parent.

4. There is a common myth amongst straight people that all gay people end up lonely and living by themselves. Of course, this is complete nonsense. Just one look at the divorce statistics show that even marriage is not a sure-fire way of living happily ever after. Gay people have a social life that cannot be compared to the straight scene. Older people are accepted into the pub/club scene in such a way that is unheard of on the straight scene, and this can be well on into their retirement. Without the financial constraints of a family you will have more security; you will be more travelled.

5. Should you be rejected by your family, rest assured that they will come around in time. Put yourself in their place: it is a shock, and there is no way of avoiding the fact that they may well be distressed. However, if they cannot accept it then it is *their problem*, not yours. You have been up-front with them and it is up to them to come to terms with it. Putting your parents in touch with your local FFLAG helpline (see the helpline listings in this book) will make it easier for them to understand exactly what you are going through.

There is nothing to say that you *must* tell all and sundry that you are gay. If you do not wish to tell anyone then you do not have to. All the choices are yours and yours alone. Of course, there are advantages of declaring your sexuality. You will not be open to blackmail. You will not be looking over your shoulder every time that you go out, wondering if anyone that knows you has seen you. You will be more relaxed with yourself and people will accept you for who you are.

For young people (under the age of 26) a good first step would be to join a local 'youth group' (see the youth group section in this book). This is a good way to make new friends and meet people who are in a similar situation to your own, people who will be able to relate to what you are feeling. Youth groups – although informal and fun – are supervised by a trained councillor. They will be able to answer all of your questions and doubts about sexuality openly and honestly. They will also be able to help you prepare a strategy for coming out if you require them to do so. Remember, the choice, at the end of the day, is yours and no-one will ever tell you that you should do something that you are not comfortable with.

Youth groups are an ideal first step on the ladder to socialising. Going to your first gay bar or club (going out on the scene) can be extremely intimidating, especially if you have not had contact with another gay person before. Having a friend with you can make it more enjoyable and you will not feel so isolated. Having said that, once you have been out, you will find it exciting and fun. You may well be surprised at how comfortable you are with other gay people. Should you, in the worst possible scenario, suffer a bad experience in a gay venue then don't think that this is reflective of all places. Try again. If you ventured out on your own, find someone who can go with you the next time. Phone the gay switchboard or any of the youth group numbers listed in this book and explain what has happened. There are many, many dedicated professionals out there who are able to help you.

One of the major worries of young people who are new to the scene is that they are not sure how to handle being approached by someone they do not fancy. It may be that the person is just being friendly (nine times out of ten this happens to be the case). However, they may just want sex. If they do and you don't, then politely say no. If you are up for it then that is equally as fine.

No one can tell you what to do in bed with another person. You will know what you want to do and what you do not want to do. No one will think any the less of you for being inexperienced; in fact it is often an added attribute.

You will read the phrase 'safe sex' or 'safer sex' throughout this book. It will be repeated and the dangers of 'unsafe sex' will be detailed. Practising safe sex should become part of your life and the consequences of not doing so are unforgivable.

Most types of gay sex are quite safe. To get infected with HIV (the virus that may lead to AIDS) you would need to get the blood or semen of someone who is infected into your bloodstream. So things like kissing or masturbating are quite safe. Oral sex carries only a minute risk of HIV infection. Out of the hundreds of thousands of HIV infection cases, only a small handful are thought to have come from sucking.

There are many myths about HIV and AIDS, some, if the subject wasn't so serious, would be laughable. Though to someone who hasn't had access to safer sex information they could be quite believable. In the chapter on HIV and AIDS, a more detailed explanation helps to separate the fact from the fiction.

For the older person venturing out onto the gay scene, you have masses of support available; groups specifically set up for people like yourself. Perhaps you are new to the area, or you just want to meet new friends. The gay switchboard should be your first calling point and they will be able to put you in touch with a group that will almost certainly meet your needs. The diversity of the gay scene is only one of its major strengths. And it is this diversity that makes the lifestyle so enjoyable. There are groups throughout the country for almost anything – big, small, hairy, smooth, black, Asian, Chinese, leather, rubber, transvestite, transsexual, uniform, sadism, masochism, sports, football, swimming, biking, walking, dining, dancing, singing, crafts – you name it and there will, without a shadow of a doubt, be a group for it. Again, phone your nearest switchboard for details of your local group.

Over the last two years the increase in women-only bars has been phenomenal. Now nearly every major city has at least one night where there is a venue specifically set aside for women only. For example, in London there is a different venue catering for women every night of the week. Manchester is quickly following suit and I'm sure that over the next year, most towns will have at least one women-only bar.

The taboo of 'single mothers' coming out has now been broken. So much so that there is even a group for 'single mothers' (surprise, surprise) enabling women to make new friends and to have an enjoyable and new found social life.

Women-only bars are usually 'hosted'. This means that you can go in by yourself and every effort will be made to ensure that you are introduced to someone who will show you around and make you feel welcome. In fact, one club gives you half a playing card, encouraging you to find the matching half.

Alternatively, most switchboards operate 'Stepping Stones', a social group for lesbians and bisexual women, usually held in the local gay centre and presided over by a trained gay counsellor. This gives you the opportunity to express concerns and ask questions regarding your sexuality, and to explore the gay scene. (More information regarding Stepping Stones is covered in the 'Switchboards and Advice Lines' introduction).

You'll find most of the gay press available free of charge in nearly all pubs and clubs. Some cities may have their own magazine or paper, catering exclusively for their own community. New papers seem to appear every couple of months or so but most don't last much longer than a few editions. (See the 'Gay Press' section of this guide for further details.)

Remember, being gay is brilliant. Don't sit at home wishing your life away – do something about it. Pick a pub or club from the listings in this book; dress however you want ('cos no-one will give a toot) and get yourself out. You have got nothing to lose and everything to gain?

London Friend

86 Caledonian Road
Kings Cross
London
N1 9DN   Telephone 0171 837 3337 daily 19.30–22.00

Nearest train station Kings Cross
Nearest tube Kings Cross/St Pancras
Car parking Available outside from 18.30, Monday–Saturday and all day
                    Sunday
A–Z ref. P61/2K
Nearest landmark Malt and Hops public house on corner of Caledonian Road/
                    Balfe Street

London Friend is a voluntary organisation affiliated to National Friend and has been in existence for over 25 years. They offer counselling and support services to gay and bisexual men and women as well as to those who may be unsure of their sexual identity. Their aim is to help men and women explore issues of sexual identity and same sex relationships, promote personal growth and self-confidence during the coming out process and beyond.

London Friend services include telephone helplines, counselling and social and support groups. All of their services are operated by trained gay volunteers. In addition to the services provided by London Friend, there are several groups run at the premises by external organisations, details of which are described as follows:

Turning Point: A coming out group for men of all ages and backgrounds who are gay or feel that they may be gay and would like to come to terms with their sexuality in a supportive atmosphere. Meet every Wednesday 19.00–21.30 at the above address. Phone for further information.

Men@Friend: A meeting place for gay men. An alternative to the pub/club scene. Evenings include guest speakers, discussions and other fun events. Meet every Thursday 20.00–22.30 at the above address. Phone for further information.

Men's Counselling Group: A closed, facilitated group which runs weekly for ten weeks. Phone for further information.

Changes: A group for women of all ages and backgrounds who are coming to terms with their sexuality, offering a chance to meet other gay women, perhaps for the first time. Meet every second and fourth Sunday of the month between 18.30 and 21.30. Phone for further information.

Lesbians at Friend on Sunday (LAFS): A bi-monthly social group with talks, discussions, videos and slide shows. Meet every first and thirrd Sunday at the above address between 18.00 and 20.30. Phone for further details.

Lesbian Bereavement Group: A closed, facilitated group which runs twice-monthly for six months. Alternatively, write to: Lesbian Bereavement Group, c/o London Friend, for more details and the starting date of the next group.

London Bisexual Group: Meets every Friday from 20.00 to 22.00. Alternatively, phone their helpline on 0131 557 3620.

Shakti: Social and support group for South Asian gay men and women. Meets second Sunday of the month, 15.00–18.00.

Housing Advice: Run by Stonewall Housing Association every Monday from 14.00 to 16.30.

Lesbian Alcoholics Anonymous: Meets every Saturday 15.00–16.30. Alternatively, phone the London regional helpline on **0171 352 3001**.

Depression Alliance: Self-help group for gay men and women with depression. Alternatively, phone the information line on **0171 633 0557**.

Counselling Service: Counselling is available for individuals and couples. The service is provided free, but donations are welcome. Counsellors are gay men and women who work to the BAC code of ethics. Phone the helpline at the top of the

page to make an appointment, or make further further enquiries at the above address.
The following groups can be accessed through London Friend either by calling personally or writing to the group direct c/o London Friend.

Orientations: A social support group for South-East Asian gay men and women

Lesbian and Gay Adoption: Fostering and parenting network

Iranian Lesbian and Gay Group

Arab Lesbian Network

Switchboards and Advice Lines

Introduction

The registered charity National Friend is the umbrella body supporting the national network of local helplines (switchboards/ lesbian lines, etc.) for those wanting support or information on issues relating to all aspects of their sexuality. Set up in 1971, National Friend is one of the longest running gay, lesbian and bisexual groups in the UK.

Recent years have seen an increased awareness of homosexuality. However, for the millions of people who do not identify as being heterosexual there is still personal confusion, isolation, discrimination, prejudice and even abuse.

The local helplines support those who are facing personal trauma and confusion about their sexuality in addition to the friends, family and colleagues of those who identify as being gay. In areas where there is not a helpline, National Friend can work with the local community to support them in setting up a new service.

The following questions and answers aim to identify some of the activities of the helplines throughout the country. The term 'switchboard' is used as a generic word for any helpline.

Who uses the gay switchboard?
Everyone. The gay switchboard is usually the first port of call for anyone who has a problem, a question or a doubt relating to any aspect of gay life. Young people who have concerns about their sexuality, parents who are seeking advice and information, gay people who require specialist information, transvestites and transsexuals (and their families), looking for advice and support, in fact the list is endless. The switchboard has a huge database of reference material and can usually direct you to the relevant organisation.

Is the switchboard confidential?
The switchboard is 100% confidential. Switchboard operators cannot even dial 1471 to see where the call is coming from. You will not be asked your name or any personal details whatsoever. A call sheet is kept for statistical purposes in order to improve services and

these only record whether the caller was male or female, an approximate age, the type of enquiry made and so on. All calls are treated in the strictest confidence and volunteers sign a confidentiality policy, which is rigidly enforced. For people making a call to a switchboard from home, it is worth remembering that the number may be itemised on your telephone bill. It may be wise to use a public pay phone or the telephone of a sympathetic friend.

My local switchboard is always engaged; can I telephone another area?
Yes. Due mainly to limited funding – as opposed to a lack of volunteers – it is virtually impossible to man the switchboard every day. There is a tremendous strain on all switchboards, particularly those in cities and major towns. London Switchboard, for example, is nearly always constantly engaged, despite the fact that it is the only switchboard in the country that operates 24 hours, every day of the year.

Apart from general advice what other services can a switchboard offer?
The Lesbian and Gay Switchboard can offer advice and information about the following distinct groups:

Stepping Stones
This is a support group for lesbians and bisexual women who are 'coming out'. The group may meet once or twice a month. Volunteers are on hand to 'break the ice' and to provide the answers to the many, many questions raised. The atmosphere is informal and friendly.

A Transvestite/Transsexual (TV/TS) Helpline
This is usually manned by transvestites or transsexuals. They are trained to offer advice and support.

Ice Breakers
A group for gay or bisexual men who are 'coming out' or are new to the area and wishing to meet like-minded people. Meetings may be more frequent than the women's group; usually fortnightly. Again, volunteers are on hand to answer your questions.

Face To Face Counselling

These meetings are on a one-to-one basis and because of their specialised nature, are conducted by highly trained councillors. There is usually a waiting list for this service. If you do make an appointment for this service and have to cancel, always inform the switchboard in order that they can re-schedule someone else.

Youth Groups

These meetings are set up specifically for young people between the ages of 16 and 26 years old. (Calls from young people regarding their sexuality rate amongst the highest 'type' of calls received.) Meetings are extremely friendly, relaxed and informal, supervised by trained volunteers who are on hand to answer any specific questions or concerns.

As stated above, the switchboard is the first port of call for any problem or anxiety and the switchboards are able to make referrals to other organisations such as Body Positive, GUM clinics, FFLAG and helplines for recreational drug users such as Lifeline and National Drugs Line. The switchboard can also act as negotiator for the Action On Hate Crime Initiative.

What is the 'Action On Hate Crime Initiative'?

Some people hate gay men and lesbians and consider them an easy target for abuse, harassment, robbery and even violence. Much of this crime goes unreported and the police can do little to deal with it without detailed information and statistics. Hate crime is not inevitable and it can be stopped if we work together.

Gay switchboards have 'incident referral forms' whereby they will complete all details of the incident (your name and address do not have to be included) and they will forward the form to the police on your behalf.

What are the commonest calls the switchboard receives?

The main issues are coming out, meeting others (particularly young people), loneliness and isolation, problems with relationships (including rape [male and female]), HIV and AIDS information, TV/TS issues and of course, the whereabouts of specific gay venues. Not all calls are of a distressing nature. The switchboard does receive calls from people that have been helped – for example, when someone meets a partner or when someone comes out to their parents or friends and has found acceptance. In fact … anything. The switchboard is your *friend*.

Continuous funding plays a vital role in maintaining all the switchboards and helplines throughout the country. If you feel that you are able to donate then please send postal orders or cheques, no matter how small, to the following address:

National Friend Limited
216 The Custard Factory
Gibb Street
Birmingham
B9 4AA

British Switchboards and Advice Lines

Bi Helpline
London
0181 569 7500
Wednesday: 19.30–21.30
Saturday: 10.30–12.30

Black Helpline
London
0171 620 3885
Tuesday & Thursday 11.00–
17.30

Diverse Divas
London
0171 267 8595
Monday: 18.30–21.30 (Women only)

Friend
Croydon, London
0181 683 4239
Monday & Friday 19.30–21.30

Friend
Lewisham, London
0181 690 6195
Thursday 19.30–21.30

Helpline
London
0171 837 3337
19.30–22.00

Irish Helpline
London
0181 983 4111
Monday 19.30–22.00

Jewish Helpline
London
0171 706 3123
Monday & Thursday 19.00–
22.00

Lesbian Line
London
0171 251 6911
Monday & Friday 14.00–22.00,
Tuesday & Thursday 19.00–
22.00

Lesbian Line
London
0171 837 2782
Sunday & Thursday 19.30–22.00

Switchboard
London
0171 837 7324
24 Hour support and advice

ENGLAND

Samaritans
0345 909 090
National, daily 24 hours

Helpline
Bedfordshire
01234 218 990
Tuesday & Thursday19.30–
22.00

Gayline
Bedworth
01203 640 171

Uni Gayline
Bath
01225 465 793
Tuesday 18.00–19.30 (term-time
only)

Friend
Birmingham
0121 622 7351
Daily 19.30–21.30

Lesbian Line
Birmingham
0121 622 6536

Switchboard
Birmingham
0121 622 6589
Daily 19.00–22.00

Lesbian Line
Bolton
01204 394 610
Thursday 19.00–22.00

Friend
Bradford
01274 723 802
Monday & Wednesday 18.30–
20.45

Lesbian Line
Bradford
01274 305 525
Thursday 19.00–21.00

Switchboard
Bradford
01274 722 206
Tuesday, Thursday & Saturday
19.30–21.30

Bi Lines
Brighton
01273 206 767
Daily 19.00–22.00 (women only)

Lesbian Line
Brighton
01273 603 298
Tuesday & Friday 20.00–22.00

Switchboard
Brighton
01273 690 825
Monday & Saturday 18.30–
22.00 & Sunday 20.00–22.00

Lesbian Line
Bristol
0117 929 0855
Thursday 19.30–22.00

Switchboard
Bristol
0117 942 0842
Thursday 19.30–22.00

Friend
Cambridge
01223 246 031
Wednesday 18.30–21.30

Lesbian Line
Cambridge
01223 311 753
Friday 19.00–22.00

Friend
Canterbury
01843 588 762
Tuesday 19.30–22.00

Lesbian Line
Canterbury
01227 464 570
Friday 19.00–22.00

Uni Gayline
Canterbury
01227 454 868
Wednesday 08.00–20.00 (term-time only)

Switchboard
Carlisle
01965 31171

Switchboard
Colchester
01206 869 191
Monday & Friday 19.00–22.00

Lesbian Line
Cornwall
01736 753 709
Thursday 20.00–22.00

Switchboard
Cornwall
01209 314 449
Monday & Friday 19.30–22.30

Friend
Coventry
01203 714 199
Monday & Friday 19.30–21.30

Switchboard
Crewe
01270 250 980
Thursday 19.30–21.30

GAD
Darlington
01325 460 287
Monday & Sat 19.00–22.00

Friend
Derby
01332 349 333
Wednesday 19.00–22.00

Helpline
Dorset
01202 318 822
Evenings

Bi Helpline
Exeter
01395 269 462

Switchboard
Exeter
01392 422 016
Monday 19.30–22.00

Uni Gayline
Exeter
01392 75007
Thursday 08.00–20.00 (term-time only)

Friend
Gloucester
01452 306 800
Monday & Thursday 19.30–22.00

Helpline
Grimsby
01472 251 818
Tuesday & Thursday 19.00–21.00

Switchboard
Harlow
01279 639 637
Tuesday, Thursday & Sunday
20.00–23.00 (Sunday for women)

Befrienders
Hastings
01424 444 777
Monday 19.00–22.00

Switchboard
Hereford & Worcester
01905 723 097
Tuesday & Friday 19.30–22.00

Switchboard
Huddersfield
01484 538 070
Tuesday & Sunday 19.00–21.00

Friend
Hull
01482 443 333
Monday & Thursday 20.00–
22.00 and Saturday 19.00–21.00

Lesbian Line
Hull
01482 214 331
Monday: 19.00–21.00

Switchboard
Ipswich
01473 232 212
Tuesday & Saturday 19.30–
21.30

Gayline
Kent
01892 535 876
Monday 20.00–22.00

Lesbian Line
Kent
01622 763 573
Friday 19.00–22.00

Helpline
Kings Lynn
01553 827 567
Tuesday 19.00–22.00 (or
answerphone)

Switchboard
Lancashire
01282 454 978
Tuesday & Thursday 19.30–
21.30

Switchboard
Lancaster
01524 847 437
Thursday & Friday 19.00–21.00

Lesbian Line
Leeds
0113 2453 588
Tuesday 19.30–21.30

Switchboard
Leeds
0113 2453 588
Daily, 19.00–22.00 (except
Tuesday)

Helpline
Leicester
01162 550 667
Monday & Friday 19.30–22.00

Lesbian Line
Lincoln
01522 535 553
Tuesday 19.00–22.00

Switchboard
Lincoln
01522 535 553
Thursday & Sunday 19.00–22.00

Lesbian Line
Liverpool
0151 7080 234
Tuesday & Thursday 19.00–22.00

Switchboard
Liverpool
0151 708 9552
Daily 19.00–22.00

TV/TS Line
Liverpool
0151 709 4745
Friday 19.00–22.30

Switchboard
Manchester
0161 274 3999
Daily 16.00–22.00

TV/TS Line
Manchester
0161 274 3705

Friend
Middlesborough
01642 248 888
Tuesday, Friday 19.30–21.30

Lesbian Line
Middlesborough
01642 217 955
Monday 20.00–22.00

Switchboard
Milton Keynes
01908 666 226
Monday 19.30–21.45

Friend
Newcastle Upon Tyne
0191 261 8555
Monday & Friday 19.00–22.00

Lesbian Line
Newcastle Upon Tyne
0191 261 2277
Tuesday 19.00–22.00

Gayline
Northamptonshire
01604 35975
Tuesday 18.30–21.30

Lesbian Line
Northampton
01604 250 887
Wednesday 18.30–21.30

Gayline
Northamptonshire
01933 271 187
Thursday 19.00–22.00

Helpline
Northamptonshire
01536 312 525
Wednesday 19.30–22.00

Friend
Nottingham
0115 947 4717
Tuesday 19.00–22.00

Gay Advice
Nottingham
01777 709 650
Monday & Thursday 09.30–
16.00

Lesbian Line
Nottingham
0115 941 0652
Monday & Wednesday 19.30–
21.00

Switchboard
Nottingham
0115 941 1454
Monday & Friday 19.00–22.00

Friend
Norwich
01603 628 055
Friday & Sunday
19.00–21.00

Lesbian Line
Norwich
01603 628 055
Tuesday 19.00–21.00

Uni Gayline
Norwich
01603 592 505
Monday 20.00–22.00 (term-time
only)

Switchboard
Oldham
0161 678 9448
Tuesday 19.00–21.00

Friend
Oxford
01865 726 893
Tuesday, Wednesday & Friday
19.00–21.00

Lesbian Line
Oxford
01865 242 333
Wednesday 19.00–21.00

Switchboard
Oxford
01865 793 999
Daily 19.00–21.00

Gayline
Peterborough
01733 706 292
Monday, Wednesday & Friday
19.30–22.00 & Sunday 12.00–
18.00

Helpline
Plymouth
01752 569 504

Lesbian Line
Portsmouth
01705 866 999
Thursday 19.00–22.00

Switchboard
Portsmouth
01705 655 077
Wednesday 19.30–22.00

Lesbian Line
Preston
01772 251 122
Wednesday 19.30–21.30

Switchboard
Preston
01772 251 122
Tuesday, Thursday & Friday
19.30–21.30

Helpline
Reading
0118 959 7269
Tuesday, Wednesday & Friday
19.30–21.30

Switchboard
Salisbury
01722 415 051
Wednesday 19.30–21.30

Helpline
Scunthorpe
01724 271 661
Wednesday & Friday 19.00–
21.00

Friend
Sheffield
0114 275 8880
Friday 19.30–21.30

Gayphone
Sheffield
0114 258 8199
Monday, Tuesday & Wednesday
19.30–21.30

Switchboard
Shropshire
01743 344 269
Tuesday & Friday 20.00–22.00

Lesbian Line
Slough
01753 823 661
Daily 16.00–22.00

Friend
Southampton
01703 630 644
Tuesday & Thursday 19.30–
22.00

Friend
Southampton
01703 637 363
Monday, Tuesday, Thursday &
Friday 19.30–22.00

Lesbian Line
Southampton
01703 405 111
Thursday 19.30–22.00

Gayline
Southend
01702 480 344

Switchboard
Southend
01702 344 355
Thursday 19.00–22.00

Helpline
St Helens
01744 454 823
Monday & Wednesday 19.00–
21.00 & Saturday 14.00–16.00

Switchboard
Stoke-on-Trent
01782 266 998
Monday, Wednesday & Friday
20.00–22.00

Helpline
Telford
01743 232 393
Tuesday, Wednesday & Friday
20.00–22.00

Info Line
Watford
01923 773 570
Daily 19.00–22.00

Lesbian Line
York
01904 646 812
Friday 19.00–21.00

Rainbow Centre
Yorkshire
01429 222 999
Gay/Bi support & advice

SCOTLAND

Friend
Scotland
01786 471 285
Monday 19.30–21.30

Lesbian Line
Scotland
01738 828 840
Monday 19.00–22.00

Switchboard
Aberdeen
01224 633 500

Switchboard
Ayr
01292 619 000
Monday, Wednesday & Friday
19.00–22.00

Switchboard
Borders
01896 756 611

Gayline
Dumfries
01387 269 161
Thursday evenings

Switchboard
Dundee
01382 202 620
Monday 19.00–22.00

Bi Line
Edinburgh
0131 557 3620
Thursday 19.30–21.30

Lesbian Line
Edinburgh
0131 557 0751
Monday & Thursday 19.30–
22.00

Switchboard
Edinburgh
0131 556 4049
Monday & Sunday 19.30–22.00

Switchboard
Elgin
01343 541 188

Lesbian Line
Glasgow
0141 552 3355
Wednesday 19.00–22.00

Switchboard
Glasgow
0141 332 8372
Nightly 19.00–22.00

Lesbian Line
West Highlands
01851 706 771
Daily 19.30–21.30

Friend
Kirkcaldy
01592 266 688
Monday 19.30–22.30 (women),
Friday (men)

Switchboard
Lothian
0131 556 4049

WALES

Friend
Cardiff
01222 340 101
Tuesday & Saturday 20.00–22.00

Lesbian Line
Cardiff
01222 374 051
Tuesday 20.00–22.00

Trans Wales
Cardiff
01222 799 441
Advice & support for TVs

Advice Line
Swansea
01792 652 902
Tuesday 18.00–21.00

Lesbian Line
Swansea
01792 651 995
Wednesday 19.00–21.00

Switchboard
Swansea
01792 301 855
Tuesday 19.00–22.00

SWITCHBOARD WEBSITES

Brighton Gay Switchboard
http://www.brighton.co.uk/
commune/switchboard

London Gay Switchboard
http://www.llgs.org.uk

Manchester Gay Switchboard
http://
www.switchboard.mcmail.com

Nottingham Gay Switchboard
http://www.geocities.com/
WestHollywood/1449/

North Wales Youth Support
http://www.mesmac-north-
wales.org/youth/

FFLAG

Introduction

'. . . If only we'd had more information, we could have understood earlier . . . '

Above: a parent's words. Families and Friends of Lesbians and Gays (FFLAG) is a national, purely voluntary organisation consisting (mainly) of parents of children who are gay, lesbian or bisexual. Each volunteer, has gone through the process of having to face that their own child is either gay, lesbian or bisexual. With hindsight, understanding and knowledge, gained over years of experience, they are willing to help other parents finding themselves in the similar situation of coming to terms with the fact that a member of their family is gay.

Although FFLAG is there for parents and families, they will also offer guidance to a gay, lesbian or bisexual child who is preparing to 'come out' to their family. The following questions and answers aim to reveal the role of FFLAG. Concerned parents should contact their nearest FFLAG helpline from the subsequent listings.

What is FFLAG?
FFLAG is a national organisation which is dedicated to supporting parents and their gay, lesbian or bisexual sons and daughters.

Who uses FFLAG?
Parents, who have just discovered that a member of their family is either gay, lesbian or bisexual. Also, concerned and caring parents or family members who need to understand exactly what 'being gay' means and to know that there is support and understanding available to them. A parent may have suspicions about their offspring and may perhaps wish to discuss their concerns with someone who is non-judgmental and impartial.

What is normally the first reaction when a parent finds out that their child is gay?
Initially, it is often shock. Most children believe that a parent already 'has suspicions' of their sexuality, but this is not always the case. The parent is anxious and frightened, worried about their child's future; their expectations of grandchildren are no longer viable. But most importantly, in a way, the parent 'grieves' over all their lost hopes for their son or daughter. At this stage, parents have no knowledge of all the 'positive aspects' of being gay.

How should a parent react when informed that their child is gay?
Despite what they might be feeling, parents should reassure their child that they are still loved and that they are willing to understand. It may (and invariably will) take time to come to terms with the fact but help and support is available from people who have been through the process.

Isn't that easier said than done?
Of course it is. However, a parent should realise that for a child to have declared their sexuality, it must have taken an enormous amount of courage and soul searching. Being honest about him or herself to a member of their family shows a great deal of respect for their parents.

Is FFLAG able to act as an intermediary for the child?
In some circumstances, a member of FFLAG may be able to meet up with the parent in order to offer support for the parent and child. It should be noted that parents might think that FFLAG is in some way a 'gay group' itself. This is not the case. Though FFLAG can help in this intermediary way, its members will not telephone the family home to disclose the news. The parent must be willing to contact the FFLAG member for advice on how to handle the situation.

What will FFLAG do when the parent calls?
They will listen. No matter how long it takes, they will listen. They understand that a parent will have questions, concerns and anxieties. What will also come out are the myths and half – truths

that the parent has been led to believe are true, regarding what it is to be gay. FFLAG members will also be able to provide the parent with accurate information and help with coming to terms with the fact of having a gay member of the family. There are support groups available in some areas if the parent wishes to attend. FFLAG will also send out (free of charge) helpful booklets and articles in addition to a quarterly newsletter available at £5.00 per annum.

What happens at the support group?
With the lack of purpose-built premises, support groups sometimes take place in the home of a FFLAG volunteer or in a room booked solely for the purpose. Set in an informal and friendly environment, a support group gives the parent the opportunity to voice their own concerns and to have the support and understanding of other parents who have had similar experiences. Information will be shared, tears may be shed, but most importantly the parent will realise that they are not on their own.

How long does it take for a parent to accept the fact that their child is gay?
It varies a great deal. Parents need to be given time to talk everything through. The hardest part is for them to change their own beliefs of what it means to be gay. These beliefs could result from years of ignorance and intolerance. Knowing fact from fiction helps the parent take a completely different outlook.

Have there been any cases where a parent totally disowns the child?
Although rare (and even then, more often than not, it is usually only a temporary situation) it does occasionally happen. The fact that a parent contacts FFLAG in the first place shows tremendous concern for the child's welfare and the willingness to understand, change and accept.

FFLAG volunteers receive no direct funding from any source whatsoever. Volunteers usually pay for stationery, telephone charges, etc. out of their own pockets. If you have had cause to use FFLAG or feel that you would like to make a donation (however small) then phone FFLAG National Co-ordinator on 0181 467 0309 or write to the address below, and rest assured that all contributions go directly towards funding much needed resources.

FFLAG
PO Box 153
Manchester
M60 1LP

British FFLAG Contacts

Parents Enquiry
London (Central)
0171 791 2854 – Eileen

Parents Together
London (South)
0181 650 5268 – Thelma
0181 467 0309 – Pat

Support Group for Jewish Parents
London (South)
0181 958 4827 – Kenneth

Telephone Contact
London (North)
0181 343 4963 – Myrna

ENGLAND

FFLAG National Co-ordinator
0181 467 0309

Parents Support Group
Birmingham
0121 742 0230 – Maureen

Telephone Contact
Brandon
01842 813 730 – Peter or Cherry

Parents Group
Bristol
01454 898 644 – Sue

Telephone Contact
Bury
01204 883 794 – Christine

Telephone Contact
Cambourne
01209 711 211 – Maureen
(Thursday evenings)

Proud Parents
Cambridge
01223 315 745 – Mary
01223 832 382 – Myfanwy

Parents Enquiry
Cleveland
01642 465 020 – Sue

Parents Group
Coventry and Warwickshire
01926 852 906 – Jan
01926 857 279 – Mo

Accept
Doncaster
01302 772 894 – Margaret
01302 782 520 – Tricia

Parents Enquiry North East
Durham
01207 509 020 – Anne-Marie
(evenings only)

Parentline
Exeter
01392 279 546 – Jenny

Telephone Contact
Kingsley
01928 787 249 – Vera

Parents Group
Leicester
01162 918 696 – Vaunda
01162 359 774 – Betty
01162 831 360 – Kath

Telephone Contact
Lichfield
01543 263 781 – Sheila

Telephone Contact
Liverpool
0151 424 1552 – Liz

Telephone Contact
Loughborough
01509 238 883 – Rachel

Parents Group
Manchester
0161 628 7621 – Joyce
0161 748 3452 – Brenda
0161 747 0976 – Cath

Parents Contact
Shrewsbury
1743 344 479 – Rose and Arthur

Parents Enquiry North East
Newcastle upon Tyne
0191 537 4691 – Pat

Telephone Contact
Northwich
01565 733 891 – Nicki and
Laurie

Telephone Contact
Rochdale
01706 712 497 – Sue and Dave

Acceptance
Sheerness
01795 661 463 – Jill and Gordon

Telephone Contact
Uttoxeter
01889 562 839 – Carol and Peter

Telephone Contact
Warrington
01925 765 139 – Inga

SCOTLAND

Parents Enquiry Scotland
Edinburgh
0131 556 8304 – Anne

Parents Enquiry
Northumberland
01670 520 992 – Anne

Parents Group
Strathclyde
01555 895 306 – Alice

WALES

The above list is exhaustive of all of the available FFLAG contacts and, unfortunately, there is no specific group for Wales. However, all groups should be willing to help you, wherever you are based. Phone the FFLAG National Co-ordinator line on 0181 467 0309 to ask for details of an appropriate contact.

Youth Groups

Introduction

Youth groups were set up specifically to help and advise young people, usually under the age of 26, with the problems and difficulties of coming to terms with their sexuality. In most cases, young people have absolutely no one to turn to and these groups are there to act solely as a friend and someone to talk over their anxieties and worries with.

In addition to the above, most youth groups offer young people the chance to meet other young people in the same situation providing opportunities to meet up for social events without the stress and trauma of having to 'go it alone'. This is particularly important for those under the age of 18, who will not have access to the gay pub and club scene.

More importantly, youth groups will be able to answer all your questions and worries regarding safe sex, 'coming out' and lifestyle. They will also supply you with condoms and offer you access to all the free gay literature available.

Having feelings that make you scared and uncomfortable about being gay is very common. Not having someone to talk to can increase your stress levels and you can actually make the problem worse by trying to supply all of the answers yourself. Some young people get into such a state that they actually consider suicide. If your feelings get this bad or you begin to think about it quite a lot, it is best to talk it over with someone who understands *exactly* what it is you are going through. Suicide is certainly not the answer; not when there are so many positive options open to you. Telephone *any* switchboard or youth group helpline that is open and talk the matter through.

Sometimes it can feel easier to pretend that you are not gay or bisexual, but this can begin to cause you more problems if you don't take a close look at your feelings for what they really are. Be honest with yourself. Speaking to a councillor or other young people at the youth group will help you to get things sorted in your head. They will be able to tell you what is true and what is not concerning the gay lifestyle. You will see that they are all like you – they are not different. Most of all you will see that they are happy.

It is important not to believe everything we see on the television or in films about gays and bisexuals. The TV can sometimes make it look bad and ugly. You will find that in real life being gay is not so bad – in fact, it's great.

The following questions and answers form many of the initial concerns that young people have regarding youth groups. They are by no means complete, but they will help you make up your mind whether or not to contact a youth group.

How do I get in touch with my local youth group?
In the listings that follow are the names and contact telephone numbers for nearly all of the youth groups throughout the United Kingdom. It takes a lot of courage to pick up the phone and ring someone and sometimes the line may be engaged. If you have got this far then don't give up; try again. Some of the groups have an address where you can write to them. For some, this might be easier than phoning.

What will happen on my first visit?
At the youth group there will be a trained councillor or experienced volunteer who will be able to answer all your questions and concerns. There will also be other young people, in the same situation as yourself; they will have the same anxieties and the same worries. The atmosphere will be friendly and relaxed. You will be able to talk to each other knowing that they understand perfectly what it is you are going through. You have to remember that the first visit is, and always will be, the hardest thing that you will ever have to do. Don't give up, see it through and then everything else will be so much easier. However, if you cannot bear to walk through the door, then try again at a later date when you are a little more prepared.

How confidential is a youth group?
Youth groups are 100% confidential. You do not have to give your real name, although there is no reason why you should have to make one up. You will not be asked for your address or any other personal details. There is often the major worry of seeing someone there that

you already know. Yet if you think about it, it would be a very good thing if there *was* someone there that you knew already; it would make it easier for you to begin talking to other people.

It is important to remember that there are many people able and willing to help youths through what is invariably a traumatic and rough time of their lives. Don't ever feel that you are bothering them – you aren't. They understand perfectly what it is you are going through and they are there to help you sort it out.

If you think that a Youth Group will be able to help you then take the first step, and call one of the numbers listed. If you cannot find a local number, then look for the next one nearest to your area.

After you do, you will wish that you had done it sooner!

British Youth Groups

Bexley Area Youth
London

Telephone 0181 265 3355
Monday–Thursday: 19.00–22.00

Croydon LGB Youth
London

Telephone 07071 225 577
Sunday 19.00–22.00

Kentish Town
Diverse Divas
London

Telephone 0171 267 8595
Monday 18.30–21.30 (Women only)

First Move
Colindale
London

Telephone 0800 389 9251
E-mail
firstmove@baeu.demon.co.uk
Monday: 16.00–18.00
Under 25s group

First Step
PO Box 1992
London
WC1N 3XX

Telephone 0181 461 4112
Monday 19.30–22.00

Forbidden Fruit
Hackney
London

Telephone 0181 533 2174
Monday 19.00–21.00
Scene alternative for under 25s
(men only)

Freedom Youth
Greenwich
London

Telephone 0181 316 4397
LGB under 25s (contact Lorraine
or James)

GB Harlow
London

Telephone 0973 541 974
Tuesday 19.00–21.30
Contact Alex

GB Male Survivors
London

Telephone 0171 388 2011
Rape and sexual assault: 16-25
peer support

Group 25 And Under
London

Telephone 0171 482 8605/267
8595

Harrow LGB Youth
Harrow Resource Centre
Marlborough Hill
London

Telephone   0181 427 1799
Friday: 18.00–20.00

Hillingdon LGB Youth Group
London

Telephone   01895 235 777
Sunday: 19.00–21.30
L&G youth under 21

Identity
Chiswick
London

Telephone   0181 742 2381
Gay and bi men's info and
support

L&G Youth Movement
London

Telephone   0181 317 9690

LGB Teenage Group
6-9 Manor Gardens
London
N7 6LA

Telephone   0171 263 5932

Lewisham Friend
Lewisham
London

Telephone   0181 690 6195
Thursday 19.30–21.30 for
advice and support

Male Out
Kentish Town
London

Telephone   0171 267 8595
Wed. 18.30–21.30

MYNORS @ Baseline
(Merton Youth Not Of Rigid
Sexuality)
Merton
London

Telephone   0181 646 3033
Daily: 12.00–18.00
G&L group, ages 14-21

NRG Youth Group
London (South-East)

Telephone   0171 620 1819
Under 25s advice, social and
friendship

Notting Hill LGB Youth
Notting Hill
London

Telephone   0171 229 3266

Outlinks LGB Youth
London

Telephone   0171 378 8732
Contact Hans or Robert

Phase (Tower Hamlets Youth Project)
London

Telephone   0171 515 4617

Streetwise Youth
London

Telephone   0171 370 0406
Working with young men under
26 who sell or exchange sex

WOW (We're Out West)
London

Telephone   0181 549 7654
Friday 19.00–21.30

ENGLAND

Gap
Andover

Telephone 01264 332 053
Monday& Friday: 11.00–15.00,
Wednesday: 12.00–17.00

L&G Youth
Barnsley

Telephone 01226 730 703

Rainbow Youth
Basildon

Telephone 01375 364 435
Contact Simon

Friend
PO Box 2405
Birmingham
B5 4AJ

Telephone 0121 622 7351

LGB Youth
Birmingham

Telephone 0121 359 3864
Contact Ian

Blackpool Young Gay Mens Project
Blackpool

Telephone 01253 476 574
Under 25s (telephone anytime)

Bypass LGB Youth
Bolton

Telephone 01204 362 002
Contact Marilyn

Youth On The Out
Bournemouth

Ring helpline for details (see
switchboard listings)

CUSU Icebreakers
Trumpington Street
Cambridge
No telephone; write for details

Freedom Club
Huntingdon
Cambridge

Telephone 01480 398 036
Wed. 19.00–20.00

Kite Club
c/o Arjuna
12 Mill Road
Cambridge
CB1 2AD

Website http://
www.youthnet.adhocity.com
E-mail kiteclub@hotmail.com
Contact Neil or Kath

Discovery
PO Box 3616
Chelmsford

Telephone 01245 280 240
Tuesday: 18.30–21.00

East Hertsfordshire Youth Support
Cheshunt

Telephone 01992 635 000

GYGL
10 Manor Road
Coventry
CV1 2LH

Telephone 01203 224 090
Weekdays: 10.00–17.00

Choices LGB Youth
Derbyshire

Telephone   01332 349 333
Thursdays 17.00–19.30
Youth support

Outhouse
Dewsbury
Ring Kirklees switchboard for
details

Friend
PO Box 171
Gloucestershire
GL1 4YE

Telephone   01452 306 800
Monday–Fri 19.30–22.00

Freedom Youth
Hampshire

Telephone   01256 376 486 / 0385
223 722

GABY
Harlow

Telephone   0973 541 974

Icebreakers
High Wycombe

Telephone   01494 473 888
Contact Paul for support and
information

Gay Under 25s
PO Box 2000
Horwich
BL6 7PG
No telephone

Friend
CVS
29 Anlaby Road
Hull
HU1 2PG

Telephone   01482 443 333

OASIS (Out And Strong In Suffolk)
Ipswich

Telephone   01473 225 344
Contact Tim or Julie

L&G Youth Group
Lancashire
Ring Lancashire switchboard for
details

Open Door
117 Granby Street
Leicestershire

Telephone   0116 254 2225

Crash
PO Box 130
Lincoln
Ring switchboard for details

GYRO
Liverpool

Telephone   0151 709 6660

Good As You
Manchester

Telephone   01253 893 127/0370
533 903
Young lesbian and bi girls
(contact Liz)

Icebreakers
Manchester

Telephone 0161 274 3999
Coming out advice and support

L&G Youth Manchester
Manchester

Telephone 0161 274 3814

42nd Street
Manchester

Telephone 0161 832 0170
LGB support for 15-21 year olds

Under 26s
Mansfield

Telephone 0115 934 8485

LGB Youthline
Milton Keynes

Telephone 01908 587 677
Meets Wednesday: 19.30–21.30

Friend
Newcastle upon Tyne

Telephone 0191 261 8555
Monday–Friday: 19.00–22.00
Operates numerous meetings
and groups

Chameleon Youth
Norwich

Telephone 01603 627 514
Contact Jenny or Scotty

LGB 51
Nottingham

Telephone 0115 952 5040
Youth support age 12-25

Way-Out
Oxford

Telephone 01865 243 389
Youth support up to age 25

Reach Out
PO Box 75
Reading
RG1 7DU

Telephone 0118 959 7269
Meets Wednesdays

LGB Youth
Rotherham

Telephone 01709 821 523
Tuesday & Friday: 18.30–21.30

Outzone
Salisbury

Telephone 01772 421 951/0468
715 548

LGB Youth
Scarborough

Telephone 01723 355 700
Contact Rob

LGB Youth
PO Box 425
Sheffield
S1 3UX
Ring switchboard for details

LGB Youth Group
PO Box 189
Shrewsbury
SY1

Telephone 01743 344 179
Wednesday 14.00–20.00

1 In 10 LGB Youth

Skelmersdale

Telephone 01695 725 665 / 0498 924 164
Tuesday & Wednesday 17.30–21.30

BLAG Youth Group

Southend on Sea

Telephone 01702 343 134

Space

Surrey

Telephone 01372 731 011
E-mail youth@esurrey-ha.sthames.nhs.uk
Groups meet near Epson

YaGAP (Young and Gay Awareness Project)

9 Devizes Road
Swindon
SN1 4BN

Telephone 01793 694 700
Monday–Thursday: 16.00–19.00

Youth Group

PO Box 130
Wellington
Telford
TF1 4NN
Write for details

LGB Support Group

7-9 Heathside Crescent
Woking

Telephone 01483 727 667
Tuesday: 19.30–22.00

SSCOG (Coming Out Group)

PO Box 59
Wolverhampton
WV10 0QX
Write for details

One In Ten Youth

10 Priory Street
York
YO1

Telephone 01904 612 629
Monday: 19.00–21.00

SCOTLAND

LGB Under 21s

Aberdeen

Telephone 01224 272 975

Dundee LGB Youth

Dundee
Ring Dundee switchboard for details

Lothian LGB Youth

Edinburgh
Ring switchboard for details

Outright Youth

PO Box 169
Edinburgh
EH1 3UU

Telephone 0131 557 2625

Stonewall Youth Project

PO Box 169
Edinburgh
EH1 3UU
No telephone, write for details

Befrienders

11 Dixon Street
Glasgow
G3

Telephone 0141 332 8372
Weekdays 19.00–22.00

Lesbian Youth Action

PO Box 686
Glasgow
G3

Telephone 0141 354 0400
Wednesday 19.30–22.00

Out And Loud

Glasgow

Telephone 0141 332 3838/01294
323 473
Contact David Bingham

Strathclyde LGB Youth

PO Box 69
Glasgow
G5 0TY
Ring switchboard for details

Youth Group

Inverness

Telephone 01463 711 585
Contact Ronald or Kerr

Forth Friend

PO Box 28
Stirling
FK9 5YW

Telephone 01786 471 285

WALES

Cardiff Gay Counselling

Cardiff

Telephone 09066 588 588
E-mail
cgc@morgraig.demon.co.uk

Cardiff Junior Youth

Cardiff
Ring Cardiff switchboard for
details

Friend South Wales

PO Box 479
Cardiff
South Wales
CF1 8JY

Telephone 01222 340 101
Wednesday–Friday: 20.00–
22.00

LGB Youth Group

Rhyl

Telephone 01745 351 293

Condoms and Lubricants

No condoms are tested and certified as suitable for anal sex, but condoms that conform to the tougher BS EN600 standard break less often in use than ordinary ones. Boys Own, Durex Ultra Strong, Forte, HT Special and Mates Super Strong all conform to this standard and the use of these is strongly recommended.

Of course, even strong condoms can break (studies involving gay couples have shown a breakage rate of anything from 1% to 4%) but you can keep the odds on your side if you:

Store them properly. Jeans pockets are out, as are any other hot places like the glove compartment of your car.

Use plenty of water based lubricant.

Get used to using them. In one study, the breakage rate decreased dramatically as time went on, presumably because the couples got used to using the condoms correctly.

Doubling up (putting two condoms on) is *less* safe than using one properly. The two condoms rub against each other causing friction that can destroy both.

Putting on a condom correctly

When you are hard, take a condom out of the wrapper carefully. It is not a good idea to use you teeth to tear the packet because you could damage the condom. Squeeze the air out of the teat (if there is one) and pop it over the end of your penis. Some people like to put a dab of lubricant inside the end of the condom, but don't use too much or the condom can slip off. Keep hold of the teat and roll it all the way down your penis. The further down it goes, the less likely it will be to slip off. If it wont unroll, you have got it on inside out – with the teat on the wrong side of the rolled-up latex (have a play with one if you don't think it can be inside out).

Once on your penis lube it up with lots of waterbased lubricant (see below), making sure that you use plenty. You can't use too much – use too little and the condom may break.

When you pull out, hold on to the condom at the base so that you don't leave it behind (it happens!). You should pull out before your penis goes soft.

It is advisable to practice using a condom by yourself in order that you will feel more confident when the time comes to using one with somebody else.

Lubricants

Stick to using lubricants that declare themselves to be *water-based* and suitable for use with condoms. The best-known brands of lube are Bodywise Liquid Silk, Boots' own brand, KY, Slick, Wet Stuff, 121, Maximus (for sensitive skin), ID, TLC, NX9 and Sex Grease. This list is not exhaustive of the brands available.

Beware oil and oil-derived products (anything from margarine to vaseline, baby oil to body moisturiser): they destroy the rubber and should not be used with latex condoms. Remember also, that if you have used oil-based products on a dildo or on your fist there will be enough either on your hands or up his anus to rot a condom if you have anal intercourse right afterwards. Polyurethane (plastic) condoms have been developed for use with almost any lubricant, but we do not know yet how suitable they are for anal sex.

GUM Clinics

No matter how careful you are, I cannot emphasise strongly enough the importance of having regular check-ups at your local GUM (Genito Urinary Medicine) clinic usually situated in your local General Hospital.

HIV check-ups are an extremely simple procedure. You do not have to give your real name although your correct date of birth and postcode is advised as these can be used to cross-reference your file on subsequent visits. The procedure is as follows:

1. Telephone the hospital (GUM department) to see what appointment system is in operation.
2. At the hospital you will be given an appointment card with an identification number and 'name' on it. Keep this card safe.
3. Initially, you will be seen by a councillor who will ask about the sexual practices that you engage in. Be honest with them. Tell

them that you go cruising; that you engage in oral sex; etc. I don't believe that there is anything you should be embarrassed about. These people hear stories such as these every day of their working life.

4. Ask for a *full* blood screening. This will include checks for syphilis, hepatitis and other sexually transmitted diseases.

5. You will be taken into a private room where a small blood sample will be taken from your arm.

6. You will then be asked to return in a couple of weeks for the results. In some instances it may be possible to obtain the results the same week.

The test itself doesn't look for HIV but for the antibodies to the virus. If antibodies are found then it is known to be HIV positive. If no antibodies are found then it is known as HIV negative. The period between infection and the time that antibodies are made can either be a few weeks or up to three months, therefore if you suspect that you have been infected you should return to the GUM clinic three months after the initial test for a follow-up test.

It is worth mentioning at this point that if you have not had the hepatitis B vaccination then it would be advised that you make a further appointment to have this done. It will not be started until you have had the results of your blood test. This procedure is also very simple and painless. The vaccination is carried out in three stages. Firstly, you will have the vaccine injected into the muscle of your arm. Secondly, you will be asked to return in one month for the second part of the vaccination. Thirdly, you will be asked to come back in a further three months for the final part. It is worth noting that if you do not return for the final dose, the previous two will not be that effective.

Sexually Transmitted Diseases

The following text has been reproduced by kind permission of Healthy Gay Manchester, 37 Ducie Street, Manchester M1 2JW:

Sexually transmitted diseases (STDs) are diseases that can be transmitted through sexual activity. STDs are more infectious than HIV and they are generally easier to transmit. However, with improvements in treatments and vaccinations, most STDs do not present the same health risks as HIV. No matter how safe your sex life is, some STDs are hard to avoid. Symptoms can take months to show and some STDs can have long-term effects. Maintaining good sexual health involves not only practising safer sex, but also visiting a GUM clinic for regular check-ups and receiving treatment when necessary.

For sexually active gay men, some STDs may be unavoidable, even if you are practising safer sex. Often you will be unaware of being infected with an STD as some STDs have no signs or symptoms and some symptoms may be hidden or disguised. The most important thing to remember is not to panic or feel embarrassed if you think that you have an STD.

It is important to seek good medical advice and to go to a GUM clinic for a check-up. How often you decide to go for a check up will depend on how often you have sex with new partners and what you do with them sexually.

GUM clinics have been established specifically to deal with the treatment of STDs and the service is provided free of charge. Don't be put off by the tales you may have heard about GUM clinics, of bizarre implements being used or of meeting someone you know. It is more important to benefit from any treatments that you may need, than it is to worry.

What you are likely to find is a relaxed and friendly atmosphere with specialist staff who are used to dealing with problems or concerns such as your own. GUM clinics are entirely confidential (even if you are admitted to the same hospital as a ward patient, you do not have to mention any previous visits to the GUM department). Your medical records at a GUM clinic are confidential by law and are not accessible to anyone else, not even your own GP, unless you have been referred by them, or you have requested otherwise.

Systems may vary from clinic to clinic, so phone for details before turning up. When you get there you are usually asked for a few personal details (name, address, etc.) although you can remain anonymous. If possible, try to give your postcode and date of birth correctly, as these will be used to cross-reference your file. Try to be honest and descriptive as this can sometimes reveal a requirement for other STD treatments. It's likely that you will be tested and treated on the same visit although you may need to make follow-up visits. It is important to follow the guidelines and advice for any treatment received.

Even if you don't think you have an STD it's a good idea to go along to a clinic for a general sexual health 'MOT' You can also get your vaccinations against hepatitis A and B while you are there.

By practising safer sex to prevent HIV transmission, you will also be taking the most important steps to prevent transmission of other STDs. Unprotected anal sex is the most risky form of sexual activity for the transmission of almost all STDs and for transmitting HIV.

Some types of sex which carry no risk of HIV transmission can be risky for transmitting other STDs. All serious STDs can be controlled with treatment as long as they are identified early enough. So, there are obvious benefits of going for regular check-ups at a GUM clinic.

The following list covers the most common STDs affecting gay men. It should be noted that, as with any medical condition, it is wise to obtain specific medical advice pertaining to your condition. This advice is available from your local GUM clinic.

Chlamydia

What is it?
Chlamydia is a common bacterial infection, mainly transmitted through unprotected anal sex, although Chlamydia can be transmitted through oral sex and 'rimming' (licking of the anus). If left untreated it can cause serious problems.

What are the symptoms?
Often hard to diagnose, as most people show no symptoms. However, if there are symptoms they include; a burning sensation and/or a white discharge when you urinate, a sore throat and a pain in the lower abdomen or anus. The eyes may also become swollen if infected.

What is the treatment?
A swab is taken to check for infection. Chlamydia is easiest to treat when spotted early. A course of antibiotics should clear up the infection.

Prevention
Use strong condoms and a water-based lubricant for anal sex and a barrier for oral sex and rimming (such as a flavoured condom for oral sex and non-microwavable cling film for rimming). It is not advisable to share sex toys. Avoid touching your eyes until you have washed your hands. It is usual for GUM cinics to test for chlamydia when you have a check-up.

Genital Warts

What are they?
Warts are one of the most common STDs. Warts can be transmitted through skin contact and are fairly easy to catch and to pass on.

What are the symptoms?
The warts usually appear on the shaft or head of the penis, or around and inside of the anus. They can grow singly (initially the size of a pinhead) or in a cluster and can appear as smooth and flat small bumps or as large pink cauliflower-like lumps. The signs may take a few weeks or many months after infection to present themselves. Occasionally, they may appear in your mouth, on your face or on other parts of your body. They are lighter in colour than the surrounding skin. Untreated, the warts can spread and get bigger.

What is the treatment?
It is important to visit a GUM clinic for treatment. The treatment can vary and includes having a chemical painted on (which burns the wart off) or having the wart frozen off with liquid nitrogen. Warts can disappear quickly after treatment or they can reappear and need further treatment. Warts must be treated by a doctor (at a GUM clinic). They can't be cured with treatments from chemists used for warts on the hand.

Prevention
Although the virus remains after the warts are gone, someone is only infectious when the warts are visible. To minimise the risk of contraction the use of strong condoms with a water-based lubricant for anal sex is necessary. However, as the virus is contracted by contact and not through semen, the use of condoms will not always be a satisfactory barrier. If you do have them it is best to get them treated as soon as possible.

Gonorrhoea

What is it?
Gonorrhoea is a bacterial infection which affects the urethra (the tube running from the bladder to the tip of the penis) anus, mouth

and throat. Very often, gonorrhoea can go undetected, although it can still be passed on. If gonorrhoea is left untreated it can cause serious illness.

What are the symptoms?
A yellow or white odourless discharge from the penis. Other symptoms include a burning sensation when urinating, a pain in the anus and a sore throat.

What is the treatment?
Gonorrhoea is easily treated with a course of antibiotics, either by injection or tablets. It is important to have a follow-on check-up to ensure that it has completely cleared up.

Prevention
Gonorrhoea is easily transmitted through unprotected anal sex, oral sex and rimming. If you are infected it is highly advisable to avoid these sexual acts until the infection has cleared up completely. It is important for current or recent sexual partners to attend a GUM clinic for screening and possible treatment.

Hepatitis A, B and C

What is it?
The hepatitis virus is a condition which affects the liver. There are several different types of the virus and those already identified have been given the letters: A, B, C, D, E, and G. In order to avoid confusion, the following guide will only deal with A, B and C, the three most common types of the hepatitis virus in this country. Sexual transmission of hepatitis A and B is currently on the increase amongst gay men and vaccinations are available from GUM clinics or your GP. These vaccinations are highly effective and can protect you from what are potentially very dangerous infections. If you are a sexually active gay man it is extremely important for you to get hepatitis A and B vaccinations. Before you are given these vaccinations, your clinic will give you a blood test to see whether you have been exposed to hepatitis before. Once the results of this test are received the clinic will be able to advise on the best course of treatment for you. If you and your partner have been successfully vaccinated against hepatitis A and B, then this is one less thing to worry about during sex. It may also make a difference to your sex life because some sex will be less risky. You will still need to think about other STDs though, including HIV, when you have sex.

Hepatitis A

What is it?
Hepatitis A is a common viral infection, found in many parts of the world and is becoming more common in this country, particularly amongst gay men. It is much less likely to lead to long-term liver disease than hepatitis B, although in a small number of cases it can still be serious and cause damage to the liver. Sexual transmission of hepatitis A between gay men is usually through oral contact with an infected person's faeces and urine (rimming and watersports). You can also contract the virus by eating unhygienically prepared food by someone who has the virus. In some parts of the world the virus is present in the water supply, so if you are travelling to one of these countries you will need to be careful with what you drink.

What are the symptoms?
Symptoms can take up to a month to present themselves and can last for up to six weeks (this is the period when you will be most infectious, so it may not be possible to identify an 'infected' person just by looking at them). They can include flu-like symptoms such as fever, nausea, exhaustion and diarrhoea. Other symptoms include weight loss, jaundice (yellowing of the skin and eyes), darkened urine and pale faeces and a distaste for fatty foods, tobacco and alcohol.

What is the treatment?
There is no treatment for hepatitis A. If you are diagnosed you will be advised to rest and avoid alcohol until your body has completely recovered from the infection .You should also avoid the use of any recreational drugs (speed and ecstasy in particular) as the risk of these causing serious damage to your liver is far greater than normal. The recovery period varies from person to person and can take up to six months depending on how severe your infection is. You will need a further blood test to ensure that you have fully recovered.

Prevention
Vaccination still remains the best way to protect yourself from infection with hepatitis A. To protect yourself you should use barriers such as a non-microwavable cling film or a dental dam for rimming. For fisting and fingering you should use surgical gloves with a water-based lubricant. You should also avoid sharing sex toys. If you do share, use a fresh condom each time and ensure the toys are washed and disinfected. If you are sexually active, it is vital

that you are vaccinated against hepatitis A. The vaccination course should protect you for up to ten years. Personal hygiene should become a habit, particularly, washing your hands after going to the toilet. Do not have sex with someone who is jaundiced (although jaundice is not a sure-fire sign that someone is infected). Remember, you might not always know if your partner is infected or not, so it is best to be safe. If you haven't yet been vaccinated, always practice safer sex.

Hepatitis B

What is it?
Hepatitis B is one of the most dangerous sexually transmitted diseases and, in a small number of cases, can lead to serious liver disease and death. Hepatitis B is also very infectious and is transmitted much more easily than HIV. What's more, hepatitis B is common amongst gay men in this country. Because of this, gay men should be vaccinated against hepatitis B. The virus can be present in all bodily fluids, more notably: blood, cum and pre-cum, and can therefore be transmitted when any of these enter your body. It may also be in saliva and urine, so it is possible to be passed on during kissing and watersports (although this *isn't* common). For gay men, hepatitis B is mainly transmitted through unprotected anal sex, unprotected oral sex, sex involving urine getting into the eyes or mouth and any type of sex which involves the faeces entering the mouth (rimming). The majority of people do overcome infection with hepatitis B fully and are not infectious afterwards. However, some can remain infectious and can develop chronic liver disease later in life. People who remain infectious are called 'carriers' of hepatitis B. If you remain a 'carrier' you can pass the infection on to other sexual partners if you don't practice safer sex.

What are the symptoms?
Many people who are infected with hepatitis B do not experience any symptoms, although they will still be infectious to others. However, some people will experience an acute period of illness after an incubation period of anything up to six months. Although people respond to infection in different ways, common symptoms include flu-like symptoms, tiredness, jaundice (yellowing of the skin and eyes, darkened urine and faeces) and loss of appetite.

What is the treatment?
There is no cure for hepatitis B and again, vaccination still remains the best way to protect yourself from infection. A booster injection will be needed, usually after 3-5 years. In both cases the clinic will be able to advise you further. Anyone who has experienced symptoms of acute infection needs to rest and avoid alcohol to allow their body to recover completely. The use of recreational drugs must be avoided as they pose a serious threat to your liver. The recovery period for hepatitis B is usually longer than with hepatitis A and can often be for up to several months. For the few men who remain as 'carriers', drugs are available which can help in treating the condition.

Prevention
Because hepatitis B is so easily transmitted, your best protection is to get vaccination. Getting vaccinated will mean one less thing to worry about during sex. If you and/or your partner is diagnosed with hepatitis B you should avoid any form of sex which could involve bodily fluids entering your body. You should follow these guidelines until the infection has completely cleared:

Use a dry or flavoured condom for oral sex.

Avoid getting urine into your mouth and eyes.

Use a barrier such as non-microwaveable cling film as a dental dam for rimming.

Avoid sharing sex toys. If you do share, use a fresh condom each time and always make sure your toys are washed and disinfected

It is *important to remember* that the symptoms of hepatitis B don't always show, so you might not know whether you or your partner is infected.

Hepatitis C

What is it?
Hepatitis C is a dangerous virus, which, like hepatitis B, can lead to severe liver disease and death. Little is known about hepatitis C but it is thought to be difficult to sexually transmit the virus. The majority of hepatitis C sufferers are injecting drug users because the main route of transmission is through blood. The hepatitis C virus was first identified in 1988 and a hepatitis C antibody test (anti-HCV) to identify individuals exposed to the virus became commercially available in 1990. In 1995 the virus was seen for the first time by using an electron microscope. A lot is still being learned about

hepatitis C and what happens if you get it. The most likely route of sexual transmission amongst gay men is through unprotected anal sex although this is not a common route to infection. Most people with it got infected from sharing drug-injecting equipment or by being given infected blood transfusions before September 1991 (when the blood supply began to be checked for the
hepatitis C virus). Using strong condoms and a water-based lubricant for anal sex should protect you against hepatitis C.

What are the symptoms?
It is possible that you'll have no symptoms when you first pick up the infection and it can sometimes take years for the signs of serious disease to show. During this period you will still be infectious to others. Like hepatitis B, these symptoms will vary, but normally include tiredness, jaundice, fever and vomiting.

What is the treatment?
Anyone thought to be infected with hepatitis C will often be referred to a liver specialist by their doctor or clinic. This will mean a visit to a hospital as an outpatient in order that a liver biopsy can be performed. Once the specialist knows the condition of your liver, a course of drugs will usually be prescribed. These are used to boost the body's immune system so that it can fight off the infection. However, a cure is not guaranteed and your liver can be permanently damaged if the infection progresses.

Herpes

What is it?
Herpes is a virus which once contracted can often remain for life and occasionally flare up from time to time, particularly when you are feeling run down. Coming into contact with the herpes virus, whether as a cold sore round the mouth or as a sore or blister around the genital area, can lead to transmission of the virus. Therefore, all forms of sexual activity are risky if someone has herpes.

What are the symptoms?
Localised itching and soreness, leading to the development of small, painful cold sores around the mouth and sores and blisters around

the genitals or anus. The blisters usually crust over within 10–14 days. Once the sores have healed they are no longer infectious. Often people with herpes show no symptoms.

What is the treatment?
No cure, but anti-viral drugs and creams can help minimise the severity and lengths of the attacks. Zovirax (available from chemists) is useful for suppressing cold sores around the mouth but is not used for the treatment of sores or blisters around the genitals or anus. You can often get pain relief by bathing the genital or anal sores/blisters in salt water or using calamine lotion.

Prevention
If you have herpes you should avoid all forms of sex which brings the sores or blisters into contact with someone else's body until the sores or blisters have healed. You can spread herpes from around the mouth to the genital area and vice versa. Don't share towels, and do not use saliva to wet contact lenses as this could cause an eye infection. It is particularly important for people with HIV to avoid becoming infected with the herpes virus as herpes can further compromise the immune system.

Non-Specific Urethritis (NSU)

What is it?
NSU, sometimes called NGU (non-gonococcal urethritis) is caused by bacteria that lives in the anus, penis and mouth. NSU is one of the most common infections and it usually affects the urethra. The urethra is the tube running from the bladder to the end of the penis. There are many infections which can inflame the urethra and cause urethritis. Often the exact cause of NSU isn't known which is why it's called 'non-specific'. You must not be fooled into thinking that 'non-specific' means 'non-serious', all infections without the correct treatment can lead to very unpleasant symptoms.

What are the symptoms?
NSU usually results in a burning sensation when urinating, which can be painful. A white discharge in the morning from the penis is also common. However, you can show no symptoms for NSU.

What is the treatment?
A complete course of antibiotics. You are likely to be asked to return to the clinic to check that the infection has completely cleared.

Prevention
As with other STDs, all sexual activity should cease until the infection has been diagnosed and successfully treated. Use of a strong condom and water-based lubricant for anal sex, and dry or flavoured condom for oral sex will prevent transmission from an infected person.

Pubic Lice (Crabs)

What are they?
Pubic lice are very small 'nits' which resemble crabs (the size of a pinhead when fully grown). Crabs live in body hair, particularly pubic hair, but not head hair. They feed on your blood but they cannot pass on HIV. Crabs are extremely easy to catch but can be treated effectively. Crabs are usually transmitted through close bodily contact, but they can also be transmitted by sharing bedding, clothing and towels as they can survive away from the body for about 24 hours. If you have a partner who has crabs it doesn't necessarily mean he has had sex with someone else.

What are the symptoms?
The first symptoms of extreme itchiness around the genital area should appear about 2–3 weeks after infection. You may also notice minute blood patches in your underwear.

What is the treatment?
A special liquid solution (available from the chemist without prescription – ask for Derbac, Quellada, Lyclear or Prioderm). These treatments are available free at GUM clinics. Follow the instructions on the bottle, which should instruct you to cover your entire body (excluding head) with the lotion and leave on for a total of 24 hours. It is best not to go out during this period as the lotion has a very distinctive smell. You should also wash bed linen, bedding and all of the clothes you have worn since contracting the crabs in a hot wash. Examine the hair carefully for any remaining 'nits'. These should be combed out and removed, using a 'nit comb'. The treatment is short-term and highly effective. Complete shaving of pubic hair will prove totally ineffective

Prevention
It is impossible to avoid crabs if you come into contact with someone who has them. If you have crabs, follow the above instructions and

avoid having sex with anybody until the crabs have cleared up. Remember to wash all bedding and clothing on a hot wash.

Scabies

What are they?
Scabies are caused by a mite which burrows under the skin, causing itching – sometimes quite severe – and can very easily be transmitted through physical contact.

What are the symptoms?
The mites are invisible to the naked eye, but the trails they leave behind show up as red marks or lines usually on your wrists and between fingers. The first symptom that you may notice is extreme itchiness on your feet and hands, particularly between the extremities. It then follows over the whole body area.

What is the treatment?
The whole body except for the head is treated with a special lotion that's left on for up to 24 hours and then washed off. Lotions are available from GUM clinics and from chemists with a pharmacy counter. You will need to wash all bedding, clothes and towels on a hot wash to avoid re-infection. Anyone who has been in close physical contact with you will need treatment too.

Prevention
Avoid physical contact until the infection has cleared. Thankfully, this does not take very long.

Syphilis

What is it?
Syphilis is an easily transmitted disease that no longer poses the threat it once did. It is important to identify a syphilis infection early. Often, if you are infected with syphilis, you will show no symptoms. There are three stages of syphilis and treatment generally occurs in the primary or second stages.

What are the symptoms?
Primary syphilis often results in sores appearing on the penis and genital area, in the throat and in or around the anus. The sores are often painless and do not bleed easily. If left untreated the sores will heal but syphilis will develop into the secondary stage. Secondary

syphilis results in a skin rash, Headaches, nausea and fever are common too. Tertiary syphilis can be extremely serious but is very rare these days.

What is the treatment?
Syphilis is easily treated with antibiotics, usually by injection and, dependent on the stage of syphilis, this can be up to a 21-day course. Follow-up visits to a GUM clinic are required to ensure the infection has completely cleared.

Prevention
Syphilis can only be transmitted through sexual contact with the sores or skin rash. If you have syphilis you should avoid all sexual contact until you have finished the treatment. It is important for previous and current partners to attend a GUM clinic for screening and possible treatment. Use of a strong condom and a water-based lubricant will help prevent the transmission from an infected person. Regular check-ups at the GUM clinic will usually include a check for syphilis.

Thrush

What is it?
Thrush is a very common fungal infection. Thrush often affects people with a compromised immune system and therefore can affect anyone with HIV. Other causes of thrush include stress, certain viral infections or use of antibiotics.

What are the symptoms?
Irritation and inflammation around the head of the penis and soreness around the anus. Oral thrush is the most common form of thrush for people with HIV. Frequent outbreaks of thrush may occur, for which anti-fungal drugs may be offered.

What is the treatment?
Using anti-fungal drugs such as Caneston (available from the chemist). If you are sexually active then you should visit a GUM clinic to ensure no other infections are causing the infection.

Prevention

Practising safer sex will usually prevent sexual transmission. Oral thrush is likely to be transmitted to the genital area.

Further detailed advice and concerns regarding your sexual health should be directed to your nearest switchboard. They will refer you to your nearest GUM clinic or sexual health helpline.

Thanks to charities such as Rubberstuffers and the availability of free contraception in most gay clubs, saunas and bars, there is absolutely no excuse for not carrying condoms with you at all times (remember to put what you can afford into the collection box attached to the dispenser). This does not mean that you are obliged to use them. You aren't, but at least you are prepared should the occasion arise.

If you have any doubts or questions regarding safe sex, then please ring one of the numerous helpline numbers for your area. All calls are treated in the strictest of confidence.

HIV and AIDS

Introduction

Fact: At current rates, someone in the United Kingdom is diagnosed with HIV every three and a half hours.

Fact: Since statistics began in the United Kingdom, over 10,800 gay men have been diagnosed with AIDS.

Fact: Since UK statistics began, over 19,700 gay men have been tested HIV positive.

Fact: One third of gay men with the AIDS virus are unaware that they are infected with HIV.

Fact: According to a recent survey; one in six young men in the UK, mistakenly believe that new HIV treatments can stop the virus being passed on.

Fact: There are an estimated 33,400,000 people, world-wide, infected with the HIV virus.

Fact: In 1996 there were over 2,800 new HIV infections reported in the UK. This was the highest recorded figure ever and shows that the problem of HIV is not going away.

Fact: One in ten HIV infections in the UK is deemed to be the result of sharing drug injecting equipment with someone who is HIV positive.

Fact: Unprotected anal sex is by far the most risky sex for gay men.

Knowledge and information will be your greatest weapon against the onslaught of HIV and AIDS and it is up to you to protect yourself against the disease by finding out as much as you can. The figures above are indeed scary and there is no need for them to get any higher if you follow the simple rules regarding safer sex. You do not have to sacrifice your sex life to stay uninfected. On the contrary; by learning what you can and can't do safely will reduce your worries leaving you to enjoy a natural part of gay life.

If you have concerns regarding any aspect of your sexual health, you can obtain up to date and accurate information from the helpline listings which follow this section. The operators will be able to answer your questions in the strictest confidence and, if necessary, refer you to a relevant organisation, depending on the nature of your query.

The subsequent pages have been adapted from text supplied by various health agencies; most notably:

GMFA
Unit 42
Eurolink Centre
49 Effra Road
London
SW2 1BZ

Terrence Higgins Trust
52–54 Grays Inn Road
London
WC1X

Separating Fact From Fiction

What does AIDS stand for?
AIDS stands for Acquired Immune Deficiency Syndrome. This is the name given to a collection of illnesses caused when HIV damages your immune system.

What does HIV stand for?
HIV stands for Human Immunodeficiency Virus. Up until 1987 the HIV virus was known as HTLV-111.

What is the difference between HIV and AIDS?
HIV is the virus that can lead to AIDS. When you contract HIV, antibodies in your blood cannot destroy the virus which continues to develop and break down your immune system. Over a period of time without drugs to stabilise the virus your immune system will break down leaving you open to the most minor infection, i.e. colds and influenza, without having an immune system to deal with it. When you develop certain infections and your CD4 count drops to a specific level you are known to have AIDS

How many people in the United Kingdom have AIDS?
Accurate statistical information first started being collated in 1985. Since then and through to the end of 1998, the number of people diagnosed as having AIDS is believed to be in excess of 15,500 cases. Out of these, it is believed that 10,700 men contracted the disease by having sex with another man.

How many people in the United Kingdom have HIV?
Between 1985 and 1998 the number of all diagnosed cases are believed to be in excess of 32,200. Out of these, it is believed that over 19,700 men contracted the virus by having sex with another man.

How is the HIV virus contracted?
To contract the HIV virus, the blood, semen (or pre-cum) of an infected person has to enter your bloodstream. This can be done in a number of ways, more notably, having unprotected anal sex, whereby the lining of the anus can easily be damaged and the bodily fluids of the infected person can enter. However, it must be said that the virus can enter the urethra (the tube that runs from the bladder to the tip of the penis) from an infected passive partner. It should be noted that HIV isn't passed on automatically with *every* instance of unsafe sex but it *can* be passed on during *any* single instance.

The other main cause is when infected and uninfected injecting drug users share injecting equipment.

What are the symptoms of HIV infection?
If you are infected with HIV there are no symptoms straight away. In the weeks after infection you may get a flu-like illness with the following symptoms: fever, swollen glands, sore throat and sometimes a rash on the body. Many people do not get these symptoms and they could be caused by lots of other infections. For months or even years after you have been infected with HIV you may not get any symptoms but over time, you may get infections and diseases caused by your immune system getting weaker.

What is safe/safer sex?
Safer sex is the term used for limiting the risk of passing on or contracting the HIV virus and other sexually transmitted diseases. This can be done in a manner of ways, depending on the type of sex you are having. For example, safer anal sex means that you should always use a *strong* condom such as Mates Super Strong, Durex Ultra Strong, Boys Own, HT Specials or Safeguard Forte. A *water-based lubricant* is also needed such as KY Jelly, Liquid Silk, or Wetstuff. A lubricant is required for ease of passage and to help prevent the condom from breaking. The use of *oil-based lubricants* should be avoided at all costs, as an oil-based lubricant will destroy the rubber of a condom. Examples of oil-based lubricants are Vaseline, baby oil, suntan lotions and creams, skin creams and food products that contain oil. Safer oral sex means that you keep your mouth healthy.

Sufferers of bleeding gums should avoid brushing their teeth before oral sex (preferably use a mouthwash instead). You should also keep semen out of your mouth. Use flavoured condoms for oral sex (these won't taste of rubber).

Risk assessment is a very complex task which we have to perform every day. Unfortunately we are not very good at it. For example, when you drive faster to make an appointment on time, do you stop and decide that arriving on time is actually worth the risk of a serious accident?

To make matters worse, no one can quantify the risk of HIV transmission associated with a particular sexual activity with any degree of precision. To be better at making these judgments we need information and we need to be in control. Reading these pages and talking about safer sex with your partner will help with both of these.

Being HIV positive may also change your view on where to draw the line on safer sex, since the consequences of other sexually transmitted diseases may now be more serious. It is important to remember that different infections have different means of transmission (see also the Sexually Transmitted Diseases section in the Health Care chapter of this book).

Are there any other sex acts that can transfer the virus?
Yes. Although unprotected anal sex is in the 'very high risk' category, the following acts are also deemed to hold some risk:

Fisting. This is a relatively low risk activity, but to be extra careful, use a strong rubber glove and plenty of lubricant. HIV can be passed through broken skin or cuts on your hands. Don't use gloves on more than one partner at a time and either wash them thoroughly afterwards, or better still, dispose of them and use new ones each time. After you've fisted someone, don't put your fingers up anyone else.

Watersports. Another low risk activity for HIV. Pissing on the skin, providing you have no cuts, is no risk at all. Drinking piss is no more risky than oral sex. But, it is worth noting that if the person has a kidney infection there may be blood in the piss.

Rimming. There is almost no chance of getting HIV from rimming, though, as always, if there is bleeding, the risk is higher. This may not always be obvious! Anal intercourse and the use of dildoes can cause internal bleeding, as can brushing and flossing your teeth, so it's safer not to rim if your mouth, or his anus, has been cut or damaged in any way. There is a risk of catching hepatitis A or B. To avoid this risk it is strongly recommended that you get vaccinated. Vaccines for both types are usually available from your GUM clinic.

Corporal punishment. C.P. is relatively safe if the skin is not broken, but again: know your limits. If you use an implement like a cane or whip that might draw blood, it should only be used on one person at a time and cleaned between partners.

Bondage. This carries no risk at all, but you are entering a situation of utmost trust and may not be able to negotiate later. Before getting in to a scene, make sure you know what your limits are. Limits aren't just S&M limits but also what you will or will not do in the way of safer sex. Discussing safer sex beforehand and knowing you can trust someone will make you more relaxed and inevitably lead to better and more exiting sex. It is better not to take a sub-servient role with a stranger.

Shaving. If you are planning on shaving any part of your own or your partner's body, always use a fresh, sharp blade. Never use the same blade on more than one person. Don't ejaculate over freshly shaven skin, as you cannot always see cuts and grazes.

Scat. Shit is very low risk for HIV, as long as there are no open cuts on your skin. You are at greater risk if you get shit in your mouth, especially if you have cuts there. You may however get hepatitis A or the more serious B or other nasty bugs. Again, vaccinations for these can be obtained at your GUM clinic.

Mutual masturbation. Carries no risk unless you use the cum of an infected person for lubrication. Even then, it is deemed to be low risk.

Oral sex. Most of us find sucking cock or being sucked pretty horny. For most of us, it is a regular part of sex. That's why it's a shame that some gay men are worried and confused about how safe it is. The actual risk of HIV infection is very low. The lining of the mouth is quite tough and saliva is a very good barrier to HIV. However, sucking cock or getting your cock sucked is not 100% safe. That's because there is evidence of a very few cases where gay men do seem to have contracted HIV through oral sex. (about 20 cases in the past 15 years – although the data on all of these cases cannot be guaranteed that the transmission *definitely* came from oral sex. Most health advisors would say that the risk of contracting HIV in giving

oral sex is negligible, and that in receiving oral sex, the risk is nil).
We know that HIV can be transmitted in blood, cum or pre-cum, so it
is theoretically possible that it could be passed on if you have cuts or
sores in your mouth, or oral piercings which should be left to heal
completely, which could take up to 12 months. So, keep your mouth
healthy, but don't brush or floss right before sucking as this can
leave small cuts in your mouth. The best way of avoiding HIV is to
not get cum into your mouth. If you do, it is slightly better to spit
than to swallow. Whilst cock-sucking is a low risk activity for HIV,
bear in mind that other STD's can be transmitted such as hepatitis B
as well as herpes and gonorrhoea. If you are still worried, the safest
thing to do would be to use a condom.

Toys. Toys that go inside you and toys that can cut you should only
be used by one person. Afterwards, they should be cleaned in hot
soapy water or a 10% bleach solution, then rinsed thoroughly and
dried.
Games with oil and wax are fun and safe but keep them away from
rubbers. Remember that if you've used a greasy lubricant on toys up
his anus, the oil will then rot a condom if you fuck him soon
afterwards.

What about saliva?
The risk of deep throat kissing is absolutely minuscule and there is
no reason at all why you should worry about it. There is not enough
HIV in spit, sweat and urine to infect anyone. So kissing, no matter
how much saliva is exchanged, is not at all risky. However, there is a
risk if your partner's mouth is damaged or bleeding.

Does the use of poppers increase the risk of HIV?
Yes. The risk is increased even further if you are having unprotected
anal sex. This is because poppers can make the lining of your anus
bleed, allowing HIV to be passed either way. Of course, use condoms
and then the use of poppers during sex is low risk. (*Low* risk rather
than *zero* risk – there is still a chance that the condom will break.)

How risky is having unprotected sex and pulling out before I cum?
Very risky. You have to remember that the lining of the anus is
extremely delicate and that the pre-cum of an infected person can
enter this way in addition to the virus being contracted by you from
an infected passive partner via your urethra.

Can you catch HIV from cutlery or from sharing a cup?
Absolutely not. Not even if the infected person spits into the cup. This was one of the myths created by the media frenzy in the eighties. It is equivalent to saying that a girl can get pregnant if a boy kisses her.

Is there a cure for HIV?
There is no cure or vaccine for HIV although many of the illnesses that people infected with HIV get can be treated or kept under control with drugs. If you have HIV, drugs can lower the amount of HIV made in your body, usually resulting in better health. These drugs are quite new and no-one knows if they will work over a number of years or if they will have to be taken for the rest of your life. For a lot of people, drug treatments don't work very well, if at all. The drugs can have unpleasant side effects and be hard to take. If you are diagnosed with HIV you may not be given drugs straight away. Tests are done to see what HIV is doing in your body before decisions are made about treatment. Treatment may be different depending on where you are being treated.

What is an HIV test?
An HIV (antibody) test, usually done on a sample of your blood, shows if you have HIV. The test does not look for HIV itself but for the antibodies to the virus. The body makes antibodies to fight infections, but antibodies made to fight HIV cannot destroy the virus. If antibodies to HIV are found then the test is 'positive' and the person is said to be HIV positive. If antibodies aren't found then the test is 'negative' and the person is said to be HIV negative. If you are infected with HIV, antibodies aren't made straight away. It can take weeks or months before they appear. This is called the 'window period' and it usually lasts for less than three months. Because of the window period, if you want to know if you have HIV you must wait three months before being tested. That's three months since the time you think you *may* have been infected. A test done before then can come back as 'negative' when really you are infected and very infectious but it's not yet showing in your blood.

As a point of note, if you go to your local GP and ask him/her for an HIV test then this will be documented on your medical records. The inclusion of these notes may make it extremely difficult for you to obtain a mortgage, insurance, etc. at a later date.

What would a positive result mean to me?
If you get a 'positive' result it means that you have been infected with HIV. You can infect others if you have unsafe sex. It doesn't say anything about how your health will be in the future and it doesn't mean that you have AIDS or will go on to develop AIDS. If people know that you have HIV, it might be that you can expect to come across hostility and prejudice. If you are tested positive you will get all of the support that you require from highly trained support staff at the hospital.

What would a negative result mean to me?
A negative result means that you haven't been infected with HIV — so long as the test was done at least three months after the last time you did something that put you at risk of getting HIV. If you do something that has a risk of contracting HIV and later get a negative test result it doesn't follow that you are immune to HIV, nor that you can take risks in the future and stay uninfected.

Can you describe HIV in a little more detail?
Like all viruses, HIV replicates by hijacking your body's cells and turning them into virus factories. It does this by inserting its own genetic information into the cell and thereby stopping its normal function. Any disease that results is just a by-product of the virus' means of reproduction.

Only certain cells are vulnerable to HIV. It can infect only the so-called CD4 lymphocytes, which play a crucial role in regulating the body's immune response to infections. These cells have a protein called CD4 (hence their name) on the surface to which HIV can attach itself. Dead CD4 cells are replaced by the body and in the first stages of infection, a battle rages with CD4 cells being rapidly destroyed and replaced. At the same time, the body's immune system kicks in and produces antibodies in an attempt to neutralise the virus. It is these antibodies that are detected by the standard HIV test but it can take up to three months for enough of them to be made for the test to show positive.

A relatively new test can measure the quantity of virus present in a sample (usually of blood) but this 'viral load' test is rarely used as a test for infection. Since CD4 cells play an important part in your body's response to infection, their loss makes you vulnerable to opportunistic infections, many of which would not normally be a problem. For this reason, counts of the number of CD4 cells, also called T-cells, (and of other important immune system cells) are used to determine what, if any, medical intervention is needed.

What is a CD4 count?

A CD4 count, or T-cell count, is a test carried out on your blood when you have HIV. They show how much damage HIV has done to your immune system. CD4 cells lead the body's fight against infections and a CD4 count measures how many are being made. Left untreated, HIV will cause the number of your CD4 cells to fall, perhaps slowly over the years as your immune system is damaged. The lower it falls, the more likely you are to have health problems. The higher your CD4 count the better your immune system is working. People without HIV usually have a count of between 500–1,200. If you have HIV and a CD4 count between these figures, your count is within the usual range for people without HIV. Your CD4 count can go up and down without any obvious reason, so decisions about treatment are made after looking at several CD4 counts, taken over a period of time.

What is a viral load test?

Viral load tests are tests carried out on your blood when you have HIV to see how well you are responding to anti-HIV drugs. They show how much HIV is being made in your body. The test shows how many 'copies' of the virus are in a sample of your blood, i.e. how many HIV particles were found in a millilitre of blood. Viral load can range from undetectable to over one million copies. The lower the figure – the better, and undetectable is the best. Less than 10,000 copies is seen as a low viral load and over 50,000 is seen as high. A higher viral load means you are more likely to get ill. You could be more infectious and there could be a greater chance of HIV being passed on if you have unprotected sex.

Drugs can often lower your viral load, meaning that you should get ill less often. Sometimes, drugs can get your viral load down to undetectable levels. Undetectable doesn't mean that HIV has gone from your body; HIV is still there, but not in levels high enough for the test to measure. If you have a low or undetectable viral load, HIV can still be in your blood, semen or pre-cum, so you could give the virus to others during unprotected sex.

Your viral load can go up and down without any obvious reason so decisions about treatment are made after looking at several viral load tests taken over a period of time.

If I am tested HIV positive, can I have unprotected sex?

Unprotected sex between HIV positive men can result in the transmission of a strain of HIV that is resistant to drugs you may never have taken. Therefore, the drugs will be less effective when you need them. Someone else's drug treatment history may include a lot more drugs than you have ever experienced, and becoming infected with *their* HIV strain could cause resistance to those untried drugs in you. By picking up strains of HIV that are resistant to drugs you will lose the benefit of the treatments that could have prolonged your life. HIV positive men *should not* have unprotected sex with anyone, either infected or not.

Is there a link between STDs and HIV?
Sexually transmitted diseases (except pubic lice and scabies) increase the chances of HIV being passed on during unprotected sex. This is true in the case of men having unprotected sex, and can be the case for sucking too. The two reasons for this are skin damage and viral load:

Skin damage. STDs often cause the skin on or in your penis, anus and throat to become sore, inflamed or sometimes to bleed. This makes it easier for HIV to get through this skin and into the bloodstream. For example, if a man with HIV cums in your mouth when you've got gonorrhoea in your throat this increases the small risk of getting HIV through sucking.

Viral load. If you have HIV, having an untreated STD usually makes your viral load (the amount of HIV in your blood and cum) go up. This is because your immune system is fighting both HIV and another STD; so it can't fight your HIV as well as usual. This increases the amount of HIV in your blood and cum, making it more likely for HIV to be passed on, if you have unprotected sex.

Because of the link between STDs and HIV it's a good idea for everyone, whether they have HIV or not, to have regular check-ups at a GUM clinic, especially as you can have infections and not notice symptoms.

What anti-HIV drugs are available?
As well as the drugs that are used to treat and prevent opportunistic infections, several drugs are available to treat the HIV infection directly. To understand how they work it helps to know a little bit about how HIV operates.

Your cells store their genetic material as DNA (deoxyribonucleic acid) – two mirrored strands of RNA (ribonucleic acid) zipped together and stored in the cell's nucleus. HIV is a retrovirus which means that it stores its genetic material as RNA rather than DNA. For it to be inserted into the target cell, the RNA must be zipped up into DNA and spliced into the DNA in the cell's nucleus. Not surprisingly, the enzyme that HIV uses to do this conversion is called 'reverse transcriptase' and the one that does the splicing is called 'integrase'.

Both RNA and DNA are long molecules made up of strings of chemicals called 'nucleosides'. The conversion of RNA into DNA involves building up the correct mirror string of nucleosides. The first family of anti-HIV drugs were all nucleoside analogues – chemicals that look much like genuine nucleosides but which, once added to the growing strand, clog up the process much like a bent tooth in a zipper. AZT, ddI, ddC, D4T and 3TC are all nucleoside analogues.

A relatively new class of drugs attacks the process at the other end. Once the viral DNA is inserted into the cell, the cell's usual processes cause it to make new HIV proteins. These must be cut up into the right building blocks for new HIV particles, which is the job of an enzyme called 'protease'. The so-called protease inhibitors like Indinavir, Saquinavir and Ritonavir all interfere with this process by binding to the HIV protease.

Drugs are also being developed that interfere with the middle stage. None of these integrase inhibitors are currently available for clinical use.

Do I have to practice safer sex whilst in a long-term relationship?
The advice that any health care worker would give is, if you are planning to have a long-term *monogamous* relationship it would be advisable to have a joint HIV test. Upon testing positive, you will have to work out between the two of you whether or not to stay faithful to each other. If there is a risk that you or your partner may be tempted to have a one night stand, then you should always practice safer sex. The answer to this question can only be decided by yourselves, and it is best to sort it out at the beginning of a relationship (after a HIV test); whether or not to use condoms. If you do decide to 'play around', then decide between the two of you what you *can* do and what you *can't* do with a third party.

HIV and AIDS are difficult subjects to cover within the resources and scope of this book. The above text is offered *only as a guideline* and to provoke you into taking the subject matter more seriously than you probably have done in the past. If you are tested positive, there are going to be literally hundreds more questions that you will need answered; for example: do you tell your GP? Do you tell your employer? Do you have to advise your insurers? What will be your expected life span? Answers to these questions will be supplied by your health care worker and numerous other agencies, who work tirelessly against the onslaught of HIV and AIDS. Only they can give the advice that will apply to you and you alone.

The numbers that follow are all for agencies set up to dispense information on HIV/AIDS, health care and *any* worries that you may have regarding your sexual health. There is no question that they have not heard before and they are willing and able to help you through any situation. If, for some reason the number you call for your area is no longer available then try the next area closest to your home town. If the matter cannot be dealt with locally you will be referred to the appropriate agency that can deal with your request. It is worth repeating that all information you supply is treated in the strictest of confidence, you will not be asked your name nor any other personal details. If you are phoning from home, it is worth remembering that some numbers may be itemised on your telephone bill. If you live with your parents you may find it safer to use a public call box for your calls. If you request printed information from any agency then this will be sent in discreet packaging.

The bottom line to this chapter is: so long as you are careful with your sexual health then you really do not have to worry *unnecessarily* about contracting HIV. The biggest threat is unprotected anal and straight sex (and then shared intravenous drug use). Knowing fact from fiction will reduce your worries and leave you to enjoy your life.

British Support Group Listings

What follows is a comprehensive list of support groups that you can either phone or write to.

ACE Centre
Croydon

Telephone 0181 665 5000
Queens Hospital. Weekdays
09.00–17.00

ACE Project
London

Telephone 0181 646 0646
Aids care and education

ACET (Aids Care Education and Training)
PO Box 3693
London
SW15 2BQ

Telephone 0181 780 0400

AIDS Support Centre
Salvation Army Hall
London
NW3

Telephone 0171 485 2466

AIDS Treatment Project
250 Kennington Lane
London
SE11

Telephone 0645 470 047

Axiom Magazine
London

Telephone 0171 383 0880

BIGUP (for black men)
Unit 75
Eurolink Centre
49 Effra Road
London
SW2

Telephone 0171 501 9264

Barnet AIDS Education Unit
Collindale Hospital
Collindale Avenue
London
NW9

Telephone 0181 905 9779

Black HIV/AIDS Network
St Stephen's House
41 Uxbridge Road
London
W12

Telephone 0181 749 2828

Blackliners
London

Telephone 0171 738 5274
Help and advice for blacks and Asians

Body And Soul
London

Telephone   0171 833 4929
For families affected by HIV and
AIDS

Body Positive (Women)
51B Philbeach Gardens
London
SW5

Telephone   0171 835 1045

Brent HIV Team
13 Brondesbury Road
London
NW6

Telephone   0181 957 4152

Camden HIV Services
Crowndale Centre
218 Eversholt Street
London NW1

Telephone   0171 911 1696

The Camden Link
7 North Studios
North Villas
London
NW1 9AY

Telephone   0171 267 1100

Cara Centre
178 Lancaster Road
London
W11 1QU

Telephone   0171 792 8299

Care
Islington

Telephone   0171 359 7829
Islington Community AIDS
Resource

Catholic AIDS Link
PO Box 646
London
E9 6QP

Telephone   0171 485 7298

Chinese HIV/AIDS Support
Queens House
1 Leicester Place
London
WC2H

Telephone   0171 287 0904

Continuum
127 Foundling Court
London
WC1N

Telephone   0171 713 7071

Cruisaid
1 Walcott Street
London
SW1P 2NG

Telephone   0171 834 7566

Cruisaid
Livingstone House
Carteret Street
London
SW1

Telephone   0171 976 8100

Cypriot HIV/AIDS Network
London

Telephone   0181 884 1065
c/o Enfield & Haringey Health
Authority

DET And PEPA
Hillingdon
London

Telephone 01895 257 285
Drugs/HIV training and
awareness

Denholm Elliot Project
250 Kennington Lane
London
SE11

Telephone 0171 820 8844

Ealing Spectrum
PO Box 8242
London
W5 4WJ

Telephone 0181 758 1351

Eddie Surman Trust
London

Telephone 0171 738 6893
Advice and support

Elton John Foundation
7 Kings Street
Cloisters
Clifton Walk
London
W6

Telephone 0181 846 9944

Facts
23–25 Weston Park
Crouch End
London
N8

Telephone 0181 348 9195

Fashion Acts
30 Elgin Crescent
London
W11 2RJ

Telephone 0171 229 7348

Food Chain
London

Telephone 0171 272 2272
Delivering food to people with
AIDS in London

Frank Foundation
Boisdale House
7–10 Rodney Street
London
N1 9JH

Telephone 0171 837 6398

GMFA
Unit 42, Eurolink Centre
49 Effra Road
London
SW2

Telephone 0171 738 6872

The Globe Centre
159 Mile End Road
London

Telephone 0171 791 2855

HIV Centre
17 Chase Side Crescent
Enfield
London

Telephone 0181 363 6660

The HIV Project
London

Telephone   0171 383 0770

HP2 Health Limited
156–158 Grays Inn Rd
London
WC1X

Telephone   0171 837 7728

The Heal Trust
41C Ramsden Road
London
SW12 8QX

Telephone   0181 265 3989

Hillingdon AIDS Response Trust
Beasleys Yard
126 High Street
Uxbridge
London

Telephone   01895 813 874

Home In My Mind
Globe House
8 Curtain Road
London
EC2

Telephone   0171 435 9510

Hounslow HIV Team
Chiswick

Telephone   0181 862 6709
Chiswick social services – advice
and support

Immune Development Trust
90–92 Islington Road
London
N1 8EG

Telephone   0171 704 1555

Immune Development Trust
London

Telephone   0171 713 0265
Homeopathy for people with
HIV/AIDS

Immunity Legal Services
London

Telephone   0171 388 6776

Information Exchange
St Stephen's Hosp'
369 Fulham Road
London
SW10

Telephone   0181 746 5929

Jewish AIDS Trust
Collindale Hosp'
Collindale Avenue
London
NW9

Telephone   0181 200 0396

Jewish AIDS Trust Helpline
London

Telephone   0181 206 1696

The Junction
207A Anerley Rd
London
SE20 8ER

Telephone   0181 776 5588

LADS
London

Telephone   0181 682 6842

LEAN (London East Aids Network)

35 Romford Road
London
E15 4LY

Telephone   0181 509 2620

LEAN (London East Aids Network)

44 Romford Road
London
E15

Telephone   0181 522 0066

LEAN (London East Aids Network)

Ilford
London

Telephone   0181 478 7619

LEAN (London East Aids Network)

Stratford
London

Telephone   0181 519 9545

Landmark

47 Tulse Hill
London
SW2

Telephone   0181 678 6686

Lighthouse

111–117 Lancaster Road
London
W11

Telephone   0171 792 1200

London East Aids Group

London

Telephone   0181 522 0999

Mainliners

38–40 Kennington Park Road
London
SE11 4RS

Telephone   0171 582 5226

Midmay Mission Hospital

Hackney Road
London
E2 7NA

Telephone   0171 739 2331

National AIDS Manual

Freepost
London
SW2 1YZ

Telephone   0171 6227 3200

National AIDS Trust

188–196 Old Street
London
EC1V

Telephone   0171 814 6767

National HIV Prevention Srvs

1 Mableton Place
London
WC1H 9TX

Telephone   0171 388 9855

Naz Project (Asian, Turk, Arab, Irani)

241 King Street
London
W6

Telephone   0181 741 1879

Newham HIV Counselling
365 High Street North
London
E12 6PG

Telephone   0181 470 9900

Oasis AIDS Care Centre
Wandsworth
London

Telephone   0181 874 3230
Tuesday – Friday 16.00–21.00

Optimum Health Services
London

Telephone   0171 635 5555 ext.
5423

Outreach Youth
Isle Of Dogs
London

Telephone   0171 538 1601
Youth support for people with
HIV/AIDS

Pace
34 Hartan Road
London
N7 6DL

Telephone   0171 700 1323

Panos Institute
9 White Lion Street
London
W1 9PD

Telephone   0171 278 1111

Pep Boys
London

Telephone   0171 955 4384
Health education for young men
in South-East London

Positive Discounts
PO Box 347
Twickenham
London
TW1 2SN

Telephone   0181 891 2561

The Positive Place
52 Deptford Broadway
London
SE8

Telephone   0181 694 9988

Positive Youth
Earls Court
London

Telephone   0171 835 1045
Advice and support for
under-25s

Positiveline
London

Telephone   0800 616 212
Monday–Friday 19.00–22.00 &
Saturday–Sunday 16.00–22.00

Positively East
PO Box 2224
London
E15 4SL

Positively Women
347–349 City Road
London
EC1

Telephone   0171 713 0222

Red Admiral Project
Earls Court
London

Telephone   0171 835 1495
HIV counselling for partners and
friends

Rubberstuffers
32 Mortimer Street
London
W1N 7RA

Telephone 0171 436 5353

Terrence Higgins Trust
52–54 Grays Inn Road
London
WC1X

Telephone 0171 831 0330

Turning Point
Ealing
London

Telephone 0181 840 3313
Advice and support

Waltham Forest AIDS Support
London

Telephone 0181 532 8738

ENGLAND

National AIDSLINE

Telephone 0800 567 123
A free and confidential service
offering advice, information and
support on HIV/AIDS issues.
Open 24 hours

Walk For Life Hotline

Telephone 0500 011 696
Phone for details

Gay Men's Health Project
Aylesbury

Telephone 01494 473 888
For gay men in Aylesbury Vale

AVVA (Aylesbury Vale Visual Aids)
PO Box 48
Aylesbury
Buckinghamshire
HP19

West Kent Lash
Aylesford

Telephone 01622 710 161
Help and advice

AIDSLINE
Barum House
The Square
Barnstaple

Telephone 01271 245 55

Gay Men's Health Project
Bath

Telephone 01225 833 900

Aled Richards Trust
Bath

Telephone 01225 444 347
Friends and relatives of PWA
(People With AIDS)

AIDSLINE
Smithfield House
Digbeth
Birmingham
B5

Telephone 0121 622 1511

Body Positive
38 Princes Street
Birmingham
B4 6LE

Telephone   0121 212 3636

Boss
146 Bromsgrove Street
Birmingham

Telephone   0121 622 6252
Drop-in and advice

Freshwinds
13 Gravelly Hill North
Erdington
Birmingham

Telephone   0121 350 8423

Body Positive
PO Box 76
Blackpool
Lancashire
FY1 4JZ

Telephone   01253 292 803

Heal
PO Box 42
Blackpool
Lancashire
FY4 1TW

Telephone   01253 290 052

Body Positive
PO Box 359
Bournemouth
Dorset

Telephone   01202 297 386

Sanctuary
Bournemouth

Telephone   01202 317 177
24 hour helpline/residential care
and resources

Pennine AIDS Link
4 Duke Street
Bradford
BD1 3QR

Telephone   01274 736 032

BAAC
Bridgewater

Telephone   01278 444 253
Bridgewater AIDS awareness
campaign

AIDS Action In Humberside
Bridlington

Telephone   01262 400 440

Body Positive
12A Circus Street
Brighton

Telephone   01273 693 266

FAB (Fighting Aids Brighton)
PO Box 49
Brighton
Sussex
BN2 3YY

Telephone   01273 723 615

Open Door
Brighton

Telephone   01273 605 706
Community support for people
affected by HIV

Wiseguys
Brighton

Telephone   01273 625 222
Men's health education

The Harbour
Bristol

Telephone   0117 925 9348
Counselling for HIV/AIDS

Aled Richards Trust
8–10 West Street
Old Market
Bristol

Telephone 0117 955 1000

Sproket Trust (Pets of PWAs)
PO Box 30
Camborne
Cornwall
TR4 9YB

Telephone 01209 712 912

AIDS Action
Cambridge

Telephone 0800 697 697 (24 hour answerphone)

Gay/Bi Health Project
The Shed
Aldenbrookes Hosp'
CB2 2QQ

Telephone 01223 216 865

AIDSLINE
Cheltenham

Telephone 01242 224 666
Monday & Wednesday 19.00–21.00

Body Positive
PO Box 135
Chester
CH1

Telephone 01244 400 415

CADAR (Chester and District AIDS line)
PO Box 315
Chester
CH1 1AZ

Telephone 01244 390 300

Connectaid (Fund-raising & support)
PO Box 1414
Chester
CH1 2WG

Healthwise
Chester

Telephone 0800 838 909
10.00–22.00 daily

CASH
Chesterfield

Telephone 01246 559 431
Health project and HIV advice

HIV/AIDS Helpline
Colchester

Telephone 01206 869 191
Monday–Friday 19.00–22.00
'buddying' service

Bethany Trust
St Mary's Road
Bodmin
PL31 1NF

Telephone 01208 790 35

Helpline
Cornwall

Telephone 01872 225 022
Aids council advice and support

Body Positive
10 Manor Road
Coventry

Telephone 01203 229 292

Body Positive
The Diva Centre
194 Three Bridges Road
Crawley

Telephone 01923 552 111

Harass
63 Susans Road
Crawley
Sussex
BN21

Telephone 01323 643 322

AIDS Relief
PO Box 47
Crewe
Cheshire
CW1 1WT

Telephone 01270 628 938

AIDSLINE
Derby

Telephone 01332 290 766
24 hours, advice and support

Body Positive
PO Box 124
Derby

Telephone 01332 292 129

Dudley HIV/AIDS Support Group
Dudley

Telephone 01384 444 300

Durham Outlink
Durham

Telephone 0191 333 3889
Groups and confidential safer sex info

Haven
East Grinstead

Telephone 01342 300 763
Meetings for people with HIV/AIDS

Gay Man's Health Advisor
Essex

Telephone 01277 232 450
Sexual health info

HANCS
PO Box 25
Essex
SS16 4AY

Telephone 01268 282 134

Man To Man Project
Essex

Telephone 01375 364 435
Group and advice for people with HIV/AIDS

Positive Connections
Essex

Telephone 01206 765 335
HIV/AIDS self-help group

AIDSLINE
PO Box 77
Exeter
Devon
EX1 2UN

Telephone 01392 411 600

Man To Man Project
Exeter

Telephone 01392 207 445
Sexual health info and advice

AIDSLINE
18–20 Pasture Street
Grimsby
Lincolnshire

Telephone 01472 240 840

Rainbow Centre
Hartlepool

Telephone 01429 222 999
Monday 19–21.00 Drop-in and
counselling

Cleveland AIDS Support
Hartlepool

Telephone 01429 868 222
Advice and support

Harass
2 Cambridge Gardens
Hastings

Telephone 01424 429 901

Gay Men's Health Project
Hereford

Telephone 01432 262 037
Advice and support

Careaid
Herne Bay

Telephone 01227 375 511
Sexual health info and advice

Herts Aid
Hertfordshire

Telephone 01992 556 616
Advice, support and
befriending

Chilternaids
PO Box 377
High Wycombe
HP13 6HV

Telephone 01494 444 818

**Avert (Aids Educational and
Medical Research)**
11–13 Denne Parade
Horsham
RH12

Telephone 01403 210 202

Kirklees AIDS Response
1 Estate Buildings
11 Railway Street
HD1

Telephone 01484 432 433

AIDS Action In Humberside
Hull

Telephone 01482 327 060

Body Positive
Hulme

Telephone 0161 873 8103
Helpline

Positive Youth Group
BP North West
Lawrence House
City Road
Manchester

Telephone 0161 873 8100

AIDS Helpline
Ipswich

Telephone 01473 232 007
Advice and support on HIV/
AIDS

POS + Helpline
Kent

Telephone 0800 435 869
Freephone helpline

AIDS Helpline
Kings Lynn

Telephone   01553 776 655
Advice and support

Action On Sexual Health
Kirklees

Telephone   01484 401 160
MSM project

Positive Action
Lancaster

Telephone   01524 424 117

Body Positive
Leeds

Telephone   01924 456 667

Bridgeside
Leeds

Telephone   0113 242 3204
HIV/AIDS helpline

Leeds HIV Support Groups
Leeds

Telephone   0113 242 3204

AIDS Support Services
Michael Wood Centre
53 Regent Road
LE1 6YF

Telephone   0116 255 9995

Positive Action
c/o Denmark Villas
Pipehill
Lichfield
WS13 8JS

Telephone   0966 237 059

AIDS Helpline
Lincoln

Telephone   01522 513 999
Advice and support

Drop In Centre
25 Newland
Lincoln
Tuesday 18.00–21.00 &
Saturday 13.00–17.00

AIDS Helpline
Lincolnshire

Telephone   0800 252 534
24 hour advice and support
helpline

AIDS Helpline
PO Box 11
Liverpool
L69 1SN

Telephone   0151 709 9000

Body Positive
PO Box 180
Liverpool
L1

Telephone   0151 707 0606

Healthwise
Liverpool

Telephone   0800 838 909
Daily 10.00–22.00 Health info
and advice

Body Positive
Luton

Telephone   01582 484 499
Advice and drop in centre

Body Positive
Luton

Telephone   01582 485 448
National Network of Body
Positive

The Lodge
Luton

Telephone   01582 875 303
Client care for people with HIV/
AIDS

Gay Men's Health Group
PO Box 94
Macclesfield
Cheshire
SK10

Telephone   01625 661 158

Body Positive
3rd Floor
Fourways House
18 Tariff Street
Manchester
M1

Telephone   0161 237 9717

George House Trust
75 Ardwick Green North
Manchester
M12 6FX

Telephone   0161 839 4340

HARPP (HIV around Positive People)
Manchester

Telephone   0161 237 3131
Support for carers

Positive Friends
Manchester

Telephone   0161 343 6637
Support group – phone for
details

MAPS
PO Box 3
Mansfield
NG16 1QT

Telephone   01623 642 304

Cleveland AIDS Support
Middlesborough

Telephone   01642 254 598
Advice and support

Body Positive
Milton Keynes

Telephone   01908 690 500
c/o Dept of GUM, Milton Keynes
Hospital

AIDS Community Trust
c/o St Gabriels Parish Centre
Heaton
NE6

Telephone   0191 224 4848

Body Positive
12 Princess Square
Upper Level
Newcastle
NE1 8EG

Telephone   0191 232 2855

AIDS Helpline
Norwich

Telephone   01603 615 816
Advice and support

Gay Men's Health Project
69 Bethal Street
Norwich

Telephone   01603 627 154

Heal (Ormskirk)
PO Box 26
Ormskirk
Lancashire
L39 2WE

Telephone   01772 555 255

Positive Gay Men's Group
Oxfordshire

Telephone   01865 243 389
Advice and info on HIV/AIDS

VITA Clinic
Oxfordshire

Telephone   02865 246 036
Lesbian sexual health – Radcliffe
Infirmary

AIDS Helpline
Peterborough

Telephone   01733 62 334
Tuesday & Thursday 19.30–
21.30

Healthy Gay Manchester
Freepost HGM
Ducie House
Ducie Street
Manchester
M1

Telephone   0161 236 7600

AIDS Support Group
Plymouth

Telephone   01752 663 609
Advice and info on HIV/AIDS

Eddy Stone Group
36 Looe Street
Plymouth
Devon

Telephone   01752 251 666

Man To Man Project
Plymouth

Telephone   01752 769 092
Health promotion

Portsmouth Buddies
45–47 Copner Road
Portsmouth
PO3 5AB

Telephone   01705 647 117

Heal (Preston)
PO Box 137
Preston
Lancashire
PR1 8UU

Telephone   01772 555 255

Family & Partners Support
PO Box 72
Preston
Lancashire
PR5 1PH

Telephone   01772 621 111

CAST (Community Aids Support Team)
PO Box 17
Preston
Lancashire
PR1 4UG

Buddies
Reading

Telephone   01734 576 164
HIV/AIDS Support: Monday &
Thursday 17.00–21.00

St Peters House Project
Redhill/Reigate

Telephone   01737 241 044
Helpline and home care support

Body Positive
St Barts Hosp
New Road
Rochester
ME1 1DS

Telephone   01634 819 071

AIDS Info
Runcorn

Telephone   01928 677 36
Monday–Friday 09.00–22.00 (24
hour answerphone)

Gay Men's Health Project
Salisbury

Telephone   01722 421 951
Advice and support on HIV/
AIDS

**SHARE (Salisbury HIV/AIDS
REsponse)**
PO Box 954
Salisbury
SP2 7EZ

Telephone   0378 603 511

Isle Of Wight Buddies
PO Box 16
Sandown
Isle Of Wight
PO36 8NH

Telephone   01976 444 317

AIDSLINE
Scarborough

Telephone   01723 275 5500
Advice and support on HIV/
AIDS

HIV/AIDS Helpline
Scarborough

Telephone   01723 500 600
Advice and support

Sheffield Centre For HIV
Scarborough

Telephone   01723 267 8806

Voluntary AIDS Liason
PO Box 816
Scarborough
S1 4JS

Telephone   01723 278 8025

AIDSLINE
Scunthorpe

Telephone   01734 276 660
Helpline and drop-in centre.
Under-25 LGB

Body Positive
22 Laneham Street
Scunthorpe

Telephone   01724 289 440

Body Positive
Abbey Yard Centre
Abbey Yard
Selby

Telephone   01757 210 030

Milburgh Hall Care Centre
Selham

Telephone   01798 867 646

SHAG (Shropshire Health Action)
Reilly Centre
Unit 3
1A Wyle Cop
SY1

Telephone   01743 344 179

AIDS Helpline (Clinic-based)
Shrewsbury

Telephone   01743 261 113
Monday all day/Wednesday
a.m. only/Thursday p.m. only

Body Positive
PO Box 241
Shrewsbury

Telephone   01743 350 075

AIDS Advice
Somerset

Telephone   01823 332 727
Advice and support on HIV/
AIDS

Gay Men's Health Project
Somerset

Telephone   01823 327 078
Health promotion

AIDS Helpline (Switchboard)
PO Box 139
Southampton
SO14 0GZ

Telephone   01703 637 363

Gay Men's Health Project
Southampton

Telephone   01703 512 900

Helpline
Southend

Telephone   01702 391 750
Monday–Friday 18.00–21.30

Body Positive
St Albans

Telephone   01462 454 744
Monday–Friday 19.00–21.00

The Crescent
St Albans

Telephone   01727 842 352
HIV Centre, BP Group, HIV
testing

South Staffs. Mesmen Project
Staffordshire

Telephone   01543 411 413
Men's health advice

Smash (Health Project)
188 Buxton Road
Manchester
SK2 7AE

Telephone   0161 487 2020

Body Positive
PO Box 474
Stoke-on-Trent
ST1 5BX

Telephone   01782 201 251

MSM Project
Stoke-on-Trent

Telephone   01782 744 444
HIV Outreach

Body Positive
241–243 Southwick Road
Southwick
SR5

Telephone   0191 549 2228

Positive Action
Surrey

Telephone   0800 980 1990

Safe Space
Surrey

Telephone   01784 434 412
Advice and support for people
with HIV/AIDS

Sussex AIDS Centre
Sussex

Telephone   0500 552 255
Helpline for people with HIV/
AIDS

Gay Men's Health Project
9 Devizes Road
Swindon
Wiltshire

Telephone   01793 514 050

SPACE
Swindon

Telephone   01793 420 620
Aids counselling and education

TAGS (Torbay Aids Group Support)
TAGS
Braddon Hill Road West
Torquay

Telephone   01803 299 266

Begin
6 Cheapside
1st Floor
Wakefield

Telephone   01924 211 117

AIDSLINE
Warrington

Telephone   01925 417 134
Monday & Wednesday 09.00–
16.00

AIDS Helpline
PO Box 138
Wigan
Lancashire
WN5 0PW

Telephone   0500 232 324

Gay Men's Health Project
Healthworks
Jessop House
Mill Lane
Wimbourne

Telephone   01202 848 567

Gay Men's Health Project
Winchester

Telephone   01962 863 511 ext.
484

Jarman Clinic
Withington

Telephone   0161 291 4939
Sexual health info and advice

AIDSLINE
Wolverhampton

Telephone   01902 644 894
Advice and support for people
affected with HIV

Wolverhampton Reach
Unit 4
Temple Street
Wolverhampton
WV2

Telephone   01902 425 702

Worcester Project
Worcester

Telephone 01905 619 884
Sexual health information

York AIDS Action
PO Box 318
York
YO3 4XY

Telephone 01904 639 595

SCOTLAND

Healthy Gay Scotland
Scotland

Telephone 0800 731 8101
Advice and info on HIV/AIDS

AIDS Helpline
Aberdeen

Telephone 01224 574 000

Body Positive
PO Box 83
Aberdeen

Telephone 01224 404 408

Body Positive
37–39 Montrose Terrace
Edinburgh

Telephone 0131 652 0754

Gay Men's Health
The Spittal Street Centre
22 Spittal Street
Edinburgh
EH3

Telephone 0131 229 5995

Milestone House
Edinburgh

Telephone 0131 441 6989
Residential AIDS care & Buddies

SOLAS
2–4 Abbeymount
Edinburgh

Telephone 0131 659 5116

SOLAS
Edinburgh

Telephone 0131 661 0982
Advice and info on HIV/AIDS

Waverlee Care House
4A Royal Terrace
Edinburgh

Telephone 0131 556 3959

Body Positive
3 Park Quadrant
Glasgow

Telephone 0141 332 5010

Phace West
49 Bath Street
Glasgow
G2 2DL

Telephone 0141 332 3838

Steve Retson Project
c/o GUM
Royal Infirmary
St Andrews Parade
Glasgow

Telephone 0141 211 4753

Reach Out Highlands
28 Huntly Street
Inverness
IV3 5PR

Telephone 01463 711 585

WALES

AIDSLINE
South Wales

Telephone 0800 454 391
Advice and info on HIV/AIDS

Sexual Health Helpline
Camarthen

Telephone 01267 221 079
Advice and info

AIDS Helpline
PO Box 304
Cardiff
CF1 9XA

Telephone 01222 223 443

Body Positive
PO Box 237
Cardiff
CF1 1XE

Telephone 01222 343 030

Body Positive
Wolfs Castle
Templeton Avenue
Cardiff
CF4 5JS

AIDS Helpline
Newport

Telephone 01633 223 456

AIDS Helpline
Swansea

Telephone 01792 456 303

Recreational Drugs: Their Use, Misuse and Abuse

Introduction

The following pages contain information on what are probably some of the more familiar drugs that have infiltrated youth and club culture throughout the last few decades in the UK. It is offered purely as a guide, in order that you are aware of the dangers and consequences of taking them, or indeed, having them in your possession.

Whilst the publishers, contributors or myself do not in any way condone the use of drugs, in any form, we feel that to be supplied with the facts and to make an informed choice is far better than to remain in ignorance.

The subsequent text has been reprinted, edited and adapted in collaboration with Lifeline Manchester, in order to provide the reader with the necessary information. There is no preaching, no exaggeration and no drama. They are just the plain facts. It tells you about the drugs that you could come across, what they can do to you and where you stand concerning the law.

Having said that, it is impossible to provide hard and fast rules because so many factors are involved. Much depends on the individual taking the drugs, their state of mind at the time, the drugs themselves, the amount taken and the surroundings in which the drugs were taken. What can be said with certainty is that all drugs are potentially dangerous in one way or another and most are illegal.

With drugs available on the black market nothing is what it seems. For example, they may have been 'cut' (mixed) with things like sugar, laxatives or even cheaper and more lethal drugs. And how do you know how strong a drug is anyway? The simple answer is: you don't. The fact is that any drugs made illegally or taken without medical supervision are not only unpredictable, they're also dangerous.

Taking drugs does involve risk. Most have side-effects that users often ignore or simply just don't know about. Mixing drugs (drug cocktails) is particularly dangerous. Combining them can do more than just mix you up. Loading any drug on top of another is risky –

very risky. Possibly the most hazardous move of all is to mix depressants such as alcohol, solvents or tranquillisers. This is because when they're mixed it takes a much lower dose of each drug to produce a 'killer cocktail'.

Although rare among young people, injecting drugs opens up a different category of risk. These include the risk of infections by viruses such as HIV (that can lead to AIDS) and the possible exposure to a number of strains of viral hepatitis, by the use of shared needles and syringes. There is also the risk of overdosing, as a result of delivering the drug directly into the bloodstream; the risk of gangrene (from hitting an artery instead of a vein) and the risk of abscesses (caused by injecting non-injectable substances, like crushed tablets or substances contaminated with infectious agents such as bacteria).

There are many different drugs available. The following pages list the key points about each of the main drugs commonly available and/or associated with club culture. At the end of 'The Facts About Drugs' section there is a 'Help Available' section, listing numbers either for the user, or for the friends and family of users. The list is by no means exhaustive of the help available. However, as an initial line of enquiry, the helpline operators can guide you to the most relevant organisation in your area.

You And The Law

If the police have reason to suspect that you are carrying an illegal drug, they have the right to make you turn out your pockets or search your vehicle. They can also take you to the police station and search you. If drugs are found, you could be charged with one of two offences: possession, and possession with intent to supply.

Possession
This means being caught with an illegal drug intended for your own use. The police can tell your parents or guardian (if you are under 17). They could also inform the social services and the probation service. As for punishment, the police have these options:

To *caution* you. This is put on local police files. If you offend again this may influence the police to charge you, rather than caution you.

To give you a *formal warning*. This is a central police record held for five years – if you offend again, this can be used as evidence against you.

To *charge* you with an offence which will lead to a court hearing. This is more likely for repeat offenders, who may end up with a fine or a custodial sentence.

If the police can *prove* that an illegal drug is or has been in your house, your car, your bag, pocket or whatever, you can be charged for *possession* of an illegal drug. Being 'done' for simple possession means that the police accept that the drug was intended for your use only.

In many places the police will be willing to caution you for simple possession (ring your nearest drug service for the local police policy). In fact the police will usually *want* to caution you. If they caution you they will only have to fill in two pieces of paper. If they charge you and take you to court they have to fill out nearly 50 separate pieces of paper!

But do you want to be cautioned?
To receive a caution you *must admit* to the offence. This amounts to admitting that the drugs found in your possession '. . . are just for my personal use'. The advantages of a caution are simple. You can be arrested and be in and out of the police station in a couple of hours. You will still have a criminal record but there are no embarrassing court appearances and nothing in the local papers telling the world you are a 'druggy'. You can also be cautioned more than once. But if you carry on getting caught, you *will* go to court.

The police themselves (generally) admit (to drugs agency workers) that they would like to caution more people. But, some of those people (who have probably watched too much television) say something like 'Fuck you copper, I'm saying nothing', which, in turn, works against them, neither helps nor appeals to the police and, consequently, they will receive a harder time.

Simple possession is one thing, but – *be warned*, you can sometimes be done for possession with intent to supply, even though you do not see yourself as a dealer. For example, you could have a big chunk of cannabis and be done for simple possession. *But*, if you got caught with the same chunk, cut into individual strips, you could be done with 'possession with intent to supply'.

Possession With Intent To Supply

If you were to have any intention of dealing (which can include giving and sharing drugs) you might be charged with this more serious offence. Decisions over whether you're charged with intent to supply are based on the circumstances in which you were caught and the quantity of drugs you were caught with. The police can take the same course of action as in simple possession cases, but this time you are more likely to be charged. If your case goes to court the penalties are likely to be heavier. Do you know what jail time you are looking at? You could be charged with 'intent to supply' for carrying as little as ten 'tabs' or tablets. You should be aware of the risks (as they vary greatly) but, as way of an example, all the case histories below are real.

1. Male: 20 years of age. He rarely made much money out of dealing and what he did make, he would spend on drugs. He got caught with 13 ecstasy tablets. Pleaded *not guilty* at the Crown Court to 'possession with intent to supply'. He was sentenced to three years in prison.

2. Female: 19 years of age and a single parent. She was holding the 25 tabs for her boyfriend who was a well-known dealer. (He had nothing on him when the police raided the club.) She pleaded *guilty* at the Crown Court to 'possession with intent to supply'. She was sentenced to one year's suspended plus supervision.

3. Male: 20 years of age. He got a real buzz out of dealing and liked everyone to know who he was. He'd only been dealing for six months. Caught with 80 acid tabs. He pleaded *guilty* at the Crown Court to 'possession with intent to supply'. Sentenced to four years in prison.

4. Male was caught with seven grams of amphetamine in separate one-gram bags. He *wasn't* a dealer. He had been using up to one gram of speed a day. The police said he must have been dealing, since the amphetamine was divided up into separate bags. He was charged at the Crown Court with 'possession with intent to supply'. He was sentenced to two years in prison.

5. Male: 22 years of age. According to him 'some people look at money and see drugs'. He looked at drugs and saw money. He got caught with 90 tabs of acid. He pleaded guilty at the Magistrates Court to 'possession with intent to supply'. He was sentenced to two years probation.

Ignorance won't wash with the law regarding drugs. The Misuse Of Drugs Act divides drugs into three classes and gives guidelines for penalties.

Class A

Cocaine/Crack/Ecstasy/Heroin/LSD/Magic mushrooms (prepared for use)/Speed or amphetamines (if prepared for injecting)
> The maximum penalties are:
> For *possession*: 7 years imprisonment and/or a fine
> For *supply*: life imprisonment and/or a fine

Class B

Cannabis/Speed or amphetamines/Codeine (and other weaker opiates) (Any Class B drug prepared for injection is considered Class A)
> The maximum penalties are:
> For *possession*: 5 years imprisonment and/or a fine
> For *supply*: 14 years imprisonment and/or a fine

Class C

Supplying of anabolic steroids and tranquillisers (Valium, Librium, Temazepam)/Possession of temazepam
> The maximum penalties are:
> For *possession*: 2 years imprisonment and/or a fine
> For *supply*: 5 years imprisonment and/or a fine

Some drugs are controlled by the Medicines Act and it isn't illegal to possess drugs such as alcohol, gases, glues, aerosols or tobacco; the law handles each of these differently.

It is an offence to allow anyone on your premises to produce, give away or sell illegal drugs. It is even an offence to offer to supply the drug free of charge. So, if a parent knows that their child is sharing drugs with a friend in their house, and does nothing to stop it, the parent has then committed an offence. Allowing the smoking of cannabis in your home is also an offence. The charges would probably be for 'allowing your premises to be used for the smoking of cannabis or opium'. The less common charges would be incitement or conspiracy, possession or joint possession. To stop someone committing an offence with a drug, you can either destroy it or hand it over to the police.

Less serious offences are dealt with at the Magistrates Court. Maximum penalties are six months plus a £500 fine for each offence. Maximum sentences vary according to the nature of the offence (less for possession, more for supply) and also with consideration given to how harmful the drug is thought to be (highest sentences for Class A, lowest for Class C).

More serious charges are dealt with at the Crown Court where penalties are harsher. For trafficking offences, such as the importing or supplying of a Class A drug (such as heroin, LSD or ecstasy), there is a maximum of life imprisonment and an unlimited fine for each offence.

Fact: 90% of all drugs offences are for possession, usually that of cannabis. Half of these receive a caution, a quarter receive a fine and less than 10% are sent straight to prison.

Remember: Drugs which have infiltrated cultures such as the club scene, ecstasy and acid for example, carry the *same penalties* as heroin.

Note: The above text is provided purely as a *guideline* and *is not* to be construed as the actual word of the law as it stands at the present time. If you find that you are in need of sympathetic legal support, then contact your nearest drugs agency helpline or local gay switchboard who may be able to refer you to a solicitor who specialises in drug use and abuse.

Drugs: The Facts

Anabolic Steroids

What other names are they known by?
Trade names include Sustanon 250, Deca-Durabolin, Dianabol, Anavar, Stanozolol. Users may refer to them as 'roids'.

What are they?
Anabolic steroids can only be sold lawfully by a pharmacist to someone with a doctor's prescription. Whilst possession isn't illegal without a prescription, supply *is* against the law and Class C penalties apply. Anabolic steroids are similar to, and include, the male hormone testosterone. They are used in medicine to treat anaemia and post-surgery muscle weakness.

Don't confuse them with the type of steroids used to treat eczema/asthma (*note*: some countries treat asthma with Clenbuterol, which is also used for its anabolic effects). Some body builders use anabolic steroids, as well as people who think it will improve their body image. Taking anabolic steroids without regular resistance training (e.g. weight training) does not provide you with 'instant muscle'. Users either swallow or inject. Users who inject do so directly into a muscle, more often into the thigh or buttocks. It is *not* injected into a vein. Use of them in sports is prohibited and a positive test for the drug can ruin a sporting career.

What are the effects?
Users claim that steroids make them feel more aggressive and able to train harder. With exercise, anabolic steroids can help build up muscle. However, there is some debate about whether they improve muscle power and athletic performance. Anabolic steroids help users to recover from strenuous exercise.

What are the dangers?
Taking anabolic steroids carries many health risks and can stop young people from growing properly (particularly, those under 18 and those that are still growing). The risks for men include erection problems, breast growth, shrinking testicles, reduced sperm count and even sterility, acne, and an increased chance of heart attack and liver failure. The risks for women include growth of facial hair, deepening voice, shrinking breasts, messed-up menstrual cycle, spots, possible miscarriage and stillbirth.

Regular use may cause aggression and severe mood swings. Some of the side-effects, such as changes in breast size, may be irreversible without surgery. Sharing needles or syringes puts users at risk of contracting dangerous infections like hepatitis and HIV. Extreme mood swings and aggression may present themselves ('roid rage').

Is the taking of anabolic steroids legal?
Yes. Anabolic steroids are a Class C drug. The supply of anabolic steroids is not legal though, and carries a maximum penalty of five years imprisonment and/or a fine. Some dealers argue that the quantity that they are carrying is for their own, personal use (as users generally possess a three month supply). Possession for personal use is not an offence.

Cannabis

What other names is it known by?
Commonly referred to as 'marijuana', 'draw', 'blow', 'weed', 'puff', 'shit', 'hash' and 'ganja'.

What is it?
Cannabis is a natural substance obtained from a plant commonly called hemp. It comes in various shades (from yellow through to black) as a solid lump known as resin or leaves, as stalks and seeds

known as grass, or as a sticky oil. It can be rolled with tobacco into a spliff or joint or smoked on its own in a special pipe or even eaten (e.g. baked in cakes).

There are different strengths of cannabis; some (such as skunk) are very strong. For example, the THC (main active ingredient) in resin is usually between 2% and 8%, whilst the THC in skunk can be up to 20%. Cannabis is a Class B drug, but Class A penalties can apply to cannabis oil.

What are the effects?
Getting 'stoned' on cannabis makes most users relaxed and talkative. It heightens the senses, especially when it comes to colours, taste and music. Cooking and eating hash makes the effects more intense and harder to control. It can leave people feeling tired and lacking energy. Hash may bring on cravings for certain foods (known as 'the munchies').

What are the dangers?
Cannabis affects short-term memory and the ability to concentrate. Getting 'stoned' affects co-ordination, increasing the risk of accidents. It impairs driving skills: so never get in a car with someone who is stoned. It can make the user paranoid and anxious (depending on their mood and situation). Smoking joints with tobacco can lead to users getting hooked on cigarettes. Smoking cannabis over a long period of time may increase the risk of respiratory disorders, including lung cancer. Some heavy users find cannabis hard to quit.

Is the taking of cannabis legal?
No. Cannabis is a Class B drug. The maximum penalty for possession is five years imprisonment and/or a fine. For supplying cannabis, the maximum penalty is 14 years imprisonment and/or a fine. For possession of cannabis oil (Class A penalties apply – though there can be some confusion about this) the maximum penalty is seven years imprisonment and/or a fine.

Cocaine

What other names is it known by?
Also known as 'coke', 'charlie', 'snow', 'C', 'toot' and 'charge'.

What is it?
Cocaine is a powerful stimulant drug. It is a white powder that is commonly 'chopped up', divided into 'lines' on a mirror and then snorted up the nose through a tube (such as a straw or rolled-up

banknote). Some users inject it and some smoke it (though smoking cocaine is an extremely ineffective way of taking the drug). Cocaine is a Class A drug.

What are the effects?
Cocaine is a powerful stimulant. The 'buzz' creates a feeling of well-being, making users feel confident and alert. The effects of cocaine usually last for about half an hour. Users are often left craving for more. People can also take more to delay the comedown (tiredness and depression).

What are the dangers?
Cocaine can cause heart problems and chest pain. Heavy use of cocaine can cause convulsions. Large or frequent doses over a short period can leave users feeling restless, confused and paranoid. Snorting cocaine may permanently damage the membranes lining the nose and/or the structure separating the nostrils. Users may find their habit expensive and hard to control.

Even if it is clear that a cocaine user is in trouble, it is often difficult to get them to seek help. They may feel full of confidence on the drug and paranoid about going to a doctor or a drug agency. Users have died from overdosing.

Is the taking of cocaine legal?
No. Cocaine is a Class A drug. The maximum penalty for possession is seven years imprisonment and/or a fine. The maximum penalty for supply is life imprisonment and/or a fine.

Crack

What other names is it known by?
Also known as 'rock', 'wash', 'stone', 'scud' and 'pebbles'.

What is it?
Crack is a form of cocaine which has been treated with chemicals to allow it to be more easily smoked and more quickly absorbed. It is a Class A drug.

What are the effects?
The effects of smoking crack are similar to those of snorting cocaine, but much more intense. The high lasts as little as ten minutes. Users

often 'chase' the high by repeating the dose. Heavy users may take heroin to dull the craving caused by crack.

What are the dangers?

Heavy use can lead to potentially fatal heart problems and heavy users are also at risk from convulsions. Smoking crack can seriously harm the lungs and cause chest pains. Crack is a habit-forming drug and is psychologically addictive. The highs can be so intense that they make the use of crack often difficult to control. After the high, feelings of restlessness, nausea and sleeplessness are all common. Effects of the comedown usually involve tiredness and depression, headaches and aching limbs. Large or frequent doses over a short period can leave users feeling restless, confused or paranoid. Regular users find their habit extremely expensive and some have died from overdosing.

Is the taking of crack legal?

No. Crack is a Class A drug. The maximum penalty for possession is seven years imprisonment and/or a fine. The maximum penalty for supply is life imprisonment and/or a fine.

Ecstasy

What other names is it known by?

Referred to as 'E', 'XTC', 'doves', 'disco biscuits', 'echoes', 'hug drug', 'eccies', 'burgers', 'fantasy' and 'Adams'. Other names simply describe what the pill looks like. Its chemical name is MDMA (Methylenedioxymethamphetamine).

What is it?

Ecstasy usually comes in tablets of different shapes, sizes and colour: brown, pink or yellow, but usually white. The effects of MDMA are unpredictable. A tablet might not contain MDMA. Other drugs, which might be sold as MDMA, can have very different effects. Ecstasy is a Class A drug.

What are the effects?

Users can feel more alert and in tune with their surroundings and with other people too. Sound, colour and emotions can appear so much more intense. The energy buzz that comes from ecstasy means users can dance for hours and hours. The effects last anything from three to six hours.

What are the dangers?
As ecstasy starts working (known as 'coming up') users may feel a tightening of the jaw (which may cause you to grind your teeth), nausea, sweating and an increase in heart rate. The comedown can leave users feeling tired and depressed, often for days, and they may have trouble sleeping. Use has been linked to liver and kidney problems. Studies into the effects of ecstasy are still at an early stage. However, inconclusive research shows that it is thought that MDMA dramatically affects the brain chemistry by depleting or destroying the Ceratonin receptors. These may or may not grow back.

Ecstasy acts as a stimulant and is potentially dangerous for anyone with high blood pressure, a heart condition or for those prone to fits. Approximately ten deaths per year are attributed to ecstasy use (there are no precise statistics, the ones available are provided by Guy's Hospital, although some of these may be based on coroners' reports). When tests are done on the tablet it is usually proved to be an 'unadulterated tablet' (i.e. pure ecstasy) and not a 'rogue tablet'.

In random tests, it has been shown that a third of ecstasy tablets contain MDMA; a third have 'some' in and the other third are 'snide', containing some kind of amphetamine instead of MDMA.

Ecstasy raises the body's temperature. Dancing for long periods in a hot atmosphere increases the chances of users overheating and dehydrating (through losing too much body fluid). This occurs because the user is dancing constantly for hours and hours and in doing so, the body temperature is rising, increased further by the ecstasy. The risks can be reduced if users regularly chill out and sip about a pint of non-alcoholic fluid such as water and an isotonic sports drink (e.g. Lucozade Sport – *not* normal Lucozade) *every* hour. People will also need to eat a salty snack to replace the salts lost from their body. Do not drink alcohol whilst taking ecstasy as alcohol dehydrates your body further.

Is the taking of ecstasy legal?
No. Ecstasy is a Class A drug. The maximum penalty for possession is seven years imprisonment and/or a fine. The maximum penalty for supplying is life imprisonment and/or a fine.

GHB

What is GHB?
GHB is short for Gamma-hydroxybutyrate and it is one of the strangest and most dangerous drugs you are likely to encounter. It is used medically in some countries as a mild anaesthetic and, because of its muscle relaxant effects, as an aid to childbirth. In America it is 'reported' to be used as a 'date rape' drug. Its main use though, is as a recreational drug taken for its euphoric effects.

What other names is it known as?
'The Big Sleep', 'GBH', 'Grievous Bodily Harm', 'Liquid X', 'Liquid Ecstasy' and 'Gamma-O'.

What GHB is not
GHB is not liquid ecstasy. It is not chemically related to ecstasy, amphetamine or LSD. Its effects at low doses can indeed seem 'ecstasy-like' and, together with the fact that Liquid E seemed a good marketing ploy, led to it being 'branded' in this way by dealers when it first appeared on the London gay scene in the mid 1990s. Reports of adverse reactions to the drug by the gay press seemed to have stopped the spread of the drug, but recently it seems to be gaining in popularity and availability.

Where does GHB come from?
GHB does not come from hospitals. It can be bought in small bottles from sex shops for around £5 (reportedly a mild dose). GHB usually appears in a powder or in a clear liquid form. Mixing powdered GHB with orange juice, water or milk is usual as GHB has an unpleasant taste. It is usually swallowed as a liquid or diluted with water and swigged at intervals. A minority of people prefer to take it intravenously. It can be bought in little phials or purchased by the cap (£3. . . 10) or in larger bottles (about £30 for a cola-sized bottle) or imported by the tub as a powder.

What are the effects of GHB?
GHB is a drug that has a wide variety of effects depending on the dose that you take. Getting the desired dose is the major problem and will be dealt with later. At low doses (3mg is considered a low dose), the effects start between 5 and 20 minutes after taking it. The effects include mild euphoria, a sense of warmth and well-being, increased confidence and a loss of inhibitions with an 'alcoholic-like' drowsiness. There is a tendency to verbalise (talk nonsense). The effects usually last between one to three hours. Quite small increases in the

dose can lead to dramatic intensification of the effects; giddiness and general silliness, slurring of speech, dizziness, loss of co-ordination and vomiting. At high doses (10–20 mg is a very high dose) GHB will induce deep sleep or literally 'knock you out'. You will probably be in a deep 'unarousable' sleep for three to five hours and if you have taken it whilst you are out you will probably wake up in casualty, surrounded by worried friends, irate medical staff and a curious police officer.

What are the dangers of GHB?
GHB is a very 'dose-dependent' drug. Up until it's ban in certain states in America the medical evidence seemed to show that it was a relatively safe drug if used 'correctly'. The problem is getting a 'correct' or 'safe' dose. There is no real way of knowing the concentration of any powder or liquid that you buy. On top of this: if badly made, GHB can result in a mix of GHB and sodium hydroxide, which can cause caustic burning of the mouth. Recent tests on randomly purchased bottles of GHB has shown that the contents not only differed from brand to brand, but also from bottle to bottle. Everybody agrees that GHB is most dangerous if either taken in high doses or mixed with alcohol. At a high dose it can lead to unconsciousness and vomiting. This is a common cause of death with any drug (including alcohol). In January 1998, six people were taken to hospital suffering from loss of consciousness, heart problems and breathing difficulties after spiking their own drinks with GHB. GHB certainly can kill. It is relatively easy to make and extremely easy to make badly. There are various sites on the Internet that will provide you with the recipe, but be warned, the Internet contains good and bad information. In America badly mixed GHB has resulted in people being admitted to hospital with burnt mouths and wind-pipes.

What are the side effects of GHB?
Many of the reported side effects are similar to alcohol and have been mentioned above. You certainly shouldn't attempt to drive a car whilst under the influence. Other side effects that have been reported include a slowing of the heart rate, a change in blood pressure, muscle contractions or seizures. It should therefore be avoided by anybody known to have a heart complaint, low or high blood pressure, eclampsia (convulsions) or epilepsy. Some people think that GHB lowers potassium levels and recommend taking potassium supplements with GHB.

How does GHB react with other drugs?
GHB is claimed to be 'synergistic'. This means that it adds to the effects of other drugs so that the combination of the two can be more powerful than the effects of either. It has been used with stimulant drugs like ecstasy and cocaine in an attempt to enhance the effects. However, whilst it may enhance the desirable effects of other drugs, it will also increase the side-effects. This is particularly dangerous with drugs such as heroin as it may enhance the effects of respiratory depression. Avoid sleeping pills (such as Valium) even over-the-counter night-time-cold-treatments that induce sleep. Drugs that depress the central nervous system such as barbiturates or alcohol should not be used. GHB reacts very badly with alcohol and the mix of the two should be avoided at all costs.

What is a safe dose?
GHB is a very 'dose-specific' drug, therefore, dosage is of vital importance. Bottles of GHB carry no dosage advice, which can result in confusion over what is an actual safe dose. Dosage is different for different people and depends – among other things – on body weight. The use of GHB is not recommended and no-one can guarantee a 'safe dose'. Having said that, it is important if you do use it, not to overdose. Drinking a pint of beer will have a different effect and would carry less risk than drinking 15 pints, for example. The problem with GHB is that the margin for error is much smaller and unlike alcohol, you have no real way of knowing the strength (particularly of the liquid). Whether you are taking GHB mixed from a powder or buying it as a liquid; start with a small amount (a half-capful of liquid or a half-teaspoon of powder) make sure you have an empty stomach and are alcohol-free. The effects should have started after 15 minutes and should last a couple of hours. Wait at least half an hour. If there is no effect then take an even smaller amount and wait another half an hour. If you are finding the desired, pleasant effects, don't be greedy and think that more will give you more of the same. It will not. It will just knock you out and cause vomiting. If you find that the desired dose is higher than the first dose you took, don't take a bigger dose next time you use it, build it up in the same way. It is worth reiterating at this point that at least two people have died in Britain from taking GHB and thousands more have suffered extreme and serious side effects.

Is GHB addictive?
There are claims that GHB can be addictive, though there is no medical evidence to back this up (that I am aware of). It is possible

that there could be a psychological addiction if used on a regular basis over a long period of time, but this could be true of just about any drug or anything enjoyable that is done on a regular basis.

Does GHB inprove sex?
GHB is also claimed to be an aphrodisiac, even by its inventor Dr Laborit. Its effects are also claimed to involve dis-inhibition, heightened sense of touch (a bit like the qualities of ecstasy) enhanced 'male erectile capacity' and an increased intensity of orgasm, particularly in women. GHB can certainly make you horny and lower you inhibitions, so make sure you still carry condoms and practice safer sex. Remember, spiking someone's drink with GHB has the potential to kill them.

How can I avoid the risks?
There is no completely safe way of taking GHB and there are no sure-fire ways to avoid the risks, but here are some tips to help you. Start with a small dose; either a half-capful of liquid or a half-teaspoon of powder. Wait at least half an hour before taking any more. Don't take too much, taking more will not enhance the desired effects but will bring on the nasty stuff.Do not drink alcohol or mix with any of the other drugs mentioned. Always take it on an empty stomach. If you take GHB after eating, the effects can be masked and it's easier to overdose, pass out and have a stomach full of food to vomit. Don't take it on your own; have someone with you who you trust (who hasn't taken GHB) in case you lose control or pass out. It is always better to take a drug in a familiar place where you feel safe. If someone is unconscious, make sure they are lying on their side so as they don't choke on their vomit. If they can't be roused (even if you think they are just sleeping) call an ambulance. Epileptics, those with heart problems, abnormal blood pressure, asthma, breathing problems or any of the other conditions previously mentioned are more at risk.

Is the use of GHB legal?
Surprisingly, yes; although there is quite a real prospect that it will become contained in the Misuse of Drugs Act in the coming year, making manufacture, supply and possession an offence. In Britain, at the present time, GHB is not covered under the Misuse of Drugs Act, so possession is not an offence. It is classed as a medicine so unauthorised manufacture and distribution *could* be an offence

under the Medicines Act. However, the law does allow the drug to be legally imported for personal use only. In the US, due to the extreme side-effects, The Food and Drug Administration declared it an 'unauthorised new drug' and several states made possession illegal.

Heroin

What other names is it known by?
Also known as 'smack', 'brown', 'horse', 'gear', 'H', 'junk', 'skag' and 'jack'.

What is it?
Heroin is a painkilling drug derived from the dried milk of the opium poppy. Street heroin is usually brownish-white (hence the term 'brown'). It is either smoked or injected. Heroin is a Class A drug. Street heroin is usually 'cut' (mixed) with other substances such as glucose or talcum powder.

What are the effects?
In small doses, heroin gives the user a sense of warmth and well being whereas higher doses can make them drowsy and relaxed. Excessive amounts can result in overdosing, comas and, in some cases, death. First time use often leads to side-effects like nausea, dizziness and vomiting.

What are the dangers?
Heroin is very addictive. Getting the next 'fix' can dominate a user's life. Tolerance and physical dependence develop quickly, which means that the user will need more heroin to get the same effect again. Users who form a habit may end up taking the drug just to feel normal. Those who start by smoking heroin invariably switch to injection to maximise the high.

As street heroin is usually 'cut' it is difficult to know how big a dose is actually being taken. The risk of overdosing is very real and can lead to coma or possible death. Injecting can damage veins and lead to gangrene. Sharing needles or syringes puts users at risk of dangerous infections like hepatitis and HIV. The contraction of hepatitis B and C is common amongst heroin users; hepatitis C being the most prevalent. Withdrawing from heroin can be very hard. Many people manage to kick the drug, but mentally, it may take years to be free.

Is the taking of heroin legal?
No. Heroin is a Class A drug. The maximum penalty for possession is seven years imprisonment and/or a fine. The maximum penalty for supply is life imprisonment and/or a fine.

Ketamine

What is it?
Ketamine is an anaesthetic with painkilling and psychedelic properties. A very similar drug is used by vets when they operate on animals. Ketamine comes in the form of tablets, or as a powder which can be snorted up the nose. Ketamine is a prescription-only medicine, and though possession without a prescription isn't illegal, supplying is against the law, and Class C penalties may apply.

What are the effects?
Ketamine makes users feel that the mind has been separated from the body. This creates 'out-of-body' and hallucinatory experiences which can last for up to three hours. Like LSD, the effects are influenced by the user's mood and environment. During this time, a user may be physically unable to move. It is said that a Ketamine 'high' (also known as a K-hole) is better suited to a quiet room rather than a clubby atmosphere.

What are the dangers?
As Ketamine numbs the body, users risk serious injury, without feeling pain. The effects can be very alarming if the user isn't expecting them. Excessive doses carry some risk of breathing problems and heart failure. Ketamine is *very dangerous* when mixed with alcohol and other drugs. The long-term effects of the recreational use of Ketamine are still not really known although it is thought to adversely affect your vision and long-term mental health.

Is the taking of Ketamine legal?
Ketamine (Ketlar) is controlled under the Medicines Act, so the supply of Ketamine without a prescription is an offence. Ketamine is

not controlled under the Misuse Of Drugs Act so possession is not an offence. It is worth noting that there are *very* few prosecutions under the Medicines Act.

LSD

What other names is it known by?
Also referred to as 'acid', 'trips', 'tabs', 'blotters', 'microdots' and 'dots'. Its chemical name is Lysergic Acid Diethylamide.

What is it?
LSD usually comes in tiny squares of paper, often with a picture on one side (a quarter or half the size of a postage stamp). The picture will tell you nothing about the likely effect or strength of the drug. They also come as pills, tablets or capsules. LSD is a Class A drug.

What are the effects?
LSD is a hallucinogenic drug. It has a powerful effect on the mind. The effects of LSD are known as a 'trip' It usually takes between 30 and 60 minutes to take effect and can then last for as long as 8 (and up to 12) hours. While a user is 'tripping' they will experience their surroundings in a very different way. The effects depend on the user's mood and also where and who they are with. Senses of movement and time may speed up or slow down and objects, colour and sound may become distorted. Dependency is not usual with LSD, but somebody who uses too much can often feel out of touch with the real world. Each trip is different from the last.

What are the dangers?
The brain is affected by the tiniest amount of LSD, and users are never too sure how much they are getting. The brain function can be permanently affected and this can trigger off long-term illness. LSD can complicate mental problems such as depression, anxiety and schizophrenia. Once the trip starts, there's no way of stopping it and a bad trip can be terrifying. Users may feel very threatened and can even forget that it is the drug that is responsible. It's impossible to predict a 'bad trip', but it's more likely to happen if the user is feeling anxious, nervous or uncomfortable. Feeling paranoid or out of control can leave users shaken for a long time afterwards. Accidents may happen whilst users are hallucinating.

Is the taking of LSD legal?
No. LSD is a Class A drug. The maximum penalty for possession is seven years imprisonment and/or a fine. The maximum penalty for supply is life imprisonment and/or a fine.

Magic Mushrooms

What other names are they known by?
They are also referred to as 'shrooms' and 'mushies'.

What are they?
Several types of magic mushroom grow wild in the United Kingdom. The main type is the liberty cup (Psilocybe Semilanceata). Magic mushrooms contain the hallucinogenic drug 'psilocybin'. There are species that look similar to magic mushrooms but which are poisonous. Magic mushrooms can be eaten raw or dried, can be cooked in food or stewed into a 'tea'. Whilst it isn't illegal to possess 'raw' magic mushrooms, it is an offence to possess any preparation of them (e.g. when they are dried or stewed). Magic mushrooms in this prepared state are designated as Class A drugs.

What are the effects?
Magic mushrooms have a similar effect to LSD but the trip is often milder and shorter. Magic mushrooms can make the user feel very relaxed and 'spaced out'. The effects depend on the user's mood and where and who they are with. Low doses produce happiness and detachment. Sometimes anxiety and panic occur. Sickness, vomiting and stomach pains are also common. Magic mushrooms may cause hallucinations, with objects, colour and sound becoming distorted. The effects begin after about half an hour, peaking at about three hours and can last for up to nine hours. You can't stop the effects once they have started.

What are the dangers?
Magic mushrooms often cause stomach pains, sickness and diarrhoea. If users feel sick they should go to the hospital with a sample of the mushroom and explain what happened. Unpleasant hallucinations can occur, usually after repeated or high doses, or, if the user is already anxious or low to start with. Bad trips can happen and can

be very frightening. Once the trip has started, there's no going back. Like any hallucinogen, magic mushrooms can complicate mental problems.

Is the taking of magic mushrooms legal?
Yes, provided they are eaten raw. Prepared magic mushrooms are a Class A drug. The possession of 'prepared' magic mushrooms is illegal and carries a maximum penalty of seven years imprisonment and/or a fine. The supply of prepared magic mushrooms carries a maximum penalty of life imprisonment and/or a fine. In reality, the law on magic mushrooms is complicated. None of them are legally restricted and there is no law against eating them raw. Once they are cooked, boiled, dried or 'prepared' in any way then they do become a Class A drug.

Poppers

What other names are they known by?
Poppers is the term applied to the group of chemicals known as alkyl nitrites. Alkyl nitrites include amyl nitrite, butyl nitrite, and isobutyl nitrite. Trade names include, Ram, Thrust, Rock Hard, Kix, TNT, Liquid Gold, Hi Tech, and Rave.

What are they?
Poppers come as a clear or straw-coloured liquid available in a small bottle or tube and usually sold in sex shops under the description of 'room odorisers'. They are used to heighten sexual arousal and to provide an immediate buzz. The vapour is breathed in through the nostrils. Over recent years, the use of poppers has become more common in dance culture. It has been extremely common on the gay scene for a number of years. This use subsided slightly in the nineties and now seems to be on the increase again. Amyl nitrite is a prescription-only medicine. Possession is not illegal.

What are the effects?
Users get a very brief but intense 'head rush'. This is caused by a sudden surge of blood through the heart and brain. The blood vessels dilate, resulting in a flushed face and neck. Some users say they experience the impression of time slowing down. The effects fade two to five minutes after use.

What are the dangers?
They can make some people feel faint and sick, especially when taken while dancing and users often experience a headache

afterwards. Regular use causes skin problems around the mouth and nose. Because the drug reduces blood pressure, taking alkyl nitrites is very dangerous for people with anaemia, glaucoma (as blood pressure is increased within the eye) and breathing or heart problems. If spilled, poppers can burn skin and if swallowed, *can be fatal*. Users of viagra should avoid inhaling poppers – it is extremely dangerous (viagra reduces blood pressure as do poppers). When used for sexual enhancement, the user should be aware of the need to practice safer sex and take appropriate precautions.

Is using poppers legal?
The legality over the sale, use and possession of poppers lies, at present, in an extremely grey area and it has been near impossible to clarify an answer to this simple question. Basically, according to the legal department of The Medicines Agency it is not illegal to *use* poppers. However, it is illegal to sell and/or manufacture poppers without a licence (subject to an appeal in a current court case), because all nitrites/nitrates (amyl, akyl and isobutyl contain one or more of a substance controlled under the Medicines Act. Poppers, no matter what guise they are sold under (aromas, room odorisers, etc.), are still medicinal. Thus, the person in possession of poppers has acquired them *illegally*. I have no evidence of a person having used poppers and then being charged with 'possession'. The Medicines Agency are at present preparing two cases against suppliers both to clarify the law and thus prohibit the sale of poppers.

Speed

What other names is it known by?
Also known as 'whizz', 'uppers', 'amph', 'billy' and 'sulphate'.

What is it?
Speed is an amphetamine and usually comes as a grey, white or dirty white powder and sometimes in tablet form. It can be snorted, swallowed, smoked or injected. Speed is the most impure drug in the United Kingdom. Amphetamines are Class B drugs but, carry Class A penalties if prepared for injection.

What are the effects?
Speed is a stimulant. It quickens the heart-beat and breathing rate. Users may experience an improved sense of confidence. Their minds

race and they may feel energetic. It suppresses the appetite, but doesn't satisfy the body's need for nourishment. Some people also become tense and experience feelings of anxiety.

What are the dangers?
The comedown (tiredness and depression) lasts for one or two days, sometimes longer. Sleep, memory and concentration are all affected in the short-term. High doses repeated over a few days may cause panic and hallucinations. Long-term users may become dependant on the buzz that speed gives them. Tolerance can develop, which means that the user will begin to need more to get the same effect. Long-term use puts a strain on the heart. Overdosing can be fatal. Use of speed can lead to mental illness, such as psychosis.

Is the taking of speed legal?
No. Speed (an amphetamine) is a Class B drug. The maximum penalty for possession is five years imprisonment and/or a fine. The maximum penalty for supply is 14 years imprisonment and/or a fine.

Tranquillizers

What other names are they known by?
Chemical names include diazepam, temazepam (mazzies), and nitrazepam. Trade names include Valium, Ativan and Mogadon ('moggies').

What are they?
The most commonly prescribed man-made drugs are called benzodiazepines and include such well-known names as Valium, Librium, Ativan and Temazepam. Nearly twice as many women than men take prescribed tranquillizers. They are prescribed by general practitioners as a short-term treatment for anxiety, depression and sleeping problems. They are misused by some people to counter the effects of stimulant drugs. They are also taken in combination with alcohol and heroin. Tranquillizers can only be lawfully supplied by a pharmacist to someone with a doctor's prescription. Though possession without a prescription isn't illegal (except in the case of temazepam, which is a Class C, Schedule 4, controlled drug and possession is an offence without a personal prescription), supplying is against the law and Class C penalties apply.

What are the effects?
Tranquillizers calm users and slow them down mentally. They relieve tension and anxiety. Higher doses can make users drowsy and forgetful.

What are the dangers?
Tranquillizers slow down reactions, making accidents more likely. They are *extremely dangerous* if mixed with alcohol. Tolerance can develop. Users can become dependant, especially if they rely on the drug to calm them or to help them to sleep. Users trying to quit may suffer panic attacks, sickness, headaches and in some cases, convulsions. Injecting crushed tablets or the contents of capsules is *very dangerous* and can be lethal.

Is the taking of tranquillizers legal?
Yes. However, the supplying of tranquillizers without a prescription *is* illegal and carries the maximum penalty of two years imprisonment and/or a fine. The supply *and* possession of temazepam carries the same maximum penalty unless tamazepam is prescribed to you in your name. The preparation of temazepam for injecting makes it a Class B drug and the maximum penalty for possession is five years imprisonment and/or a fine. The supply of (prepared for injection) temazepam carries the maximum penalty of 14 years imprisonment and/or a fine.

British Helpline Listings

You can talk to your doctor about general health problems. General practitioners can also offer advice and help on treating drugs problems. There are a wide range of specialist drugs services in England, Scotland and Wales. The type of help available will vary from agency to agency but many offer more than just one service. Services can include:

- General advice and counselling about drugs
- Support, counselling and aftercare services for drug misusers and their families
- Needle and syringe exchange schemes for those who inject drugs to help prevent infections * Out-patient clinics for treating people with a drug problem (e.g. prescribing substitute drugs)
- In-patient facilities for people with serious or complicated drugs problems
- Residential rehabilitation services for drug misusers (these provide extended programmes of care and many require the person to be drug-free on admission)

Services can be provided from a number of different locations, for example: hospital clinics, community centres, drop-in centres, and home-visiting teams. They may be provided by the NHS, voluntary organisations or self-help and volunteer groups and they can link in with other services, such as social care, housing and legal advice.

Some pharmacists provide needle and syringe exchange facilities. Opening hours can vary and some may have an appointment system or require a referral. You can check by phoning the agency concerned.

The following contact organisations represent only a handful of specialist agencies who are able to offer confidential advice and support. All of them will be able to refer you to an agency in your area. It is worth noting that the lines may appear to be constantly engaged, but you should keep trying in order to get through. Further details of services are also available from The National Drugs Helpline or SCODA. Your local Yellow Pages directory may be able to give you a local advice and support number to contact under 'Counselling and Advice'.

The National Drugs Helpline

Telephone   0800 77 66 00

Gives free advice about drugs, including personal advice on how to talk to your children about drugs, confidential counselling or information on anything to do with taking drugs. It can tell you about local services in your area, what help they can give and how people can be referred on to more specialist services, such as hospital clinics or residential rehabilitation programmes. The lines are open 24 hours a day, every day. Anyone can call, whatever their age and interest in drugs. All calls are free and confidential.

The Standing Conference On Drug Abuse (SCODA)

Waterbridge House
32. . . 36 Loman Street
London
SE1 0EE   Telephone   0171 928 9500

SCODA is the independent national co-ordinating body for drug services. It provides specialist advice on local services and best practice information on drug treatment, care, prevention and education. The Institute for Drug Dependence (ISDD) provides a comprehensive library service and research department on various aspects of the use and misuse of drugs.

ADFAM National

Telephone   0171 638 3700

This is the national charity for families and friends of drug users which runs the National Helpine for families, offering confidential support and information. Callers can ring as often as they need and ADFAM will call people back if the cost of a call is a problem.

Families Anonymous

Telephone   0171 498 4680

Is a self-help support group for parents of drug users with branches in various parts of the country. Phone the above number for further details.

Release

Telephone   0171 603 8654

Offers a 24 hour confidential helpline providing advice on drug use and associated legal matters. Useful if someone has been arrested for a drugs offence

Release 'Drugs In Schools'

Telephone   0345 366 666
(10.00–17.00 Monday – Friday)

Offers advice, information and support for those concerned with a drug incident at school.

Scottish Drugs Forum

5th Floor
Shaftsbury House
5 Waterloo Street
Glasgow
G2 6AY   Telephone 0141 221 1175

Will provide information on services in Scotland.

The Welsh Office

Cathays Park
Cardiff
CF1 3NQ   Telephone 01222 825 592

Will provide information on services in Wales.

Legal Concerns

Introduction

This section has been designed to give you an insight into the various aspects of legal representation that we will almost certainly require at some stage in our lives. Particularly: wills, living wills and powers of attorney. Not to mention conveyancing and – more common than you may realise – divorce. It is with this in mind that you choose your solicitor carefully; one who thoroughly understands the gay lifestyle and can advise on the *implications* of your actions with more authority than a solicitor picked at random from the Yellow Pages.

It should be noted that the following text is a guideline and a guideline *only* to the procedures in each given field and it is not to be construed as the final word of the law. There are subtle differences between English and Welsh law and Scottish law, and the text has been designed to give an overall picture of procedure rather than to describe the differences between the countries.

The following text has been supplied, edited and reprinted with kind permission from David Terry and Co. Full details of his services are outlined in the subsequent listings

Buying Property And Living Together

Buying Property Together
In the UK there is a very big difference between property rights as between married couples and an unmarried couple (whether of the same sex or not). Any gay man or woman contemplating buying a property with his or her partner should almost certainly talk the matter through with a solicitor first. Since same sex marriages are not permitted in the UK it is vital that anyone who is living with a partner is fully aware of what the legal position is with regard to ownership of property. There are so many misconceptions in this area, that it is best to be absolutely clear about it. Gay men and women who find themselves in a lasting relationship very often buy houses or flats together. It is important to think this through

carefully at the time of buying because gay relationships can (and do) break down just like any others. If this happens, there is then the question of what is going to happen to the property.

The basic position between an unmarried couple (whether gay or not) is that each owns their own property and continues to own it separately. If the relationship breaks down each party simply takes out their own property and that is theoretically the end of the matter. But where a couple live together for any length of time, it becomes increasingly difficult to establish who owns what. It is not commonly appreciated, for example, that property often belongs to the person who paid for it rather than in whose possession it may be (although this is a very technical subject upon which the advice of a lawyer is almost always necessary if there is a dispute).

The whole problem becomes very much more acute when you start talking about assets with a substantial value, such as a house or flat. It is very common, for example, for the deposit money to be divided unequally or for the contributions to the mortgage to be different. Later on this can easily lead to quite complex disputes about who is entitled to what. So it is usually far better to avoid this type of problem by thinking ahead.

It is very much easier to deal with this situation at the very beginning by having a proper agreement rather than hoping for the best if the relationship breaks down. For example, each partner may have contributed unequally to the initial deposit. This is an easy matter to record in the beginning, but if the relationship breaks down it is very likely to become the subject of dispute.

In fact gays have something of an advantage over married couples in this respect. It is not actually possible for a married couple to come to an agreement as to who is to have what in the event of divorce: the courts have the last word, and the courts can, and usually do, divide up all the matrimonial property – his, hers and theirs – in whatever way they think best. A gay couple (or indeed, any unmarried couple) can come to whatever agreement they want as to what should happen in the event of a split and such an agreement will be binding.

It is particularly important to do this where, say, contributions to buy a house or flat have been substantially different. Or, it is if you want to preserve the right to your own money at least – some people are more relaxed about it. If there has been no agreement, then either party who owns a jointly-owned house, for example, can force a sale in the event of a separation. This may not be sensible. It may be better, say, for one partner to be allowed to buy the other's interest out.

It is also not often well understood that there are two different ways of holding property together: as joint tenants or, as tenants in common. Sometimes one is appropriate; sometimes the other. For example, in the case of joint tenants the property automatically goes to the other on death *no matter what any will says*. In the case of a tenancy in common however, each partners share can be left by will *in whatever way you wish*. Similarly, a tenancy in common allows a property to be owned, say, 60% by one and 40% by the other (depending perhaps on their contributions).

The way in which property is held between an unmarried couple is vitally important in case something should happen to either of them. In the case of a jointly-owned property the house or flat belongs automatically to the survivor on the death of one of the partners. That is not the case with a tenancy in common. In this latter case, the share of the property belonging to the deceased passes with his or her estate, and that may mean it passes to his or her partner or it may not. Whether it does will depend on the wording of any will or on the operation of the intestacy rules. The very worst scenario that can happen in these circumstances is that one of the partners dies thinking that his/her partner will inherit the house, but in fact, his/her family do and then force the sale of a home in which the surviving partner may have previously lived for many years. This can all be avoided by making proper provisions and it is often sensible to make a will at the same time as buying the house or, at the very least, to understand something about wills and intestacy so that the obvious risks can be avoided.

In short, when buying property together it is almost always sensible to take legal advice, and ordinary conveyancing solicitors are not *necessarily* the persons to give that advice, unless you are quite sure that they fully understand your particular lifestyle and specific concerns. Too often, joint purchases by gay couples go through without these issues ever being discussed. It is very important to discuss these matters carefully with a solicitor and if the solicitor acting for you on the purchase of a property does not do so (as many do not), then you should make sure that *you* raise the subject. Dealing with this properly at the beginning can save a great deal of trouble later.

The Costs Of Buying A Property

In practice, clients rarely have any complaints over the amounts that they are charged by solicitors (or licensed conveyancers) to buy or sell ordinary residential property in England. This is because it is a very competitive market. Also, of course, when a client buys a property, the legal costs are low in comparison to the estate agent's commission and/or stamp duty.

Most clients can soon find the going-rate for such services in their area by phoning around and asking for quotes, which are normally very easily obtained. In fact, the Law Society is very concerned that the prices charged for conveyancing are sometimes too low because if the solicitor skimps on the job there may well be a call on the profession's compulsory public indemnity insurance for which the whole profession pays. Such insurance claims have been increasing at an alarming rate in recent years and this would tend to suggest that the Law Society is correct – conveyancing charges tend, if anything, to be lower than they should be, rather than higher. Naturally, this is good news for clients. It is only fair to point out, though, that if solicitors do have to cut corners in this area because of the cut-throat competition, they do also sometimes have to cut those corners in terms of client service, and so the client may not be as well informed about the progress of the transaction as he would wish. This isn't always the case but in this field, as in many others, a client often gets what he pays for and a rock-bottom price doesn't necessarily ensure a top-of-the-range service. Trade-offs do have to be made and the choice must ultimately rest with the client as to what sort of service he/she wants.

As well as the legal costs (quotes for which can easily be obtained over the phone from any number of firms) there are so-called 'disbursements' involved in buying or selling properties. These are sums paid by the solicitor to third parties as necessary expenses in property purchase and they vary slightly, depending on whether one is buying or selling a property. Of course, if one is selling one home in order to buy another, then both sets of disbursements will be incurred. Since these are sums paid out by the solicitor to third parties they will remain constant from solicitor to solicitor and they are inevitable and unavoidable expenses in the great majority of instances.

Selling A Property
The normal disbursements are:

1. The cost of obtaining the title deeds. Some banks or building societies charge for this, although the charge is not always obvious because it simply gets added to the mortgage debt in most cases, and is paid when the mortgage is redeemed. If it is charged it is normally in the region of £25.

2. It is the seller's obligation to provide so-called 'office copies' of the title to the purchaser's solicitor. These documents are obtained from the Land Registry and the fee is about £10, although the Land Registry periodically changes its various charges.

3. Very often there are quite large sums of money involved in buying and selling properties, so the client will be anxious to receive the money due to him as soon as possible. For this reason (and for other practical conveyancing reasons) money is usually transferred by 'telegraphic transfer' and the banks charge for this service. Normally they charge in the region of £20 to £25.

4. The estate agent's commission. This is normally a percentage of the sale price and will have been agreed between the client and the estate agent beforehand. It almost invariably dwarfs all other disbursements (and the legal costs).

Buying A Property

There are more expenses involved in buying a property, particularly if the property is being bought with the assistance of a mortgage. Clients do not always realise that in the latter case, their solicitor is usually also acting for their lender. (This is done to save costs. Basically, to prevent the client having to pay separate legal costs for his own solicitor and for the lender's solicitor because the lender would almost certainly make payment of its legal costs a condition of the loan.) Nevertheless, because the solicitor is also very often acting for the client's lender it means that it is not possible to cut corners. The solicitor owes a duty of care to the lender as well as the purchaser and so he must be particularly careful to investigate the title thoroughly.

Lenders can and do very frequently sue solicitors where this has not been done and all conveyancing solicitors are acutely aware of this risk. The main disbursements on buying a property are therefore:

1. The local authority search (necessary in order to find out, for instance, whether the local authority intends to build a road through the front garden). The cost of this varies from authority to authority, but it is in the general region of £100.

2. Stamp duty. This is typically a large disbursement because it is based on a percentage of the value of the property. Properties worth under £60,000 (currently) are exempt while properties over that value have to pay 1% of the value of the transfer as

stamp duty. More expensive properties may have to pay an even higher rate. The Land Registry will not register details of a property transfer if the stamp duty is not paid; nor can the transfer be used as evidence in any court proceedings. There are also penalties payable if the duty is not paid within 30 days of the transfer. In practice, therefore, the duty must be paid. Sometimes, on properties at the boundaries of the exempt or higher-rate bands of stamp duty, it may be possible to save considerable sums by attributing a proportion of the purchase price to 'contents' and so reducing the value of the transfer. However, this only applies to properties near the relevant price boundaries and, of course, the apportioning of value to the 'contents' has to be done in good faith.

3. Land registration fees. Once a property has been bought, it will need to be registered at HM Land Registry and a lender will certainly insist on this. There are scale fees for such registrations, which vary depending on the value of the property. In effect, they range from approximately £40 for properties of modest value to hundreds of pounds for more expensive properties.

4. In order to obtain 'priority' for an intended registration it is necessary to do a special type of Land Registry search before the formal registration. (If the property was sold to someone else as a result of not effecting this protection the client would not be very pleased.) The cost of this is approximately £10.

5. Where a property is being bought with the aid of a mortgage, the lender will insist on a 'bankruptcy search' being carried out against the borrower. The cost of this is quite modest (less than one pound) but if it were not done there would be a risk that the sum advanced by the lender to purchase the property would end up paying the borrower's creditors.

6. Bank charges – as in the case of selling a property.

It has to be said that these are the minimum disbursements in most cases. In some cases, there are rather more. Leasehold properties, for instance, often require payments of sums of money to register the new owner and the lender with the freeholder and the managing agent may need to be paid to provide copies of the service charge accounts. The precise sums due will depend upon the terms of the lease, but it is certainly the case that there will normally be higher disbursements in the case of a purchase (or sale) of a leasehold property. Even in the case of freehold properties there may be additional disbursements in certain circumstances. In Cornwall, for instance, it is quite common to have to do a 'mining search' to establish whether the property might be situated on an old mine working, and it can readily be seen that local and particular circumstances such as these might come into play in any conveyancing transaction.

The client may be sure, though, that the reason for such a disbursement will be given and that they are almost invariably necessary and/or advisable if the circumstances are such that they come into play. Conveyancing charges are rarely a problem for clients but nevertheless you should always ensure that they are agreed in advance. A client who does not do this runs the risk of paying a 'reasonable price' and in this field a reasonable price may actually be higher than the market rate.

Living Together

The law relating to cohabitees is entirely different from the law relating to married couples, so far as property rights are concerned, although issues involving children and injunctions are dealt with in broadly similar (although not identical) ways. It is important to remember of course, that 'cohabitees' means any couple that live together, and that may include same sex relationships. The law is the same whether the parties are of the same sex or not. The big difference is between the status of marriage and that of cohabiting children are very rarely an issue in same sex relationships but the law as it affects property rights is the same whether the cohabitees are of the same sex or not. It is only the focus of any disputes which is likely to be different.

If the relationship between two unmarried people breaks down, their property rights are unaffected. The distinction between 'his', 'his and theirs' or 'hers', 'hers and theirs' is very real in this situation and each person is entitled to claim their own property. This is in marked distinction to the position between married couples where the courts can divide all property (his, hers and theirs) in whatever way they think best, regardless of who actually owns them. In the case of divorce following marriage breakdown the courts have a very wide jurisdiction over all the marital property and broadly speaking, such property is usually divided between the parties according to *their perceived needs*.

It is important to appreciate the importance of this distinction. For example, it is quite common following a divorce for the former matrimonial home to be transferred into the sole name of the ex-wife who continues to live there with the children of the marriage. The ex-husband may also be obliged to pay maintenance for his children and/or his ex-wife. The reason this often happens is that the *need* of the children to have a stable home environment and a roof over their heads quite frequently dictates that the house be transferred into the sole name of the ex-wife. This may be despite the fact that all mortgage payments, for example, may have been made by the ex-husband. Such a situation often causes bitterness for understandable reasons.

The case of an unmarried couple is quite different. Their property rights remain exactly the same after the split as before. Any property continues to belong to its owner and that is usually the person who paid for it. Naturally, there is some room for dispute over this, but that is the overriding principle and the courts have no jurisdiction to ignore it. So, if, for example, one man owns a house and moves his boyfriend in but the relationship subsequently breaks down there is no question but that the house remains the property of the owner whether there are children involved or not.

People often refer to a 'common law wife' in this connection and there is a widespread misconception that after a certain period of time a 'common law wife' acquires the same rights as an 'actual' wife. This is not the case. There can be complications in that there may be a dispute over who owns what or who contributed how much to a given purchase but, in principle, the answer is always the same: each is entitled to keep their own property. This may involve the sale of jointly-owned property (which either can usually insist upon) but the proceeds of the sale will be divided according to strict property rights.

Same sex couples (or indeed any couple) can come to an agreement about what is to happen in the event of subsequent separation and, insofar as it affects property, such an agreement will be legally binding. Such an agreement made by a married couple could be ignored by a court in dividing the matrimonial assets, but that is not the case where the couple is not married. Indeed, that could be said to be one of the advantages of not being married; that the jurisdiction of the courts to interfere with property rights is almost entirely excluded where the partners are not married.

People often mention the possibility of 'pre-nuptial agreements' which would regulate what would happen to the property of a married couple after divorce. These agreements are possible in other jurisdictions such as the Unites States of America and it is probably as a result of US influence on the media that so many people are aware of this but, pre-nuptial agreements are *not* binding in the United Kingdom. The courts retain absolute jurisdiction as to how to divide the matrimonial property after a divorce and they would not flinch from ignoring such an agreement. They cannot do this where the agreement regulates property rights between an unmarried couple.

In the case where, say, a house is to be bought jointly by an unmarried couple it is sensible to enter into a written agreement as to who has contributed what and what is to happen if the parties later split up. This can save a lot of acrimony later and is something that a solicitor can easily do. In the case of a joint house or flat purchase by an unmarried couple it is a matter of elementary prudence to make such an agreement, and it is a lot easier to do at the outset rather than later, when difficulties may have arisen.

There are a lot of other issues that an unmarried couple may want to consider. For instance, they are not actually legally related in any way and so if either wants to benefit the other in the event of death it is usually sensible to make a will to that effect. If that is not done, then the beneficiaries may well be the next of kin who were not intended to be beneficiaries at all.

Similarly, there may be issues such as involvement in decisions on medical treatment to consider, since it should always be remembered that the partner of someone who is unmarried is not the next of kin.

Wills And Intestacy

Making A Will
If a gay man or woman lives with a partner outside of marriage (and of course gay marriages are not allowed) then, no matter how long you may have been together, your partner is not legally related to you *in any way*, and in the event of death, he/she would be very unlikely to receive anything, if you were to die without making a will. If you want your partner, as opposed say to relatives who might detest your partner, to benefit in the event of your death then a will is *absolutely essential*.

Of course there is no reason why a gay relationship need follow the standard monogamous heterosexual pattern anyway. Gay men and women often have a wide circle of close friends without necessarily having one exclusive partner. The same rule would apply here: such friends cannot benefit automatically on your death as relatives can, under intestacy rules. If you specifically want your partner or friends to benefit then you must make a will, for the intestacy rules only benefit 'family' and in this context your partner is not family at all.

What makes the situation very often worse of course is that the family can quite often detest the partner and/or friends and so the bitterness of callous treatment at the hands of the family is then added to the grief of loss. This does not always happen of course, but it is a common enough situation, which can be avoided by taking elementary precautions. A will which makes provision for your partner may also appoint him/her executor, so that you know that your estate will be dealt with in the way that you would have wished following your death.

Of course, no-one likes to think about death very much and many people feel they do not have much to leave anyway. But it is surprising what comes to light in the way, for example, of insurance policies, benefits from pension plans at work, policies which pay off mortgages, etc.

Naturally, you will also have to make sure that your will is kept up-to-date from time to time so that it reflects your real wishes. Gay relationships tend to be more fluid than conventional ones and so this is a point particularly worth bearing in mind.

It is also worth considering a 'living will'. This is not strictly speaking a will at all, because it operates during life rather than after death, but most gay men or women with partners would prefer their partners to be involved with any medical decisions affecting them if they become ill and incapable of taking decisions for themselves. It is possible, for instance, to direct that your partner be contacted in the event of any accident or illness or that he/she be consulted if medical treatment requires consent. There are few things more frustrating than to be excluded from such decisions affecting your partner by his/her family even though you may have lived together for many years and the so-called family was estranged from the patient when he/she was well.

In order to make sure this does not happen it is sensible sometimes to have several copies of a living will which can be kept, for example, with your GP as well as at home.

Incidentally there is a very useful book containing a wealth of information which many gay men and women may find helpful entitled *The Natural Death Handbook* and obtainable from:

> The Natural Death Centre
> 20 Heber Road
> London
> NW2 6AA

There are a number of pitfalls involved in making a will and most of them are very easy to avoid. Above all, never attempt to do it yourself. Drafting a will is a very technical business and it is exceptionally easy to get it wrong. If you do get it wrong your intended beneficiaries could be involved in costly litigation (the costs of which will very likely come out of your estate) and they will have no-one to sue if you did get it wrong. Use a solicitor to draft your will. It should only cost a modest amount and, at the very least, if he/she does get it wrong your intended beneficiaries would have some remedy.

Secondly, do not appoint a solicitor or other professional as an executor of your will unless there is very good reason for doing so. Sometimes there is a good reason such as, for instance, where you want to make sure that a trust for the benefit of children is scrupulously observed.

Professionals who act as executors usually have a charging clause in the will which enables them to charge for things which a lay executor could perfectly easily have done – selling a house and liaising with estate agents, for example.

The very worst scenario is for a bank or other institution to be appointed executor. If you have such a will – *change it now*. Banks and institutional executors usually charge a great deal for everything they do and having such an executor will very soon make a substantial hole in the estate. They are also often very cautious and slow in their administration, which can add very considerably to the costs. For example, a bank will very often have shares valued by its stockbroking arm or a house sold by its estate agency, and there are fees and delays usually involved at every step. If it really is necessary to appoint a professional executor (and it sometimes is) then it is almost invariably cheaper and quicker in the long run to use, say, the family solicitor or accountant but always consider whether you need to do so carefully in the first place.

Thirdly, it is a little known fact that wills can be deposited for safekeeping at the Principal Probate Registry in the Strand, London, for a one-off fee (currently) of £1. Such wills cannot get lost and it saves the hassle of contacting many banks or solicitors particularly where the deceased may have moved home on several occasions. Searching to see whether a will has been deposited at the Principal Probate Registry is part of the routine whenever an application is made for probate or letters of administration and so it will always come to light.

Although solicitors very often do not charge for holding a will for safekeeping (hoping, in general, that they will get the probate work in due course), banks do usually charge. So, you should therefore simply file the original at the Principal Probate Registry (where it will be quite safe and must come to light as soon as anyone tries to administer your estate). You should also keep a copy at home for reference purposes. Incidentally, with regard to the latter event there will be no prospect of a disgruntled beneficiary destroying the will after your death as, regrettably, does sometimes happen.

Although there are many other things to bear in mind when making a will, do remember that you should always make one if what you wish to do is *not what would happen* under the intestacy rules. And also bear in mind that marriage and divorce affect wills in very significant ways so it always pays to reconsider your will after such an event.

Making a will is by no means straightforward, but there are often quite considerable benefits to be had by doing so and the cost is usually quite modest.

Making A Living Will

Although they are not wills as such, more and more clients do enquire about whether it is possible to make provision for a time when they may be physically or mentally incapable of taking medical decisions for themselves by making a 'living will'. Many people fear the prospect of degeneration and/or indignity as much, if not more than, death and in these circumstances, a living will may be of very real assistance.

Every person has the right to die in dignity, free from efforts to prolong terminal illness, just because the technology is available to do so. In fact, it can be a very heavy burden for doctors and family to decide whether or not to keep a patient alive when there is no real hope. The family and hospital often do not know what to do and people are left wondering if they have made the right decision. A living will can help solve this problem and it can also mean that the patient him/herself has been involved in the decision making process. Even the catholic church in the 1980 Declaration Of Euthanasia accepted that 'when inevitable death is imminent, it is permitted in conscience to take the decision to refuse forms of treatment that would only secure a precarious and burdensome prolongation of life.'

A living will can, for example, indicate whether in certain circumstances medical treatment should be directed to saving life at all costs or merely relieving suffering, even if such relief could shorten life. Or, it may express a wish that a certain person be involved in decisions about medical care or be contacted if death is imminent. The latter point is extremely important in the case of cohabiting couples. It is bad enough to be terminally ill without having one's loved one pushed out of the picture by 'family' who are technically the next of kin. In these circumstances it can well make a great deal of sense to name your partner as the proxy who can and should be involved in all medical decisions.

A solicitor can draft a document appropriate to the needs of a particular client. Quite comprehensive forms, covering most eventualities can be obtained from the Terrence Higgins Trust or the Natural Death centre.

In the event of mental or physical incapacity, a power of attorney or an enduring power of attorney may also have important roles to play in dealing with non-medical aspects such as the operation of bank accounts, paying bills, etc.

Intestacy – What Happens If You Die Without Making A Will

Although it is usually advisable for most people to make a will, if no will has already been made, then the deceased's property will devolve according to the intestacy rules. In fact, those rules are based upon an analysis of what most people actually do in their wills and so the intestacy rules very often correspond to what the testator would have done by will anyway. The rules are periodically revised as will-making patterns change.

Having said that, making a will can have considerable advantages over dying intestate for any of a number of reasons. For instance, the unmarried partner of the deceased would not benefit under the intestacy provisions, nor would any friend or charity that the deceased wished to favour be able to benefit, unless there was a will. Similarly, a person making a will might very easily want to leave different amounts to relatives of the same degree, who would otherwise receive equally under the intestacy rules. There could also be inheritance tax benefits to be obtained by disposing of one's property in a certain way by will. Bearing in mind that inheritance tax is levied at the rate of 40% over the exempt threshold this can be a very significant fact in larger estates.

These are simply examples of the sorts of reasons why people might choose to make a will rather than dying intestate and it has to be said that not making a will in some of these situations would be quite irresponsible. There is also a non-legal factor which most solicitors will have observed often enough: even though what a client wishes to do by will would also be achieved by the intestacy rules, many clients do gain satisfaction from 'having put their affairs in order'. Although that may sound illogical it is as equally true, and most solicitors would be able to confirm it. For the relatively small amount it usually costs to make a will, many clients undoubtedly obtain peace of mind.

The three most common situations which arise on intestacy are:

1. Where the deceased leaves a spouse, but no children and no near relatives, in which case the spouse takes all.
2. Where the deceased leaves a spouse and children, in which case, provided the estate exceeds a certain amount, the property is divided between the spouse and children.
3. Where the deceased leaves neither wife nor children, in which case certain near relatives benefit in a given order of priority.

It can readily be seen from the third situation, that the surviving partner of a cohabiting couple can be left high and dry, so it is almost always the case that clients in such a position should make a will. In the case of intestacy, one needs *letters of administration* to deal with the estate of the deceased rather than probate, but the one procedure is quite as simple as the other except, of course, that one can appoint an executor by will, whereas only certain specified people in a given order of priority would be eligible to request letters of administration.

Enduring Power Of Attorney

An enduring power of attorney, unlike an ordinary powder of attorney, remains valid not withstanding the donor's subsequent incapacity. Such a power of attorney needs to be executed in a prescribed form and, if the attorney has reason to believe that the donor is becoming incapable, then it has to be registered with the court.

Just like an ordinary power of attorney, an enduring power can be restricted in any way the donor sees fit, but, unlike an ordinary power, it can be used after the donor has become incapable.

This is an invaluable power where a client has become incapable, mentally or otherwise, of managing his or her own affairs. If it were not for this possibility, no-one would be able to operate the bank account (and pay the bills) of someone who had become incapable without going through the much more cumbrous and expensive procedure of applying to the Court of Protection. One should always think about an enduring power of attorney whenever there is a possibility that someone might become mentally or physically incapable in the near future. This might arise, for instance, from the onset of dementia or as the result of an illness or accident.

It is important to stress that an enduring power of attorney can only be executed by the person giving the power, while he or she has the mental capacity to do so. Once mental capacity has been lost, for whatever reason, it is too late (unless there is recovery) and so everyone would be well advised to consider this possibility at some point.

An enduring power of attorney is a relatively simple and convenient way of dealing with the affairs of someone who is incapable of handling business matters for him/herself by reason of incapacity. In fact, because this can happen to anyone without warning, as a result of an accident or illness perhaps, it is probably a good idea to execute an enduring power of attorney at the same time as executing a will. In the case of elderly clients, executing an enduring power of attorney is almost always a very sensible precaution which can prevent the great deal of inconvenience and expense which occurs if it is left too late.

Issues For Gay Parents

Gay men and women do marry – just like anyone else, and they also have children. Unfortunately, such marriages do also sometimes break down and as with any other marriage, this may lead to disputes over financial matters and/or the children. In point of fact, in the case of most marriage breakdowns, questions relating to the children are resolved by agreement between the parents. The intervention of a court is very much the exception, although it has to be said that such cases are not uncommon.

Sometimes of course, a marriage including a gay man or woman breaks down precisely because his/her partner becomes aware of the spouse's true sexuality for the first time. Cases such as these can involve particular difficulty if there are children involved, because it is much more likely for there to be problems over contact, access and residence, etc. The non-gay spouse may be outraged and refuse all contact with the children. Although this is a difficult situation, the gay parent can in fact be helped by modern divorce law.

Firstly it is important to understand that the reasons for a divorce have, in almost all cases, no bearing whatsoever on any questions which may arise as to, (a) the division of the matrimonial property or, (b) any question affecting the children of the marriage. It is surprising how deep the folk memory of 'blame' runs in matrimonial law because there is still a widespread belief that issues of 'conduct' do affect decisions relating to property and/or the children. One often hears the expression 'unfit mother' in relation to allegations of adultery, for instance (and, indeed, very frequently in relation to a lesbian mother). In fact, nothing could be further from the truth. Just as a mother who has committed adultery can be (and usually is) a perfectly good mother to her children, so also can a gay man or woman be a good parent, and the law recognises this. It matters not a jot that the divorce may have been obtained on the basis of the gay parent's 'unreasonable behaviour'. However outraged the 'innocent' party may be, the fact remains that a good parent remains a good parent and that is the case whatever the sexuality of the parent may be.

Secondly, matters affecting children are decided solely on the basis of what is in the particular child's best interests. That is the *paramount* consideration in the law relating to children and it is demonstrated in many principles constantly reiterated by the courts. For instance, the following factors are emphasised over and over again in such cases:

1. A court should not deprive a child of contact with a natural parent, unless wholly satisfied that it is in the interests of the child that it should cease, and the court should be extremely slow to arrivè at that conclusion.
2. It is the normal assumption that a child will benefit from contact with the natural parent.
3. It is the right *of the child* to have a relationship with each parent and cogent reasons must be given for denying the child contact with a parent.
4. Contact is necessary as the separation of parents involves a loss to the child which should be made good, as far as possible, by contact with the absent parent.
5. Direct contact should only be refused when a child would be put at serious risk of major emotional harm.

Contact with an absent parent has been shown to fulfil a number of important psychological and emotional needs:

1. It diminishes the child's sense of vulnerability in depending totally on one parent.
2. It enriches the child's family life by the knowledge of all it's biological relations, rather than being focused entirely on those of the mother or the father.
3. It provides knowledge of origins and a greater sense of identity.
4. It tends to diminish any unrealistic fantasies about the absent parent.

5. It spares the child any underlying nagging doubts about the possibility of being rejected.

It can readily be seen that the sexuality of the parent does not, in general, enter into these factors at all and the important thing to grasp is that the court looks at it from the child's point of view – not that of the possibly outraged 'innocent' parent. Therefore, if a gay man or woman is deprived of contact with his/her children by a non-gay spouse for, basically, homophobic reasons the courts can and will provide a remedy. They will do so because it is in the child's interest (in almost all cases) that contact be maintained with both parents.

Having said all of that, if this type of problem does arise, it can be difficult to resolve because of the implacable hostility of the non-gay parent, which very frequently accompanies these cases.

In most divorces, disputes about the children are resolved by agreement and, of course, that is always the best outcome. Even if they are not resolved by agreement immediately, the parties are usually offered the services of a conciliation officer, which may resolve matters. If that is not successful, a court welfare officer usually prepares a report and again, that may contain constructive proposals to resolve the dispute.

These steps will also be taken if the dispute is between a gay and non-gay parent but it has to be said that they are less likely to result in agreement if the marriage has recently broken down because of the discovery of the gay element. The same is true incidentally, of marriages which have broken down because of a recent discovery of adultery. A mother in the latter case for instance, will very often not want 'her' children to have contact with 'the other woman'. Where the marriage has broken down because of the discovery of a gay relationship, this feeling can be intensified and reinforced by prejudice. These disputes can, therefore, be difficult to resolve quickly and it may be necessary to go to a full hearing before a judge.

It is also fair to say that the 'implacable hostility' of the non-gay parent to any form of contact can lead to further complications, and cases may be more complicated than mere implacable hostility. A case, for instance, where the husband has had a sex change, now lives as a woman and wishes to have contact with her children might require the involvement of an official solicitor, because such cases are sufficiently unusual not to permit of easy answers and need very careful consideration. Luckily, cases such as the latter, with all their difficulties, are rare, but most disputes concerning children in this area need to be dealt with administering more than usual care.

Fortunately, the law is mainly on the gay parent's side in such disputes.

Divorce

Grounds For Divorce

'Unreasonable behaviour' is the most frequent ground for divorce in and solicitors are frequently asked what constitutes 'unreasonable behaviour'. As you probably know, divorce is based on an 'irretrievable breakdown' of the marriage but this breakdown must be proved by evidence of one of five 'facts':

Adultery
Unreasonable behaviour
Desertion
Two years' separation with consent
Five years' separation without consent

Three of these grounds – desertion, two and five years separation – involve considerable periods of delay before obtaining a divorce is possible at all. At least two years in the case of the first two and five years in the case of the other. Similarly, the parties cannot use adultery if there has been none. This means that 'unreasonable behaviour' is the method of choice for most couples who want an 'instant' divorce in cases where no adultery is involved.

People often approach a solicitor and say they want a divorce based on 'irreconcilable differences'. This happens so often that it is perfectly obvious that there are very many couples in this position. They are in an unhappy marriage and want to bring it to an end. This is perfectly natural and understandable. Nevertheless, it is not possible to obtain a divorce based on 'irreconcilable differences'. This is perhaps wrong but there it is – what the law demands is rather different.

The law insists that, (a) that the marriage has broken down irretrievably and, (b) that one of the parties to the marriage has behaved in such an unreasonable manner that the other finds it intolerable to live with him or her. Or, at least, that is what it requires if divorce is sought on the grounds of unreasonable behaviour. Although this sounds rather a difficult thing to prove, the reality of the matter is that the courts do not set a very demanding standard, and in practice it is not normally too difficult to find some examples of 'unreasonable behaviour' sufficient to satisfy a court when a marriage has broken down. The courts adopt a realistic attitude.

They know that if one party to a marriage feels so strongly about it as to issue a divorce petition, then the marriage has irretrievably broken down so far as that person is concerned and it would be futile to pretend otherwise. The courts therefore adopt quite a relaxed attitude to the exact type of 'unreasonable behaviour' which one has to allege in order to get the divorce. It is important to understand this. It is a pity that couples are forced to do this because there are very many cases where the couple has simply drifted apart and they do not really hold any especial animosity towards one another. They do, nevertheless, want to obtain a divorce now rather than in two years time. They are therefore obliged to fall back on 'unreasonable behaviour' if there has been no adultery. If they want an 'instant' divorce, one of them must divorce the other on the grounds of unreasonable behaviour. Really it does not matter who does it.

People often think that if they do not 'defend' a divorce based on unreasonable behaviour they will suffer in some way when it comes to the division of the matrimonial property and/or any questions relating to the children. In point of fact, the reason for the divorce has no impact whatever on these two latter issues in the overwhelming majority of cases and so there is no reason to be concerned about it. However, this is something which does need to be explained and it often has to be explained carefully.

The other thing to bear in mind is that divorce is private. Details of unreasonable behaviour in an undefended divorce petition are not divulged to the general public and so in general, no-one but the parties themselves need ever know what was in the petition. Indeed, it is quite common for the respondent (the person who receives the divorce petition as opposed to the person who issues it) to agree not to defend the divorce on condition that no use is made of the lack of defence to allegations of unreasonable behaviour in any other proceedings (such, for instance, as those relating to children or the matrimonial property).

The respondent might also want to make it a condition of not defending that there is some agreement as to who bears the costs of the divorce and the reasons for this are explained on the relevant page about divorce costs.

Very often clients ask what constitutes 'unreasonable behaviour'? Obviously, it covers extreme types of behaviour such as habitual drunkenness or violence, but it is by no means necessary to allege anything near as serious in a divorce petition. In fact, because no-one likes receiving a petition based on their unreasonable behaviour, it is very often sensible to keep the allegations to the bare minimum that will suffice to obtain the divorce even in circumstances where very much more could be added. A few paragraphs are normally sufficient and in a case where a marriage has in fact irretrievably broken down it is unusual not to be able to find some instances of unreasonable behaviour which will suffice for the purposes of obtaining a divorce. It is important to understand that the courts are not too demanding about this – particularly where the parties are agreed on a divorce. Naturally, if the parties are not agreed on this, the requirements of the courts are much stricter because the allegations will be subject to scrutiny but in the overwhelming majority of cases the allegations are unchallenged because very few divorces indeed are ever defended.

Something which it important to bear in mind is that there are time limits involved. In general, one must present a divorce petition within no more than six months from the last incident of unreasonable behaviour relied upon if the parties are continuing to live together. There are two reasons for this. Firstly, it is perfectly easy to accept unreasonable behaviour and many people do. For instance, if both parties are heavy drinkers and have been so throughout their married lives, it would lack any credibility if one of them suddenly decided to petition for divorce based on the other's heavy drinking. The second reason is rather more important because it does sometimes catch people out. It is that it is a rule of law. Perhaps this is best explained by example. Suppose a husband hits his wife and as a result the wife decides that the marriage is over but does nothing about it. She continues to live with her husband but there is no further incident of violence. At any time within six months from being hit by her husband the wife could present a petition for divorce based on this unreasonable behaviour if she wished. But once they have lived together for more than six months afterwards she can no longer rely on this incident. However, this rule only applies if the parties continue to live together after the latest incident of unreasonable behaviour. If the wife in the above example had immediately left her husband after being hit and gone to live with her parents she could still petition for divorce based on her husband's unreasonable behaviour in hitting her, even though more than six months had passed since the incident. Even in this case, though, one should not wait too long. There gets a point where one simply cannot credibly complain about the behaviour of one's spouse if he/she is not actually there to be unreasonable. If it looks as though six months since the last incident of unreasonable behaviour occurred will soon elapse it is normally sensible to consider whether one should petition for divorce.

If one leaves it too long the parties may then have to wait two years from the date of the separation before one of them can petition for divorce based on two years' separation. And this is dependent upon the other's consent. If that consent is not forthcoming, the person who wants the divorce may have to wait until the separation has lasted five years unless in the meantime his/her spouse relents. This can be extremely awkward if the reason for wanting the divorce is to remarry, so it is worth bearing these formal and practical time limits in mind. They do sometimes catch people out and to many minds, they are defects in the law, but they are defects which can have very inconvenient consequences if one of the parties wishes, for example, to remarry but the opportunity for relying on unreasonable behaviour has passed.

People often think they can get a divorce based simply upon 'irreconcilable differences'. The truth of the matter is that this usually means 'unreasonable behaviour' and in order to obtain a divorce on the grounds of unreasonable behaviour, one has to comply with the rules applicable to that particular ground including any time limits.

How Divorce Affects Men

Men, in particular, often come out of the divorce process feeling aggrieved and embittered. A very common scenario is that the house is transferred to the wife's sole name, the children live with the wife and the husband pays maintenance for the children until they leave full-time education, while at the same time losing meaningful contact with them. All too often the man feels he has lost everything under such circumstances – wife, home and children – and that what he has spent years building up has suddenly been snatched away from him.

This situation can be made to feel infinitely worse if the man feels that the wife has been to 'blame' for the break-up by, for instance, committing adultery. He very often feels that this 'fault' ought to be taken into account in some way.

To understand why this happens so often it is important to know precisely how the divorce process works. There are, in effect, three *separate* issues.

Firstly, there is the divorce itself. This is the process by which the marriage is brought to an end so that the parties are free to remarry. The conclusion of this process is the *decree absolute*.

Secondly, there is the process by which the marital assets are divided and financial provision is made for all the parties affected. This is described as 'ancillary relief' although, in practice, it is often the most contested part of the proceedings and is very much central rather than ancillary. This part of the process may go on long after the decree absolute has been granted.

Thirdly, there may be proceedings relating to children – with whom the children are to live with, contact arrangements with the absent parent, etc. Very often, matters relating to children are resolved amicably and by agreement, which is by far the best way. But if they are not and a court is asked to decide questions of residence and/or contact, these proceedings can be very bitter indeed.

Getting A Divorce

The law on this is in the process of being changed but one thing will remain constant: it takes two people to make a marriage. This may seem obvious but it has a very important consequence: if one of the parties decides the marriage is at an end then, effectively, it is.

There is no way round that fact. Parliament and/or the courts can establish various criteria which have to be met before a divorce can be granted and those criteria can be more or less demanding. But no-one outside the marriage can force husband and wife to make it work if either thinks that it has broken down. For that reason, it is extremely difficult to defend a divorce.

The very fact that one of the parties has presented a divorce petition is a fair indication that at least one of the parties to the marriage thinks it is over. There are some very limited circumstances under which one party can prevent the other from getting a divorce, but cases which fulfil such criteria are very rare. In practical terms, the vast majority of husbands cannot prevent their wives obtaining a divorce (and vice versa).Defending such a petition would almost invariably incur substantial legal costs and in all probability the attempt would fail unless the circumstances were wholly exceptional. It is important to understand this. In practical terms, it means that one party to a marriage cannot prevent the other obtaining a divorce and there is little that can be done about it. This has the following important knock-on effect. When a marriage is dissolved by a court, that court has almost unlimited powers to divide up all the marital assets in whatever way it sees fit (although the courts in fact make such divisions according to well-understood rules). That is, it is not an arbitrary process but, equally, it is not one which either party to the marriage can prevent. It is not possible in the UK to enter into binding pre-nuptial agreements which determine what is to happen to the marital property in the event of divorce. The courts have complete and almost absolute jurisdiction. What this means is that one party to the marriage can force a divorce and have the courts decide how the marital assets ought to be split up. Short of not getting married in the first place, these consequences cannot be escaped for the overwhelming majority of husbands and wives.

Ancillary Relief

Once divorce proceedings have been commenced and, in particular, once *decree nisi* has been granted, the courts have power to make various final orders in respect of maintenance, transfer of property and/or capital, etc. If husband and wife cannot reach agreement then a court will be asked to decide. There are several important points to be aware of here. Perhaps the most important, and the one which causes greatest resentment and confusion, is the fact that in the overwhelming majority of cases the reasons for the divorce are not relevant in coming to any decisions on the subsequent financial arrangements. It does not matter who divorced whom for what – that almost always has no impact whatever on the decision making process when it comes to resolving financial issues. This can seem hard when one of the parties feels the other has been almost exclusively responsible for the breakdown of the marriage. It is a particularly common feeling in the case of adultery, for example. There is a widespread feeling that the 'guilty' party ought to, in some way, 'pay' for what they have done, and it often comes as a complete shock to discover that this is not the case at all. In deciding financial issues the courts are not concerned at all about who was to blame and simply do not want to know about the conduct of either party during the marriage unless the circumstances are wholly exceptional. This is not prejudice on the part of the courts: the rules which they have to apply are laid out clearly in the law as laid down by Parliament and an enquiry into the respective degrees of fault of the parties does not feature in the list. The relevant criteria are set out in the Matrimonial Causes Act 1973. If you read those criteria, they seem at first sight perfectly plain and reasonable. A lay client who takes the trouble to read the relevant section will see, for instance, that it reads in part, "It shall be the duty of the court in deciding whether to exercise its powers . . . to have regard to all the circumstances of the case . . . and so to exercise those powers as to place the parties, so far as it is practicable and, having regard to their conduct, just to do so, in the financial position in which they would have been if the marriage had not broken down"

Most people are likely to seize on those words 'all the circumstances of the case' and 'having regard to their conduct' as meaning that their spouse's bad behaviour can and should be taken into account; but it does not quite work out like that. Husbands (and it is usually the husband) who are inclined to think like that soon discover that the words 'so far as it is practicable' have a much greater weight than they could possibly expect.

It is probably easiest to explain by example. Say there is a husband and wife who live in a modest home together with two young children. There is a mortgage on the home and some equity. There are no other capital assets. The husband has paid the mortgage instalments while the wife has remained at home to look after the children from the time they were born. At first glance, the husband might expect the home to be sold and the proceeds divided equally between himself and his wife. That will almost never happen. What happens in this case is that the court will look at the 'needs' of the parties and it will be found that the 'need' of the wife and children to have a roof over their head will vastly outweigh the 'need' of the husband to have some part of the capital which was tied up in the matrimonial home. Young children almost always remain with the mother, and so the overwhelming likelihood is that a court would order the matrimonial home to be transferred into the sole name of the wife. This is despite the fact that the husband may have made all the financial payments. The courts regard the needs of the wife and children to be much more important in cases such as these. The truth of the matter is that is very rarely practicable to put both the parties into the financial position they would have been in if the marriage had not come to an end. In the overwhelming majority of cases there is simply not enough money available to enable both the husband and the wife to buy themselves suitable alternative accommodation and so a choice has to be made as to who has the greatest 'need'.

It is almost invariably the case that the courts put the needs of the wife and children before that of the husband. This can seem, and is, very hard to the man. Theoretically, the law is equal for husband and wife but in practice, because the residence of young children tends to be with the mother, financial settlements of capital or transfers of property to the wife are almost always very substantial, unless the marriage has been very short or there are other truly exceptional circumstances. This is the hard fact of the matter and it is difficult enough for most husbands in this position to accept but there are many additional factors which are likely to add to the man's sense of grievance. Not least of these is the very unfair effect of legal aid.

Typically, a wife who remains at home to look after the children will be eligible for legal aid in matrimonial proceedings because she has little or no income, and the income of her partner is not taken into account for this purpose. The husband, on the other hand, will typically not be eligible for legal aid because of his income. The first significant effect of this is that the husband will usually be charged very much more for the same legal advice than the wife. This is because lawyers – barristers and solicitors – almost invariably charge 'private clients' considerably more than legally aided clients. It can sometimes be almost twice as much. The reason for this is that legal aid rates of payment are fixed, whereas it is the market which determines the going rate for private client work.

Whether it is justified is another matter and a husband who finds himself in this position should *always* (unless money is not a problem) find out exactly how much he will be charged and ask how that compares to the legal aid rate for the same work. By doing it this way, he is probably more likely to be able to negotiate a lower rate of charging. It is important to remember that the market works both ways! Nevertheless, this is the unfortunate position many men find that they are in. This obviously puts pressure on them to settle on terms which are quite unreasonable and unfair, but which, if they do not have the funds to continue, they have little choice other than to accept.

The second significant effect is that the wife often has a very deep purse to fund her legal action, despite the fact that she may have no income or capital of her own. Legal aid is not actually free in these circumstances. The wife's, solicitor's and barrister's bills will be paid for the wife by the Legal Aid Board, out of taxpayers' money, although if a legally aided litigant recovers any money or property with the help of legal aid, the Legal Aid Board can recover the money it has spent from the property recovered.

If, for instance, the wife makes a claim to have the matrimonial home transferred into her sole name, and that is what happens at the end of the day, then she has 'recovered' the house and the Legal Aid Board can put a charge on it (called 'the statutory charge' because it is laid down by act of Parliament) to get back the money spent on the case. In effect what this means is that the wife can mortgage the house to pay for her legal costs. Interestingly enough, the husband cannot do the same. If the house is in joint names, the wife obviously would not agree to such borrowing and if the house is in the husband's sole name the husband will soon find he is on the receiving end of an injunction if he attempts to do any such thing.

The wife's lawyers cannot lose either way – they will be paid by the Legal Aid Board no matter what the outcome. Legal aid is not usually limited in matrimonial proceedings (presumably because the Legal Aid Board is fairly confident of recovering its money via the statutory charge) and so, in effect, the lawyers know they are dealing with a client who has a bottomless purse. The husband is *not* usually in that position.

This does not end the list of disadvantages for the husband. Ordinarily the rule in litigation is that the loser has to pay the winner's legal costs (as well, of course, as their own). There is some obvious sense to this. If, for instance, A owes money to B and B has to resort to court proceedings to recover the debt, it is only fair that A should have to pay B's legal costs for doing so. This is the general principle and it encourages people to be reasonable in the proposals which they make to settle any given dispute: they know that if they do not make reasonable proposals but choose instead, say, to put up a defence which they know to be worthless, they will have to pay their opponent's legal costs.

It is fair to say that in matrimonial proceedings this general rule is applied in a more relaxed way, but nevertheless, that is the general rule and there is good reason for it. So, for instance, if a non-working wife from a short marriage demanded that her former husband should transfer the former matrimonial home into her sole name and pay her half his net salary for the rest of her life so long as she remained unmarried it is almost certain that such a claim would fail. And if the husband were to spend money in defending such an unjustifiable claim, most people would think that the wife ought to bear those costs which her unreasonable stance had occasioned.

It cannot be stressed too much that where the wife is legally aided this is *not* the case. Legal aid gives such a wife an extremely unfair advantage: surprising though it may seem the general rule is that costs *cannot* be awarded against a legally aided person. The rule (laid down by the Legal Aid Act 1988) reads:

'An order for costs (against such a person) can only be made if:

(a) – the court is satisfied that the unassisted party will suffer severe financial hardship unless the order is made; and

(b) – the court is satisfied that it is just and equitable in all the circumstances of the case that provision for the costs should be made out of public funds.'

It is very rare for these conditions to be satisfied and what it means, in effect, is that a legally aided litigant can pursue litigation without being at any real risk of paying the costs of the other side if the litigation is unsuccessful. This rule is almost certainly only in existence to save the public purse but it places the husband facing a legally aided wife or ex-wife who is completely unreasonable in her demands at a huge disadvantage. Everyone involved in the system knows this and it encourages unreasonable demands by legally aided litigants such as many wives in matrimonial proceedings. It is quite wrong but the financial consequences for the husband can be very serious indeed.

Once again the scales are not evenly balanced, because if the non-legally aided husband loses the case because it is adjudged that his proposals to settle were unsatisfactory the wife's lawyers will ask for, and almost certainly get, an order that the husband pay the Legal Aid Board's costs. This situation happens time after time in the courts and it is not surprising that many men rail at the injustice of it all.

Given this context of the Legal Aid situation it is not surprising that it affects how cases are conducted. It is always open to husband and wife to come to an agreement between themselves as to what the financial settlement should be and, if at all possible, this is usually the best course of action because it is agreed and because it leads to least acrimony, bitterness and cost. But for such an agreement to be really final it needs to be sealed by a court as a 'consent order'. This means that the agreement is embodied as an order of the court, and in that way it can conclude matters once for all.

A simple agreement between husband and wife is not final unless this step is taken (although, of course, some couples might be satisfied with such an informal arrangement). What is more than likely to happen is that one or other of the parties will consult a solicitor at some stage. This may be at the very outset to determine what the actual legal position is (and anyone involved in a divorce would usually be well advised to do this) or it may be that husband and wife want their own informal agreement 'legalised'.

In this latter case, a solicitor is likely to reply that he/she cannot give full and considered advice without having all the relevant financial information. That is quite a proper position to take although the client should always remember that he/she is the client and that it is open to him or her to say, 'I don't much care about that. I know what the financial position is. Please draft a document which reflects our agreement and submit it to the court so that everything can be finalised.' A solicitor faced with such a client would almost certainly seek to protect him/herself against a future negligence claim by insisting such instructions were in writing but with that proviso, there is no reason why such instructions should not be carried out after suitable explanations and disclaimers.

However, such clients are very rare. What is much more likely to happen is that the client will be guided by the solicitor as to what the best course of action is. If the client is a wife who is eligible for legal aid then she will almost certainly be advised to apply for it and once it has been granted, the work will commence in earnest. Her solicitor will wish to be sure that he/she has the *full* financial picture before even considering what settlement proposals should be made in this particular case. Since the lawyers know that a legally aided client has, in effect, a bottomless purse, there is no especial incentive to be anything less than extremely thorough.

In point of fact most husbands do not have bank accounts in Switzerland or the Cayman Islands but the scope for requesting information is much wider than one might imagine. The following list gives a flavour of some of the documents or details which might routinely be requested even in quite ordinary cases:

- bank statements for each and every account covering the last six months
- statements covering a similar period for any building society, post office or other account which contains any funds over which the husband has any control whether as beneficial owner or otherwise
- copies of all credit card statements for the same period
- copies of pay slips and any other sources of income for the same period
- details of any expenses necessary to earn the above income
- copy of most recent P60
- details of any necessary expenditure on providing yourself with a place to live – community charge, water rates, mortgage interest and repayments, premiums on endowment insurance, etc.
- ownership of any car (make, model, year of manufacture, estimated value)
- any property in which you have an interest, including jointly held property, and articles of any substantial value such as jewellery or furniture
- any unpaid debts including hire purchase debts
- any endowment insurance policies giving details of any premium, date of maturity, surrender value, etc
- details of any pension scheme including details of what the spouse would be entitled to on death, the transfer value, what would be lost on decree absolute, etc.

It will readily be seen that it might take some time to get all this information and all sorts of further questions could be asked about any particular parts of it or about details which were incomplete, and this assumes that the recipient is co-operative about the whole process. In reality it is not uncommon for people to resent such intrusion and to be less than fully co-operative which obviously lengthens the whole process still further. And, of course, some of these details require applications to be made to third parties such as insurance companies or pension trustees who have no especial incentive to answer by return of post.

All of this takes up time and runs up costs but what is even worse is if the correspondence becomes acrimonious. It is especially easy for this to happen in divorce cases. An overly blunt letter asking, say, for details of a co-habitee's income can result in point-blank refusal, which in turn can soon lead to court applications, 'unless orders' and/or contempt proceedings. It is all too easy for the emotions to take over and in those circumstances, no-one benefits but the lawyers. Dealing with all these matters and avoiding all the pitfalls requires considerable skill, and even with such help it will be appreciated that sometimes husbands come out of the process feeling very aggrieved indeed because of all the ways in which the system is weighted against them. The choice of lawyer is crucially important in this area because poor advice can very easily make a bad situation many times worse.

Children

After ancillary relief, probably the most contentious and bitter struggles are fought over the children. In most cases, questions relating to the children are not an issue and arrangements are made voluntarily which are quite satisfactory to husband, wife and children. It is only a small minority of cases which involve disputes about children, but when they occur such disputes can be very difficult indeed.

In point of fact when there are dependent children of a relationship, it is a part of the divorce process to file a 'Statement of Arrangements' in respect of the children at the same time as filing the divorce petition. The person filing the divorce petition will complete a form setting out the arrangements which proposes for the children where they will live, which schools they will attend, contact arrangements with the absent parent and so on. The petitioner will certainly sign the form and there is provision for it also to be signed by the respondent. If both husband and wife do sign the Statement of Arrangements then questions involving the children rarely become an issue.

The court has to be satisfied that satisfactory arrangements are in place for the children before granting a decree of divorce and that requirement will usually be met if husband and wife have agreed what those arrangements are to be and completed the relevant form. In the majority if cases this tends to be that the children will continue to live with the mother but have contact with the father. The court will read through the arrangements and if it has no query, the court will sign a certificate saying it has considered the arrangements and that they are satisfactory. That is then the end of the matter.

There is only one point which is worth commenting upon in this very common situation. *Young children almost invariably continue to live with their mother.* There is no rule of law about this but it is the way it most often works out. The reason is usually that the mother has been at home looking after the children during the marriage while the husband has gone out to work. Or perhaps the mother has worked part-time to fit in with the children's school day. It is therefore natural for this situation to be preserved after the divorce for practical reasons if for no other.

It will be remembered, though, that in arriving at the financial settlement between husband and wife the court has to take into account various factors and one of these will be the needs of the children. Obviously, the children need a roof over their head and to the extent that they live with their mother her need to be accommodated and theirs coincide. What this means in practice is that the mother's claim to have the matrimonial home transferred into her sole name is immeasurably stronger than the father's in the majority of cases. This is one of the main reasons why orders for the transfer of the matrimonial home into the sole name of the wife are so common.

It should be remembered also that the divorce process is divided into three parts: the divorce itself, ancillary relief and any proceedings relating to children.

The key question in each part is quite different. In the case of the divorce, the key question is whether the marriage has irretrievably broken down. For ancillary relief the key questions are set out in Section 25 of the Matrimonial Causes Act 1973 and, basically, amount to what the respective needs of the parties are. In disputes involving children, the central issue is quite different again and it is important to understand this.

Where children are involved, the central question is what is in the child's best interests. The welfare of the child is paramount and that is always the guiding light by which a court operates. This causes problems to parents if they do not understand that this is the *only* issue so far as children are concerned. Take the following examples:

(a) A father does not think his wife should have custody of the children because she has committed adultery. In his eyes she is 'an unfit mother' or, alternatively, she should not have custody of the children because she does not deserve it after what she has done. This reasoning is bound to fail. An adulterous mother (or father) can still be a caring parent and adultery as such usually hardly has any impact upon what is in the child's best interests, so far as residence is concerned.

(b) A mother does not believe the father should have contact with the child because he does not pay maintenance. Again, this is wrong. A skinflint father can still be a caring father and contact is granted for the benefit of the child. The child may benefit from contact with his/her father regardless of whether maintenance is paid.

(c) The father is a thief who has spent time in prison. Again, it is likely that he will be allowed contact with his children if he wishes it. The contact is granted for the benefit of children rather than their parents and there is a general presumption that contact with both parents is a good thing. It takes truly exceptional circumstances to displace this presumption.

In point of fact, there are obvious trends that are noticeable to anyone who has experience of these matters. Young children tend almost invariably to live with their mother but as they get older what they want matters more and more. If an older child wishes to live with one parent rather than another then, ultimately, that is what will probably happen. There is also a strong presumption not to disturb the status quo unless the reasons are truly compelling. This is another reason why children tend to stay with their mothers. More often than not it is the husband who leaves the matrimonial home – whether as a result of choice or following an injunction. The children tend to live in the same place, to attend the same school and to play with the same friends. It would have to be exceptional for a court to disturb this and say the children ought to go to live with their father elsewhere, attend a new school, make new friends, etc.

Something which does cause a great deal of grief is the following scenario: husband and wife are divorced. The children live with their mother and have contact with their father on a regular basis. The mother then meets someone else and decides to move to another part of the country or even abroad to be with her new partner. She wishes to take the children with her and, indeed, to continue to receive maintenance from their father for the children's benefit, even though in practical terms it means that the father is now very unlikely to see his children at all regularly. Most fathers feel very bitter about this scenario and understandably so. There is indeed a certain amount of tension in this case about preserving the status quo because a major part of it is going to change. In the case of older children, it would be difficult to force them to go with their mother if they expressed a clear and strong wish to remain with their father, but more often than not, the father has to accept that he will no longer see the children on a regular basis. No court would order the mother not to relocate and so the father has to accept what is undoubtedly a very difficult situation.

The other problem which undoubtedly causes a lot of anguish is the question of child maintenance. In point of fact, every parent has a legal duty to support their children while they are still dependent and that has always been the case. Most parents would not quarrel with that. What has happened relatively recently is the creation of the Child Support Agency (CSA) which many fathers regard as having far too great a power over their income. It is now the CSA which deals with most child maintenance cases, although its power is not exclusive. In particular, the courts retain power to vary child maintenance orders which were previously made by a court *and* have the power to award *more* maintenance than the CSA has power to award, if the financial circumstances justify it.

Now that the system has bedded down, what seems to be happening is that the CSA is very slow and bureaucratic, which often causes short-term problems for mothers. On the other hand, it seems that the CSA is mainly concerned with saving the public purse in that above all it wants to ensure that fathers pay maintenance for their children and that the State does not have to pay in their place. But, provided this is achieved, the CSA does not appear to delve too deeply into whether the financial information given by absent fathers is correct. Obviously, it is an offence to misrepresent one's income and out-goings to the CSA but the truth of the matter seems to be that, provided the State is not required to make any benefit payments, the figures given by the father are accepted with minimal checking.

All of the above makes the divorce process a particularly difficult one for most husbands. The system is weighted against them in many different ways, although, of course, one can argue about whether or not that is proper. The point remains though, that divorce can lead many men to feel that they have suffered major injustice and some of the factors above explain why this happens. This does not mean to say that nothing can be done about it. In particular, it is very important for the man not to make a bad situation worse and it is essential that he receives sound advice at an early stage. There are pitfalls which can be avoided and there are ways to minimise the damage, but that almost certainly requires professional advice. It is all too easy to stumble along in this process until at the end of the day the man is left with an overwhelming sense of grievance against his ex-wife, the lawyers, the courts and the CSA.

Divorce – How Long It Takes

How long it takes to obtain a divorce is a question which clients frequently ask their solicitors, so it may be helpful to outline the various steps involved and give an indication of roughly how long they take:

1. The first step is to lodge the divorce petition with the court (and the Statement of Arrangements for Children form if there are any dependent children of the marriage). Once the court receives this it will then post (usually by second class post) a copy of the divorce petition (and the Statement of Arrangements if applicable) to the respondent, together with a document called an Acknowledgment of Service.

2. The Acknowledgment of Service is basically a document which the respondent is requested to return to the court indicating, (a) that he/she has received the petition and, (b) whether he/she intends defending the divorce. If the respondent is resident in the UK, the acknowledgment will state that the respondent has seven days in which to reply. At this point most people who receive a divorce petition consult a solicitor, if they have not done so already. Whether they do in fact return the acknowledgment within the seven days varies greatly and much depends on how the matter has been handled up until that point.

3. When the Acknowledgment of Service is returned to the court a copy will be sent to the petitioner (or the petitionerp's solicitor if the petitioner is legally represented). Assuming that the respondent has indicated that he/she will not be defending the divorce (as it almost invariably the case because it is so difficult to 'defend' a divorce) then the petitioner now has to file an affidavit with the court. The affidavit will confirm that the details in the divorce petition are correct and that the signature which appears on the Acknowledgment of Service (and the Statement of Arrangements for Children in some cases) is that of the respondent. Once this affidavit has been sworn, it is returned to the court with a request that the court considers the evidence and decides whether the matter should proceed.

4. On receipt of this affidavit and request the file is placed before a district judge who considers all the paperwork. If he decides that it is in order he will grant a certificate to this effect and send a

copy to the petitioner giving a date when decree nisi will be pronounced.

5. Decree nisi will be pronounced on the date which the district judge has previously indicated in his certificate. It is very rare for anyone to attend court on this occasion and it is neither expected nor necessary. All that happens, in effect, is that a judge says in open court, 'I pronounce decree nisi in cases numbered ABC to XYZ'. In fact, many judges dislike being used as a rubber stamp in this way but that is the system and it is rare for any of the parties to attend court.

6. After decree nisi has been pronounced the petitioner must wait for six weeks before applying for the decree nisi to be made absolute. The decree nisi does not end the marriage and is in the nature of a provisional decree. In order to be able to remarry, a decree absolute has to be applied for and obtained. The delay of six weeks is compulsory and cannot be abridged. After that period of time has elapsed the petitioner may apply for the decree to be made absolute and does so by making a request and paying the necessary fee. On receipt of these the court normally pronounces the decree absolute within a few days and sends a copy of the decree to both parties or their solicitors. If the petitioner does not apply for the decree nisi to be made absolute within three months, the respondent may do so although he/she cannot do so before then. Judicial separation is slightly different in that there is only one decree rather than two. A decree of judicial separation is pronounced instead of a decree nisi and nothing further needs to be done in that case.

All of the above steps may take about three to four months from start to finish and you will see that the compulsory delay of six weeks between the decree nisi and decree absolute accounts for a great deal of this. How long exactly a divorce takes does rather depend on the speed with which third parties (the court and the respondent) deal with their respective parts and it is not all dependent upon the petitioner. If the respondent is resident overseas, for example, the time for returning the Acknowledgment of Service is extended from the normal seven days to thirty.

If the respondent does not return the Acknowledgment of Service this can cause additional delay because it is necessary to prove that the respondent has received the divorce petition before matters can proceed. It may therefore be necessary for the petitioner to arrange to have another copy of the divorce served on the respondent by a court bailiff or to arrange another form of personal service which can be proved. Similarly, the respondent can cause delay by indicating that he/she will defend the divorce and going through the first motions of doing so. This rarely results in a defended divorce at the end of the day, but it can slow matters down.

There are many things which can be done to speed the process up (except for the compulsory delay of six weeks between decree nisi and decree absolute). For instance, the petitioner's solicitor can ask for the divorce petition to be returned to him for service rather than waiting for the court to do it (by second class post). This can be particularly useful if the petitioner knows that the respondent might not co-operate in the divorce, because by the petitioner's solicitor effecting personal service at this stage the petitioner does not have to wait to see if the respondent will respond to the court and then wait seven days after before taking action. If the petitioner's solicitor is aware of potential delays like this at the outset a great deal can be done to minimise them. Naturally, if there are difficulties of this nature and additional court applications, etc. have to be made in order to deal with them, it might have an effect on the costs of the divorce.

It can sometimes take a frustratingly long time to obtain a divorce – particularly if the respondent is uncooperative, living overseas or untraceable. The best way of dealing with these problems is to engage a competent lawyer, because in practice that can make a big difference to the time scale.

Divorce Petition

The are various things which might hold up the timetable of a divorce and not least of these is that the respondent (i.e. the person who receives the divorce petition) does not fully understand it and therefore delays dealing with it. Bearing in mind that no-one likes receiving a divorce petition and that each party is understandably suspicious that the other is trying to steal a march on him/her, it is quite natural that people want to understand what is happening before committing themselves.

In practice, most of the words of a divorce petition are self-explanatory and simply recite the details of the marriage. The part which almost invariably does cause difficulty (and often concern) is the so-called 'prayer' with which the petition ends. This is normally pre-printed on the divorce petition and in most cases it reads something like the following:

The petitioner therefore prays:

1. That the said marriage may be dissolved

2. That the respondent may be ordered to pay the costs of this suit
3. That she may be granted the following ancillary relief:
   (i)   an order for maintenance pending suit
   (ii) a periodical payments order
   (iii) a secured provisions order
   (iv) a lump sum order
   (v)   a property adjustment order

Point (1) is clear enough and causes no problems.

Point (2) is more significant. In cases involving unreasonable behaviour or adultery the courts usually order the respondent to pay the costs of the divorce unless there is agreement to the contrary. It is therefore sensible to come to an agreement with the petitioner over this. 'I will not defend the divorce on the condition that you do not seek the costs of the divorce from me', for example, often secures an agreement about costs which both parties are happy with (because it speeds things up for the petitioner and costs less for the respondent) but the agreement can be of any kind. If there is no agreement, the court will make the usual order and that is normally pre-printed on the divorce petition as in this example. If it were not included here the petitioner would not be able to seek costs against the respondent, and so it is sensible to leave it in until there is agreement.

Point (3) is what causes most difficulty because people do not understand it (and, indeed, there is no obvious way they could unless it was explained to them). What worries most respondents when they read this is that they think that the petitioner is claiming all these things and that if they return the divorce petition they will in some way have conceded these points. That is not the case.

Those points numbered (i) to (v) are simply the orders which may be made by a divorce court but a court cannot make such orders unless it is asked to do so. Very often, when a divorce petition is filed, the parties do not know what the final financial settlement will be (and neither do their lawyers). Therefore, all the possible options are included on the divorce petition, although in practice only one or two of them may eventually turn out to be relevant. 'Secured provision orders', for instance are quite uncommon.

The reason all the possible remedies are included on the petition is so that the court does not turn round at a later date and say, 'But you didn't ask for this particular order so we cannot give it to you.' In circumstances such as that, it would be necessary to seek leave, to amend the divorce petition. In practice, it is just better to ask for all the orders at the outset so as to avoid this difficulty.

It is also necessary to have these orders mentioned here if only to have them formally dismissed by the court at a later stage. For instance, both parties might want a 'clean break' in which neither pays maintenance to the other. This is very common and it is what many couples want. In such a case the eventual court order may formally 'dismiss' the petitioner's claim for periodical payments.

Once that has been done the petitioner cannot re-open the matter in the future and there truly is a 'clean break'. If this request for periodical payments were not included in the divorce petition and the final consent order did not mention it either, then, theoretically, the petitioner could then seek maintenance from the respondent at any time in the future. It is therefore in the respondent's interests to ensure these words are included as well as in the petitioner's.

This is all very technical and it is a pity that these things are not straightforward, but the bottom line is; that there is good reason why these words are included on the petition. They do not necessarily mean that the petitioner is going to seek them all and the respondent is not prejudiced in any way by agreeing not to defend a divorce petition containing these words. The respondent is just agreeing to the divorce *but not to anything else*. His/her rights in respect of the financial settlement remain quite unaffected. It is important to understand this because this is the very difficulty which usually causes people to bring a divorce petition to a solicitor. The matter needs to be carefully explained. (And there is a similar need for explanation of the so-called Acknowledgment of Service for slightly different reasons).

Acknowledgment of Service

The Acknowledgment of Service is the document which is sent by the court to the respondent at the same time as the divorce petition, and which the respondent is requested to complete and return to the court. Most of the document is quite straightforward and causes no problems. Essentially, the respondent is asked to sign and return the document to the court, after answering the following questions:

1. Have you received the divorce petition?
2. On which date and at which address did you receive it?
3. Are you the person named as the respondent in the petition?
4. Do you intend to defend the case?
5. Do you admit the (adultery, unreasonable behaviour, etc.)?
6. Even if you do not intend to defend the case, do you object to paying the cost of the proceedings?

7. Have you received a copy of the Statement of Arrangements for the children? Do you agree with the proposals?

How to answer these questions, very frequently causes concern (just as the wording of the divorce petition does) and it is delay on the part of the respondent in dealing with the divorce petition because of his/her doubts about the wording of the divorce petition and how to complete the Acknowledgment of Service that often causes delay to the timetable of the divorce. If these doubts are resolved quickly (or, indeed, explained even before the documents are received) it can speed matters along considerably. It is also a good thing in itself that people know exactly what is happening and why.

In practice, only points (4) to (7) cause any difficulty with the first three being self-explanatory. It may, however, perhaps be worth mentioning that the respondent cannot stop the divorce simply by not returning the Acknowledgment of Service. If he/she does not do so within a reasonable time scale, what is likely to happen is that another copy of the petition will be served personally, by a court bailiff or the petitioner's solicitor, or there may be alternative methods of service. If this happens it will inevitably incur extra costs which the respondent will almost certainly be asked (or made) to pay. It is, therefore, usually a bad idea *not* to send the Acknowledgment of Service back to the court simply because the respondent wants to 'frustrate' the divorce. Not returning the Acknowledgment of Service for that reason is very rarely a sensible choice.

Hardly any divorces are defended for the very good reasons that, (a) the presentation of a divorce petition is a fairly clear indication that the marriage has broken down and, (b) because it can cost a lot of money to do so, with no obvious benefit to be gained at the end of the day.

When it is also explained to the client that agreeing to a divorce does not affect his/her rights in respect of the property and/or children most people see the sense of agreeing not to defend. It is more convenient and cheaper in the great majority of cases, although one should not agree until the subject of costs has also been dealt with. Again, many people hesitate about whether they should 'admit' unreasonable behaviour or adultery. The fact of the matter is that one cannot get a divorce (on these two grounds) unless the court is satisfied that the grounds exist, and the easiest (and cheapest) means of proving that is an admission. If the behaviour or adultery were not admitted it would have to be proved by means of evidence and this could soon incur considerable cost – again for no especial benefit. The point to remember is that the reason for the divorce (in

95% of cases) *does not affect any other issue* – whether to do with children or property. So the admission can safely be made in the knowledge that neither of these other two issues is being prejudiced. In the case of there being some anxiety about this, it would be possible to limit the uses of the admission to obtaining the divorce only, and making it clear that the facts would have to be proved in any other proceedings. This is sometimes advisable. It is usually the case that the respondent is ordered to pay the costs of the divorce, and so it is not normally sensible to return the Acknowledgment of Sevice *until* agreement has been reached on this (although one should be careful not to delay so long that the petitioner is able to proceed anyway). One should also be aware that merely *indicating* that you intend to defend the divorce does not automatically mean that the divorce will not still proceed as undefended, and that the respondent will be ordered to pay the costs. This does trip people up and so most Respondents do need advice at this point.

The final worry is that whether by agreeing to the Statement of Arrangements, the respondent is in some way giving away rights over the children. This not the case, although this question does cause a great deal of anxiety. In fact, the Statement of Arrangements form is designed to establish to the court that the interests of the children have been taken into account and it is sufficient if it is in the most general terms. Normally it is best if mother and father agree the arrangements about the children between themselves, with no interference from anyone else and that is what happens in the vast majority of cases. If father and mother do disagree about some question relating to the children in the future, either of them can bring it back to the court for decision regardless of what was in the Statement of Arrangements. Neither party (nor any child) loses any right as a result of agreeing to the Statement of Arrangements now. In fact, it can often be sensible to agree to it even though it may contain something that one is not entirely happy with, because many of these things can be resolved satisfactorily over time. If they are not, then both parents will always retain the right to ask the court to decide.

It can be seen why the questions which are raised by receiving the divorce petition and the Acknowledgment of Service often need the help of a solicitor. Although these things are simple and can be explained if one is familiar with them, they are not regarded (and quite naturally) in this way by a person who is reading them for the first time. It is the receipt of these documents which often prompts people to seek legal advice about a divorce for the first time and they have to be explained very carefully.

Many of the 'technicalities' which are familiar to lawyers on the various papers relating to divorce, are confusing to people who read them for the first time and the explanation is by no means always obvious. Explaining their significance often requires legal help.

Calderbank Letters

'Calderbank letters' (so-called after a case of that name) are routine parts of any UK divorce where the 'ancillary relief' claims are contested. The loser is usually ordered to pay the winner's legal costs and the same is true (in general) of matrimonial cases.

In any case where significant legal costs have been incurred a litigant will want, so far as is possible, to minimise the risk of having to pay his/her opponent's legal costs and the Calderbank letter is intended to address this problem. Drafting such a letter and pitching it at the right level is a skilled art and one in which a mistake can cost dear or, if done well, reap handsome dividends.

So if, for instance, a husband and wife have a jointly owned house worth, say, £100,000, free of mortgage, and it is agreed between them that the property should be sold and the proceeds divided between them, the ancillary relief dispute might be about what percentage of the proceeds each should get. (And this very much depends on their needs and circumstances.) The wife might want, say, 70% and the husband, say, might only be prepared to divide the proceeds 50/50. Since one is talking about a difference of £20,000, this is quite likely a case where there will be a legal dispute and it may end up in court if the parties do not reach an agreed settlement.

If neither party is legally aided (because legal aid can affect the calculation very significantly), then each party is at risk of paying the other's legal costs (as well as their own) if he/she loses. So if, for instance, the judge decided the wife should get 70% of the proceeds he will almost certainly order the husband to pay the wife's legal costs. Similarly, if the judge were to order a 50/50 split the wife would very likely be at risk of having to pay her husband's legal costs.

In order to lessen the risk of this, the husband (or, more likely, his solicitors) might write a 'Calderbank letter' to the wife's solicitors offering to let her have, say, 60% of the proceeds of sale and they would head such a letter 'Without prejudice save as to costs'. What this heading means is that the letter cannot be produced to the court as it is deciding the issue of what percentage of the proceeds should go to each. The judge would decide the matter without knowing anything at all about the letter. But then say the judge decided to split the proceeds 60/40 in favour of the wife (which he might easily do on the basis of just splitting the difference between the husband's position and that of the wife): at that point there would be an argument about who should pay the legal costs of the proceedings and the husband's lawyers would produce the Calderbank letter to show that he had already offered a 60/40 split.

In circumstances such as these, the judge would almost certainly order the wife to pay the husband's legal costs from the date of the letter, because all legal expenses since that date would have arisen as a result of the wife's refusal to accept the offer.

Notice that it would have been possible for the husband to have made his offer of 60% of the proceeds in so-called 'open correspondence' or, indeed, in one of his affidavits sworn during the course of the case. If he had done this, the court would be aware of the offer as it was making its decision about what percentage to grant to each. Very often, it is undesirable that the court should know the parties' 'bottom line' in this way, because it will naturally tend to use the husband's offer of 60% as its base figure and might then, perhaps, have awarded the wife, say, 65% of the proceeds. For this reason it is sometimes sensible to keep the court in the dark while still protecting one's own position as far as possible, by means of a Calderbank letter. That is why the letter is headed 'Without prejudice save as to costs'.

It is fair to say that the courts do not apply costs rules in matrimonial cases anywhere near as strictly as they do in, say, commercial litigation cases. Also, the matrimonial courts do normally require an indication of both sides' legal costs before coming to a decision, because they know these can affect the fairness of their decisions. Nevertheless, the general rule is still that 'costs follow the event' – i.e. that the loser pays the winner's legal costs – and it would be very unwise of any party to matrimonial proceedings to ignore that fact.

Knowing exactly where to pitch the level of a Calderbank letter is a difficult matter of judgement which, basically, involves 'second guessing' the court. For that reason it needs professional expertise and it would be a rash practitioner who could guarantee never to get it wrong. It is a guess, but a guess based on informed knowledge of what and how the courts decide these cases is the best advice on offer. Done well, it can save a client a great deal of money; handled badly, it can have quite the opposite effect.

It can probably be seen that this is a technical and quite important part of divorce law in which the competence of one's lawyer can make a great deal of difference to the eventual outcome.

The Costs of Divorce

The first thing to remember about solicitors' divorce charges is that there are normally three possible legal issues involved in a divorce:

1. The divorce itself. It is obtaining the divorce – and, more particularly, the decree absolute – which enables both parties to remarry if they wish. This part is simply what brings the marriage to an end and it is legally distinct from the two following issues.
2. Issues involving the matrimonial property – basically, deciding who gets what and whether any maintenance will be paid, etc. The technical words for this are 'ancillary relief'.
3. Issues involving children – access, contact, residence, maintenance, etc.

It will be appreciated that not every divorce involves a dispute over all of these issues. Very often, for example, there will be no children and/or matters involving the children will have been resolved by agreement rather than by court action. In fact, the latter is what happens in the majority of divorces where there are children, and disputes involving children, while not exactly rare, are nevertheless not normally a feature of most divorces. It is more common to have disputes over the matrimonial property – who gets what and whether any maintenance will be paid, etc.

Both of these problems, namely problems relating to children and/or the matrimonial property, are legally distinct from the mere process of obtaining the divorce and usually have to be charged for on a quite different basis. The truth of the matter is that these two problems can usually only be charged for on a time basis, as is the case with most litigation. Some of these disputes can be resolved very quickly but others can be very much more difficult and correspondingly require a greater amount of legal input. It is, however, usually possible to charge a more or less fixed fee for obtaining a divorce – i.e. the first of the three legal issues mentioned above – because in practice, the overwhelming number of divorces are not contested and proceed, essentially, by agreement. Contested divorces are very rare and would have to be charged for on the same basis as any other contested matter, just as the other two contentious matters mentioned above normally are. Assuming that the divorce is not contested, the first element in the cost of obtaining a divorce is still the court fees. There is a court fee (currently) of £150 to issue the divorce petition, which has to be paid to the court. Similarly, there is a court fee of £20 payable to obtain the decree and (normally) there is an affidavit which needs to be sworn during the proceedings, which costs approximately £7 in most cases. This means that the total 'disbursements' are therefore in the region of £177.

It should perhaps be mentioned that these figures are not cast in stone. For instance, sometimes the respondent fails to respond to the petition and so it may be necessary to arrange personal service by means of a bailiff or some other course may need to be adopted. Steps like these incur additional court fees (and possibly legal costs) but in the majority of cases the 'disbursements' amount to £177 or so.

After the court fees have been taken into account, the solicitor needs to be paid for the legal work involved. Naturally, this varies from solicitor to solicitor and the client is recommended to get a firm quote on this in advance. It is likely to be in the region of £350 or so, plus VAT. So the total cost of obtaining a divorce will probably be something in the order of £600, once the court fees and VAT, etc. have been taken into account. There is no especial reason why this sum cannot be shared equally between the petitioner and the respondent (because the respondent usually incurs no significant separate legal costs in obtaining the divorce) and this can often be agreed. Such an agreement sometimes takes the form of, 'Alright, I will not defend the divorce if you agree not to ask for the divorce costs from me', and that may well be acceptable, but in fact, the costs of the divorce can be split in whatever proportion the parties wish to agree upon.

Sometimes, the respondent will be a non-working wife and the petitioner will agree to bear the costs of the divorce. At other times the divorce is 'amicable' and the petitioner and respondent bear the costs of the divorce equally. (At other times the petitioner wants the full pound of flesh and demands all the divorce costs! This is understandable, but also often counter-productive unless there are good reasons for it on other grounds.) It is worth mentioning this because the most common ground for divorce is 'unreasonable behaviour'. The reason this is so is because it enables the parties to get an 'instant divorce' and it really does not matter who divorces whom for what. That does not normally affect any subsequent issue – such as questions of maintenance or relating to the children, for example – and so it is sufficient that one of the parties files for divorce based on the unreasonable behaviour of the other. In practice, when a marriage breaks down, it is not so difficult to find examples of unreasonable behaviour on both sides and very often it is 'six of one and half a dozen of the other'. The important thing is simply that the marriage be brought to an end, because that is what is best for both parties and it really does not matter who issues the petition in many cases. It is, however, simpler and cheaper if only one party does it, and the other simply indicates to the court that he/she will not defend the petition.

So long as it is explained, neither party usually has much difficulty in accepting this. It does usually need to be explained though, because no-one really likes receiving a petition based on their unreasonable behaviour and a very common reaction is, 'I'm not having this. I'm going to defend it and issue a petition based on your unreasonable behaviour.' In most cases there would be no purpose in doing this and it would be counter-productive in that it would just serve to increase costs, delay the whole proceedings and the parties would be divorced just the same at the end of the day. Only the lawyers would gain. It is worth explaining this in some detail because the normal rule in divorces involving unreasonable behaviour is that, unless there is agreement between the parties to the contrary, the courts order the respondent to pay the whole of the divorce costs. Very often, this is not what the parties themselves want and the fact that the respondent may be ordered to pay the court costs is frequently a deterrent to returning the papers to the court quickly or at all. It is therefore frequently helpful for the subject of who is to pay what costs to be agreed at this point if it has not been agreed before.

Incidentally, it is normally unwise for a respondent to return the Acknowledgement of Service without agreeing the subject of the costs.

If one fails to do this, the court makes the usual order that the respondent does pay the divorce costs and it will be appreciated that when the petitioner's solicitor submits a bill which he knows is not going to be paid by his own client, there will be a risk that the bill might be higher than it would have been had there been an agreement. It is worth bearing this in mind.

Finally, it is probably worth mentioning that it is sometimes possible to get a limited form of legal aid called 'green form assistance' to obtain a divorce. However, there is a strict means test applied and in practice it is only available to those on income support or in receipt of some such benefit.

Nevertheless, if the circumstances do apply, it is worth consider-ing, especially if there are no significant matrimonial assets. If there are such assets and the petitioner recovers them in due course in the 'ancillary relief' proceedings the Legal Aid Board will recoup its costs from the assets recovered by means of the 'statutory charge'. Under these circumstances, legal aid is not quite as 'free' as people often imagine.

People very often have the most exaggerated fears about the legal costs of a divorce and, although it would be wrong to suggest that at least a few of the horror stories might not have some foundation in fact, the costs are generally more modest than one might imagine. Also, choosing the right lawyer can save a great deal of money in the long-term, so it pays to choose carefully.

General Costs

How and how much solicitors charge for their services in the UK is not well understood by their clients although the Law Society of England & Wales, for instance, does have clear rules about how it should be done. One common misconception, for instance, is that solicitors 'hold onto' clients' money for as long as possible in order to earn (and keep) the interest on that money. In fact, this does not happen (unless it has been expressly agreed in advance with the client) because interest on clients' money belongs to the client as much as the money itself. The Law Society has strict rules about it and every solicitor is aware of them. Nevertheless, the fact that this notion is so widespread amongst the public is an indication of how bad solicitors sometimes are at explaining their charges to clients. It has to be said that solicitors are often their own worst enemy in this instance because the subject of solicitors' charges (which they refer to by the arcane word 'costs') is bedevilled by the use of unnecessarily complicated words and charging methods. This is a pity, because the actual rules which govern solicitors' charges to their clients are designed to be fair and transparent. For instance, 'secret commissions', which are commonplace in some professions, and of which the client is absolutely unaware, are not permitted to solicitors, and all charges and commissions must be fully disclosed. Some people, for example, have found to their cost that the 'endowment policies', which they have taken out to secure repayment of their mortgages, have little or no surrender value in the policy's early years because the premiums have gone towards the payment of the salesman's commission. Nevertheless, many clients are still confused about how much they will be charged by their solicitor for a given piece of work, and it has to be said that they often are right to be confused. The golden rule if you are not sure is to ask. It is surprising how many clients do not ask. Although the precise basis on which a client is to be charged should be given in writing at the outset this sometimes does not happen and clients rightly feel aggrieved if they are 'ambushed' by an unexpectedly large bill at the end. Always ask on what basis you will be charged and be sure to ask if there is anything about it which is unclear.

In some cases (buying or selling a house or flat is the most common), a solicitor will agree a fixed fee in advance, and this usually presents few problems. The costs of obtaining a divorce are normally another such example. However, even in this case, it is sensible to be quite clear about what is and what is not included in the fixed fee. So-called 'disbursements' usually are not. In most cases this simply means costs such as Land Registry fees, local search fees, etc. which the solicitor has to pay on behalf of the client and for which he will seek to be reimbursed. These do not usually cause a problem and they will be the same from solicitor to solicitor. However, there are still some solicitors who charge for such things as photocopying under this same heading and it is as well to be aware of it.Incidentally, it is also worth bearing in mind that you should choose horses for courses. It would be silly to pay a partner in a large City of London firm to buy or sell your house (even if he were prepared to do it) because the cost would be quite disproportionate. A High Street solicitor will usually be much more competitive for this type of work. Conversely, if you need specialist advice on, say, corporate de-mergers you will almost certainly need to engage a specialist or specialists and correspondingly pay more for it.

What is probably less well realised is that even within quite small firms, there can be a range of charging levels depending on the person who is dealing with your work. Typically, this will range from a partner at the top end of the scale, through to an assistant solicitor or perhaps a legal executive in the middle, to a legal clerk at the bottom. It is always worth asking if a firm has different charging levels that depend on who carries out the work and to consider whether the work you want done can be done more economically and effectively by, say, a legal executive as opposed to a partner.

For work which is not carried out on a fixed fee basis, (litigation is generally one such example because it cannot usually be foreseen how long a given case might last), solicitors normally charge for each incoming and outgoing letter, for telephone calls and for time otherwise spent (for example, interviewing the client, drafting documents, etc.). These charges vary quite considerably from solicitor to solicitor and it is vitally important that the client understands them in order to make the best use of his solicitor's time and to keep some control over costs. For an example of how this works (and how the costs are calculated is by no means self-evident unless you choose to ask) take a look at the Legal Aid Board's scale of costs applicable in family matters, in force since 1 November 1997. Understanding how this works will give you an idea of how solicitors' charges are calculated (and why they sometimes seem to be more than the client had expected).

It is quite possible to ask to be informed if costs exceed a given point. Sometimes, too, it may be possible for the client to act in person for some matters and only to seek specific legal advice as and when he needs it. In the event that you are unhappy with your solicitor's bill you should in the first instance take it up with your solicitor. He is obliged to give you a detailed breakdown of how the bill is made up and this may be sufficient to resolve matters.

If it is not, you do have the right to have the bill scrutinised by a third party and the result of that may be that the size of the bill is reduced. Your solicitor will explain the procedures by which you may do this. In the case of contentious issues (that is, those involving court proceedings) the process usually adopted is called 'taxation' and in the case of non-contentious matters the client may have a right to obtain an adjudication from the Law Society confirming that the bill is fair and reasonable or otherwise. It is fair to say that there is a cost to both procedures, and who will pay those costs rather depends on whether the original bill was deemed fair and reasonable or not but it is certainly the case that there are procedures by which a solicitor's bill can be questioned. It is usually better though, to make quite sure where you stand at the outset and agree a proper framework of how you will be charged.

There is no reason why solicitors' charges should be a subject of such terror, but the truth of the matter is that they often are. Understanding them is vital if a client wants to make the best use of his solicitor's time and if the solicitor-client relationship is to be built on a firm foundation.

There is no long-term benefit to either solicitor or client if at the end of a given piece of work the client is left feeling dissatisfied because of the costs. It is in both the solicitor's interest and that of his client that the solicitor's charges are fair, reasonable, comprehensible and (in the last resort) subject to independent review.

Legal Aid

Whether you are entitled to legal aid or whether your opponent in litigation is legally aided can have very important consequences in litigation. Your solicitor will be able to tell you if you are eligible for legal aid and will be able to provide you with the necessary forms although not all solicitors do legal aid work. Basically, legal aid is granted on the basis of financial need and so you will have to give details of your income and expenditure to the Legal Aid Board. There are, however, certain types of legal work – wills and conveyancing for example – for which legal aid is not generally available.

The board also has to be satisfied that you have good legal grounds for starting or defending a case before it will grant legal aid. Preliminary advice can often be given by a solicitor under the 'green form scheme' which is a sort of limited and instant form of legal aid which is available if your means justify it. Legal aid proper has to be applied for if the case is going to involve litigation and/or substantial legal input.

It is often thought that legal aid is free whereas that is often not so. In criminal cases and ones where no property is at issue it can sometimes be 'free' although the client may still have to pay contributions depending on his or her income. More commonly, the Legal Aid Board recovers the money which it spends on a case from the property which is recovered by a successful legally aided client. This is particularly applicable in matrimonial cases. It is true that a certain amount (currently £3,000) is exempt and also that payment can, and very often is, deferred by the Legal Aid Board placing a charge on the property, such as a house, but in those cases legal aid is not 'free'.

The Legal Aid Board describes it thus:

'If you get legal aid, your solicitor's and barrister's bills will be paid for you by the Legal Aid Board out of taxpayers' money. But, if you get money or property with the help of legal aid you may have to put it towards these bills. This is called the statutory charge. It means that the Legal Aid Board can get back some of the millions of pounds spent each year with their legal costs. You will not have to pay if you lose, or if your case is exempt, or if the other side pays all your bills.'

It can be seen that there are some technical rules which may need careful explaining. Legal aid plays a particularly important role in divorce proceedings or, more accurately, in proceedings concerning the matrimonial property, and has an unfair effect on the legal costs of the respective parties in any proceedings where one party is legally aided but the other is not. If one party is legally aided and the other is not, then even if the party who is not legally aided is successful in the proceedings, he/she cannot usually recover his/her costs from the loser, as would usually be the case.

On the other hand, if the legally aided party is successful then he/she will usually ask for (and receive) reimbursement of his/her legal costs from the losing party. This puts a legally aided client at a considerable advantage and correspondingly disadvantages the other.

In point of fact, what very often happens in matrimonial proceedings is that the husband cannot obtain legal aid because he is in full-time employment. The wife however, is very often at home looking after the children and so she has no income of her own. This often means that the wife is eligible for legal aid in matrimonial proceedings whereas the husband is not. For reasons such as these the availability or otherwise of legal aid can have important effects in any litigation whether or not one is eligible for it oneself.

British Solicitor Listings

The following listings represent only a fraction of solicitors' firms that are able to advise on specific gay and lesbian matters. For firms of gay-friendly solicitors in your area you should phone **London Gay Switchboard** on 0171 837 7324 who hold the complete database of firms willing and able to assist in gay legal advice. It is our aim that the next edition of The Ultimate Gay Guide will have the complete listings of gay-friendly solicitors. If you have any comments relating to this section please forward them using the contact facilities listed in the Introduction to this guide.

LONDON

Aitchison Shaw Solicitors
United House
North Road
Holloway
London
N7 9DP   Telephone 0171 700 0045   Fax 0171 700 6288
                E-mail aitchison.shaw@virgin.net

Specialists in all aspects of family law.

Andrew Keen & Company
Solicitors
Enterprise House
113–115 George Lane
South Woodford
London
E18 1AB   Telephone 0181 989 3123   Fax 0181 989 3223
                E-mail askeen@cwcom.net

A gay-run firm providing a comprehensive legal service, including wills, probate and contested estates, family law, divorce and relationship breakdown, property disputes, Children Act matters, injunctions, criminal cases (including cottaging), landlord, tenant and housing, sale and purchase of residential and business property, debt actions and consumer issues. Legal aid available. Andrew Keen & Company is regulated by the Law Society in the conduct of investment business.

Belmont Hodgson
Solicitors
Heal House
375 Kennington Lane
Vauxhall Bridge
London
SE11 5QY   Telephone 0171 787 6777   Fax 0171 787 6782

Aiming to provide you with the legal help that you need, whatever the problem or transaction. With their American associates (Pisapia & Lipsig, New York) they may also be able to assist with claims for injuries suffered in the US, immigration, employment and other matters involving both jurisdictions.

Outlines   from Absolute press

A delightful collection of monographs detailing the loves and lives of some of the most prolific gay and lesbian creative artists of this century.
Titles in the series:
David Hockney
Benjamin Britten
Bessie Smith
We are Michael Field
Federico Garcia Lorca
Arthur Rimbaud
k.d. lang
Armistead Maupain
Tallulah Bankhead

belmont hodgson
solicitors

london   * new york

We aim to be able to provide you with the legal help that you need whatever the problem or transaction. With our American associates we may also assist with claims for injuries suffered in the U.S., immigration, employment and other matters involving both jurisdictions.

**For further information
or a conveyancing quotation
telephone
0207 787 6777**

Heal House
375 Kennington Lane
Vauxhall Bridge
London, SE11 5QY

*In association with Pisapia + Lipsig,
The Lincoln Building, 60E, 42nd St.
New York, NY 10165

Cornish & Company

Solicitors
Lex House
1–7 Hainault Street
Ilford
London

IG1 4EL	Telephone 0181 478 3300 Fax 0181 553 3418 Fax 0181 553 3422
	Contact Alan Rees

Providing a comprehensive legal service in all matters relating to your personal and business affairs both in the UK and abroad. Cornish & Company have a supportive and positive approach to providing legal services to the gay community. They are members of the Gay Business Association. Contact Alan Rees without obligation for advice and information on all of the following services; overseas property; litigation; trusts and tax; corporate and commercial affairs; timeshare; probate and wills; conveyancing; franchising and licensing.

David Clark Solicitor

38 Heath Street
Hampstead
London

NW3 6TE	Telephone 0171 433 1562 Fax 0171 433 1625

A gay firm dealing with crime. Experienced in criminal defence work, including sexual offences, conveyancing (advice on mortgages and buying with your partner), homophobia (warning letters, injunctions and civil proceedings), immigration, wills and probate, and family and civil matters.

GLAD (Gay and Lesbian Legal Advice)

c/o Central Station
37 Wharfdale Road
Islington
London

N1 9ST	Telephone 0171 837 5212
	(Helpline hours: Monday – Thursday: 19.00 – 21.30)

GLAD provides a telephone helpline offering free and confidential legal advice to the lesbian and gay community on any legal issue. The helpline is staffed voluntarily by qualified lawyers. Bear in mind that Central Station is used only as a mailing address.

Gherson & Company

Immigration Solicitors
1 Great Cumberland Place
London

W1H 7AL	Telephone 0171 724 4488 Fax 0171 724 4888
	Website http://www.gherson.com
	E-mail gherson@macline.co.uk
	Contact Anne Morris

Gherson & Company is a firm of solicitors based in London's West End, specialising in UK immigration and nationality law with over 18 years worth of experience. They offer advice and legal representation regarding the Home Office concession to allow same sex couples in long-term committed relationships to apply for residency in the UK. Additionally, Gherson & Company can advise in connection with visa applications for business investors, persons of independent means, work permits, media representatives, writers and artists, students, au-pairs, registration and naturalisation. Gherson & Company is regulated by the Law Society of England and Wales and is a member of the Immigration Law Practitioners Association.

Hamiltons Solicitors

42B Independent Place
London
E8 2HE   Telephone 0171 923 7823   Fax 0171 923 0758
               Website http://www.btinternet.com/~hamiltons
               E-mail Hamiltons@btinternet.com
               Contact Angus Hamilton or David Campbell

Hamiltons was established in 1997 by leading gay rights lawyer Angus Hamilton. The firm offers services to the lesbian and gay community in the areas of criminal litigation (including a 24 hour police station service), computers and the law, data protection, regulation of the Internet, wills, living wills and powers of attorney. The firm specialises in criminal litigation. Angus Hamilton has had substantial experience in dealing with sexual offences and prosecutions relating to pornography (including Internet pornography) and indecency and has been involved in many of the gay-related civil liberties cases of the past decades. Angus writes regularly for the magazines *PC Pro* and *Gay Times* on legal issues. He is also a contributor to the 1999 publications *Advising The Lesbian and Gay Client* and *Liberating Cyberspace*. He is co-author of *Sweet and Maxwell's Guide to the 1998 Data Protection Act*. Angus is the former Chair of the Board of Trustees of the National Aids Manual and a long standing volunteer with the Terrence Higgins Trust.

Judith Burton & Company

Solicitors
Museum House
25 Museum Street
London
WC1A 1JT   Telephone 0171 636 2448   Fax 0171 493 9241
               E-mail j-burton@dircon.co.uk

An all-lesbian firm providing a full range of legal services to lesbians and gay men including: sale and purchase of your home and business; company and partnership advice; relationship breakdown; family and Children Act matters; wills and probate; employment; landlord and tenant; debts. The firm is also authorised by the Law Society to conduct financial investment business.

Kaltons Solicitors

9 White Lion Street
London
N1 9PD   Telephone 0171 278 1817   Fax 0171 278 1835
                Website http://www.kaltons.co.uk
                E-mail lawyers@kaltons.co.uk
                Contact Amanda Woolven

Kaltons are a team of lawyers specialising in IT/Internet law, business law, property (including both business and domestic conveyancing), property disputes (including 'gay divorces'), wills, probate, estate and tax planning. Particularly popular with the gay community are their business services (especially to charities, bars, restaurants and pubs, and now to Internet businesses), conveyancing work (including contracts between co-owners), living wills, wills, powers of attorney and probate. Over the years, they are proud to have sponsored, acted for and/or supported some of the leading gay organisations such as Stonewall, Pride, LAGER, Lesbian & Gay Bereavement Project, Lesbian & Gay Christian Movement and AIDS Treatment Project, and they have one of the highest profiles in the community. Maitland Kalton was listed by *Gay Times* as one of 'the country's 200 leading gay figures'. He established Kaltons over 10 years ago. The firm's team consists largely of 'refugees' from large city firms, which means that they offer legal advice of the highest standards but at far lower rates that their former colleagues.

Outlines   from Absolute Press

A delightful collection of monographs detailing the loves and lives of some of the most prolific gay and lesbian creative artists of this century.
 Titles in the series:
 David Hockney
 Benjamin Britten
 Bessie Smith
 We are Michael Field
 Federico García Lorca
 Arthur Rimbaud
 k.d. lang
 Armistead Maupin
 Tallulah Bankhead

Engleharts solicitors

We serve the needs of our many lesbian and gay Clients

Property sales and purchases.
Including a range of living together agreements.

Buying and selling businesses
Ancillary business advice and commercial agreements generally.

Dealing with and advising on liquor licensing
Including advice as to the best licence to apply for, making introductions to appropriate sources to sell and buy licensed premises and undergo necessary licensing training.

**David Englehart
18 Blatchington Road
Hove BN3 3YN
T: 01273 204411
F: 01273 204207**

Lesbian & Gay Employment Rights (LAGER)

Unit 1G Leroy House
436 Essex Road
London
N1 3QP   Telephone 0171 704 2205 (General enquiries)
                Telephone 0171 704 8066 (Lesbian helpline)
                Telephone 0171 704 6066 (Gay men's helpline)

Hours for advice are Monday – Friday: 12.00 – 16.00. Phone or write (enclosing SAE) for experienced and free legal advice on any employment problems, including discrimination.

McGlennons Solicitors

Park House
158–160 Arthur Road
London
SW19 8AQ   Telephone 0181 946 6015   Fax 0181 946 8803
                E-mail mcglenn@dircon.co.uk

Main areas of practice include wills, probate and contested estates. The firm is also authorised by the Law Society in the conduct of investment business.

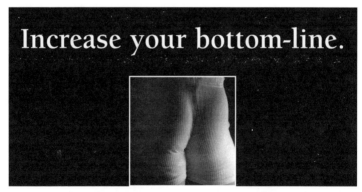

Increase your bottom-line.

For tighter financial management contact John Holding
for your free initial consultation.

HOLDINGS CHARTERED CERTIFIED ACCOUNTANTS & MANAGEMENT CONSULTANTS

40A High Street Welwyn Hertfordshire AL6 9EQ
TELEPHONE: 01438 840333 FAX: 01438 840700
EMAIL: johnholding@msn.com WEBSITE:http://www.holdings.co.uk
DTI/TEC LISTED CONSULTANTS -
MEMBERS OF THE CHARTERED ASSOCIATION OF CERTIFIED ACCOUNTANTS

Simon Woods & Co. Solicitors
18 Broadwick Street
Soho
London
W1V 1FG   Telephone 0171 434 3996   Fax 0171 434 3997
                 E-mail simonwoods@compuserve.com
                 Contact Simon Woods or Ruth Ross

Simon Woods & Co. is a 100% lesbian and gay firm and a member of the Gay Business Association, specialising in the areas of conveyancing, wills and probate, small business work and entertainment law. Ruth Ross has, for the past five years, specialised in criminal law – in particular, gay-specific sexual offences, property disputes, divorce and child contact disputes – acting for lesbians, gay men and transsexuals. Simon Woods & Co. offer a free initial advice chat over the telephone and, for the present can do legal aid work.

Stonewall Immigration Group
                 Telephone 0171 336 0620

Week days: 12.00 – 17.00. Offering free immigration information and advice to same sex couples and gay asylum seekers.

When you need the professionals ...

for your taxation, auditing and accountancy needs,

rely on the practised service of Chartered Accountants hescroff bevan

call Chris Bevan

London   T 0171 491 8660
           F 0171 491 8665

Poole   T 01202 685351
           F 01202 669532

           E enq@hescroff-bevan.co.uk

hescroff bevan

Chartered Accountants

Taylor Willcocks Solicitors

7 Old Town
Clapham
London
SW4 0JT   Telephone 0171 498 2244   Fax 0171 498 2255
                 E-mail petersibley@taylorwillcocks.co.uk
                 Contact Peter Sibley

They deal with gay legal representation, specialising in property, cohabitation agreements, relationship splits, wills and probate, trust deeds, commercial matters, mortgage and finance planning and medical negligence. Taylor Willcocks is a member of the Gay Business Association.

Winstanley-Burgess

378 City Road
London
EC1V 2TQ   Telephone 0171 278 7911   Fax 0171 833 2135
                 E-mail wb@gn.apc.org

This large, well-established law firm in Angel Islington has lesbian lawyers with expertise in the areas of crime (including 24 hour police station) and all aspects of family and housing law. Work is undertaken by lesbian and gay-friendly lawyers in other areas including personal injury, actions against the police, immigration, conveyancing and wills and probate.

ENGLAND

Pritchard, Joyce & Hinds Solicitors

St Brides House
32 High Street
Beckenham
BR3 1AY   Telephone 0181 658 3922   Fax 0181 658 8694
                 Contact Andrew Ransley or his secretary Julie Wilson

For all business, commercial and personal legal requirements.

Bradley & Cuthbertson

47 Newhall Street
Birmingham
B3 3QU   Telephone 0121 233 2644   Fax 0121 233 2196

Areas of legal speciality include property purchase and ownership, wills, probate and inheritance, partnership breakdown and children.

David Laing & Company

Solicitors
22 Ship Street
Brighton   Telephone 01273 323 113/01903 761 136 (Out of hours
                 answerphone)   Fax 01273 770 913
                 Contact Monica Deeming

Caring for the legal needs of the gay community in Sussex and specialising in the following areas; personal injury; employment; wills and probate; family law;

commerce and conveyancing. For sympathetic and experienced legal advice contact Monica Deeming.

Linda Filby
Solicitor
6 Hamilton Court
Brighton Marina
BN2 5XD   Telephone 01273 695 321   Fax 01273 605 924

Linda Filby has been offering her legal services to the gay community in Brighton for many years. For further information and details phone the above number.

Shanahan Bull Solicitors
Regent House
Prince's Place
Brighton
BN1 1ED   Telephone 01273 220 813   Fax 01273 747 807

Friendly legal service to the lesbian and gay community specialising in accident claims, family and cohabitation, children, injunctions, crime, conveyancing, landlord and tenant, wills, probate and trusts. Legal aid too.

Janis Purdy Solicitor
11 St Edwards Road
Clifton
Bristol
BS8 4TS   Telephone 0117 923 0307   Fax 0117 925 6178

Specialists in split-ups, property, wills and probate, accidents and all court work. Cottaging cases are welcome too.

Terry & Co. Solicitors
23 Pemberton Avenue
Ingatestone
Essex
CM4 0AG   Telephone 01277 354 518   Fax 08700 547 975
               E-mail dterry@terry.co.uk

The firm mainly deals with divorce work, and in that context has vast experience of the particular problems faced by gay men, women and transsexuals who 'come out' during their marriage. These issues can cause all sorts of difficulties, not normally encountered in the average divorce. The firm can also offer advice on wills and probate, powers of attorney, enduring powers of attorney and living wills.

Glaisyers Solicitors

6th Floor
Manchester House
18–20 Bridge Street
Manchester
M3 3BY   Telephone 0161 832 4666   Fax 0161 832 1981
                E-mail email@glaisyers.com
                Contact Helen Benson

Supportive assistance in all areas of the law. Glaisyers is a major legal practice with a long reputation within the gay and lesbian community, specialising in family breakdown, contact/residence, domestic violence, claims to property, living together agreements, wills and probate, powers of attorney, all criminal matters, conveyancing and financial/property claims after the death of partner.

Booth & Barker. Solicitors

1 Dean Street
Stalybridge
Cheshire
SK15 2JD   Telephone 0161 338 2335   Fax 0161 338 8250
                E-mail bkaatbb@aol.com

Gay-owned and -run solicitors.

the ultimate GAY guide

Tell us what you think

Ultimate Guides
PO Box 64
Manchester
M7 4NZ

email
ugg@ic24.net

(or you can use the form at the back of this book)

Outlines   from Absolute Press

A delightful collection of monographs detailing the loves and lives of some of the most prolific gay and lesbian creative artists of this century.
Titles in the series:
David Hockney
Benjamin Britten
Bessie Smith
We are Michael Field
Federico García Lorca
Arthur Rimbaud
k.d. lang
Armistead Maupin
Tallulah Bankhead

O'Neill Morgan Patient. Solicitors

251 London Road
Hazel Grove
Stockport
SK7 4PL   Telephone 0161 483 8555   Fax 0161 483 0333
                 E-mail Patient@omp.u-net.com

Gay solicitors for gay people. Offering their legal services for all your business and personal needs. Early morning, late evening and weekend appointments available. Office also situated at Prudential Buildings, 61–63 St Petersgate, Stockport SK1. Use the same contact details as above.

Young & Co. Solicitors

Edward House
Uttoxeter Road
Longton
Stoke-on-Trent
ST3 1NZ   Telephone 01782 599 222   Fax 01782 599 005
                 E-mail young-co@dircon.co.uk
                 Contact Jane England/Martin Leeke/Deirdre Gough

Legal advice on family and child law, domestic violence and injunctions, criminal litigation, marriage and cohabitation breakdowns and contact and residence disputes.

The Bradin Trubshaw Partnership: Solicitors

36 Lichfield Street
Walsall
WS1 1TJ   Telephone 01922 612 444   Fax 01922 612 999
                 Contact Lee Trubshaw or Helen Bradin

A Midlands-based firm providing a full range of legal services including the sale and purchase of your home, wills and probate, cohabitation agreements, personal injury claims, company and partnership and employment law including discrimination. Free initial interview. Open on Saturdays.

WALES

Dawn A. Tindall, Triangle Legal Services
                 Telephone 01222 238 232

Dawn Tindall is a gay-friendly solicitor offering effective, efficient advice in Cardiff, Wales and throughout the UK. Specialist legal services include wills and probate, living wills, welfare benefits, trusts and tax, court of protection and enduring powers of attorney.

Margraves Solicitors
Old Court Chambers
Spa Road
Llandrindod Wells
Powys
LD1 5EY   Telephone 01597 825 565   Fax 01597 825 220
                 E-mail law@margraves.co.uk

Margraves is an established private client niche practice, specialising in wills and probate, trusts, estate and inheritance planning. The field is covered by the firm's principal, Clive Margrave-Jones, who is an established authority in his field with a particular interest in providing estate and inheritance tax planning for gay couples. Although the practice is physically based on the Herefordshire/Welsh border, its client base is throughout the UK. Clive has devoted the whole of his professional life to the area of wills, trusts, probate, estate and inheritance tax planning. In addition to his wide practical experience, Clive has written and lectured extensively in these and other related areas of law, and many practitioners are currently using publications in which he is involved. He is also currently a member of the Law Society's Wills and Equity Committee.

SCOTLAND

Bovey and Bovey
126 Morningside Road
Edinburgh
EH10 4DT   Telephone 0131 452 8770   Fax 0131 452 8770
                  Contact Keith Bovey

Deals only with cases regarding possession of drugs and possession with intent to supply drugs.

Trevor Davis: Consultant Peden & Patrick: Solicitors
13 Bath Street
Glasgow G2   Telephone 0141 333 0175   Fax 0141 333 0334
                  E-mail tsdavis@peden-patrick.co.uk

Wills and executry (probate), living wills, powers of attorney, deeds of trust, house purchase and sale, mortgages and commercial and investment property. Trevor Davis has a mainly personal client base as a consultant with this long-established and well-respected firm in Glasgow. He prepared the Scottish version of a 'Will Pack' for the Gay and Lesbian Bereavement Project and took part in the Scottish Equality Project 1998, with particular reference to gay partnership.

Levy & McRae. Solicitors
266 St Vincent Street
Glasgow
G2   Telephone 0141 307 2311   Fax 0141 307 6857
                  Contact Margaret Morton

Wills and probate, living wills, powers of attorney, divorce and relationship breakdown.

Biggart Bailey & Giffard

310 St Vincent Street
Glasgow
G2   Telephone 0141 228 8000   Fax 0141 228 8310
                      Contact Sian Warren

Wills and probate, living wills, divorce and relationship breakdown, criminal litigation.

Transgenderism

Introduction

It is a common misnomer – even to some people on the gay scene – that transvestites and transsexuals are all gay. This is certainly not the case. However, like any group of people there can be transvestites, cross-dressers or transsexuals that *may* be gay or bisexual.

TVs, TSs and CDs use the gay venues because, unlike the straight establishments, they allow them the opportunity to be themselves without fear of ridicule and/or ignorant abuse.

The following text has been edited from various reliable sources, the aim being to give the reader an insight of all the resources available to the TV/TS/CD in the UK. It should be noted that as the subject matter is as diverse as it is complex, the text, although detailed for the amount of space available, is *only* a guide in order to direct you to the relevant organisation suitable for your proclivities. It is anticipated that further detailed resources and an expansion of the medical text of this most important subject will be included in the next edition of *The Ultimate Gay Guide*. Responses and suggestions from all parties concerned (particularly young people) are welcome. Please write to the address given in the introduction of this book.

As you will discover, the majority of the following text is aimed at *male-to-female* transsexualism (MTF), however, it is recognised that *female to male* transsexualism (FTM) exists in the same numbers and that the anxieties of the person concerned are probably greater than MTF. However, space prohibits a separate classification although, the format has taken in a generalisation of them both.

The inclusion of any organisation, product or service is by no means an endorsement. Again, these are included as a starting point for you to conduct your own research.

Finally, the gay scene itself can at times be ignorant and cynical to minority groups within the gay community. As a minority group ourselves, we should show and offer support and respect to the transgendered community by recognising, at the very least, their discrimination in a misinformed world. To go one better would be to take the time and effort to speak to transgendered people in order that you can understand some of the hostilities encountered by them.

Special thanks and credit are due to the following organisations for their part in supplying text towards this section: The Northern Concord; Pamela Sexton; The Beaumont Society and to others – contributors whose names were not available.

Definitions

Transvestism

Transvestism is cross-dressing with the desire to adopt the clothes, appearance and behaviour normally associated with the opposite gender. For some it is simply 'dressing up', while for others, known as 'dual role transvestites', it is a need to adopt the opposite role as fully as possible on a temporary or full-time basis.

Transvestism tends to be little understood, though work in recent years to change public attitudes means that it is perhaps no longer a subject of fear, but is seen more as being harmless. It is a subject commonly treated in the press in a way that exploits it as sensationalist. However, women's magazines seem to be more sympathetic. Perhaps it does not feel such a threat to women as it does to men. When one is very close to the person however, it may well be a different matter. Among families it seems to be very threatening at first. Understanding is not as good as it might be amongst people in the caring professions, the clergy, the police and social workers to name but a few, who may be called upon to offer help.

The unhappiness often experienced by many transvestites comes from loneliness and anxiety about their situation and considerable confusion about their feelings. In a sense, they are a minority group who fail to conform to what is regarded as 'normal behaviour' and may therefore fear the consequences, should their activity be discovered. Society's acceptance of females who choose to dress in traditionally male clothes is widespread in the West, but cross-dressing by males is much less accepted. Throughout history, women adopting the male role have largely gone unremarked. Partners are often concerned that their man may *become* homosexual or transsexual, though this is extremely unlikely to happen, once the person is sure of himself. Some transvestites do opt to live full-time as a woman and some may be homosexual or bisexual by coinci-dence.

The majority of transvestites are heterosexual men who are often married with families. The desire to cross-dress usually seems to begin at an early age when the only available clothes may be those belonging to female members of the family. A transvestite boy may suffer feelings of isolation and guilt, but is often too young to realise the reasons for the need. At first, cross-dressing is often non-sexual, but during puberty it may take on erotic overtones.

In many transvestites however, the urge to cross-dress is irresistible. Belief in society's lack of approval may make the transvestite attempt to suppress the behaviour, or to keep it a secret from those whom he loves for fear of destroying the relationship. This may lead to a depressive phase where counselling by understanding professionals is crucial. Self-help organisations around the country provide an outlet for transvestites and their families to meet socially, to combat the sense of isolation.

The incidence of transvestism is estimated at approximately one in every hundred of the male population. It has never been accurately estimated in the female population.

Transvestism is not a disease and therefore the term 'cure' does not apply. It is a behaviour pattern that may have underlying reasons, which are not yet fully understood. In some societies it might be perceived as a harmless quirk. It may however be regarded as threatening in a relationship. Often, the transvestite has avoided telling his partner, believing it may pass once he is married, only to be discovered accidentally at a later stage when it emerges. The female partner may feel let down or angry at not being told. Often cross-dressing is simply a safety valve and a form of escape from the pressures and responsibility of work and social demands.

A partner may react with complete revulsion, leading to separation and divorce. At the other extreme, the partner may find the behaviour pattern intriguing, perhaps even stimulating. The majority of partners will fall within these two extremes and form some sort of compromise and tolerance, though without *necessarily* approving.

A transvestite who indulges in cross-dressing at the expense of time spent with his wife and family, and at the cost of purchasing a double wardrobe, risks alienating both wife and family. If the couple can work together in mutual acceptance of feelings, and support the partnership, there is a real possibility that the marriage may be strengthened and enhanced. Such transvestites may have developed a better understanding of the opposite sex.

Many partners lack knowledge and assume that cross-dressing equates with homosexuality.

They may also fear the possibility of contracting a sexually transmitted disease. A transvestite is no more at risk in this than any other member of the public. More commonly, a partner may feel inadequate and believe that somehow she must have failed her husband as a woman. Often, the most damaging is the feeling of being deceived and that the secret has gone unshared, despite the intimate life that they may otherwise have. Like the transvestite himself, the partner may fear adverse reaction from parents, relatives, friends and particularly the children of the marriage.

Cross-Dressing

Cross-dressing refers to the adoption – fully or partially – of the clothes identified normally as belonging to the opposite sex. People may cross-dress for a variety of reasons, of which transvestism, transsexualism and fetishism are the commonest. Some people may also cross-dress as part of a disguise or for entertainment. Others may cross-dress as part of masochistic activities.

Gender Dysphoria

Gender Dysphoria refers to the dissatisfaction with one's gender (masculinity or femininity) which is in conflict with one's physical sex. The term is usually restricted to those who seek medical and surgical assistance to resolve their difficulty. The cause of gender dysphoria remains uncertain and may well be a combination of internal hormonal and learning mechanisms in the early environment. There is no clear evidence of an inherited or familial factor. Both transvestism and transsexualism often lead to social consequences, which often require skilled specialist counselling. Neither condition is amenable to 'cure', any more than is homosexuality or left-handedness. At one end of the scale is the occasional crossdresser, who perhaps adopts the clothing of the opposite sex for fetishistic reasons. At the other end of the spectrum is the transsexual, who, with thoughtful and carefully directed therapy, usually becomes happier as an individual after the gender reassignment process. Between these two extremes of cross-dressing are gradations, with the transvestite functioning somewhere in between. The transvestite who knows that he – or she, in rare cases – is not alone and not insane is more able to come to terms with the condition and learn to live with it. Gender possibilities are broad, as are those of sex. People can exist anywhere along the continuum.

Transsexuality

Transsexuality is a profound form of gender dysphoria, where there is a conviction of being 'trapped in the wrong body' and the need to express oneself and to be as far as possible in the gender to which one feels comfortable.

This is usually characterised by a continuing conviction that the physical anatomy is incompatible with the true gender role. Thus, a female to male transsexual (FTM) will feel she has 'a man's mind trapped in a female body' and vice versa. Surgical attempts to allow such individuals to live in their chosen gender role, known as gender reassignment surgery (or more commonly, 'sex change operations') are less complex for the male to female (MTF) than for the FTM clients. However, entering the adopted social role is often much simpler for the FTM. Hormone prescription for MTF transsexuals is said to lower sexual appetite, while in the FTM's case, it is said to be the opposite. However, it is not likely that it will alter sexual interest. Transsexuals may be heterosexual or homosexual like the rest of the population. Sexual orientation is a variable, and some transsexuals are content to remain celibate.

There is no need for transsexuals to suffer in the late twentieth century, as treatments are already available. The first thing a transsexual would need to do on discovering there is something wrong is to see their own doctor and ask for a referral to a psychiatrist who has knowledge of gender issues. You will usually be evaluated by a psychiatrist *and* a psychologist to ensure that you are indeed transsexual, and not a confused transvestite or a person who suffers from delusions. These tests are absolutely necessary for your own protection, and the protection of the psychiatrist, surgeon and hospital where you are treated.

If you are diagnosed as transsexual, the psychiatrist will usually prescribe hormones for your correct gender. In the case of MTF transsexuals, the psychiatrist will prescribe oestrogens, progestins and anti-androgens. In the case of FTM transsexuals the psychiatrist will prescribe testosterone. It is possible to obtain hormones without the psychiatrist consultation. However, this course of action can be extremely dangerous: it is absolutely essential that you are monitored correctly.

The next part is extremely difficult to start, but an absolute necessity. In order to progress, a transsexual must spend one or two years living in the opposite biological role whilst integrating themselves into society. This is called the real life test (RLT). An MTF transsexual must spend at least one year living as a woman, working as a woman and be accepted as a woman in society to be recommended for the next stage.

They will continue to be evaluated by a psychiatrist during this period. This can be extremely difficult, as many transsexuals spend large periods without employment. The sex discrimination law prevents transsexuals being discriminated against in employment, but it doesn't need much imagination to deduce that very few transsexuals would be prepared to go to a tribunal where the press may be present. Some psychiatrists accept college as employment and in the UK, most colleges have full equal opportunities policies to protect the transsexual student.

If a transsexual is successful during the RLT the psychiatrist will usually introduce a plastic surgeon who is a specialist in sex confirmation surgery. The surgeon will have access to all your notes and will decide whether to operate to rectify nature's mistake. If the surgeon is satisfied, the operation will take place soon after.

The operation can take one of two general methods. The most common is the inversion method. This involves the penis being cut open and the spongy tissue inside being removed, the scrotum being opened and the testicles being removed. The skin of the penis is then inverted and fits inside the body. The scrotum is used to form new labia lips and a new clitoris can be formed. Using this method the new vagina has to be dilated regularly to stop it shrinking and/or atrophying. This involves using special dilators and/or regular sexual activity. Dilators do not look at all comfortable but are extremely necessary to prevent the new vagina from closing.

The other method of sex reassignment surgery involves removing part of the colon to use as the new vagina. This method leaves scarring similar to that of a hysterectomy. It remains attached to the body throughout surgery and is self-lubricating which doesn't happen with the other method. This method is not common in the United Kingdom.

The National Health Service isn't, in general, the best provider of any treatment for any transgender conditions. There are still too many providers of health services who genuinely believe that transsexuality is a life choice rather than a condition that you were born with. They are not allowed by law to refuse treatment, so instead they try to put obstacles in the way.

They might refuse to prescribe hormones on the NHS, or refer you to a psychiatrist hundreds of miles from your home. The waiting lists are often over 18 months. (Bear in mind that the count starts from when you hear from them and that could take months!)

However, if you are unemployed or low paid then you probably have no other option than to use the NHS for all your treatment. In that case, you must see your family doctor GP. Your GP is the only person who can refer you to a National Health psychiatrist. Try to have a talk with your GP. It is likely that he/she will have never come into contact with a transsexual before and may have very little idea about the condition, or worse, may have pre-conceived ideas. If they seem interested or sympathetic to your condition then you are ready to begin your long journey. In those cases where a doctor has no interest or seems unwilling to help, then see if there is another doctor within the practice who is willing to help. If you still have no luck then consider finding a new GP. You can get a list of GPs from your local Family Health Services Authority (number in the phone book). It is important to have the right doctor involved in your treatment because the journey will take a long time using the NHS. If you have a little more money then the private way is usually better and much quicker.

However, you must do your research. A psychiatrist who has no knowledge of any of the transgender conditions isn't much use, because the journey will be a lot slower. Psychiatrists sometimes know as much as the general public; they just don't like to admit that they sometimes know less than their patient. Their job is to make sure that you are a transsexual and that you can cope as a member of your correct gender for the rest of your life. A psychiatrist with no knowledge of transsexuality could make mistakes that could affect your whole life.

If you are a child who is transgendered then your options are reduced. If you are under 16, then you are only allowed to visit the only Gender Identity Clinic (GIC) in the UK for children and adolescents, as long as you are accompanied by a parent, school teacher, social worker or other responsible adult (further information is contained in the 'Mermaids' section that follows this text). You can refer yourself to the GIC if you are 16–18 years of age.

In the NHS, when you have found a GP who is willing to treat you, you need to ask him to refer you to a psychiatrist, or better still, a GIC. But, as in the private sector, do your own research and try to find out as much as you can on the subject. If you live in Yorkshire you will usually be referred to St James University Hospital in Leeds. This is probably the best GIC in the country. They take only referrals from Yorkshire. For areas that do not have their own GIC, you will most probably be referred to Charing Cross Hospital (London). If you can avoid it, then do so. There is a problem though, as many health authorities will have contracts with only one hospital, but there is a way of getting around it. When you have found a psychiatrist or GIC that you have heard good reports about, then approach your GP. Your GP may say that they cannot refer you because the health authority does not have a contract with them. That may be true, but you can ask your doctor for an extra contractual referral. This means that your health authority may buy in the services of a psychiatrist or GIC from an area that they don't have a contract with. This is a perfect way of avoiding the Charing Cross nightmare.

When you have got your appointment with a psychiatrist, you will then have to wait. If you go private you will have a wait of anything up to six weeks. If you go the National Health Service route it can be two years or longer.

At your first visit you will be assessed by a psychiatrist. It is important that you answer all their questions with complete honesty. There are people who read other people's tales of how they got treatment and then proceed to use exactly the same story. The psychiatrists can see right through this. If you genuinely felt as if you were born into the wrong body then say so, but, if you had other thoughts and feelings then be completely honest. Not every transsexual is the same and an experienced psychiatrist will know much of the spectrum of gender identity issues. You wont get thrown out of treatment if you tell the truth, even if your tale is different to everyone else's. However, the course of treatment may be different if the psychiatrist suspects that you are trying to conceal the truth and it may take you longer to complete.

A good suggestion for many NHS hospitals is to wear a dress or skirt, at least for your first visit. Many NHS psychiatrists have pre-conceived ideas of the way they think women should look and behave. They also seem to confuse transvestism and transsexuality at times. Do not say you have transitioned if you haven't. To an experienced psychiatrist you will usually give yourself away.

In the private sector, if you have told the truth, then hormones will usually be prescribed on the first or second visit. It is always a good idea to have a blood test before your first hormones, in order to have a base for future testing and to make sure that you don't have any liver or blood problems. Hormones are dangerous and you *must* be monitored on a regular basis. Your GP will normally arrange for this to be done. If travelling the private route then ask your GP to convert your private prescription to an NHS one. Some will and can make the journey much cheaper.

In the NHS, expect a longer wait for hormones. This appears to be another obstacle that is often put in your way. At Charing Cross Hospital for example, there have been tales of patients being told that they must live 'in role' for one year before you can receive hormones. This is relatively new. In the late eighties hormone prescription was available on the second visit despite the MTF being a long-way-off transition. It has also been reported that patients who have been referred to Charing Cross after they have started hormones have been asked to stop. Although you may have to wait, do not, under any circumstances attempt to buy hormones illegally. They are dangerous, there is a possibility of a stroke or serious injury that could delay, or stop altogether any further treatment. Herbal hormones are not safe either, unless monitored.

In the private sector you will normally have interviews for one to two years before you are referred to a second psychiatrist to confirm the diagnosis of the first. In the NHS, it can take up to six years, which appears to be yet another obstacle. If your second referral is positive then you will be referred to a surgeon.

After you have been through all the hurdles you finally get to the pre-surgery stage. In the NHS you will usually have a surgeon appointed for you but there are ways round this. Again, you need to do your research. Different surgeons have different methods. If you find a surgeon that you like but the hospital doesn't use then you can ask your health authority for an 'extra contractual referral' to the surgeon of your choice. If you are going the private way then you still need to do your research but cost may come into your decision too. It is worth remembering that although most are good at the surgery, some may have more experience and this will be reflected in the price.

You will initially be interviewed by the surgeon and must answer all their questions honestly. As in the case of the interview with the psychiatrist, they will want to know everything. They will also tell you a few things that you must do. If you don't, you wont get the surgery. This includes stopping oral hormones – if you don't you risk dying. Some surgeons will test your blood to make sure that you have stopped.

The day will approach for your surgery and you do need to prepare. In the case of MTFs, you will need to buy your first sanitary towels for after the operation, and you will also need loose night-clothes to keep good circulation. You can expect to be confined to bed for a while and your stay in hospital will usually last about ten days. After your operation, you will still need to visit your surgeon from time to time to check that everything is healing correctly. Some psychiatrists may also ask you to return post-operatively.

It is a good idea to take these visits. Not only do they want to ensure that you are adjusting properly, but, for the treatment of future patients, the research opportunities are valuable. Some people believe that surgery will make everything better and that is not always the case. Sometimes there are other underlying problems that the doctor would like to help with. The subsequent helpline numbers and addresses will be able to offer you more detailed information on all of the subjects covered within this text..

Hermaphroditism

Hermaphroditism or intersexuality is where the physiological sex is ambiguous. The situation may, or may not, be accompanied by various degrees of gender dysphoria. The condition may be due to chromosomal complexes such as Turners or Klinefelters syndromes, congenital errors of metabolism such as androgen insensitivity syndrome and adrenogenital syndrome. There may also be effects from the hormone balance in the foetus or the placenta.

Gender Identity in Children

Gender identity issues vary considerably. They may arise when a child exhibits gender behaviour to some degree or other. Some may be boys who prefer to take the female role or vice versa; others may have a compulsion to play with toys mostly used by the other sex (for instance, a boy who predominantly plays with dolls, or a girl who always plays with Action Man or army toys. Some children may only feel comfortable when playing with peers of the other physical sex, or may cross-dress from time to time. Some children may be unhappy about their own biological sex and wish to belong to the other one. Some adolescents may experience a crisis over a problem of sexual orientation. The situations may lead to considerable concern and distress for all those involved.

At school, a child or teenager with a gender identity issue may come in for a great deal of bullying, mickey-taking, name-calling or even physical attacks. The child or teenager may have great difficulty in responding appropriately. However, the education of people about gender identity issues in the school environment is very important in dealing with these problems. Many adults with gender identity issues describe difficulties in childhood. Often, they complain of having been very unhappy teenagers and that their suffering had not been recognised early enough by parents and professionals. If this suffering can be recognised early in life, then with the right help, support and 'treatment', young people can be helped to tolerate living through these distressing conditions and find a solution to this identity conflict. Their childhood can become happier and less traumatic.

Gender identity is the sense of 'I am male' or 'I am female'. A child becomes aware of its gender identity before or around the age of five years. In most people their gender identity is the same as their sex, i.e. a woman or girl feels that she is female and a man or boy feels that he is male, but in a few people their gender identity and sex do not match, and this can cause problems.

Sexual orientation is separate from gender identity – it is simply a case of whether one is sexually attracted to men, women, both or neither.

Police Policy – Dealing With Transsexuals And Transvestites

The big question is: Under the law, what rights do you have when you go out cross-dressed?

The answer is, very few. UK law does not operate under a constitution that guarantees fundamental rights. Instead of being given rights we are free to do as we please, unless something has been forbidden by the law. Cross-dressing has never been legislated against in modern times but there are laws one should be aware of which could affect you. For instance, under the Public Disorder Act, the police have the power to arrest anyone that they think is likely to cause a breach of the peace. In the past, this power has been used to arrest two gay men kissing at a bus stop and in theory could easily be used to arrest a cross-dresser when, for example, she encounters verbal abuse from ignorant yobs. Although the police will realise that it is the cross-dresser who is the 'victim', they could construe the incident in such a way that would target you, dressed as a woman, as the provocation for the disturbance, and as such, responsible for a breach of the peace. Breaches of the peace are the commonest offences that the police deal with on a day-to-day basis and, dependent on the nature of the trouble, the police officer could do one of three things:

a)   Ask you to leave the area.
b)   Escort you away from the area.
c)   Arrest you (the worst case scenario).

If the officer chooses the last course of action, you will be taken to the police station, where upon arrival, you will have to give your correct name, date of birth, address and any other information that is required of you. Failure to provide your correct name will result in you having to remain at the police station, until your identity can be established.

Having given all of your correct details you will be thoroughly searched (see procedure for TVs/TSs below) and all monies and personal effects will be removed from you and booked into property. A breach of the peace is a straightforward process requiring no interview. The officer will just complete the relevant forms. Remember that you are entitled to a solicitor, should you feel the need for one. If you don't know one yourself you can ask to speak to the duty solicitor, free of charge.

Breach of the peace is one of the few offences that has no bail, because it is believed by the arresting officer that a breach of the peace would reoccur if you were allowed to return to the situation. This means that you will be detained overnight and then be taken before a court in the morning; the crunch being that you would be dressed as you were arrested. Depending on your ability to pay, you would either be fined or given a spell in prison.

This scenario is not intended to scare you witless and is certainly not intended to put you off going out cross-dressed. It is just to make you aware of what could, in the worst possible case, happen. Most police do not enjoy arresting people for this offence, especially if the matter can be resolved in another way. Just remember that if you are daft, it could happen to you.

Using a credit card whilst out dressed can also give rise to police involvement. You may have gone to a lot of trouble to obtain a credit card in your *femme* name, probably by deception, even though the card is registered to your own account. Think about it; the shopkeeper will see a man dressed as a woman trying to use a credit card with a woman's name on it. The police will be called, and they will have to investigate who you really are.

One of the most common dealings that transvestites have with the police is probably whilst driving a car. It's very easy for everyone to help themselves and avoid being stopped in the first place by making sure that their vehicle is 100% mechanically and electrically road-worthy. If your car appears normal and doesn't arouse the suspicions of the police in any other way, then there is no reason for them to stop you. The golden rule is 'don't attract attention' and they will pick on someone else.

Let's say now that you are stopped whilst driving. It is an offence not to give your real name, address and date of birth. You will also have to say who the registered keeper or owner of the vehicle is. Now, don't try to be clever here. By the time you are stopped, the police will probably know who the registered owner is, having already conducted a routine computer check over the radio. So don't, whatever you do, try giving a false name and address. Section 25 of the Police and Criminal Evidence Act allows him to arrest you and take you to the police station until he can verify who you are. If the car is a company car, say so. Tell the officer which company it is so as they needn't phone them or inform on you. All they are trying to do is establish that the car is being driven by the person it's supposed to be driven by.

One final piece of advice is never use a ladies' public convenience unless you are a card-carrying male-to-female transsexual. To do so would put yourself at real risk of being arrested. Try to use the unisex disabled facilities instead.

The following edited text is taken from PACE (Police Code Of Guidelines) with additional text used for clarification:

Definitions

Transvestite A person who dresses in clothes of the opposite sex.

Transsexual A person who has the physical characteristics of one sex, but with certain characteristics of the other sex. Surgery may have taken place and a person may exhibit features of one or both sexes. Potentially, there is a wide variation in the stage of change from one sex to another.

Officers who deal with transsexuals and transvestites in the course of their duties must ensure that they are treated with the same level of respect and dignity as any other member of the public. If there is any doubt as to a person's gender they should be asked whether they are a transsexual or a transvestite. If the person states that they are a transvestite, they should be treated as the gender which is registered at the time of birth. This must be done in a sensitive manner so as not to offend the dignity of the individual concerned. If the person states that they are transsexual, they should be asked what their preferred gender is for the purpose of police procedures. They should then be asked to sign the custody record or other document. For example, where a stop-search in the street takes place, and the gender of the person being searched is in doubt, then a pocket notebook entry should be made indicating their preference and they should be asked to sign it.

If the person is unwilling to make such an election, the officer should try to determine the *predominant* lifestyle of the person. For example, if they appear to live predominantly as a woman then they should be treated as such. If there is still any doubt, the officer will have to resort to dealing with the person according to the gender of which they were born.

Transsexuals, transvestites and persons of doubtful gender must always be accommodated in a cell or detention room on their own.

Once a decision has been made about what gender a transsexual, or, a person of doubtful gender is to be treated as, every officer having further contact with that person should be advised of the gender that that person is to be dealt with as. This is important so as to maintain the dignity of the individual and the officer(s) concerned.

Searching should be conducted in accordance with PACE. The code states that 'any search involving the removal of more than an outer coat, jacket, gloves, headgear or footwear may only be made by an officer of the same sex as the person searched, and may not be made in the presence of anyone of the opposite sex unless the person specifically requests it.'

With this in mind, a *technical* breach of the codes could occur in that an officer of the opposite sex could be present, *if* the person being searched, is searched as their preferred sex, and not as the sex shown on their birth certificate. If the search can be shown to have taken into account the sensitivity of the subject '*in order to reduce the embarrassment of those present*', it is believed that such a breach of codes of practice can be upheld or justified. This should only relate to transsexuals, and custody officers should fully detail any such action and record the consent of the person being searched as to the preferred sex of the searching officer.

It should not be forgotten that 'in law', the sex of a person is that which was registered at the time of birth, a fact that remains unchanged regardless of any subsequent medical treatment or surgery. However, a rigid adherence to this principle has been found to be too inflexible and led to unnecessary confrontations. Experience in other forces has shown that where transsexuals are treated according to their preferred sex, they are more likely to be cooperative during their dealings with the police – for example, in being interviewed or as a witness to a crime.

National Organisations

The Beaumont Society

27 Old Gloucester Street
London
WC1N 3XX
(Janett Scott – President)
                Telephone   01582 732 936

Note: The address above is a post-office for the collection of mail – so please, no personal callers.

The Beaumont Society is an organisation run for, and by, people who like to wear the clothes of the opposite gender and people who may be transsexual. It is a society dedicated to the special needs of those who feel the desire, or compulsion to express a feminine side to their personality by dressing, or living as 'women'.

The society was founded in 1996. The name Beaumont was taken from the Chevalier D'Eon Beaumont, a celebrated French transvestite of the 18th century.

The Beaumont Society is a national organisation, run on a regional basis. There are members throughout the country, with local groups in most areas. The Society also has many overseas members. The Beaumont Society is run voluntarily, by members who have been elected as 'officers' of the society. Besides national officers there are regional organisers with assistant and area organisers who are responsible for looking after the membership at the local level. An executive committee of the national officers and the elected organisers meet several times a year to deal with the organisations business at the local level.

Some cross-dressers have feelings of guilt, shame and self-disgust and a fear of what they feel to be an inexplicable desire to cross-dress. Usually, membership of the Society will help overcome these feelings by providing mutual support and so help to develop self-acceptance, peace of mind and understanding. The knowledge that there are so many others who have similar feelings is often a great comfort in itself. Considerable help with practical matters concerned with cross-dressing can be gained through being able to meet and talk to others, or just by reading the Society's magazines.

The Society may also be of help in gaining acceptance by partners, relatives and friends. For the more self-assured, the Society offers a social scene where they can meet others, make friends and more fully enjoy their cross-dressing. Some of the meetings are open to non-members.

Once your membership has been accepted you will become a provisional member. This places a few minor restrictions on the facilities you can use, but you can become a full member without further charge by meeting an officer of the Society who will sponsor you. This is simply a formality to make sure the Society is right for you, and that you are right for the Society. It also acts as a safeguard to help protect the rest of the membership and to introduce you to at least one other Society member.

In practice, sponsorship is quite informal. It is a meeting which will give you the opportunity of asking further questions about the Society and, if you wish, of discussing your own cross-dressing. Sometimes this may be the first time the new member has actually spoken face to face with another cross-dresser. However, there is no pressure to become sponsored. If the prospect worries you there is no need to actually meet anyone to become, or remain, a member of the society. Sponsorship can take place at any time whilst you are a provisional member. It is not a necessity to be 'dressed' for a sponsorship meeting.

The Society is very much aware that most cross-dressers are very concerned that their personal details should not become known to others. The Society operates a strict code of confidentiality and guarantees that all information given on your application form, or to any Society officer, will only be seen by those officers responsible for considering and administering your membership. No personal information is passed to other members and the Society never supplies names and addresses to anyone inside or outside the Society without the member's express permission. It is not even necessary to give your real address on your application form, so long as you provide some means for the Society to communicate with you by post (e.g. an accommodation address or post-officce box number). Within the Society you will be identified by your membership number and if you choose one, your 'femme name'. There is no pressure for you to adopt a special name but most members prefer to use one as part of the feminine image they wish to project.

The Beaumont Magazine and *The Beaumont Bulletin*, are the Society's own magazines. They are published quarterly and come free with the membership fee. *The Beaumont Bulletin* contains Society business and members' adverts and is only available to members. *The Beaumont Magazine* is more general in content with features, colour photo pages, readers' letters, and many articles on social events and helpful tips. It provides a lifeline to those members who for one reason or another are unable to participate in many of the social activities. For those who do, the magazine also provides news and information on social activities of interest to members.

The Beaumont Trust

BM Charity
London
WC1N 3XX

Helpline   07000 287 878 (Tuesday & Thursday evenings 19.00–23.00)
          Registered Charity No: 297527

All communications will be strictly confidential and it would be greatly appreciated if enquirers enclose a stamped addressed envelope.

The Beaumont Trust is a registered charity that was established in 1975 and is funded voluntarily by donations. Its aim is to assist those who are in any way troubled by gender dysphoria, or who are involved in such peoples' care and provides referrals to appropriate organisations, professional counsellors and self-help groups. Its aims are to advance public education about all aspects of gender dysphoria related to transvestism or transsexualism and to protect the good mental and physical health of such individuals. It also aims to support the friends and families of transvestites and transsexuals. It fosters research into both psychological and social aspects of transvestism and transsexualism and can provide speakers to address other organisations. It produces literature, arranges with workshops, develops befriending facilities and assists with conferences.

The Beaumont Trust includes professionals and members of other relevant organisations as trustees and officers.

Women Of The Beaumont Society (WOBS)

BM WOBS
London
WC1N 3XX

Helpline 01223 441 246 or 01684 578 281 or 01389 380 389

WOBS is a group run by and for wives and partners, providing support and helping to support those whose husband's or partner's behaviour is difficult to understand. The above numbers are for wives and partners, where you can call to speak to another woman.

Gendys Network

BM Gendys
London
WC1N 3XX

The enclosure of an SAE would be appreciated.

Gendys is a network for all those who have encountered gender identity problems personally: transsexuals, transgendered people and gender dysphoric people of either sex and for those that provide care, both professional and lay. Members can be entirely open with other members or remain anonymous. This is a matter of personal choice. All personal information is entirely confidential and members are expected to respect this. Subscriptions support the network and help provide the various services. The network hopes to help transsexuals and intersexed people see themselves not as victims, but as survivors of their gender identity difficulties.

The next Gendys Biannual Conference is at Manchester University in 2000.

The Gender Trust

BM Gentrust
London
WC1N 3XX

Helpline 07000 790 347 (before 22.00)

This is a registered charity for transsexuals and transgenderists. It publishes a quarterly newsletter on many issues affecting transsexuals. The Gender Trust also produces a handbook giving full details of all aspects of transsexualism and is given free to members when they first join. It explains about the young transsexual and their parents, the operation (in more detail than in the previous text), Female to male transsexuals, discovery and denial and many other topics. Members are from all over the world and the patrons include: Professor John Money, Professor Richard Green, Professor Louis Gooren, Professor Steven Hirsch and Doctor D. Montgomery.

Mermaids

The Mermaids Support Group
BM Mermaids
London
WC1N 3XX

Helpline   07071 225 895 (12.00 – 21.00)

The enclosure of an SAE would be appreciated.

Calls are charged at 27.23p per minute up to 18.00/18.72p after 18.00/8.93p at weekends. Registered Charity No: 1073991 (Make donations payable to Mermaids)

Mermaids is a support group formed by a group of parents, each bringing a child to a Gender Identity Development Clinic (GIC) and brought together as a result of their children's long standing gender identity issues. They have been able to support each other and their children through the difficulties and trauma that gender issues commonly bring to families. They have identified a need to form a support group to aid other families' children and teenagers in similar situations.

Mermaids recognises that awareness of gender identity issues at an early age should be promoted, and help provided to families or individuals in order to alleviate any problems that might arise. It is often helpful to talk to others who have gone through, or are going through similar problems to one's own. Contact with others, whether it is by telephone, letter or in person, can alleviate the feelings of loneliness and alienation that can arise. Discovering that one is not alone can bring strength and understanding to very difficult situations.

The Northern Concord

PO Box 258
Manchester
M60 1LN

The Northern Concord is a completely voluntary organisation with no commercial ties whatsoever and is the largest social and self-help group in the North of England for cross-dressers, transvestites, transsexuals, their wives or partners. The group is based in Manchester and meets every Wednesday night, 52 weeks a year, and has done successfully for over 13 years. For the first 10 years they used to meet in the upstairs bistro at The Rembrandt Hotel; for one year, in the basement club rooms at The Blooms Hotel, and now the Wednesday night meeting is at The Hollywood Showbar on Bloom Street, Manchester (see Pubs and Clubs listings). The Northern Concord night is open exclusively to members from 19.30 to 23.00 each Wednesday. After 23.00 the doors will be open to the public until 02.00 and Concord members are welcome to stay if they wish.

For first-time visitors, the most common question asked is what should they wear when they come to visit. The choice is entirely yours, the only given is that they expect smart-casual male or female attire. If you are confident enough to come dressed *en femme* that's fine, or you can bring your clothes and make up and get ready at the club. Alternatively if you are not sure and want to come along and just have a look, then come dressed as your 'normal' self. It is not a problem and you will still be welcomed. For those that do require a changing facility, the doors will be open at 18.30 and a changing area is available to change on arrival and departure.

A charge of £2 for members and £3 for non-members is set to help cover the costs.

The Northern Concord was conceived and created in 1986 out of the ashes of the original TV/TS group, which had been running since 1965 in one form or another. The aims were, and still are, to be a self-help and social group for cross-dressers and people who consider themselves to be transsexuals. They are listed with every major help organisation around the region i.e. Samaritans, Relate, MIND, Citizens Advice, etc. National Concord set out to provide an infrastructure in which people would be able to dress in safety and enjoy themselves. They also run many other social events and organise events that benefit their members, make-up demonstrations, fashion nights, jewellery nights, etc. Information on how and where to obtain clothes, services and accessories at the right price from TV-friendly suppliers can also be gained.

Wives and girlfriends are more than welcome, and indeed they have had mothers, aunts, daughters, sons and even fathers attend some of their events. To encourage family members there is no charge for them to enter the club.

Their magazine *Cross Talk* might give you a flavour of their approach to cross-dressing, for it is their philosophy that you need to be able to laugh at yourself and not take your little idiosyncrasy too seriously. *Cross Talk* costs £3.50 in the UK, £5 in Europe and £5.50 in the USA. If you become a member of National Concord, which costs £15 per annum in the United Kingdom, £20 for Europe and £25 for the USA, the magazines will be sent as part of your membership package. Back issues of the magazine are available to anyone with an interest and can be obtained by sending a cheque or postal order, made payable to The National Concord. All other letters of interest are to be sent to the address above (SAE appreciated for reply).

Press For Change
BM Network
London
WC1N 3XX

A campaigning organisation looking for equal rights for transsexuals.

Regional Organisations

LONDON

F to M Network
BM Network
London
WC1N 3XX

The Female to Male Network is an organisation for female to male transsexuals. People who are genetically female have the same problems as male to female transsexuals. Their surgery is much more painful and less satisfactory.

ENGLAND

Renaissance 2
Blackpool   Telephone 01253 400 160
               E-mail Lynda@renaissance2.demon.co.uk

Social and support group meeting on the second and fourth Tuesday of the month. Lynda is also proprietor of the fabulous Renaissance Guest House in Blackpool (see 'Accommodation Listings'). Phone the number above for further information.

TS/TG Support
Blackpool & North-West

Helpline 01253 623 044

A new support group for TSs in the Blackpool and North-West areas. Meetings are held on the third Thursday of every month in the home of the organiser, close to Blackpool's town centre.

Brighton TV Social Group
Brighton

Helpline 0127 332 8968 (24 hours)

A TV/TS social group holding weekly meetings every Friday. Phone the above number for further information.

TV/TS Helpline
Cambridge   Telephone 01223 861 167

This helpline offers support and advice in all areas south of Kings Lynn. The helpline is staffed daily from 15.00.

TV/TS Helpline
Coventry   Telephone   0120 367 5535

Helpline for TVs/TSs, their partners and friends.

Devon TV/TS Group
Devon   Telephone   0175 260 6965 (Donna)/0175 266 7859 (Michelle)

Contact either of the above numbers for details of the support group.

Self-Help Essex
Essex   Telephone   0125 586 1432 (18.00 – 21.00)

A helpline run by transsexuals for transsexuals and cross-dressers.

Transessex
Essex

Helpline   01268 583 761 (Thursday 19.00 – 22.30)

Transessex is a support group based in Essex. Phone the above number for further information.

Liverbirds
(Currently meeting at)
36 Bolton Road
Liverpool
L3 5SX

Helpline   0151 709 4745 (Friday 19.00 – 22.00)

The Liverpool TV/TS group, established for many years, meet at various venues throughout the city. Meetings are every Friday night from 19.00 through to 23.00. Excellent changing facilities, tea, coffee, soft drinks and light refreshments available. If you are attending for the first time, ask for Allison or Lynn and they will make you feel welcome.

TV/TS Helpline
Manchester   Telephone   0161 274 3704/5 (Wednesday 19.00 – 22.00)

This number can also give details of the Manchester TS group.

Chameleon Group
Nottingham   Telephone   0115 928 9479

A support group that meets every Thursday from 20.00 to 23.00. Phone for venue location and further details.

Oxford TV/TS Support
Oxford   Telephone   0179 342 0262 (Fridays 19.00 – 23.00 only)

Meeting on the first Saturday of each month.

Swindon TV Forum
Swindon

Helpline   0179 342 0262 (Friday 19.00 – 23.00 only)

The forum holds events on the second Saturday of each month. Phone the number above (within the hours stated) for further information.

Transgender Support Group
Torquay
The Torbay Sexual Health Centre
Bradahn Hill Road West
Torquay   Telephone   0180 320 1763

St Michael's TV/TS Support Group
West Midlands

Helpline   0121 559 3181 any Tuesday – Thursday: 19.00 – 22.00

Helpline and support.

Michelle Wilson
PO Box 171
Woking
Surrey
GU22   Telephone/Fax   0148 377 3428

Michelle Wilson is a transsexual lawyer who will be ready to listen and help with your problem if she can. It is advisable to write (with SAE) first, unless it is an emergency.

SCOTLAND

Edinburgh TV/TS Group
c/o Outright
58A Broughton Street
Edinburgh
EH1 3SA   Telephone   0131 556 4049

Write with an SAE or phone as per the details above. Meetings are held on the last Saturday of the month.

Crosslynx Glasgow
SLGS
PO Box 38
Glasgow
G2 2QF   Telephone 0141 332 3333 (Monday: 19.30 – 21.30)

Write with an SAE for details. West of Scotland TV/TS group which meets the
second Wednesday of every month. Phone the above number for further details.

Grampian Gender Group (3G)
Grampian

Helpline 01224 633 108 (Monday – Tuesday: 18.00 – 21.00)

W A L E S

TransWales

Helpline 0122 279 9441

A relatively new helpline for TVs/TSs in Wales.

TV/TS/CD Resource Directory

One of the problems with being transgendered is how to buy clothes, make-up, wigs etc., without being ripped off. Many transgenderists are nervous in the early days and will probably spend more than is necessary on basic essentials.

In the early days most transgendered people don't go into straight shops. They use mail order. Beware! Not everybody who claims to be working in the interests of the transgendered is doing so. There are some who will try and make as much profit as they can knowing that people will not have the confidence to shop at non-transgender shops. This is why you can pay £10.00 for a pair of knickers from a transgender store when they would only cost £1.00 from a straight store. You may also have the disadvantage that certain items may not be returned. For example, if you purchase a wig or any item that goes around the groin (knickers, a cache sexe), then they may not be returned if they have been worn. If you use a general mail order catalogue from one of the well-known companies you have a better chance of returning goods. Many now include a crotch cover so that you can even try on swimming costumes and bikinis, and as long as the cover is not removed they may be returned.

Shoes are another problem by mail order. Most catalogues have shoes up to a size 8 (UK) at best. A few of the smaller companies may go up to size 9 or 10 but the styles are limited. Companies that specifically aim at the transgender community may go up to size 12 but, in general, the shoes are not designed for everyday wear and they may be a little narrow for the average male foot. Many transgender shoe companies don't supply flat shoes and heels are not practical for everyday wear. When shoes are available by mail order they are usually priced more expensively than going into a local shop, where you may get bargains in the sales.

Make-up by mail order is always difficult. What may look good on a model may not look good on you. You need to experiment with colours and types that are suitable for your skin colour and texture. You need to ensure that your make up co-ordinates with your clothes, hair colour skin colour and eye colour. There are mail order companies that do let you have free samples. These should be taken advantage of as this gives you the opportunity to experiment to find the right colour for you.

Avoid like the plague any company that offers any type of hormone by mail. Some companies may offer hormone creams. Don't touch them. They would only be available on prescription. The UK government regulates oestrogen and testosterone hormones very strongly. Also, it is extremely unwise to buy hormones from a country where they are not regulated. Without exaggeration; there is a great risk that you can die. Hormones require proper monitoring by a GP, a psychiatrist or an endocrinologist. Regardless of any pain, physical or psychological, the risks from hormones are extremely serious. You are at risk from liver damage, thrombosis, kidney damage, heart damage, strokes etc., Some of you who are not TS will become sterile or impotent (not usually a problem with TSs). You will usually be quite safe if you are monitored, but black market and mail order hormones (including herbal ones) are dangerous.

People do reach the time when they like to go shopping themselves and leave behind the mail order companies. Before they go 'dressed' they go in all male mode. To do this you will have to prepare yourself, especially if you are nervous. You may think that the shop assistant will think you weird for buying women's clothing but this is not always the case. Many shop assistants are on commission and will just want to make a sale. However, there are 'excuses' that can be used if still nervous: 'I'm buying for my wife/girlfriend/sister/mother' is a common one used, but don't be too quick to use the excuse. It often looks rehearsed if you tell the assistant in advance. It is unlikely that you'll even be asked but it's there in reserve if you feel you need it. Another excuse of a similar nature is to carry a shopping list as if you were buying for a relative who is ill. It will help if you have details written down of what you want including size.

As you get more confident, you can, if you like, tell the shop assistant that you are buying for yourself. In many towns and cities you may find the staff very helpful. Where single changing rooms are available they will sometimes let you try on the items that you wish to buy. This is the best option as assistants will usually advise you on whether an item is suitable for you. Too many people buy clothes that are too old or too young for them and really stand out when they change to their *femme* selves. It is often better for a person brought up as male, who initially has no idea of fashion for their age, to seek the advice of a genetic female when shopping for many items. By being out in the open, items such as wigs and shoes can be tried for appearance and underwear and outerwear can be browsed to find suitable items for oneself rather than selecting hurriedly.

In the UK, many stores are seen as transgender-friendly for normal shopping. Marks and Spencer's are known to train their staff on how to deal with transsexual and transvestite customers with sensitivity and understanding. All customers, whether male or female are treated equally. Shoe City is a large UK chain of shoe stores. Many of their ladies fashions go up to a UK size $10^{1}/_{2}$. These stores are very popular with the transgendered, whose shoe sizes are above size 8. Crispins is a less well-known chain of shoe shops. They do women's shoes up to size 12. They sell more fashionable ranges than Shoe City. They can be rather pricey but their shoes are manmade using leather, rather than being machine-made. They also have a mail order service.

It is my intention for the next edition of *The Ultimate Gay Guide* that a considerable expansion on the subject of Transgenderism be included. Everyone associated with this guide feels it is an important subject that needs further coverage. In particular, personal case histories that could help someone in the same situation as yourself and personal recommendations of products and organisations that you would like passed on to others.

The following list of mail order companies is provided to help you with your own research. The listing of a company does not in any way mean that it is endorsed and no responsibility can be accepted from any resultant complaint. As with all forms of purchase, it is better to get a few prices together before finally deciding. Before sending money off for a catalogue or article, an initial letter of enquiry is recommended to establish the company is still in operation.

LONDON

Cover Girl Shoes
44 Cross Street
London
N1

Everything you may need to get started, although prices may be a little expensive.

Crispins
28–30 Chiltern Street
London
W1M 1PF

This is a chain of shoe shops with a mail order service. Although expensive, they are extremely well made.

Leatherworks Limited

77–79 Southgate Road
London
N1 3JS   Telephone 0171 359 9778

Manufacturer of leather boots and shoes. Catalogue £6.

Magic Shoe

Unit 6
88 Mile End Road
London
E1 4UN

Manufacturers of boots and shoes in wild designs.

Small and Tall Shoe Shop

71 York Street
London
W1

Shoe shop which also has a mail order service.

ENGLAND

Cocoon

182 High Street
Digbeth
Birmingham
B12 0LD   Telephone 0121 772 2882

Supplying a special range of TV wear. All the clothes featured in their catalogue can be made up using their special TV size chart.

Trans Wigs

PO Box 2361
Bournemouth
BH1 1XU   Telephone 0120 274 7177

Good range of wigs for cross-dressers. Catalogue £4 (refundable against first order).

Button, Boot and Spatterdash

Freepost
(UK Only)
Brigg
Humberside
DN20 9BR   Telephone 0165 265 0651

A fabulous catalogue will introduce their wide range of corsets made to original patterns.

Altered Image

PO Box 3050
Colchester
CO1 2QQ   Telephone 0120 623 0708

Write or phone for a comprehensive 28 page full-colour catalogue designed by transsexuals for transsexuals. You can see every item that you require in this book.

Long Tall Sally

Unit B
Pioneers Industrial Park
Beddington Farm Road
Croydon
Surrey
CR0 4XB

This chain of shops and mail order businesses provide clothes for the taller woman; size 12–20 (UK). No more short-sleeve worries.

Fantasy Girl

PO Box 313
Folkestone
Kent
CT20 1DG

This mail order company offers a comprehensive range of products for cross-dressers.

Beesley Hair and Wig Fashions

100 High Street
Sandhurst
Guildford
GU17 8EE

Over 350 wigs in stock.

Westwood Bound

Freepost (UK only)
Launceston
Cornwall   Telephone 0156 677 7797

Mail order for shoes, lingerie, wigs, fetish, fashion and accessories.

Hay Way Shoes

Unit 1
Abbey Court
Corporation Road
Leicester   Telephone 0116 266 3444

Shoes and boots up to a size 13 (UK). Free catalogue too.

Hidebound
Unit R1A
Rocket Trade Centre
Liverpool
L15 3NZ   Telephone 0151 252 2272

Leather, rubber and PVC clothing.

Wiggins
119 Penny Lane
Liverpool
L18 1DF   Telephone 0151 733 5826

Wig shop with a mail order service.

Midnight Lady
20–24 Cardigan Street
Luton
Bedfordshire
LU1 1RR   Telephone 0158 239 1854

Midnight Lady supplies unusual lingerie, leather clothing, shoes and boots.

Transformations
413 Bury Old Road
Manchester   Telephone 0161 773 2572

Shop with a large selection of TV/TS items. Comprehensive mail order service available. Also operates 'Changeaways': a complete makeover session for a day (phone for details).

Vollers
112 Kingston Road
Portsmouth   Telephone 0171 566 0740

Classic corsetry in many styles. Catalogue £10.

Suzi Mail Order
41 Canarvon Road
Southend On Sea
Essex
SS2 6LR

Wigs at reasonable prices. Catalogue £2.

Lady Elizabeth Shoes
PO Box 2
Ellesmere Port
South Wirral
Merseyside
L65 3EA

Lady Elizabeth specialises in high-heeled boots and shoes in leather and PVC.

Alter Ego

Showgrade Ltd
PO Box 10
Bramhall
Stockport
SK7 2QF

The Alter Ego range caters for the taller, larger cross-dresser who loves exotic materials and designs. They understand the need for figure controlling devices and sizes that suit larger frames. Catalogue £2.

Incognito

10 Ashfield Road
Davenport
Stockport
SK3 8UJ   Telephone 0161 483 3194

High fashion wigs available at reasonable prices.

Sarah Heart Limited

PO Box 488
Cheadle
Stoke-on-Trent
ST10 2QJ

Provides lingerie and the following: baby wear, school girl knickers, french maid outfits, Directoire knickers, plastic pants, shoes and wigs. Catalogue £4.

Victoria Regine

PO Box 192
Wolverhampton
WV4 5TS

Sells breast forms, boots and shoes.

Swingtime Collection

14 Oval Way
Ferring
Worthing
Sussex   Telephone 0190 324 3392

Fifties fashion clothes and the necessary underwear. Catalogue free with A4 SAE (UK only).

SCOTLAND

Catherine Robertson

PO Box 86
Falkirk
Scotland
FK1 5YG

Manufacturer of 'masquerade' foundation garments. These are fully padded, curve-forming panty girdles specifically designed for the cross-dresser.

WALES

Wilbru Corsetry

PO Box 12
Lampeter
Dyfed
South Wales
SA48 7XU

Mail order corsetry specialists.

the ultimate guide to
Pubs and Clubs

Introduction

Over the past ten years or so, the gay club and pub scene has gone through some remarkable changes. Gone are the locked doors with the sliding shutter down some dubious side street far away from the town centre, and in come some of the trendiest bars in the country that make the straight scene green with envy. So much so that it has become the victim of its own success.

Now the straights are clamouring to be seen in the trendy gay pubs and clubs around the country, giving them the excuse that if they are seen in a gay venue they are there because it is trendy, not because they are looking for a bit of how's your father!

The downside to all of this 'integration' is the fact that trying to pick someone up in a bar is a teensy bit more difficult if you are not sure whether your 'dreamboat' is straight or gay. The fact that a 'straight' person is in a gay bar may give rise to some doubts, but, there are some 100% heteros who prefer going to gay bars because they know that they are able to enjoy themselves more than going to an attitude filled straight bar. Approaching these people have never been a problem, they know the score that they may be chatted up and they will inform you right away that they are not gay.

Attitudes towards gays are changing, which can only be a good thing. Not more than a generation ago there was so much stigma about being gay that only a course of electrotherapy and a good seeing to by the right woman (or man) could ever put you on the straight and narrow. But now? Hey, It's the nineties. Being gay is as acceptable as the colour of your skin. Of course the bigots in our society have yet to discover all of this, but, I'm sure they are too busy with their white pointy hats and burning crosses to take the time to look around them and see that times are changing.

The listings that follow offer the most complete guide ever published. They are designed to show you instantly what to expect prior to going into the venue itself. For example, if you are just planning to go out for a quiet drink then you do not want to go to a place where there is loud dance music being pumped out. Alternatively, if you are after some place that's cruisy and dark then you will certainly not want to go to a 'traditional' establishment.

Some listings guides may include bars that are described as 'gay friendly' and some of these have been included here if they have shown that being 'gay friendly' means that they cater in some way to and for the gay community. The majority have not been included when the gay friendly tag has been added in order to get some extra revenue in the till. However, the majority of the subsequent listings are of gay majority venues and as explained in the introduction some landlords have given more than enough information for you to decide which venue to patronise and the rest have given only the briefest details. It seemed to me that the busier and more popular the venue the more forthcoming the information was. The establishments with lack of entertainment and facilities seemed to be reluctant to disclose more than was absolutely necessary.

During 1998–99 every gay and 'gay friendly' venue in the United Kingdom was contacted twice by letter and then with a follow up phone call to impart details of their establishment. You may know of a venue which 'should' have been included but by glancing through the listings notice that it hasn't. The reason for this may be that a) The proprietor did not, for some reason known only to himself, want his venue to be listed (perhaps they have enough customers and have no need for any more) b) could not be bothered to respond to any request for information or c) the venue has only recently opened or received a change of ownership and current details were not available. The lack of a listing for any known venue should not be construed as 'unsuitable'. It is my intention for the next edition to have all gay venues visited and reviewed with additional comments (both negative and positive) provided by yourselves to be included in order to generate a more detailed picture of the establishment. Venue proprietors who receive negative remarks will of course have the opportunity to respond to criticism and these too will be noted.

If you have any feedback or comments that you feel would be beneficial for the next edition and/or subsequent reprints then please use the contact addresses in the introduction section at the beginning of the guide

Finally, If you have never been to a gay venue before and are wary about going in alone, contact your nearest switchboard to find out the details regarding 'Icebreakers' for men, 'Stepping Stones' for women or a youth group for the over 18s. This will give you an ideal opportunity to experience the gay scene with someone who is in exactly the same situation as yourself. Age has never been an issue in gay establishments whereby young and old(er) mix extremely well in all venues and if you do think of yourself as being 'past that sort of thing' then think again – you are missing out on an awful lot and now is the best time to start a new social life.

Venue Proprietors Note:

If your venue has not been included, or indeed lacks relevant information then please contact me in order that any amendments can be made for subsequent reprints and editions.

British Pub and Club Listings

79 CXR

79 Charing Cross Road
London
WC2H 0NE   Telephone 0171 734 0769

Nearest train station Charing Cross
Nearest tube Leicester Square
Car parking Don't even try
A–Z ref. P61/7H
Nearest landmark Leicester Square Tube Station

Membership details None required
Opening hours   Monday–Thursday: 13.00–02.00
                       Friday–Saturday: 13.00–03.00
                       Sunday: 13.00–22.30
Admission charges   Admission charges apply after 22.30
Food available No
Regular entertainment No scheduled entertainment although there is a resident
DJ from Thursday to Saturday.

This extremely busy bar is spaced out over two floors and is jam-packed most
nights with some of the best looking guys in London. The lighting is on its lowest
setting so everyone looks good! A fun party atmosphere, through to the early
hours and one of the places to be after the local pubs close. Both floors can be
pretty cruisy. The first floor balcony enables you to select your 'victim' before
descending to make your move. During the day there are tables and chairs on the
street which give you a good opportunity to just sit, relax and watch the world
go by. Very nice.

MON-THU 1pm - 2am   SUNDAYS ALL DAY
FRI & SAT 1pm - 3am   1.00pm TO 10.30pm

SOHO'S FRIENDLIEST, BEST VALUE LATE BAR

PINTS OF STELLA ★ BACARDI BREEZERS
BOTTLE HOLSTEN PILS
HOUSE DOUBLE & MIX*

HAPPY HOURS FROM 8pm - 10pm
EVERY NIGHT & ALL DAY SUNDAYS   *CURRENT SELECTION - SUBJECT TO CHANGE

79 CHARING CROSS ROAD WC2

Admiral Duncan

54 Old Compton Street
Soho
London
W1V   Telephone 0171 437 5300

Nearest train station Charing Cross
Nearest tube Piccadilly/Leicester Square/Tottenham Court Road
Car parking NCP close by
A–Z ref. P61/7H
Nearest landmark McDonalds on Dean Street

Membership details None required
Opening hours   Monday–Saturday: 11.00–23.00
                       Sunday: 12.00–22.30
Admission charges None
Food available Tea and coffee available
Regular entertainment There is no scheduled entertainment

The Admiral Duncan has been a mixed gay, homely venue in the heart of the gay village for over two years. A busy place at weekends, offering great value for money. Friendly staff, good atmosphere, brilliant jukebox and an excellent range of traditional beers (which are sometimes hard to obtain in gay establishments around Soho). The venue itself consists of one open-plan room opening onto the street in the summer. The Admiral welcomes all gay and straight walks of life with TVs/CDs more than welcome.
In memory of those that died in the bombing of The Admiral Duncan on Friday 30th April 1999 – may they rest in peace.

The Artful Dodger

139 Southgate Road
Islington
London
N1   Telephone 0171 226 0841

Nearest train station Essex Road
Nearest tube Angel (A good ten minute walk away)
Car parking Street parking
A–Z ref. P62/1D
Nearest landmark Balls Pond Road (Southgate Road runs off)

Membership details Available at £5 per year, which entitles the holder to reduced door entry (you can complete a form at the door)
Opening hours   Monday–Wednesday: 18.00–24.00
                       Thursday: 18.00–01.00
                       Friday–Saturday: 18.00–02.00
                       Sunday: 13.00–24.00
Admission charges   Monday–Tuesday: Free
                       Wednesday–Thursday: £2 after 22.00
                       Friday: £3 guests/£2 members
                       Saturday: £4 guests/£3 members
                       Sunday: £3 (includes clothes check) from 15.00
Food available Traditional Sunday lunch (14.00–18.00)
Regular entertainment Monday: Cheap cruise night

Tuesday: Another cheap cruise night
Wednesday: Yet another cheap cruise night
Thursday: 'Afrika Jumbo' (men of colour and admirers)
Friday: Cruisy party night/stripper/DJ
Alternate Saturday: DJ Lord Kaos (hard dance)/stripper
Alternate Saturday: 'Stuff: Version 2.0' (big beat, left field, indie, dance, old skool hip-hop)
Sunday: 'Undies On Sundays' (dress code of underwear and footwear–phone for further details)

One of the nicest things about this place is that you can wear what you like and no-one will give a toss, be it feathers, leathers, rubber, ballgowns or uniforms. It is an extremely busy traditional men-only cruise bar, although women are welcome in the front bar only (well that's where the pool table is). The age range is like everywhere else: mixed, although the predominant age is somewhere between the twenties and thirties. The venue is laid out well over three floors. The ground floor has a main bar area with seating and a pool table and a back bar with camouflage nets and a dance floor; all dark and cruisy. Upstairs is the main cruise bar (well-known to all). Downstairs in the cellar is a new facility consisting of a gym, sauna and shower block (you will have to phone for further details regarding membership and prices for these facilities).

Quality has a name ...

LONDON MEN

TOP CLASS GUYS

Carefully screened and tested to ensure professional services

London . Paris . New York

Open 7 Days A Week   12noon till late

Phone us for an accurate and honest description
HOME/HOTEL VISITS WELCOME

☎
0207 553 2112
FAX: 0208 519 9440
Website with portfolio: http://www.londonmen.com

Limited vacancies for quality guys   Full discretion assured
Call us for an interview   Major credit/debit cards accepted

Try the best! Quality has a name

Backstreet
Wentworth Mews
(Off Burdett Road)
London
E3   Telephone 0181 980 8557 (Club hours)/0181 980 7880 (Outside
                club hours)

Nearest train station None
Nearest tube Mile End
Car parking Ample side-street parking/floodlit space for motorbikes outside
door
A–Z ref. P64/4A
Nearest landmark Mile End Tube Station (practically next door)

Membership details None required
Opening hours   Thursday: 22.00–02.30
                       Friday–Saturday: 22.00–03.00
                       Sunday: 21.00–01.00
Admission charges   Thursday: £2.50
                       Friday: £4
                       Saturday: £4
                       Sunday: £2.50
Food available No

Backstreet operates a strict dress code of leather and rubber, and at least one item
of rubber or leather *must* be worn: for example, a jacket, jock strap or hat. Men
totally dressed in rubber will be allowed in for free!

Bar Aquda
13–14 Maiden Lane
Covent Garden
London
WC2   Telephone 0171 557 9891

Nearest train station Charing Cross
Nearest tube Covent Garden
Car parking None
A–Z ref. P61/7J
Nearest landmark The Strand

Membership details None required
Opening hours   Monday–Saturday: 12.00–23.00
                       Sunday: 15.00–22.30
Admission charges None
Food available Full menu available till 19.30 and light bites after
Regular entertainment No scheduled entertainment

Bar Aquda is situated behind The Strand off Bedford Street. This is a stylish and
modern venue catering for a very mixed gay and lesbian crowd. The atmosphere
is relaxed and social as opposed to the typical West End gay pub. A full menu is
available throughout the day and the prices are affordable, which for the location
is quite rare. It's popular with the local office crowds and a relaxing place to
unwind after a hard day's work. In the evening the lighting and music are at just
the right pitch so you do not have to shout inanely at your friends. All in all, Bar

Aquda seems to be the right place to meet up with your friends in a delightful atmosphere and plan for the night ahead.

Barcode

3–4 Archer Street
Soho
London
W1   Telephone 0171 734 3342

Nearest train station Charing Cross
Nearest tube Piccadilly Circus
Car parking Local NCP if you must
A–Z ref. P61/7H
Nearest landmark Windmill Theatre

Membership details None required
Opening hours   Monday–Thursday: 13.00–24.00
                      Friday–Saturday: 11.00–01.00
                      Sunday: 13.00–22.30
Admission charges Nominal £2–3, depending on night
Food available Yes
Regular entertainment No regular scheduled entertainment

A busy young bar over two large floors, filled to capacity with sexy 'blokes'. The downstairs dance area with DJ plays up-to-the-minute dance tracks, whilst the quieter upstairs bar with ample seating gives you a chance to get your hearing back. The atmosphere is clubby and friendly with a predominantly young male crowd, although women will be made more than welcome (well, after all there is a pool table!). The full range of draught beers are available in addition to a huge selection of continental and standard bottles. At the time of going to print there were plans of opening a Barcode in Earls Court at 181 Finborough Road. Unfortunately no venue details were available at the time.

The Black Cap

171 Camden High Street
London
NW1   Telephone 0171 428 2721
                Website http://www.ourworld.compuserve.com/homepages/chris

Nearest train station Camden Road
Nearest tube Camden Town
Car parking Street Parking–limited during the day although easier at night
A–Z ref. P45/7F
Nearest landmark Camden Tube Station (two minute walk)

Membership details None required
Opening hours   Monday–Thursday: 12.00–02.00
                      Friday–Saturday: 12.00–03.00
                      Sunday: 12.00–24.00
Admission charges   Monday: Free before 23.00/£1 after
                      Tuesday–Thursday: Free before 23.00/£2 after
                      Friday–Saturday: Free before 22.00/£3 before 23.00/£4 after

Sunday: Free all day
Food available Full menu in The Shufflewicks Bar from 12.00–18.00
Regular entertainment Monday: 70s and 80s trash disco
Tuesday: Drag cabaret with resident Regina Fong
Wednesday: Cabaret/DJ
Thursday: 90s night (very busy)
Friday: Drag cabaret/DJ/live monthly top PAs
Saturday: DJ (hard house)/strippers
Sunday: Cabaret/DJ

This is one of those venues that is ideal for the male venturing out on to the scene for the first time or rediscovering a social life after a failed miserable relationship. It has *everything*. If you want to cruise then there is a space for that, a space too for cabaret and a space to be social. All combine and create a very, very nice friendly atmosphere.

The Black Horse
168 Mile End Road
London
E1 4AQ   Telephone 0171 790 1684

Nearest train station Bethnal Green (five minutes)
Nearest tube Stepney Green (opposite)
Car parking Ample street parking
A–Z ref. P63/5J

Membership details None required
Opening hours   Monday–Thursday: 20.00–24.00
                       Friday: 20.00–02.00
                       Saturday: 18.00–02.00
                       Sunday: 14.00–24.00
Admission charges Friday: Free before 23.00/£2 after
                       Saturday: Free before 23.00/£2 after
Food available Yes
Regular entertainment Wednesday: Drag cabaret
Thursday: Cabaret
Friday: Cabaret and DJ
Saturday: Cabaret/DJ
Sunday: Strippers and cabaret

Situated opposite The Globe Centre, this is a cosy East End gay bar with an excellent cabaret and entertainment policy. At the time of going to print, The Black Horse was planning on opening a new night for women only. Phone the venue for further details.

The Box
32–34 Monmouth Street
Seven Dials
Covent Garden
London
WC2   Telephone 0171 240 5828   Fax 0171 836 8033

Nearest train station Charing Cross
Nearest tube Covent Garden/Leicester Square
Car parking Not on your Nelly
A–Z ref. P61/6J
Nearest landmark Cambridge Theatre (opposite)

Membership details None required
Opening hours   Monday–Saturday: 11.00–23.00
                     Sunday: 12.00–22.30
                     (Last Friday of the month: bar extension till 01.00)
Admission charges None
Food available Full menu served up until 17.30 every day and 18.30 on Sunday
Regular entertainment No scheduled regular entertainment except for the last
Friday of every month which is 'Fab Friday': DJs, dancers, cabaret and all sorts
of other goings on including the late bar licence.

Another '3-in-1': coffee shop, diner and bar. Cafe society at its best–chic, and oh
so elegant. The menu has been devised by top cookery writer Jane Pettigrew and
changes seasonally. A huge variety of teas and coffees are available along with a
marvellous selection of continental ale on tap (not Red Barrel). Tables and chairs
that spill out on to the pavement, giving you a good opportunity to relax and just
take it all in. That is until the weekend, when the music is turned up and
supported by live house DJs. Attracts a good-looking crowd of cosmopolitan
girls and boys (this bar was voted 'best bar for women' by the *Pink Paper* and in
addition was listed as one of the top 100 London bars in *Time Out*). It is a friendly
and welcoming venue for a no-attitude crowd. The free gay press, literature and
flyers for most of the London clubs can be collected from here in addition to the
discounted tickets (Q- Jumpers) for Heaven, DTPM and Coco Latte. The
downstairs bar is open over the weekend and is available for private hire (phone
for details).

The Brewery Tap

78 Lingham Street
London
SW9   Telephone 0171 738 6683

Nearest train station Wandsworth Road
Nearest tube Stockwell
Car parking Street parking
A–Z ref. P93/2J
Nearest landmark Stockwell Tube Station on Clapham Road

Membership details None required
Opening hours   Monday–Friday: 17.00–23.00
                     Saturday: 16.00–23.00
                     Sunday: 12.00–22.30
Admission charges None
Food available Bar snacks only
Regular entertainment No scheduled entertainment

A local no-attitude gay bar. The kind of bar where you can walk in and say 'usual
please Gloria' and you'd probably get a drink in your own pewter tankard (or
Waterstone crystal tumbler . . .); do you get the picture? A pool table (for the
more than welcome lesbian clientele) and bar stools for the local drunks. During

the fine weather the beer garden opens up with the usual BBQ burnt offerings–until they get the hang of how the 'fire thingy' works and then it's too late, the winter sets in again. Cheap drinks, good company and the sister bar to The Joiners Arms. What more do you want?

Brief Encounter
42 St Martins Lane
Soho
London
WC2 4EJ   Telephone 0171 557 9851

Nearest train station Charing Cross
Nearest tube Leicester Square
Car parking Local NCP (and that's all there is)
A–Z ref. P61/7J
Nearest landmark McDonalds

Membership details None required
Opening hours   Monday–Saturday: 12.00–23.00
                               Sunday: 12.00–22.30
Admission charges   None
Food available No
Regular entertainment No scheduled entertainment

A delightfully tacky (in the nicest sense) cruisy venue. An extremely busy bar and disco, split over two floors. The heaving basement disco plays commercial pop music as well as classic club anthems. The upstairs bar, although a bit quieter is still heaving. It is a predominantly male venue and as the name suggests (however slightly) it is a fun and cruisy venue.

Bromptons
294 Old Brompton Road
Earls Court
London
SW5 9JF   Telephone 0171 370 1344

Nearest train station Kensington (Olympia ten minutes away)
Nearest tube Earls Court (Warwick Road exit)
Car parking Extremely limited
A–Z ref. P75/5J
Nearest landmark Earls Court Exhibition Centre

Membership details None required
Opening hours   Monday–Saturday: 18.00–02.00
                               Sunday: 18.00–24.00 (no entry one hour before closing)
Admission charges   Monday–Thursday: Free before 23.00/£2.50 after
                               Friday–Saturday: Free before 23.00/£3.50 after
                               Sunday: £2 after 22.30
Food available 18.00–21.00
Regular entertainment Monday: DJ
Tuesday: 'Chaps': men only night/stripper
Wednesday: DJ

Thursday: Cabaret (see gay press)
Friday: DJ except every 1st Friday of the month, which is 'Red' (phone for further details)
Saturday: DJ
Sunday: 'Strippers': 18.30/19.30/20.30/21.30

During the week, this large cruisy bar/disco is popular with the leather, cloney crowd. Whilst at all times over the weekend just about anybody and everybody joins in the no-attitude fun. The friendly, quieter upstairs bar is an area where you are most likely to actually hear what the other person is saying to you and if you are in before the club opens, you can wander between the two without paying any admission charges whatsoever. The club downstairs is a very large open-plan room with the DJ box and dance floor taking up one end of the room and a sea of men everywhere else. Always busy over the weekend with plenty of standing space to watch the new talent trip over the step dividing the dance area from the bar (always a laugh). Bromptons host many themed evenings (e.g. 'Red' every 1st Friday) and it is wise to phone the venue to see what is on their calendar for the coming months.

The Candy Bar

4 Carlisle Street
Soho
London
W1   Telephone 0171 494 4041

Nearest train station Charing Cross (ten minutes)
Nearest tube Tottenham Court Road
Car parking Difficult
A–Z ref. P61/6H
Nearest landmark Soho Square

Membership details Membership details were being finalised at the time of going to print, but it is likely that a day membership will be introduced (phone for further details)

Opening hours	Monday–Thursday: 17.00–24.00 (the downstairs club is closed on a Tuesday)
	Friday: 17.00–02.00
	Saturday: 12.00–02.00
	Sunday: 17.00–23.00
Admission charges	Monday: £2
	Tuesday: Free
	Wednesday: £3
	Thursday: £2
	Friday–Saturday: £5/£3 Members (free before 22.00)
	Sunday: £2–3 (various depending on themed evening)
	(Monday–Thursday: Admission to ground floor and cocktail bar is free)

Food available Bar snacks available
Regular entertainment Monday: 'Suffragette City': A mixture of sleaze, glam and bubblegum pop, hosted by Debbie Smith
Tuesday: 'Disco Bunny'/Social in the bar

Wednesday: 'Opportunity Knockers' (karaoke with the Cuervo Tequila Girls)
Thursday: 'Kix': hard house with DJ Smalls
Friday: 'Booby Trap' with Princess Julia
Saturday: 'Dolly Mixtures' with DJ Slamma
Sunday: First of the month: 'Sweethearts' with Amy Lame (20s to 40s sounds); second:
'Firmed Up' (R&B, soul and garage); third: 'Chocolate' (Reggae, disco and funky classics)
fourth: 'Precious Brown' (drum 'n' bass, jazz and garage)

A women's bar where men are welcome as guests of a female (men alone will not be allowed in). Excellent music policy hosted by some of the top names on the DJ circuit, with the best themed evenings in London. Well laid out on three floors, there is the basement where you'll find the disco/dance floor, the ground floor which is the main bar area, and then upstairs, which accommodates the cocktail bar, offering a more comfortable place to chill and relax.

Central Station
37 Wharfdale Road
Kings Cross
London
N1 9ST   Telephone 0171 278 3294

Nearest train station Kings Cross/St Pancras

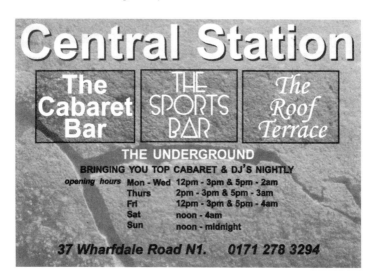

Nearest tube Kings Cross
Car parking Local NCP/street parking not too bad
A–Z ref. P61/2J
Nearest landmark Off York Way by Kings Cross Station

Membership details None required
Opening hours   Monday: 06.30–Late
                      Tuesday–Wednesday: 12.00–15.00/17.00–02.00
                      Thursday: 12.00–15.00/17.00–03.00
                      Friday: 12.00–15.00/17.00–04.00
                      Saturday: 12.00–04.00
                      Sunday: 12.00–24.00
Admission charges   Monday: Free to bar
                      Tuesday: Free to bar/free to Bridge Club upstairs (phone)
                      Wednesday: Free to bar/sometimes nominal to club
                      Thursday: £3 to club/admission to pub is free
                      Friday: £1 after 22.30/£2 after 23.30/£3 thereafter
                      Saturday: £2 after 22.30/£3 after 23.30/£4 thereafter
                      Sunday: Themed evenings–admission prices vary (phone
                      for details)
Food available Sunday lunch 01.00–18.00, available in sports bar
Regular entertainment Monday: 'Post Melt Chill Out' in the basement
Monday: 'Ray's Greatest Tits'/'Blacksmiths': LRU basement
Tuesday: Cabaret/'Meatpackers' (Cruise Bar–no dress code)/Bridge Club
Wednesday: 'Bulk': big boys and their raunchy friends/cabaret
Thursday: 'Glory Hole' (fortnightly) alternates with 'Locker Room'/stripper
Friday: 'Strictly Handbag'/cabaret
Saturday: 'Hunk': hard music and hard action
Sunday: Basement: themed nights (phone for event)/karaoke upstairs

Three floors of men! What more can one ask for? The basement (The Underground) is the area (well-) used for the various themed evenings to be had here. For example: once a month is 'GUMMI' (see GUMMI, London listing for membership details); 'PIS' (Pleasure In Streams) is every first Sunday; 'Aural' and 'MIB' (Men In Briefs), every third Sunday. For full further details of these events telephone the venue (please note that Sunday's themed events are regular private functions organised by separate promoters and are consequently subject to change throughout the year). The ground floor is a crowded cabaret room and bar, hosting frequent shows. In contrast, the first floor is the new sports bar, home of Stonewall FC/Gay Wrestlers, etc. (For further information regarding any gay sports group please write or telephone the venue.) The sports bar will serve food, show sports on TV screens (no! not *water sports*) and display trophies from individuals and gay sporting groups. Music policy is well and truly diverse, from trashy pop to club anthems and techno. For newcomers to the scene, this venue is worth a visit to find out about all the groups that meet in the venue (around 50 in all). Central Station is totally attitude-free and is a true community-based venue. You will not be disappointed.

Central Station
80 Brunner Road
Walthamstow
London
E17 7NW   Telephone 0181 520 4836

Nearest train station St James Street/Walthamstow Queens Road
Nearest tube Walthamstow Central
Car parking Adequate street parking
A–Z ref. P32/5A
Nearest landmark Markhouse Road roundabout

Membership details None required
Opening hours   Monday–Wednesday: 12.00–15.00/17.30–01.00
                       Thursday–Friday: 12.00–15.00/17.30–02.00
                       Saturday: 12.00–02.00
                       Sunday: 12.00–22.30
Admission charges Monday–Thursday: Free
                     Friday: £1 after 22.30/£2 after 23.30
                     Saturday: £1 after 22.30/£2 after 23.30
                     Sunday: Free
Food available Sunday lunch
Regular entertainment Monday: Quiz night
Tuesday: Karaoke
Wednesday: 'Golden Oldies'/'Ray's Disco and Video Show' (busy)
Thursday: 'The Jean T Show'
Friday: Cabaret/DJ (handbag)
Saturday: Cabaret/DJ (commercial)
Sunday: Party-mix disco

The sister venue to Central Station at Kings Cross and this place is just as good. A slightly younger clientele, predominantly male with a few no-attitude straights who enjoy the atmosphere of this friendly club. One large level with plenty of quiet corners, a pool table (oh yes, women are welcome) and the busy dance floor and stage. There is a large beer garden adjoining the venue which is open most weekends to cater for the overspill from the club (absolutely packed during the hot summer months). The scene in this venue is not as heavy as its sister venue and is a perfect place to just enjoy yourself.

Centre Stage (formerly The Orange)
118 Lower Road
Surrey Quays
London
SE16   Telephone 0171 394 9766

Nearest train station South Bermondsey
Nearest tube Surrey Quays/ Canada Water
Car parkin g Ample side-street parking
A–Z ref. P79/2J
Nearest landmark Surrey Quays Tube Station is on Lower Road

Membership details Membership not required but available
Opening hours   Monday–Wednesday: 19.00–24.00
                       Thursday: 19.00–01.00
                       Friday–Saturday: 19.00–02.00
                       Sunday: 15.00–24.00
Admission charges Friday: Free before 22.00/members £1 and guests £3 after
                     22.00
                     Saturday: Free before 22.00 /members £1 and guests £3
                     after 22.00

Andrew and Craig welcome you to the all new

CENTRE STAGE

**The Grande Dame of the South London scene and
the nearest gay club to the millennium dome.**

**118 Lower Road, Rotherhithe, London. SE16 2UB
Tel: 0171 394 9766**

**Tube: Canada Water (1 mins walk) Surrey Quays (30 secs walk)
Busses: 1, 47, 188, N47, P13, P14.
(run by two bikes - what more transport do you need?)**

Thursday
open from 7pm-1am
High Energy
Trash Disco
Entrance free B4 10pm
£1 after ○ Members free

Fridays
open 7pm ○ Entrance free B4 10pm
Members/flyers/ad £1 ○ Guests £3
FRESH
Commercial anthems with resident
D.J. Myra on the mix
'The Well Party'
first Friday of every month

Saturdays
Open 7pm ○ Entrance free B4 10pm
Members/Flyers/ad £1 ○ Guest £3
SHOWTIME
with Andrew Swan and Guests

Sunday Lunch
open from 3pm - 7pm
Entrance £12.50/£10 with flyer or ad
Sundays will never be the same
TWO SOUPS
Entrance fee includes free roast
dinner and all you can drink! for four
hours (3pm-7pm) from our extensive
range of house spirits and beers,
YES believe it! you can't a££ord to
miss it!

Sunday Evening
open 7pm-midnight ○ free entry
'Stars of the new millennium'
to enter call 0171 394 9766
0961 995557

Mondays
open 7pm-midnight, free entry
QUIDS INN
you extend your weekend and we'll
extend our happy hour! Doubles
all night long. Vodka, Brandy, White
Rum, Whisky and selected beers
all £1.00

Tuesday
open 7pm-midnight ○ free entry
team up for
GAY GAMES
Centre Stage presents a night of
utter madness where anything goes,
yes, another pub offers you bingo
and quizzes. But this pub takes it
one step further with Electra Voltage.

Wednesday
open 7pm-midnight ○ free entry

Piano bar night with
Lewis + Swan

Sunday: £12 from 15.00–19.00 includes full Sunday lunch and as much as you can drink

(concise details can be gained by phoning the bar direct)

Food available Sunday lunch: 15.00–17.00

Regular entertainment Monday: 'Quids In' (all drinks £1)

Tuesday: 'Gay Games' with Jessica Woodchip

Wednesday: Piano bar with Peter Lewis and Andrew Swan (very popular night)

Thursday: 'Hi Nrg' dance night

Friday: 'Fresh'(upliftin' house with special PAs)/first Friday of the month: 'The Well' (top

dance night–individually promoted: phone for details)

Saturday: Top cabaret/ DJ

Sunday: Regular cabaret

What was once the home of the Oi! club is now a completely revamped and stylish dance club. New sound and lighting system, completely refurbished and an excellent entertainments policy will ensure that the Centre Stage becomes one of the major players on the London gay club scene. Upstairs is now a large chill out bar and lounge area. Downstairs is the dance floor, pool room and numerous chill out areas. Friday nights are individually promoted, so it is advisable to phone to receive up-to-the-minute details (admission charges may apply).

Quebec (formerly City of Quebec)

12 Old Quebec Street
Marble Arch
London
W1H 7AF   Telephone 0171 629 6159

Nearest train station Paddington (taxi from here or a 10 minute walk)

Nearest tube Marble Arch

Car parking NCP

A–Z ref. P60/6D

Nearest landmark KFC on Marble Arch

Membership details None required

Opening hours   Monday–Wednesday: 11.00–23.00

Thursday: 11.00–01.00

Friday–Saturday: 11.00–02.00

Sunday: 12.00–22.30

Admission charges None

Food available Sandwiches and snacks available in the evening

Regular entertainment Monday: 'Monday Chill Out'

Tuesday: Social

Wednesday: Social

Thursday: 'Golden Oldies'

Friday: 'Hi Nrg' (downstairs)

Saturday–Sunday: DJ

Traditional venue, popular with the thirty-something set. From Thursdays, the downstairs dance bar opens till late for the younger crowd.

Club Travestie @ Stepneys Nightclub

(Rear of The George Tavern)
373 Commercial Road
London
E1 0LA   Telephone 0181 788 4154 (infoline)

Nearest train station Shadwell DLR
Nearest tube Aldgate East
Car parking Street parking on the junction of Jubilee Street
A–Z ref. P63/6J
Nearest landmark The George Tavern

Membership details Available but not neccessary. Enquire at desk for further details
Opening hours   Saturday: 20.30–02.30
                         (Every second and fourth Saturday only)
Admission charges   Saturday: £5
Food available No
Regular entertainment Saturday: (Alternate Saturdays) Live cabaret/stripper, etc.

Based in Stepneys Nightclub adjacent to (the rear of) The George Tavern. The entrance to the club is on Aylward Street, which is off Jubilee Street. (Are you still with me?) Club Travestie is a well-established club, now in its 19th year for cross-dressers, TVs, TSs, their friends, admirers and their families. Having said that, the club is extremely popular with the mainstream gay and lesbian crowd in addition to 'no-attitude' straights who thoroughly enjoy the relaxed, friendly, fun-filled atmosphere. The only downside is that it is open only twice a month and not every night. The dance floor may be reminiscent of *Saturday Night Fever* but the venue is plush and comfortable, with tiered staging in order that you can see the stage and not the back of someone's head. Staff are friendly and welcoming (even the lovely doormen, which makes a pleasant change) and are committed to ensuring your night out is enjoyable. Excellent cloakroom and changing facilities are available in the club and taxis home can be booked at reception. For first-timers and newcomers to the scene, who want to gain more information or be shown around the venue, then please phone the lovely Ron Storme on the above number. Ron is always on the door to welcome you to the club and will do his utmost to help and assist you.

The Cock and Comfort

359 Bethnal Green Road
London
E2 6LG   Telephone 0171 729 1090

Nearest train station Liverpool Street (and then No. 8 bus)/Bethnall Green
Nearest tube Bethnal Green
Car parking Street parking
A–Z ref. P63/4F
Nearest landmark Tesco (next door-ish)

Membership details None required
Opening hours   Monday–Thursday: 14.00–23.00
                         Friday: 14.00–02.00
                         Saturday: 13.00–02.00

Sunday: 12.00–24.00

Admission charges None

Food available Sunday: 14.00–18.00 (very busy: book upfront): Aunty Rachel's Kitchen = big portions, small prices (all home-cooked food)

Regular entertainment Monday: Social

Tuesday: Cabaret

Wednesday–Thursday: Social

Friday–Sunday: Cabaret

The Cock is a large, lively, friendly, typically East End boozer (just like the one off the telly, only there isn't a Pauline moaning continuously). It is certainly *not* a trendy West End bar. Emphasis is on booze and not bopping and the clientele is a good mix of lesbian and gay with a smattering of gay-friendly straights who 'just love the atmosphere'. The age range is anything from 18 to death! all coming together (oo-er missus) in a no-attitude environment. Drinks are very cheap (and so are the staff). The cabaret acts are usually the top names on the circuit (you will have to look at the listing in the pub to see who is due to come on, or alternatively look out for the ads in the gay press). The upstairs restaurant is packed on Sundays and you will have to book in advance for a table.

The Cock Tavern

340 Kennington Road

London

SE11   Telephone 0171 735 1013

Nearest train station Waterloo (5 minutes)

Nearest tube Kennington/Oval

Car parking Street parking

A–Z ref. P78/5A

Nearest landmark Waterloo Station

Membership details None required

Opening hours   Monday–Saturday: 11.00–23.00

                        Sunday: 12.00–22.30

Food available Full menu available 12.00–21.00 every day

Regular entertainment Monday: 'Monday Madness'/'Free Pool'

Tuesday: Stripper

Wednesday: 'Killer Pool'

Thursday: 'Amateur Strip'

Friday: PA or cabaret/DJ

Saturday: Stripper/cabaret

Sunday: Afternoon cabaret/traditional Sunday lunch

Large traditional gay pub with regular cabaret and so on. A new late licence is being applied for, so the above details may be changing some time in 1999

The Colherne

261 Old Brompton Road

Earls Court

London

SW5   Telephone 0171 244 5951

CHAMPION

drink
eat
relax
chat
meet
talk
dream
chill
watch
smile
enjoy

eat —a delicious choice of food served daily from midday

relax —unwind from the day in our courtyard

enjoy —life in Notting Hill!

Find us by Underground: Central, Circle & District lines or by Bus route: 27, 28, 31, 52, 70 & 94

CHAMPION

1 Wellington Terrace
Bayswater Road
London W2 4LW
Tel: 020 7243 9531

Nearest train station Kensington (ten minutes)
Nearest tube Earls Court
Car parking None
A–Z ref. P75/5J
Nearest landmark Brompton Cemetery

Membership details None required
Opening hours   Monday–Saturday: 12.00–23.00
                       Sunday: 12.00–22.30
Admission charges None
Food available No
Regular entertainment No scheduled regular entertainment

Located in the middle of Earls Court's gay neighbourhood, close to Clone Zone, Bromptons et al. Recently refurbished, the bar is now one large open-plan room with a first floor gallery area and smaller bar (this opens at 20.00 until close). The Colherne is an extremely cruisy venue both night and day, not only attracting the leather and denim crowd from all over the capital, but also a handful of locals taking a break from walking around the nearby haunts. A few dark corners well worth exploring.

Comptons Of Soho

53 Old Compton Street
Soho
London
W1V   Telephone 0171 479 7961/0171 437 4445

Nearest train station Charing Cross
Nearest tube Piccadilly/Leicester Square
Car parking NCP close by
A–Z ref. P61/7H
Nearest landmark McDonalds on Dean Street

Membership details None
Opening hours   Monday–Saturday: 12.00–23.00
                       Sunday: 12.00–22.30
Admission charges None
Food available No
Regular entertainment Friday: DJ
Saturday: DJ
Sunday: 'Anthems': post-Trade party

Comptons = a man's bar popular with everyone. Always very busy. State-of-the-art sound and lighting system. Very cruisy and a DJ most nights. The music policy is the heavier side of techno, helping to create a fun, party atmosphere. Saturday nights and Sunday afternoons tend to be extremely busy, although considering the sheer volume of talent that passes through the portals this is definitely not a problem. Flyers for most of the major clubs can be picked up from here, offering discounted door charges, as well as the free gay press. Well laid out over two floors (the venue that is, not the punters!), the top room being a little bit more intimate, with small tables and chairs, and quieter than the ground floor. Free entry flyers and Q-Jump tickets for G.A.Y Monday and Thursday, (see G.A.Y., London listing) are available from behind the bar (these are not put out on the table, so please ask).

Crash

Arch 66
Goding Street
Vauxhall
London
SE11   Telephone 0171 278 0995

Nearest train station Vauxhall
Nearest tube Vauxhall
Car parking Side-street parking
A–Z ref. P77/5J
Nearest landmark Vauxhall Tavern

Membership details Available, but not necessary (enquire at venue)
Opening hours Monday–Thursday: 22.30–03.00
Saturday: 22.30–05.00
Sunday: 22.30–03.00
Admission prices
Sunday–Thursday: Enquire at venue
Saurday: £10 (Discount for members)
Food available No

One of London's top mixed gay, bisexual and TV cruizing and boozing venues, just south of the river in the biker bar of Crash. With four bars, large main dance floor, industrial-look second room and the hottest and sexiest men. Top DJs and New York-style bar with top go-go dancers too.

O

Outlines   from Absolute Press

A delightful collection of monographs detailing the loves and lives of some of the most prolific gay and lesbian creative artists of this century.

Titles in the series:
David Hockney
Benjamin Britten
Bessie Smith
We are Michael Field
Federico García Lorca
Arthur Rimbaud
k.d. lang
Armistead Maupin
Tallulah Bankhead

k.d. lang

ROSE COLLIS

5 NIGHTS A WEEK OF LONDON'S
HOTTEST MEN, CRUISING AND BOOZING
JUST SOUTH OF THE RIVER IN THE BIKER BAR OF CRASH,
THE CAPITAL'S SEXIEST VENUE
DJS & NEW YORK STYLE BAR TOP GO-GOS

CRASH 2 – ENTRANCE ON ALBERT EMBANKMENT
(OPPOSITE MI5) VAUXHALL, LONDON, SE11
CRASH 2 – SUNDAYS MONDAYS TUESDAYS
WEDNESDAYS THURSDAYS 10.30PM–3AM

DTPM @ The End

18 West Central Street
London
WC1   Telephone 0171 419 9199/0181 586 0344 (DTPM infoline)   Fax
             0181 470 4250

Nearest train station Euston/St Pancras/Kings Cross
Nearest tube Tottenham Court Road
Car parking Limited street parking/ 24hr NCP opposite venue
A–Z ref. P61/6J
Nearest landmark Extreme end of Shaftesbury Avenue (away from Piccadilly)
or, from New Oxford Street (going east) turn right into West Central Street
when you come to McDonalds on the left

Membership details Membership not necessary but available at £20 per
annum/£15 renewals. Apply in person at the club on Sundays only. For other
information on the venue or to submit test tapes write to the following address:
Lee Freeman, DTPM, PO Box 23508, London E13 9RY
Opening hours   Sunday: 20.00–04.00
                     Every Sunday only
Admission charges £7 before 23.00/£7 after 23.00 for NUS and members and
                     £10 guests
                     Advance ticket holders receive priority queuing (advance
                     tickets can be bought at: Seven @ A.K.A., West Central
                     Street; The Edge, Soho Square (see listing) and The Box,
                     Monmouth Street (see listing)
Food available A.K.A. club bar and restaurant–a recent addition to the club
with a full à la carte menu.

Hosts weekly Sunday parties known as 'Seven', serving food from 14.00–19.00
with DJs (including showcase) on from 18.30–22.30. The perfect prelude to
DTPM downstairs. DTPM was established in 1993 and has been at The End since
January 1996. The move here catapulted the club to new heights, drawing
numerous awards and wide acclaim from most of the music and fashion press
including *DJ Magazine*, *I-D*, *The Face*, *Mix Mag* and *Attitude*. The venue has also
received wide acclaim too with its ultra-modern decor, state-of-the-art sound
system and capacity for over 1,000 sophisticated and fashionable gay and
gay-friendly clubbers, all of whom are serious about their music and expect
excellence from their night out. DTPM is foremost a gay club night, however, the
emphasis is 'the right attitude' and thus attracts a wide range of young friendly
people–gay and straight–and in particular, people who are involved in the club
scene itself, including high profile DJs such as Danny Rampling, Pete Wardman,
Fat Tony and Boy George, with many, many other celebrities, too numerous to
mention. Current DJs include Smokin' Jo, Steve Thomas, Malcolm Duffy, Jeffrey
Hinton, Alan Thomson, Guy Williams, Craig Daniel, Princess Julia, Felix, Tony
Sapiano, Oscar Goldenchild, Jamie, Miguel P and Laurent R. Almost all have
been DJing for at least five years with most of them having doubled that. This,
not to mention the new talent coming forward who DTPM are encouraging and
nurturing to become tomorrow's great DJs (test tapes are welcomed). DTPM also
hosts and organises the main music area at London Mardi Gras (formerly known
as London Pride) along with much smaller events at notable clubs throughout the
country and abroad. The club has never worked as most clubs do, that is to say
they do not employ big name DJs to pull in the crowds, instead they promote the

night as a whole, so the success of the night is not determined by which DJ is playing. That is not to say they do not employ top DJs–they do, however, this is rarely advertised and the DJs have requested to play at the club 'for pleasure' because they believe in the direction it is going and the credibility associated with it. The venue is divided into two main arenas. The Lounge plays acid jazz, funk, soul and R&B, with a little hip-hop and disco. It's a relaxing and sophisticated environment where people can dance, chill out on a sofa or stand near the bar and socialise. This room is also used to showcase new talent with music that fits into the above categories. The Vaults is the other area; the music here is more uplifting but with a deeper and harder edge: garage, deep American house and hard house. All in all, DTPM is a 'unique' venue. Their hard core of customers (known as the family) are very loyal and return regularly to receive a warm welcome from the long suffering ... erm ... standing staff and the promoters, who do take a genuine and personal interest in the club. A 'family' has been created and this is a large contributing factor which has helped sustain the success of DTPM.

Diamonds @ Jaque Of Clubs

47 Ossory Road
London
SE1 5AS   Telephone 0171 252 0007

Nearest train station South Bermondsey (five minute walk)
Nearest tube Elephant and Castle (ten minute walk)
Car parking Ample space outside the club
A–Z ref. P79/6G
Nearest landmark McDonalds on the Old Kent Road (venue is behind)

Membership details Phone for details. Non-members welcome. Instant free membership at the door
Opening hours   Saturday: 21.00–04.00
Admission charges   Never above £5
Food available No
Regular entertainment No scheduled entertainment
Happy hour from 21.00–23.00

Exclusively women only. Extremely popular and was one of the first venues to offer a Saturday night exclusively to women. Very friendly, no-attitude atmosphere, with a wide range of music tastes catered for, i.e. dance, house, pop and reggae. Fully air-conditioned venue with a good light and sound system. The bar area is a plush clean open-plan space, with small tables and chairs for those intimate moments. Easily accessible by tube (Elephant and Castle) off the Old Kent Road behind McDonalds. Drinks prices are as close to pub prices as you can get in a late-license bar with happy hour(s) running from 21.00–23.00. The age range is from 23 upwards but most of the customers are around the thirty-something bracket (all good time girls!). If you are new to the scene and would like to be introduced around, then please phone the bar beforehand to make arrangements. Alternatively, if you are spotted by yourself then every effort will be made to make you feel welcome. Taxi service available on request.

The Dome
1 Dartmouth Park Hill
Tufnell Park
London
N19   Telephone 0171 272 8153 (Dome)

Nearest train station Upper Holloway
Nearest tube Tufnell Park
Car parking Street parking
A–Z ref. P45/3G
Nearest landmark Tufnell Park Tube Station/Club Kali entrance is next door to
The Boston Arms pub

Membership details None required, although a mailing list is in operation
giving details of current and future events and mailing list forms are available
from the club. Alternatively you can write to the PO box number below for
inclusion (remembering to state your name and address)
Opening hours   Friday: 22.00–03.00 (every first and third Friday of the
                        month only)
Admission charges   £5 before 23.00/£6 after
                        Concessions: £3 before 23.00/£4 after (identification
                        required)

Club Kali is the world's largest South Asian music based lesbian and gay club
(attracting regular crowds in excess of 800) with DJs' Ritu and Riz playing
Bhangra, Hindi and Arabic, mixed with more Western tunes. The atmosphere is
totally attitude-free, friendly and electric–so much so that the popularity of Club
Kali has enabled it to increase to twice a month. Bear in mind that these
bi-monthly events are always extremely busy, so early admission is advised
otherwise you will have to queue. Coach trips to Club Kali are organised from
Leicester (Dover Castle), Coventry and Birmingham, details of which are
available from the PO box address that follows, or by phoning 'Sonny' on 0116
254 1747 (c/o Leicester Gay Men's Health). Additionally, if you are gay and Asian
and wish to experience the phenomena that is Club Kali then write to the PO Box
number for further information and advice. Club Kali, PO Box 25628, London
N17 6ZJ. Also checkout the listing For Baghdad @ The Oak Bar.

The Duke Of Wellington
119 Balls Pond Road
London
N1 4BL   Telephone 0171 254 4338

Nearest train station Dalston Kingsland
Nearest tube Highbury and Islington
Car parking Limited side-street parking
A–Z ref. P46/6E
Nearest landmark Dalston Kingsland BR (more or less opposite)

Membership details None required
Opening hours   Monday–Saturday: 12.00–23.00
                        Sunday: 12.00–22.30
Admission charges   None
Food available Very busy Sunday lunch and bar snacks available too
Regular entertainment Monday: Chill out and social

Tuesday: Bingo
Wednesday: Social
Thursday: Trivia quiz
Saturday: Karaoke
Sunday: Trivia quiz

A cosy, intimate and friendly venue. Mixed gay and lesbian crowd of all ages and types. A large room with a central bar, with the games room (pool table) leading off and another room used as an overspill which can also be hired out for private functions.

The Edge

11 Soho Square
Soho
London
W1V 5DB   Telephone 0171 439 1313   Fax 0171 434 4516
E-mail edgesoho@aol.com
Website http://www.theedge-group.com

Nearest train station Charing Cross (five minutes)
Nearest tube Tottenham Court Road
Car parking Extremely limited
A–Z Ref. P61/6H
Nearest landmark Soho Square

Membership details None required
Opening hours   Monday–Thursday: 12.00–01.00
Friday: 12.00–01.00
Saturday: 12.00–01.00
Sunday: 12.00–22.30
Admission charges None
Food available 12.00–01.00: Full menu available (menu changes each month)
Regular entertainment Thursday–Saturday: 21.00–01.00: In-house DJ

A comfortable and friendly bar in Soho Square, with seating spilling out on to the pavements when the weather permits. This makes spending a Sunday, or indeed any afternoon or evening at this venue a pure joy. With four floors of bars and a friendly young clientele The Edge should be a regular drinking den on anyone's list. The top floors are available for private hire (more information can be gained by visiting the website or calling the venue direct). Weekends tend to be packed, especially when the weather is dry and the street becomes the focal point of the area, so much so that actually getting a drink at the bar becomes near impossible. Flyers and ads for entry to most of the major events in London can be obtained from the information point at the bottom of the stairs.

Father Redcap

319 Camberwell Road
Camberwell Green
London
SE5 0HQ   Telephone 0171 708 4474

Nearest train station Loughborough Junction

Nearest tube Elephant and Castle/Oval (taxi required from here)
Car parking Street parking
A–Z ref. P94/1D
Nearest landmark Camberwell Green

Membership details	None required
Opening hours	Monday–Saturday: 19.00–02.00
	Sunday: 12.00–4.00
Admission charges	Monday–Wednesday: Free before 23.00/£1 after
	Thursday: Free before 23.00/£1.50 after
	Friday–Saturday: Free before 22.00/£3 after
	Sunday: Free before 14.00/enquire after
	(Last admissions: 01.00 Monday–Saturday/23.00 Sunday)

Food available No
Regular entertainment Monday: Dance Club
Tuesday: 'Trance Session' (dance)
Wednesday: DJ
Thursday–Saturday: Cabaret/DJ
Sunday: Chill Out/DJs

A large open-plan venue which is more of a club than a pub. However the atmosphere is still friendly and welcoming. The dance floor and stage at the back of the room is well used and packed from Thursday onwards with a young, predominantly gay male crowd. It doesn't cater for any particular type, the crowd is more the jeans and T-shirt crowd, bent on having fun and partying.

The Fort
131 Grange Road
London
SE1 3AL   Telephone 0171 237 7742

Nearest train station Elephant and Castle
Nearest tube Elephant and Castle
Car parking Ample facilities adjacent
A–Z ref. P78/3E
Nearest landmark Tower Bridge (Grange Road is off Tower Bridge Road)

Membership details	None required
Opening hours	Monday–Friday: 20.00–23.00
	Saturday: 14.00–18.00/20.00–23.00
	Sunday: 14.00–22.30
Admission charges	Monday: £2
	Tuesday–Wednesday: Free
	Thursday: £2
	Friday–Saturday: Free
	Sunday: £2

Food available No
Regular entertainment Monday: 'Underwear Party'
Tuesday: 'Cruise In The Dark'
Wednesday: 'Leather, Rubber, Uniform' (no strict dress code)
Thursday: 'Underwear Party'
Friday: 'Cruise In The Dark'
Saturday: 'Cruise In The Dark'

Sunday: 'Underwear Party'

An obviously very popular (and well-known) gay men-only venue. Dark, cruisy atmosphere with an interesting mix of all age groups and types, including many local guys and international visitors too. There is absolutely no attempt to disguise the fact that this place is an indoor cruising ground, with the added bonus of alcohol being available. The other bonus is that it is a safe environment with a choice selection of men, including many straightish lads who like to sample the delights on offer. Underwear parties are always busy with the stipulation that footwear and underwear must be worn (the admission charge is for the clothes check). Phone the venue for further details about this event. The following bus services stop right outside the venue: 1, 199, 78, N1.

The Freedom Café Bar
60–66 Wardour Street Soho
London
W1V 3HP   Telephone 0171 734 0071

Nearest train station Charing Cross
Nearest tube Piccadilly
Car parking NCP Brewer Street
A–Z ref. P61/6G
Nearest landmark Soho Square

Membership details None
Opening hours   Monday: 11.00–02.00
                         Tuesday–Saturday: 11.00– 03.00
                         Sunday: 11.00–24.00
Admission charges   Monday–Thursday: Free
                         Friday–Saturday: £3 after 21.00/£5 after 22.00
                         Sunday: Free
Food available Extensive menu available at all times
Regular entertainment No scheduled regular entertainment

An extremely stylish, young, individualistic and friendly venue, believing in integration not segregation (I think that means gay-friendly) which makes this establishment a popular haunt for the most fashionable of people. There's a dance club with DJ in the basement, which opens on Tuesday through to Saturday from 21.00 to 03.00 each night.

G.A.Y @ The London Astoria
157–165 Charing Cross Road
London
WC2   Telephone 0171 734 6963
             Website http://www.G-A-Y.co.uk

Nearest train station Charing Cross
Nearest tube Leicester Square
Car parking Possible side streets (but doubtful)
A–Z ref. P61/6H
Nearest landmark Leicester Square Tube Station

Membership details None required
Opening hours   Monday & Thursday: 22.30–04.00 LA 2
                         Friday & Saturday: 22.30–05.00 LA1

Admission charges   Monday & Thursday: £1 with flyer ('Pink Pounder')/£3
                      without
                      Friday: £1–3 with flyer ('Camp Attack')/£5 without
                      Saturday: £6–£10 depending on P.A. (usually big names)
                      Use flyers/*Boyz* ads for discounts
                      Students and UB40 concessions (positive identification
                      required)
                      Free admission to Positive Discount card holders
Food available Food area in venue
Regular entertainment Monday & Thursday: G.A.Y. 'Pink Pounder'
Friday: 'Camp Attack @ The Astoria'
Saturday: G.A.Y. regular major P.A.s

G.A.Y. = Good As You. *Gay Times'* and *Boyz'* 'Best Club Of The Year 1998'. Busy, busy, busy. One of only a couple of major clubs in Soho. The talent is awesome and so is everything else about this club. The music can be pretty much mainstream but the dance floor is always packed to breaking point. There is plenty of seating in the galleries, ideal for chilling out and scanning the talent. Saturday nights in the cavernous 2,000 capacity LA1 is even more packed, with spunky young party-goers. The music is less mainstream and the atmosphere is always electric, usually with the appearance of a top P.A. Friday night is 'Camp Attack @ The Astoria'. A popular and crowded night with the best and worst music from the 70s and 80s. Positive Discount cardholders are (quite rightly) allowed free admission and to queue-jump on all nights–so don't go shouting your mouth off. If you want to queue- jump then buy 'Q-Jumper' tickets from the Astoria on Saturday between the hours of 14.00– 19.00, or, from The Box or Ku Bar in the evenings. Flyers to all nights can usually be found in most bars on the evening.

Gay Tea Dance @ The Limelight

136 Shaftsbury Avenue
London
W1V 7DN   Telephone 0171 437 4303 (c/o The Ku Bar)

Nearest train station Charing Cross
Nearest tube Leicester Square
Car parking In Brixton (you must be joking)
A–Z ref. P61/7H

Membership details Available at the venue on first visit
Opening hours   Sunday: 18.00–23.00
Admission charges   £3 before 19.00 members
                       £4.50 after 19.00 members
                       £6 at all times non-members
                       (No admission after 22.00)
Food available No

Get here early or you wont get in! The Sunday Tea Dance at The Limelight is five hours of non-stop classic pop from the 70s, 80s and 90s, with a weekly P.A. from the likes of Bucks Fizz, Lonnie Gordon and Sonia. Five bars and two dance floors, split over three levels joining together lots of cruisy corridors and stairwells–it wont be that difficult to find a dancing partner. An old converted church forms these premises and it was probably the first venue to hold openly gay parties.

When you choose an escort agency, make sure it's a CAPITAL *experience*

At Capital we believe it's the quality of *our* experience which guarantees the quality of *yours*. We're not some big anonymous company, but a small, long-established consultancy which really takes the time and trouble to listen to your needs.

We're friendly, professional and totally discreet. Whether you want a companion at home or abroad, for a brief meeting or a longer encounter, Capital will arrange it quickly, efficiently and with pleasure. That's why so many of our clients return to us again and again.

So why risk a disappointing experience, when you could have a Capital one? Call us today and find out why *nobody does it better.*

★ Hotel or home visits, dinner evenings, theatre trips, sightseeing, weekends or longer.

★ Visit our central London office to see the Capital portfolio of London's most attractive young escorts and masseurs.

★ Carefully vetted to be friendly, educated and good company.

★ Escorts are London-based and are happy to travel throughout the UK, Europe and further.

CAPITAL
0171 630 7567
London's most exclusive escort agency

The Limelight has been going for what seems like for ever, and is now firmly established as a traditional gay Sunday night out. For cheaper admission prices, look out for the discount flyers in the bars, or scour *Boyz* for promotional ads.

George and Dragon
2 Blackheath Hill
Greenwich
London
SE10   Telephone 0181 691 3764

Nearest train station Greenwich/Lewisham
Nearest tube None
Car parking Limited street parking
A–Z ref. P96/1E
Nearest landmark The Point (common)

Membership details None required
Opening hours   Monday–Friday: 15.00–23.00
                         Saturday: 12.00–23.00
                         Sunday: 12.00–22.30
Admission charges   None
Food available Light snacks
Regular entertainment Tuesday: 'Big Boyz Night' (for big men and their admirers)
Wednesday: Karaoke with The Duchess
Thursday: DJ
Friday: Cabaret
Saturday: Cabaret and DJ
Sunday: 'Camp Attack' disco in the afternoon/cabaret in the evening

A lively and friendly venue with a full entertainment policy.

Gladstone Arms
64 Lant Street
London
SE1 1QD   Telephone 0171 407 3962

Nearest train station London Bridge
Nearest tube Borough
Car parking Difficult, but easier over the weekend
A–Z ref. P78/2C
Nearest landmark Borough Tube Station

Membership details None required
Opening hours   Monday–Friday: 11.00–23.00
                         Saturday: 12.00–23.00
                         Sunday: 12.00–22.30
Admission charges   None
Food available Yes–lunch-times and early evenings
Regular entertainment No scheduled entertainment

The Gladstone Arms is a traditional gay venue that could be described as an alternative to the West End scene. A social and friendly venue with the emphasis on conversation rather than dancing. The well-used free juke box and the occasional quiz night provides the entertainment for the predominantly male clientele, although lunch-times see the local office workers popping in for a pint and a bite to eat. Easily accessible by tube, with Borough Station on the corner of Lant Street.

The Glass Bar

190 Euston Road
London
NW1   Telephone 0171 387 6184

Nearest train station Euston
Nearest tube Euston
Car parking Street parking is easy in the evening
A–Z ref. P61/4F
Nearest landmark Euston Station

Membership details Daily membership: £1 at the door (women members-only bar)

Opening hours   Monday: Closed
                         Tuesday–Friday: 17.00–Late
                         Saturday: 19.00–Late
                         Sunday: 14.00–19.00
                         (No admission after 23.30)
Admission charges £1 day membership at all times
Food available No
Regular entertainment Tuesday: 'Bridge Night'
Thursday: 'Singles Mingles'
Friday: 'Jazz Junkie'/live jazz every last Friday of the month
Saturday: 'Groove and Swing'
Sunday: 'Relax'

The longest running, indeed, the only permanent women-only bar in London (men are not even accepted as guests). Now over three years old and a membership list in excess of 10,000 proves the popularity of this place. Comfortably laid out over two floors; the downstairs being the main bar whilst upstairs are the toilets and chill out area (soft comfortable furnishings, etc.). The venue has a homely atmosphere that could be described as 'walking into your living room' (that's if you have a nice living room—not a bedsit or squat!) Partly disabled access, namely to the ground floor and help is available to carry people to the toilets upstairs. If you have not been out on the scene before or indeed, if you have just left a long-term relationship and are looking to start your social life again, then Thursdays would be an ideal night to start. 'Singles Mingles' is a friendly introduction night giving you the opportunity to meet new people in a welcoming and safe environment. All the free gay press is available, along with pertinent lesbian literature. Such is the friendliness of this venue that you are welcome to phone beforehand if you are a little bit nervous about coming in alone. The recent introduction of 'gay mothers and kids' every second Tuesday of the month is another first for The Glass Bar and is sure to be copied around the country. Another excellent night to be hosted here is the Jewish Lesbian Group evening, taking place every first Wednesday of the month. There is talk about starting a monthly 'eating out group'—not for sampling fine cuisine and wine but just another excuse for stuffing your face and getting pissed. For further information of this event and others please phone the above number or, ideally, just pop in.

GUMMI

BM 414
London
WC1N 3XX   Telephone Apply in writing only–there is no published number for this
              club
              Website http://www.powerhouse.co.uk/powerhouse/gummi/

Membership details Annual membership from the postal address, or guests allowed in with a member
Admission charges   Members £4/guests £5

In central London, details from the postal address. GUMMI is the foremost rubber club for gay men in the world, now in it's seventh year. The club meets monthly at a central London venue and attracts around 2–300 guys to each event. There is a strict rubber dress code; at least one item of rubber-wear in addition to any rubber boots or gloves. The one item of rubber-wear can be anything from a full one-piece rubber suit with hood and mask to a rubber jock! GUMMI has a membership running into hundreds of members, who not only receive reduced admission price to events but also a bi-monthly newsletter 'The Rubber Sheet', discounts at many major rubber suppliers in the UK and abroad, discounts with other gay venues, and news of GUMMI members-only events. A member's monthly free raffle, with £100 and £50 prize vouchers for rubber gear at Rob. There is a bar and food is also usually available. Changing room and coat check. Despite the large numbers of gay men who attend GUMMI events, the atmosphere is friendly and talkative, making newcomers to the scene feel welcome.

Halfway To Heaven

7 Duncannon Street
London
WC2 4JF   Telephone 0171 321 2791

Nearest train station Charing Cross
Nearest tube Charing Cross
Car parking Limited street parking close-by
A–Z ref. P61/7J

Membership details None required
Opening hours   Monday–Saturday: 12.00–23.00
                       Sunday: 12.00–22.30
Admission charges   None
                       Traditional pub, good beer, friendly crowd and a great
                       place to meet up with friends prior to an evening of sex and
                       debauchery.

Heaven

Under The Arches
Off Villiers Street
Charing Cross
London
WC2 6NG   Telephone 0171 930 2020/9604   Fax 0171 930 8306
               E-mail info@heaven-london.com
               Website http://www.heaven-london.com

Nearest train station Charing Cross
Nearest tube Charing Cross
Car parking Street parking
A–Z ref. P77/1J
Nearest landmark Charing Cross Station

Membership details To be announced (phone for details). Membership required for The Long Yang Club (see below)

Opening hours   Monday: (mixed) 22.30–03.00
Wednesday: (gay/TV/TS) 22.30–03.00
Thursday: (straight) 09.00–03.00 (every second Thursday only)
Friday: (straight) 22.30–06.00
Saturday: (gay) 22.30–06.00
Sunday: (gay) 20.00–01.00 (members only)

Admission charges   Monday: £1 with flyer before 23.30/£3 after
Wednesday: £1 with flyer before 23.30/£4 with flyer after/ otherwise £6
Thursday: £6 before 23.30/£8 after
Friday: £4 before 23.30/£8 after
Saturday: £8 with flyer before 23.30/£10 after/£5 after 03.00
Sunday: details on request from Heaven

Food available Fully functional coffee shop and chill out area has been introduced serving hot and cold food throughout the night
Regular entertainment Heaven is spilt up into three main rooms, each following its own musical direction, from hard house with a twist, all the way to rare groove. They are the Main Floor, Room 2 and The Dakota Piano Bar.
Monday: 'Popcorn': pop to harder commercial/indie and alternative/live cabaret
Wednesday: 'The Fruit Machine'/'Powder Room' (TV/TS) and 'R+B'
Thursday: 'Bedrock' (every second Thursday with John Digweed)
Friday: 'Urban Torque'
Saturday: 'Heaven'–The Ultimate Gay Night Out
Sunday: 'Long Yang Club': members only–for men from the orient and their admirers

Probably the most famous London gay club in the world. Now, after its massive £3m refurbishment the venue has gone from strength to strength and from very busy to very, very busy, averaging over 7,000 customers a week. Q-Jump tickets are available from Kudos Bar. You will also be able to pick up reduced admission flyers from here (remember to pick up your flyer first before buying your ticket). Also check out the current gay press for promotional ads. Remember that on some nights, Heaven may have the venue hired out for a straight or mixed event (if you are interested in mixing with breeders then telephone for further details or checkout the website). However, Saturday's is the flagship in Heaven's fleet of nights and still has a strict 'lesbian and gay' door policy. There is also a spectacular private members' bar, 'Departure Lounge' offering a space of pleasure and anonymity for any celebrities that may be passing through. Membership enquiries for access to this room are to be made to the above number. Finally, if you do not want to queue then get here very early.

The Hoist

Railway Arch 47C
South Lambeth Road
Vauxhall Cross
London
SW8 1RH   Telephone 0171 735 9972
               Website http://www.expectations.co.uk

Nearest train station Vauxhall
Nearest tube Vauxhall (exit 1)
Car parking Plentiful parking outside venue
A–Z ref. P77/ 6J
Nearest landmark Vauxhall Cross

Membership details (Optional) £15 per year
Opening hours   Monday–Tuesday: Closed
                       Wednesday: 21.00–01.00
                       Thursday: Closed except for third Thursday of the month
                       Friday–Saturday: 22.00–03.00
                       Sunday: 21.00–01.00
Admission charges   Wednesday: £2.50
                       Thursday: ('SM Gays') £3.50/£2.50 concessions
                       Friday: £4
                       Saturday: £5
                       Sunday: £2.50
                       (Members free at all times)
Food available No
Regular entertainment Thursday: 'SM Gays' every third Thursday of the
month: 20.00–24.00
Friday–Sunday: 'Hoist Club Night'

The Hoist is an exclusively gay men-only venue with a dress code of leather,
rubber, uniform and industrial. A large very cruisy area situated in an old
railway arch with full air- conditioning, constructed of brick with an industrial
feel. Separating the two floors is a metal mezzanine level. An additional third
floor has recently been added. 'SM Gays' is a monthly social and cruising ground
for those who like it rough (phone prior to arrival for entry requirements). There
is no (strict) dress code although newcomers should phone for further details
prior to arrival. Checkout the website.

The Horse and Jockey

128 Wellesley Road
Croydon
Surrey
CR0 2AH   Telephone 0181 689 3473

Nearest train station West Croydon
Nearest tube None
Car parking Ample street parking
A–Z ref. P134/1C
Nearest landmark Council offices

Membership details None required
Opening hours   Monday–Saturday: 11.00–23.00

Sunday: 12.00–22.30

Admission charges None
Food available No
Regular entertainment No regular scheduled entertainment but occasional cabaret

A typical pub/club over two floors, the basement being a dance area which was formerly known as The Pink Parrot Club, now returning back as an extension of the upstairs bar. Upstairs the atmosphere is more relaxed and social.

Jacomo's

88 Cowcross Street
Farringdon
London
EC1   Telephone 0171 553 7641

Nearest train station Farringdon
Nearest tube Farringdon
Car parking Plenty of space in the evening, but difficult during the day
A–Z ref. P62/5B
Nearest landmark Smithfield Market

Membership details None required
Opening hours   Monday–Friday: 12.00–23.00
                        Saturday: Closed (available for private hire)
                        Sunday: Closed
Admission charges None
Food available Full menu 12.00–15.00/bar snacks18.00–20.00
Regular entertainment No regular scheduled entertainment

Jacomo's is a mixed gay and lesbian venue, formerly the home of the Her/She bar, one of the first women only venues in London, which has now sadly finished. The venue is a bright modern venue with wooden floors and a minimalist decor. The room itself is divided with sofas and comfy chairs in addition to the traditional small bar-tables and chairs. The clientele during the day sees a mix of locals and suits from the nearby offices. However, the evenings seem to cater for a younger, more trendy crowd. Entertainment comes courtesy of the CD stacker and occasional DJ-hosted party nights.

The Joiners Arms

116–118 Hackney Road
London
E2 7QL   Telephone 0171 739 9854

Nearest train station Old Street
Nearest tube Old Street
Car parking Limited street parking but generally okay
A–Z ref. P63/3F
Nearest landmark Old Street Tube Station

Membership details None required
Opening hours   Monday–Saturday: 11.00–02.00
                        Sunday: 11.00–22.30
Admission charges None, except an occasional charge for specialist events
Food available Bar snacks available

Regular entertainment Tuesday–Wednesday: 'DJ Try-Outs' (new DJ talent): phone for further details
Thursday: Drink promotions/DJ
Friday–Saturday: DJ
Sunday: DJs all day

At the time of going to print the Joiners Arms were planning on opening the bar at 06.00 in the morning (Saturday–Monday) in order to accommodate the post-club crowd, offering hot drinks and refreshments (so for confirmation please phone the venue direct). At other times The Joiners is a large friendly traditional bar, open to all, irrespective of gender and creating a lively and fun atmosphere. There is a good mix of all ages, although at weekends, as you would expect, it is predominantly the eighteen to thirty-something crowd. There is a well- used pool table which is free every day from 12.00–17.00.

Jonathan's
1st Floor
16 Irving Street
Leicester Square
London
WC2   Telephone 0171 930 4770

Nearest train station Charing Cross
Nearest tube Leicester Square
Car parking None
A–Z ref. P61/7H

Membership details Membership is required–for details contact the club direct (new members welcome). Members' bona fide guests allowed
Opening hours   Monday–Saturday: 15.00–23.00
                       Sunday: 13.00–15.00/19.00–22.30
Admission charges None
Food available No
Regular entertainment There is no scheduled entertainment although there are happy hours daily:
Monday–Friday: 15.00–20.00
Saturday–Sunday: 15.00–22.30 (spirit and mixer £1!)

Jonathan's is a private West End drinking club which is over 50 years old and popular with locals, visitors and celebrities. The photographs on the wall show

Jonathan's

First Floor 16 Irving St
London WC2

☎ 0171 930 4770

Private west end drinking club, new members welcome. Friendly atmosphere with background music.

★ Happy Hour 3pm-8pm ★

(Open 3pm-11pm Mon-Sat and 3pm-10.30pm Sun.)

that the club has been (and still is) frequented by many gay media icons over its 50 year history, from Francis Bacon to Lily Savage. Situated in the heart of the West End the atmosphere, likened to a gay version of Cheers! where people actually talk to each other, is intimate, friendly and relaxed, with light background music and subdued (not dark) lighting. Situated on the first floor, Jonathan's is not the ideal place for the disco bunny, more for the intimate discreet rendezvous with a certain gentleman friend. This is strictly a members-only club and for details of this and their pricing system, then phone the venue direct. New members welcome.

King Edward VI

25 Bromfield Street
Islington
London
N1 0PZ   Telephone 0171 704 0745

Nearest train station Highbury and Islington (ten minute walk)
Nearest tube Angel Islington
Car parking Outside venue
A–Z ref. P62/2A
Nearest landmark Bromfield Street is off Liverpool Road

Membership Details None required
Opening hours   Monday–Sunday: 12.00–24.00
Admission charges   None except on scheduled party nights (nominal)
Food available Full restaurant facilities upstairs (very relaxing). Traditional Sunday lunch from 12.30 to 16.00 (free bottle of wine if two meals are ordered)

The Edward is one of North London's oldest gay bars and is well-known and very busy and is situated very close to The Complex (Popstarz' new home). Popular value-for-money Sunday lunches. Hosts of regular charity weekends in aid of worthy charitable organisations; always well-attended and always with top-of-the-range raffle prizes. In May 2000, they, along with about 15 other gay venues, will be part of the eleventh annual 'Pink Angels' weekend. This is a massive HIV/AIDS charitable event, so keep an eye on the gay press or enquire at the venue for details. During the summer months, their secluded beer garden opens up, offering you the opportunity to drink and dine *al fresco*.

King William IV

77 High Street
Hampstead
London
NW3 1RE   Telephone 0171 435 5747

Nearest train Hampstead
Nearest tube Hampstead
Car parking Always difficult during the day (easier at night)
A–Z ref. P44/4B
Nearest landmark Hampstead Tube Station

Membership details None required
Opening hours   Monday–Saturday: 12.00–23.00

Sunday: 12.00–22.30
Admission charges   None
Food available Full menu served Monday–Saturday: 12.00–18.00
Regular entertainment No scheduled regular entertainment

Probably one of London's oldest and truest pubs. 'Olde worlde' style setting with a relaxing front bar and cruisy rear bar. With its close proximity to Hampstead Heath (which is about a ten minute walk away) it doesn't take a brain-of-Britain to understand why this bar gets as busy as it does (there is even a boot scraper outside the front door!). When they were doing the quiz nights the most popular question was 'How many did you have?' It must be said that this isn't a cruise bar in the strictest sense of the word, although the, erm . . . *subtly lit* back bar does offer scope for those wet and windy nights if the Heath is out of bounds. During the summer, the colourful beer garden is opened up, offering the ideal venue for those lazy hazy afternoons.

Kings Arms

23 Poland Street
London
W1V 3DD   Telephone 0171 734 5907

Nearest train station Charing Cross
Nearest tube Oxford Circus
Car parking NCP close by
A–Z ref. P61/6G
Nearest landmark HMV on Oxford Street (Poland Street is opposite)

Membership details None required
Opening hours   Monday–Saturday: 11.00–23.00
                      Sunday: 12.00–22.30
Admission charges   None
Food available Full bar menu served up until 16.00
Regular entertainment Sunday: Karaoke (very busy)

Conveniently situated close to the shops at Oxford Circus, this traditional English pub offers a pleasant atmosphere with equally pleasant bar staff. Located several streets away from the Soho scene and attracting a smaller crowd, it still appeals to the 'after work' crowd. The venue is well-patronised for various

You want to see London?
call Pink Travel
The only way to really experience gay London

Londons only specialised in-bound gay and lesbian walking tours • hotels • transfers • guides.
Office hours 2-5pm

Contact Ralf@ Pink Travel
Studio 1, 51 Shirland Road London W9 2JD
T: +44 (0) 171 289 9744 F: +44 (0) 171 289 9744
E: pinktravel@btinternet.com

weekly and monthly meetings, such as 'Bear Hug' (for big men and their admirers) who use the upstairs bar on a Thursday, and interested parties can find out more by popping upstairs and speaking to the organiser. The venue can be pretty cruisy at times, although it is more of a social venue rather than a fully-fledged cruise bar. The age range is mixed, predominantly male and the atmosphere is friendly. Full range of gay press, maps and flyers available.

Ku Bar

75 Charing Cross Road
London
WC2H 0NE   Telephone 0171 437 4303

Nearest train station Charing Cross
Nearest tube Leicester Square
Car parking No chance
A–Z-ref. P61/6H

Membership details None required
Opening hours   Monday–Saturday: 12.00–23.00
                       Sunday: 12.00–22.30
Admission charges   None
Food available No

A large trendy bar over two levels, catering mainly for young gay men and women and their friends. A friendly establishment with candlelit tables upstairs and jukebox entertainment on the lower floor. The clientele tends to be a mix of suits and trendy guys and girls preparing to take on the town. Unfortunately, there is no draught beer or lager, only the bottled stuff which tends to be a little bit more expensive, but hey, who cares? We're on the pull. Situated next door but one to 79 CXR, this venue makes an ideal meeting place during the day with tables on the pavement or for a meeting place in the evening. Cocktail happy hours every day from 12.00 to 19.00.

Kudos Café Bar

10 Adelaide Street
London
WC2N 4HZ   Telephone 0171 379 4573
                Website http://www.kudos-bar.co.uk

Nearest train station Charing Cross
Nearest tube Charing Cross
Car parking NCP close by
A–Z-ref. P61/7J
Nearest landmark Charing Cross Station (across the road)

Membership details None required
Opening hours   Monday–Saturday: 11.00–23.00
                       Sunday: 12.00–22.30
Admission charges   None
Food available Full menu available at lunch-times
Regular entertainment Monday: 'Double Trouble' (cheap spirits)
Tuesday: 'Boogie Nights' (Retro)/cheap cans

Wednesday: Pre-Fruit Machine warm-up
Thursday: 'Crush Bar'
Saturday: Pre-Heaven warm-up

Down to earth, friendly cafe bar and restaurant. Seemingly very popular with businessmen during the day. Happy hour in the downstairs video bar is between 16.00–18.00. Thursday evenings offer 'Crush Nights', whereby every time a selected artist appears on the large screen video, all spirits are two for the price of one. The crowd is young and energetic and its prominence to Heaven makes it a natural staging area for all the disco dollies. Q-Jumper tickets for Heaven can be purchased here. Flyers for most of the major gay events happening in London and the complete range of the free gay press is also available.

Matrix
125 Cleveland Street
London
W1P 5PN   Telephone   0171 637 5352

Nearest train station   Euston (five minutes)
Nearest tube   Warren Street/Great Portland Street
Car parking   Limited street parking available
A–Z ref.   P61/5G
Nearest landmark   Post Office Tower

Membership details   None required
Opening hours   Monday–Saturday: 12.00–23.00
                                    Sunday: 12.00–22.30
Admission charges   None at present
Food available   Full menu at lunch-times and snacks in the evening
Matrix is the latest up-market gay bar to open in London. Stylish and trendy with a basement dance area featuring resident and guest DJs. A late licence has been applied for and once it comes through a scheduled entertainment policy can be arranged. Keep an eye on the gay press for further details.

Mis-Shapes @ The Crossbar
257 Pentonville Road
Kings Cross
London
N1   Telephone   0171 738 2336/0956 549 246 (Infoline)

Nearest train station   Kings Cross Thameslink
Nearest tube   Kings Cross/St Pancras
Car parking   Difficult
A–Z ref.   P61/2K
Nearest landmark   St Pancras Tube Station

Membership details   None required
Opening hours   Sunday: 20.00–02.00
                                    Every Sunday only
Admission charges   Free before 21.00/£2 between 21.00 and 21.30
                                    £2 NUS/UB40 all night (positive identification required)
                                    £3 with flyer or ad after 21.30

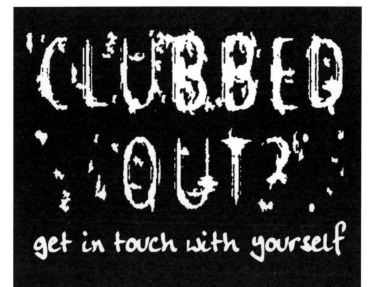

get in touch with yourself

chill out

with Isabella Sommerville

For a brochure, or an appointment
call Isabella on:

0171 610 1967 (24 hr)

Your **FREE** 30 mins consultation is
the first step in helping you find out
how easily you can get what
YOU want from life

Note: Licensing rules prohibit any entry *after* 22.30

Food available No

Regular entertainment Sunday: The official Popstarz Sunday Session. A mischievous mix of indie, rock, alternative pop, funk 'n' swing and the 80s thing, plus regular cheap drinks with a special £1 pint of lager between 21.00 and 22.00 (subject to change)

Due to the abrupt closure of Plastic People nightclub, Mis-Shapes suddenly became homeless to the homos! So where better to go than to its original home, The Crossbar. This time they are able to offer you so much more. The Crossbar has now been radically revamped (just like the Complex was) and now has a dance/club area and chill out space, combined with loads of special offers. You will be soooo impressed.

New Beginnings @ Central Station

37 Wharfdale Road
Kings Cross
London
N1 9ST   Telephone 0171 265 9655

Nearest train station Kings Cross/St Pancras
Nearest tube Kings Cross
Car parking Local NCP/street parking not too bad
A–Z ref. P61/2J
Nearest landmark Off York way by Kings Cross Station.
Admission charges None
                    Meeting times are Saturday: 19.45–20.45.

Founded in 1985, New Beginnings is a friendly and informal discussion group for people of all ages coming to terms with their sexuality. Each week there will be a different series of questions to be discussed on themes ranging from 'law and politics' and 'relationships' to 'soap operas' and 'spare time'. The hour-long discussion is only a means to an end: to break the ice and allow people to get talking to each other, and the question sheets are only there if people need them. Everyone is free to talk about whatever subject they want. The group arrives relatively early in order that they can carry on talking in the bar afterwards or go onto a club later. The group is there for people who are 'coming out': to help make the process a little less stressful, and to assure them that they are not alone. Those running the group have themselves been through exactly the same experiences, so anyone who comes on a Saturday night can be sure that everyone knows how they feel. To find out more about the group or to get someone to meet you there, phone the above contact number. You won't be sorry.

The Oak Bar

79 Green Lanes
Islington
London
N16 9BU   Telephone 0171 354 2791

Nearest train station Canonbury
Nearest tube Manor House or Angel
Car parking Ample side-street parking
A–Z ref. P46/4D
Nearest landmark Newington Green roundabout

Membership details None required
Opening hours   Monday–Thursday: 17.00–24.00
                                    Friday: 17.00–02.00
                                    Saturday: 17.00–02.00
                                    Saturday ('Baghdad'): 21.00–02.00
                                    Sunday: 17.00–24.00
                                    (Strictly no admissions after midnight)
Admission charges None except for club nights which are never above £5 and
                                    are usually cheaper before 23.00
Food available Bar snacks available daily
Regular entertainment Monday: 'Happy Mondays DJ' (60s-90s) and cheap
drinks
Thursday: Pub quiz night
Friday: 'Kiss': women only (house, garage and trash)–very popular
Saturday: Every first Saturday of the month is 'Odyssey' (deep soul, jazz and
house); every
third Saturday is 'Baghdad' (Asian feel) and every last Saturday is 'Club Ha'de'
(Turkish,
Greek and Arabic, mixed with soul, funk and garage)
Sunday: 'Tequila Rush Hour' (50p when you hear 'that' tune)/MTV/karaoke
(Happy hour is Monday–Thursday: 17.00–20.00, with all pints at £1.50)

'Kiss' is a popular women-only weekly night with resident DJs Heidi High and
Little Miss Twins. 'Odyssey' is a once a month club night with DJs Nikki Lucas
and Ms Bailey (Precious Brown) and David Campbell. 'Baghdad' is a once a month
lesbian and gay event brought to you by the people who run Club Kali, with DJs
Nikki Lucas and DJ Ritu plus special guests playing Salsa, Rai, Bhangra,
Zoukous, etc. Phone 0181 809 1777 for further information. Recently refurbished, The Oak Bar is a great venue, particularly popular with the ladies. Stylish
furnishings, fantastic atmosphere, friendly helpful staff and an unpretentious air
. . . is it 'freaky' or 'unique'? You decide!

The Penny Farthing

135 King Street
Hammersmith
London
W6 9JG   Telephone 0181 600 0941

Nearest train station Hammersmith
Nearest tube Hammersmith
Car parking NCP/street parking/meters
A–Z ref. P74/4E
Nearest landmark Hammersmith Palace

Membership details None required
Opening hours   Monday–Saturday: 12.00–02.00
                                    Sunday: 12.00–22.30
Admission charges Monday–Wednesday: Free
                                    Thursday–Saturday: £2 after 22.30
                                    Sunday: Free
Food available
Sunday: 12.00–16.00

Regular entertainment Tuesday: Quiz night
Wednesday: Social
Thursday: DJ/cabaret
Friday: Cabaret
Saturday: Drag cabaret/ DJ
Sunday: Cabaret/karaoke

A busy little pub in the evenings and at weekends. Good cabaret policy throughout the latter part of the week. When the sun shines the beer garden out the back gets absolutely packed. New female management team took over in January 1999 and aims to adapt the cabaret to cater for the ever increasing girl crowd.

Pleasure In Streams (PIS) @ Central Station
Skins FC @ Central Station
37 Wharfdale Road
Kings Cross
London
N1 9ST   Telephone 07970 467 343 (info)/0171 278 3294 (Central Station)
E-Mail (PIS) pislondon@hotmail.com/(Skins FC) skinsfc@hotmail.com
Website http://www.jadzia.demon.co.uk/pis/

Nearest train station Kings Cross/St Pancras
Nearest tube Kings Cross
Car parking Street parking not bad
A–Z ref. P61/2J
Nearest landmark Off York Way by Kings Cross Station

Membership details None required
Opening hours   PIS: Every first Sunday of the month: 15.00–24.00
                         Skins FC: Every fourth Sunday of the month: 17.00–24.00
Admission charges £5 each event
                         Free entry to Skins FC if you are wearing a Spurs football
                         shirt!

Pleasure In Streams is the United Kingdom's first watersports club, taking place in the basement of Central Station on the first Sunday of every month. The first event in January was a raging success with more than 150 enthusiasts turning up to enjoy what was on offer. Since then the event has attracted notoriety nationwide as the place to go for wet fun and games with an average attendance of over 300 passing through the doors at each event. The 15.00 start attracts a lot of early risers, and the pleasure is definitely coming in streams by 16.00, with no shortage of tap heads and willing drinkers, with the momentum carrying on all through the night. The clientele are stunning; a great mix of skins, bears, footie lads, the odd muscle guy and of course the obligatory walking plumbing-supply-catalogue fan. If you have ever thought that you might like to try it, but don't want to invest in a full-face rubber mask and matching suit (or just don't want to wear one then either turn up at the door or phone the above numbers for further details. (The promoters will show you around and introduce you to the 'scene'.) Please bear in mind that the phone number belongs to Central Station. The infoline number and e-mail address belong to PIS promoters who will be able to supply you with all the information you require. Alternatively, you can write to PIS, c/o Central Station and the letter will be forwarded on.

Skins F.C. is London's newest club night run by the same promoters that stage PIS, so you know this event is going to be huge. For Skins F.C. there will be a strict dress code of skinhead gear, and rugby/footy kit. As far as the music policy goes, it will obviously include a mix of ska, 2-tone, indie, pop, etc. The atmosphere at the club will of course be cruisy but overall, the emphasis will be friendly and strictly 'no politics'. Further information is available through the above contacts.

Popstarz @ The Complex

1–5 Parkfield Street
Islington
London
N1   Telephone 0171 738 2336/0956 549 246 (infoline)/0973 739 534
                   (infoline)

Nearest train station Kings Cross (walk up Pentonville Road)
Nearest tube The Angel
Car parking Side-street parking
A–Z ref. P62/2A
Nearest landmark Angel Tube Station

Membership details None required
Opening hours   Friday: 22.00–04.00
Admission charges   NUS/UB40: £4 before 23.00/£5 after
                      With flyer/ad: £5 before 23.00/£6 after
                      All others: £8

Food available No

Popstarz has now well and firmly settled into their new home at The Complex (formerly The Paradise Club) which was the original place where the innovation began. The venue has been totally transformed into a state-of-the-art club whilst retaining the original feel of The Paradise. It is now twice as big and spans four floors, enabling Popstarz to offer even more to London's gay clubbers. Level one (Beats Basement): Take a fast pace forward through big beat, breakbeats, alternative dance and old school hip-hop. Level two (Common Room): The Popstarz Allstarz' DJs playing top indie and alternative 'toonz' to keep you jumping. Level three (The Rubbish Room): The best, worst and simply the most inspired 80s trash and triumph known to London's gay scene. Level four (The Love Lounge): Sensational 60s and 70s sounds centring on funky Motown and dynamic disco in this red velvet room. Popstarz brought gay London its first major indie club based at the Paradise. Now, the return to The Complex after three years will bring London its *ultimate* indie alternative night, putting to shame other alternative clubs on either the gay or straight scene. Q-Jump tickets for £5 are available every Friday night at 'The Pre-Popstarz Penniless Piss-Up' at The Retro Bar (see separate listing). See listings also for Mis-shapes @ The Crossbar and Wig Out @ The Tube.

The Princess Of Wales

18 Wilmont Street
Woolwich
London
SE18   Telephone 0181 316 0229

Nearest train station Woolwich Arsenal

popstarz

every Friday

10pm at THE COMPLEX, **4am**
1-5 PARKFIELD ST.,
ISLINGTON, LONDON N1

LEVEL ONE: BEATS BASEMENT
Take a fast paced trip through
Big Beat, Chemical Beats,
Breakbeats, Old School Hip
Hop and Alternative Dance.

LEVEL TWO: COMMON ROOM
The popstarz allstarz DJ's
playing top Indie and
Alternative toonz to keep
you jumping.

**LEVEL THREE:
THE RUBBISH ROOM**
The best, the worst and
simply the most inspired
80's trash and triumph
known to London's gay
scene.

**LEVEL FOUR:
THE LOVE LOUNGE**
Sensational 60's and 70's
sounds centering on funky
motown and dynamic disco
in this swish red velvet
room!

**advance QJump tickets
and 2 for 1 drinks offers
available Every Friday from:**

CENTRAL ▫ The Retro Bar,
2 George Court (off the Strand,
by the Halifax) 8pm-midnight
0171-321 2811

NORTH ▫ The Angel Bar,
65, Graham St, Islington N1
8pm-midnight 0171-608 2656

NUS/UB40 - £4 B4 11pm / £5 after
FLYER/AD - £5 B4 11pm / £6 after
otherwise £8

info: 0171-738 2336 / 0956-549246

Nearest tube None
Car parking Street parking
A–Z ref. P83/4F
Nearest landmark Somerfields Supermarket

Membership details None required
Opening hours   Monday–Saturday: 12.00–23.00
                                 Sunday: 12.00–22.30
                                 Late licence applied for, so opening times may be extended
                                 in the coming year
Admission charges None
Food available Food facility planned for the future
Regular entertainment Monday: 'That Monday Feeling'/drink promos
Tuesday: 'Tuesday Teaser'–quiz with a difference (it could be that you are given the answer
and you have to guess what the question was–perhaps not!)
Wednesday: 'Comedy Night'–stand-up comedy
Thursday: 'Various'–A pot-pourri of pure pleasure from live music to 'search for a star'
Friday: 'SEX' (Seventies-Eighties Xtravaganza)
Saturday: 'SHAG': Saturday Handbag And Garage (very busy)
Sunday: Alternating between 'Krazy Karaoke' and 'Fun and Games'

One of the trendiest and smartest bars in East London without the high drinks prices. Recently refurbished to make one large open-plan room with a separate games and pool room. The Princess is billed as an Attitude-Free Zone, which

**the
ultimate
GAY
guide**

Tell us what you think

Ultimate Guides
PO Box 64
Manchester
M7 4NZ

email
ugg@ic24.net

(or you can use the form at
the back of this book)

Princess
of
Wales

*Friendly south east London gay
local with a mixed clientele.
A welcoming relaxed atmosphere,
Popular music policy.
Recently refurbished bar plus
garden and games room.
Open normal pub hours.
Occasional entertainment and
special nights.*

**18 Wilmount Street
Woolwich SE18
0181 354 3403**

means that age and sex will not be an issue. New manager Chris (top bloke) is going to ensure that this friendly venue provides you with non-stop fun and games from Monday to Sunday guaranteeing that you will be coming back for more. Age range is predominantly young (with a high proportion of students) and the music is loud. Excellent! Checkout the listing for sister venue The Ram Bar in Islington.

Queens Arms
203 Hanworth Road
Hounslow
Middlesex
TW3 3UA   Telephone 0181 230 0700

Nearest train station Hounslow
Nearest tube Hounslow Central (ten minutes)
Car parking On-site/street parking after 18.30
A–Z ref. P87/4F
Nearest landmark Community Centre on Hanworth Road

Membership details
None required
Opening hours   Monday–Friday: 12.00–23.00
                         Saturday: 11.00–23.00
                         Sunday: 12.00–22.30
Admission charges   None (except for special cabaret nights)
Food available Full menu available lunch-times/snacks available evenings
Regular entertainment Tuesday: 60s and 70s
Friday: 'Nikki's Strut' (cheesy disco and well-known sounds)
Saturday: 'I Want Candy' (cover version classics brought into the nineies)
Sunday: 'Jules Sorta Soul' (soul sounds/classic disco)

Exclusive gay and lesbian venue. Sundays tend to get a large lesbian following. Lots of newcomers to the venue who are always made to feel welcome by the friendly staff (they even advise that you pop in during the day for a chat). Another excellent place for the newcomer to the scene to start with. There's a large, imposing waterfall on the dance floor! This is an anti-drug venue (if you take them when you're out–go somewhere else!).

The Queens Arms
63 Courthill Road
Lewisham
London
SE13   Telephone 0181 318 7305

Nearest train station Ladywell/Lewisham
Nearest tube None (DLR coming shortly)
Car parking Street parking
A–Z ref. P96/4E
Nearest landmark Jasmin's Bingo Hall

Membership details None required

Opening hours	Monday–Friday: 14.00–23.00
	Saturday: 12.00–Late
	Sunday: 12.00–22.30

Admission charges None
Food available No
Regular entertainment Monday: Social
Tuesday: Vocalists
Wednesday: Quiz night (£1 entry: winner takes all–cash prize)
Thursday: 'Guyz meet Guyz' (singles night)
Friday: 'Boogie Night' (70s and 80s)/resident DJs
Saturday: Top cabaret night
Sunday: Vocalist

South-East London's smart up-market and friendly gay bar. Bar prices are amongst the lowest in the area with the addition of regular happy hours which means that the bar is nearly always busy, with a predominantly young crowd getting pissed for a lot less moolah. Beer garden and BBQ opens up in the Summer.

The Queens Head

27 Tryon Street
Chelsea
London
SW3 3LG   Telephone 0171 589 0262

Nearest train station Victoria (ten minute walk)
Nearest tube Sloane Square (five minute walk)
Car parking Limited street parking
A–Z ref. P76/5D
Nearest landmark Sloane Square

Membership details None required
Opening hours   Monday–Saturday: 11.00–23.00
                                      Sunday: 11.00–22.30
Admission charges None
Food available Simple food at reasonable prices 11.00–21.30

A cosy and traditional single floor venue with three bars. A gay bar even before it was legal (knock three times on the shutter and say 'I'm a friend of Quentin's')! Every month or so they organise a themed party, such as a 'beach party', when all the floor is covered in sand, sun loungers, pina coladas, etc. or, a 'garden party', where the floor is covered in turf, with more than one queen roaming around, cucumber sandwiches, etc. (phone the venue for details of the next spectacular). Mixed age range from 18 upwards and the friendly atmosphere ensures everyone gets along just fine.

The Railway Tavern

576 Commercial Road
London
E14 7JD   Telephone 0171 790 2360

Nearest train station Limehouse DLR

Nearest tube Tower Hill
Car parking Limited street parking
A–Z ref. P64/6A
Nearest landmark Rotherhithe Tunnell Approach

Membership details None required
Opening hours   Monday–Saturday: 11.00–23.00
                        Sunday: 11.00–22.30
                        (Late licence applied for at time of going to print–phone for
                        new opening hours)
Admission charges None
Food available Main menu 12.00–15.00/18.00–19.30 and bar snacks are
available at all other times
Regular entertainment Monday: Social night
Friday: DJ/cabaret
Saturday: DJ/cabaret/karaoke (alternating)
Sunday: Cabaret

Another venue that has recently undergone a complete refurbishment programme. This venue is now a modern, bright and very trendy open-plan room
with two raised areas with comfortable seating.

The Ram Bar
39 Queens Head Street
Islington
London
N1 8NQ   Telephone 0171 354 0576

Nearest train station Essex Road
Nearest tube Angel Islington
Car parking Street parking
A–Z ref. P62/1B
Nearest landmark Islington Green

Membership details None required
Opening hours   Monday–Friday: 17.00–23.00
                        Saturday: 14.00–24.00
                        Sunday: 14.00–22.30
Admission charges None
Food available Snacks only
Regular entertainment No regular scheduled entertainment

The Ram Bar has been operating as a gay-only bar since 1992. The present owners
have been here for three years and have gradually improved the decor and
facilities. The bar is attended by a largely mixed gay and local crowd. It
comprises a lounge bar with seating and an intimate atmosphere. In addition to
this there is also a second bar with darts and a pool table.

Reflex
184 London Road
Kingston upon Thames
Surrey
KT2 6QW   Telephone 0181 549 9911

Nearest train station Norbiton BR

Nearest tube None
Car parking Ample street parking
A–Z ref. P118/2F
Nearest landmark Kingston Hospital (two minutes walk)

Membership details £99 per year (phone or enquire at the club for details)
Opening hours   Monday–Thursday: Closed (available for private hire)
                       Friday–Saturday: 21.00–03.00
                       Sunday: Various event (see gay press or phone venue for
                       details)
Admission charges Friday: £3 before 23.00/£5 after
                     Saturday: £5 all night
                     Sunday: Various
Food available Bar snacks available
Regular entertainment Friday: Dance anthems/Cabaret
Saturday: 'Dance Party Night' (hot and horny)

A fully air-conditioned, friendly, attitude-free gay club, with happy uplifting
sounds from resident DJs Steve Lush and Miss Annabelle. There are different
events running through the week organised by various promoters. Keep an eye
on the gay press or phone the venue direct for further information.

The Retro Bar

2 George Court
London
WC2   Telephone 0171 321 2811

Outlines   from Absolute press

A delightful collection of monographs
detailing the loves and lives of some
of the most prolific gay and lesbian
creative artists of this century.
  Titles in the series:
  David Hockney
  Benjamin Britten
  Bessie Smith
  We are Michael Field
  Federico Garcia Lorca
  Arthur Rimbaud
  k.d. lang
  Armistead Maupain
  Tallulah Bankhead

The Ram Bar
39 Queens Head St.
Islington London N1
☎ 0171 359 6258

**Friendly North
London local Bar.
Pool and darts
bar popular with
the lads!
Relaxed and
comfortable main
bar attracting a
mixed crowd.
Great place to
meet and make
friends.
Party music
and warm-up
atmosphere at
the weekends.**

Nearest train station Charing Cross
Nearest tube Charing Cross
Car parking Difficult/possible street parking in evening
A–Z ref. P61/7J
Nearest landmark Charing Cross Tube Station (George Court is off St Martins Lane)

Membership details None required
Opening hours   Monday–Saturday: 12.00–23.00
                       Sunday: 12.00–22.30
Admission charges None
Food available No
Regular entertainment Monday: 'Room 2': indie dance club
Tuesday: 'Pop Quiz'
Wednesday: Retro Karaoke
Thursday: 'DIY DJ' (new DJ try-outs)
Friday: 'Pre-Popstarz Penniless Piss Up' (very busy)
Saturday: 'DJ Lush'
Sunday: Social/chill out

Friendly young gay bar playing the best in music from the 70s and 80s as well as loads of indie thrown in to please just about everybody. The most important night will be Friday when the Retro Bar becomes the official Pre-Popstarz meet-up bar. Cheap drinks ensure that the brilliant Popstarz night goes with a bang (see separate listing for Popstarz).

The Rocket

10–13 Churchfield Road
Acton
London
W3 6BD   Telephone 0181 992 1545

Nearest train station Acton Central
Nearest tube None
Car parking Ample side-street parking
A–Z ref. P73/1J
Nearest landmark Acton Central Station (practically next door)

Membership details None required
Opening hours   Monday–Friday: 18.00–23.00
                       Saturday: 12.00–23.00
                       Sunday: 12.00–22.30
Admission charges None except for £2 cloakroom charge on Sunday
Food available Sunday: snacks available
Regular entertainment Monday: 'Singles Night' in Kirks
Tuesday: Film night (large screen TV)
Thursday: Quiz night
Friday: Drag cabaret
Saturday: Drag cabaret/'Cruise In The Dark' (upstairs)
Sunday: 'Underwear Day' (men-only upstairs)

The Rocket is divided into two parts. 'Kirks' club is the upstairs part and hosts the popular 'Underwear Day' on Sunday and the even more popular 'Cruise In

The Dark' on Saturday. There's also always something going on in the downstairs cabaret bar.

The Royal Oak

73 Columbia Road
Bethnal Green
London
E2 7RG   Telephone 0171 739 8204

Nearest train station Bethnal Green
Nearest tube Old Street (five minutes)
Car parking Side street parking
A–Z ref. P63/3F
Nearest landmark Old Market Square

Membership details None required
Opening hours   Monday–Thursday: 13.00–23.00
                         Friday–Saturday: 13.00–Late
                         Sunday: 08.00–Late
Admission charges None
Food available Sunday morning breakfasts

A large old-fashioned pub with a lot of character and history. It is the very pub that *Goodnight Sweetheart* (amongst others) was filmed in. The Sunday 08.00 breakfast licence is that old it's probably carved in stone, and was granted for the famous flower market right outside the pub (providing ample opportunity to do your Eliza Dolittle and Mr 'iggins repertoire). Sunday mornings do see an influx

Outlines   from Absolute Press

A delightful collection of monographs detailing the loves and lives of some of the most prolific gay and lesbian creative artists of this century.
 Titles in the series:
 David Hockney
 Benjamin Britten
 Bessie Smith
 We are Michael Field
 Federico García Lorca
 Arthur Rimbaud
 k.d. lang
 Armistead Maupin
 Tallulah Bankhead

The Royal Oak
73 Columbia Road
London
E2 7RG
Tel: 0207 739 8204

The Place To Be!!!

Monday-Saturday: 11.00-Late
Sunday: 08.00-14.00
(for Full English and Full Vegetarian English breakfasts)

Private parties catered for, see listing

of late-night clubbers poppping in for a bite to eat and to chill out from their late night revelling. Also hosts popular once-a-month charity nights in aid of various worthy charities and the party atmosphere ensures the place is packed to the rafters to watch the drag acts (singers/cabaret/strippers/etc.). Predominantly a mixed (90%) gay bar but all are welcome.

Royal Vauxhall Tavern

372 Kennington Lane
London
SE11 5QH   Telephone 0171 582 0833

Nearest train station Vauxhall Cross
Nearest tube Vauxhall
Car parking Limited street parking
A–Z ref. P77/5K
Nearest landmark Vauxhall Cross mainline station

Membership details None required
Opening hours   Monday–Saturday: 21.00–02.00
                       Sunday: 12.00–24.00
Admission charges   Monday: Free admission
                       Tuesday: £2 after 23.00
                       Wednesday–Thursday: Free admission
                       Friday: £3 (women only night)
                       Saturday: £4
                       Sunday: £2 between 15.00–18.00/£3 after
Food available No
Regular entertainment Monday: Karaoke
Tuesday: Youth club
Wednesday: 'Wig 'n' Casino' (Homo northern soul review)
Thursday: Cabaret with Regina Fong and DJ Simon Le Vans
Friday: 'Vixens' (women only–infoline: 0181 671 1221)
Saturday: 'Duckie'–with Amy Lame
Sunday: 'Dame Edna Experience' Cabaret/Evening Disco 'Chill Out After 4'

This was one of Lily Savage's early hangouts (and you can see where she gets it from). A lively venue where there is strictly no attitude and every evening is rife with fun. Weekends tend to be packed to capacity, particularly on Saturday evening with 'Duckie' (a different theme every week). *Note*: This venue is under threat of closure by developers and there is no guarantee as to how long they will leave this national institution alone. Only time will tell.

Rupert Street

50 Rupert Street/Archer Street
Soho
London
W1V 7HR   Telephone 0171 292 7141

Nearest train station Charing Cross (taxi from here)
Nearest tube Piccadilly Circus/Soho
Car parking No, no, no . . .

A–Z ref. P61/7H
Nearest landmark Windmill Theatre

Membership details None required
Opening hours Monday–Saturday: 12.00–23.00
Sunday: 12.00–22.30
Admission charges None
Food available Yes

One of the newest bars in Soho. Very up market and so is the clientele. Good place to bring someone whom you are trying to impress, although you will soon be sussed when you go to pay the bar tab!

The Sister George (formerly The Wonder Bar)

Hugh Street
Victoria
London
SW1   Telephone 0171 592 9911

Nearest train station Victoria Mainline
Nearest tube Victoria (two minuutes)
Car parking Limited street parking difficult during the day/car park
A–Z ref. P77/4F
Nearest landmark Behind Victoria Station

Membership details Free at venue
Opening hours Monday–Wednesday: Closed
Thursday–Saturday: 17.00–23.00
Sunday: 14.00–22.30
Admission charges None
Food available Value for money Sunday lunch
Regular entertainment Thursday: 'Sin-Girls Night'
Friday: 'Disco Party Night'
Saturday: DJ (commercial dance)
Sunday: Chill Out/pool and games

The Sister George is situated in the basement of The George (a straight pub popular with business folk). However, there is absolutely no conflict and over time the two bars work extremely well. This is a women's only bar with men allowed in (at the manager's discretion) as guests. The atmosphere is friendly and welcoming, with people willing to come over and introduce themselves. There is no attitude and never any trouble. The age range is across the board. At the 'Sin-Girls (Singles) Night' you are handed half a playing card. You are then supposed to find the corresponding half-card for you and your new partner to claim a free drink. You don't have to take it seriously and you will not be expected to shack up with your new found lover. It's just a brilliant way to meet new friends.

The Spiral Staircase

138 Shoreditch High Street
London
E1 6JE   Telephone 0171 613 1351

Nearest train station Liverpool Street
Nearest tube Liverpool Street/Old Street
Car parking Limited side-street parking
A–Z ref. P62/4E
Nearest landmark Opposite Shoreditch Church

Membership details Not necessary but available for discounted door entry
(enquire at venue)
Opening hours	Monday–Tuesday: Closed (available for private hire)
	Wednesday–Thursday: 22.00–02.00
	Friday–Saturday: 21.00–04.00
	Sunday: 21.00–03.30
Admission charges	Wednesday: Free
	Thursday: £1
	Friday–Saturday: Free before 23.00/£2.50 members/£3.50
	non-members
	Sunday: Free before 23.00/£2.50 members/£5 non-members
	(No admission after 03.30)

Regular entertainment Wednesday: Chill out (something major happening soon)
Thursday: 70s-90s Disco (trash and handbag)
Friday: Karaoke (very busy)
Saturday: Cabaret/DJ Gibbo (camp, trashy handbag)
Sunday: 'Piano Bar' with (well-known) popular pianist Ian Parker
(Drink promotions always available)

Entertainment may change over the months but the regular discos are always on.
Newly refurbished with video cameras showing the punters in the venue on
large TV monitors. I think it's for saving you the trouble of trolling around the
joint. Excellent new sound and lighting system installed. Very busy venue at all
times.

Substation @ Soundshaft

Hungerford Lane
Charing Cross
London
WC2   Telephone 0171 278 0995

Nearest train station Charing Cross
Nearest tube Charing Cross
Car parking Limited street parking
A–Z ref. P77/1J
Nearest landmark Charing Cross Station

Membership details Available at £15 per year (entitles reduced door charges)
Opening hours	Tuesday–Wednesday: 22.30–03.30
	Friday: 22.30–05.00
	Saturday: 22.00–05.00
Admission charges	Tuesday–Wednesday: £3/£2 Members
	Friday–Saurday: £7/£6 Members
	(Promotional flyers/ads available for reduced admission)

Regular entertainment Tuesday: 'Twisted' (New York house and garage)
Wednesday: 'Love Bite' (indie)/cheap drinks
Friday: 'Spunk' (underground house)

Saturday: 'Renegades' (uplifting dance from the Renegades crew)
(phone for details of Monday, Thursday and Sunday events (not available at
time of press)

Well and truly settled down in their 'new' venue, following the recent move
from their old home at Dean Street. A little bit of a name change from Substation
Soho to Substation @ Soundshaft, but still the same old late-night-slut-hut. Just
as cruisy and still loads of men. Not as hard as Substation South, but definitely
not for the faint of heart and prudish. Dont say you weren't warned. Door policy
of mixed gay and TV crowd–mainly male. See listing for Substation South also.

Substation South

Units 1–4
9 Brighton Terrace
Brixton
London
SW9 8DJ   Telephone 0171 737 2095

Nearest train station Brixton
Nearest tube Brixton
Car parking Residential streets
A–Z ref. P93/4K
Nearest landmark Top of Brixton Hill (by station)

Membership details Available at £15 per year (entitles reduced entry fee)
Opening hours   Monday: 22.00–03.00 (Gay and bi men only)
                         Tuesday: 22.30–02.00 (Gay and bi men only)

Outlines   from Absolute Press

A delightful collection of monographs
detailing the loves and lives of some
of the most prolific gay and lesbian
creative artists of this century.
 Titles in the series:
 David Hockney
 Benjamin Britten
 Bessie Smith
 We are Michael Field
 Federico García Lorca
 Arthur Rimbaud
 k.d. lang
 Armistead Maupin
 Tallulah Bankhead

ROSE COLLIS

SubStation South

**LONDON'S HOTTEST
CRUISE BAR**

Mon - Thurs 10.30pm - 2am
Fri 10.30pm - 5am
Sat 10.30pm - 6am
Sun 10.30pm - 3am

DJs Every Night,
Pool & Videos

9 Brighton Terrace,
Brixton, SW9
Brixton Tube
0171 737 2095

	Wednesday: 22.30–03.00 (Gay and bi men only)
	Thursday: 22.30–03.00 (Mixed gay/bi/TVs)
	Friday: 22.30–05.00 (Mixed gay/bi/TVs)
	Saturday: 22.30–06.00 (Mixed gay/bi/TVs)
	Sunday: 22.00–Late (Mixed gay/bi/TVs)

Admission charges   Monday: £4/£3 Members
Tuesday–Thursday: £3/£2 Members
Friday: £5/£4 Members
Saturday: £6/£5 Members
Sunday: £3/£2 Members
(Promotional ads available in most gay press for reduced door entry)

Food available No
Regular entertainment Monday: 'Y-Front Night'
Tuesday: 'Massive'
Wednesday: 'Bootcamp'
Thursday: 'Blackout'
Friday: 'Dirty Dishes'
Saturday: 'Queer nation'
Sunday: 'Marvellous'

Cruisy, dark, dancy, fun, and sexy basement bar catering for a wide range of gay boys and girls. Changing area available for underwear parties. This large late night bar is a lot cruisier than its older sister at The Soundshaft, hosting some well hot and sleazy nights. There are door policies for each night (see opening hours above). Further to this, each night of the week is also themed. Monday is 'Y-front night' (dress code: underwear only). Tuesday is 'Massive' (for big guys, bodybuilders and their admirers). Wednesday is 'Bootcamp' (dress code: preferred uniform, leather, jocks and boots; music: commercial house and disco). Thursday is 'Blackout' (dark and cruisy fun). Friday is 'Dirty Dishes' (hard house–very busy mixed gay night). Saturday is 'Queer Nation': (garage+) guest DJs. Sunday is 'Marvellous' (indie/Brit- pop/new wave/punk). If you are not sure what is happening when, then give them a ring.

Ted's Place
305A North End Road
Fulham
London
W14   Telephone 0171 385 9359

Nearest train station Kensington Olympia
Nearest tube West Kensington
Car parking Immediate side roads
A–Z ref. P75/5H
Nearest landmark West Kensington Tube Station

Membership details £15 per annum for free admission (non-members are also welcome)
Opening hours   Monday–Wednesday: 18.00–23.00
Thursday: 19.00–23.00
Friday: 18.00–23.00
Saturday–Sunday: Closed

Admission charges   Guests £2/members free
Food available   Snacks only
Regular entertainment   Monday–Tuesday: 'Seed': men-only night (for men who like their men rough!)
Wednesday: Karaoke/Quiz Night
Thursday: 'TV/TS' (limited changing facilities available)
Friday: 'Seed' men-only night

Situated on the junction of Lillie Road, this predominantly men-only basement bar is extremely popular with TVs/TSs on Thursday evenings, and rough trade during the week. The clientele are extremely diverse (not your average 'in crowd') which makes the place more of an experience. Although the 'Seed' nights are strictly men-only, on Wednesday and Thursday the doors are open to all.

The Townhouse

3 Green Street
Mayfair
London
W1Y 3RG   Telephone 0171 499 4489   Fax 0171 493 7342
                 Website http://www.thetownhouse.co.uk

Nearest train station Marylebone/Victoria
Nearest tube Bond Street/Marble Arch
Car parking Free off-street parking after 18.30, Monday–Friday and after 13.30 on
Saturday and all day Sunday
A–Z ref. P60/7E
Nearest landmark Marble Arch (venue is just off Park Lane)

Membership details Membership is structured to various levels: Junior £50/ Country & Overseas £90 (limited to 12 visits per annum)/Silver £175/Gold £350/ Life £850 (temporary membership is available upon request–phone for complete membership structure)

Opening hours   Club bar and lounge:
                       Monday–Saturday: 18.00–01.30
                       Sunday: Closed
Admission charges   Members free
                       Up to four guests admitted free on a member's Gold and
                       Life membership card
                       One guest allowed in for free on all other types of
                       membership and additional guests (up to a maximum of six)
                       will be charged at £5 per guest
                       Higher number of guests admitted with prior arrangement
                       with the management
Food available
Conservatory restaurant/private dining room: open for dinner (last orders for dinner at midnight). Snacks available until midnight

The Townhouse is London's most exclusive gay members-only club aimed at professional gay men and their friends, enabling them to meet in luxurious surroundings for drinks, meals, conversation or just to relax. Monday sees 'Monday's Child' where 19–25 year-old studying professionals and young professionals join the regulars (annual membership £10/£2 on the door for non-members). On Tuesday evenings from 18.00 to 01.00, The Townhouse plays host to 'Gay London Professionals' (GLP). Membership to this 'club' is only £75 per year. Members of GLP are able to sign in one guest and additional guests will be charged £5. Wednesday welcomes the members and guests of 'Significant Others', London's premier gay introduction agency. Thursday is 'Thursday International', where the many ethnic and multi- cultural groups meet together to socialise with the Townhouse members–a very lively event. Facilities at the club include a club lounge with an intimate atmosphere and pre-restaurant drinks making for a good meeting place. There's also a conservatory restaurant which is glass roofed and extends from the club lounge. It serves modern European food and vegetarian meals are also available. The club bar (maple and ash panelled walls) has a lively atmosphere and there is also a dining room with traditional décor, which is available for private hire–complete with it's own butler. Otherwise it is open as a more formal environment in which to dine than the conservatory restaurant. Dress code is smart/smart-casual. Write or phone for further details.

The Tube

5–6 Falconberg Court
London
W1   Telephone   0171 287 3726/0171 738 2336 ('Wig Out' infoline)

Nearest train station Charing Cross or Kings Cross
Nearest tube Tottenham Court Road
Car parking Extremely limited
A–Z ref. P61/6H
Nearest landmark The Astoria, Tottenham Court Road

Membership details None at present
Opening hours   Wednesday: 22.30–03.30
                       Friday: 22.00–06.00
                       Saturday: 22.00–04.00
Admission charges Wednesday: £3 all night
                       Friday: £6 (with flyer/ad)/£5 concessions/£7 other
                       Saturday: £6 (with flyer/ad/£5 concessions/£7 other
Food available Limited snacks
Regular entertainment Wednesday: 'Mama Mia' (commercial pop)
Friday: 'Rush'
Saturday: 'Wig Out' (trash disco)

'Wig Out' is a trash disco night promoted by the boys who bring you 'Popstarz'. This night is popular with students and disco bunnies alike, who all have one thing in common–get pissed and party! 'Rush' was recently launched by David Cross (Melt) as a replacement for 'Babe'. The first to take the decks is Diddy at 22.00 for a two hour set, followed by Marc Andrews till 04.00, with Wayne G taking over to bring the night to a close at 06.00, leaving the massive crowd screaming for more. Situated behind The Astoria (G.A.Y), The Tube has now been open for over three years and has established itself as one of London's more diverse West End clubs. Music policy is varied throughout the week. Although it is a predominantly gay venue, a small percentage of gay-friendly straights are allowed in, ensuring a good mix of clientele. The Tube does have its fair share of cruising going on, plenty of secluded areas, nooks and crannies, etc. Dance, cruise . . . what more do you want?

Turnmills

63B Clerkenwell Road
Farringdon
London
EC1   Telephone 0171 250 340/0171 607 5700 (Trade infoline)/0171
               250 3409 (Melt infoline)
               Website (Melt): http://www.tagrecords.co.uk/melt

Nearest train station Farringdon
Nearest tube Farringdon
Car parking Easy street parking all night
A–Z ref. P62/4B
Nearest landmark Farringdon Stations (one minute from entrance)

Membership details
Trade: £35 per year and then £25 renewals (apply by phone). Although membership is not required, admission priority is given to members
Melt: None required but available for reduced entry
Opening hours   Trade: Sunday: 04.00–13.00
               Melt: Sunday: 22.00–08.00 (Sunday into Monday)
Admission charges   Trade: £10 for memebers/£15 for guests
               Melt: £5 before 23.00/£10 after
               (Discounts with flyers from gay press and bars. Priority
               entrance given to members at busy times)

Either night at Turnmills is an absolutely unique experience. This place has to be seen to be believed. Held in what was once an old gin mill, the lighting and overall atmosphere makes this place what it is; hard, hot, topless (male and female!) with spunky, hedonistic boys and babes–not for the faint-hearted. Trade, without exaggeration, is a world-famous dance night, always packed out, and unless you are a member it is highly unlikely that you will get in. Now in its tenth year, this is one serious party that should not under any circumstance be missed. Despite the fact that it starts at 04.00 (the very early hours of Sunday morning) the queue is massive (well into the hundreds by 03.00) with plenty of disappointed punters turned away when its full up. Trade attracts the beautiful bodies (some can be found in the saunas on a Saturday night, prior to Trade opening), but is still every bit as serious about partying. The music is a touch lighter than Melt and is a little less intense and probably a bit younger crowd. Trade Lite Lounge with the Sharp Boys, Fat Tony and guests. Melt comprises very hard techno and house, with resident DJs Blu Peter and Jon the Dentist, plus guests. Again, despite the fact that you will not be in a fit state for work on the Monday morning this night is just as busy as Trade. Remember the all-important 'dark glasses' accessory for when you return to the real world on a Monday morning. Plenty of post-Trade/post-Melt chill-outs in various venues nearby on Sunday/Monday afternoons. Checkout the listings for details. Also checkout the listing for Trade Up North @ The Arches, Glasgow. *Note*: As of 5th June 1999, Trade has taken up temporary residence at the London Astoria 2 (see G.A.Y. listing for details). From 3 July they will probably be moving to Crash until October, when they will be finding permanent residence at a venue still to be named. Phone infoline for up-to-the-minute details.

The Two Brewers

114 Clapham High Street
London
SW4 7UJ   Telephone 0171 498 4971

Nearest train station Clapham High Street
Nearest tube Clapham Common
Car parking Ample off-street parking
A–Z ref. P93/4H
Nearest landmark Clapham High Street Train Station

Membership details None required
Opening hours   Monday–Thursday: 12.00–02.00
                         Friday–Saturday: 12.00–03.00
                         Sunday: 12.00–24.00
Admission charges Monday: Free
                     Tuesday–Thursday: £2 after 23.00
                     Friday–Saturday: £3 after 21.30/£4 after 23.00
                     Sunday: Free
Food available Full menu till 18.00 and bar snacks after
Regular entertainment Monday: Karaoke/cabaret
Tuesday: 'Corruption' with Sandra/cabaret
Wednesday–Saturday: Cabaret
Sunday: Cabaret lunch-time and evening

After a recent million pound refurbishment this well-known bar, close to the infamous Clapham Common, is now barely recognisable. It has been transformed into a modern and lively club without losing the appeal and charm of the old venue. The club bar is now similar to an industrial warehouse whilst the dance club has had a state-of-the-art sound and lighting system installed. The Two Brewers always had a reputation for the top cabaret on offer and now it could quite possibly be one of the premier gay cabaret bars in London. Weekends tend to be very busy as everyone is trying to get in before the 21.30 deadline, in order that they'll not have to pay an admission charge. If you arrive here later than that then expect to queue. There are no specialist evenings anymore although you will find a complete range of the gay community in evidence. The friendly and welcoming atmosphere has been retained ensuring you of an exceptional evening (particularly for newcomers to the scene).

The Viaduct (formerly The Dungeon)

39–41 Parry Street
Vauxhall
London
SW8   Telephone 0171 932 0755/0171 237 2299 ('Bulk' infoline)
             Website (Bamboozled) http://www.xanadu.freeserve.co.uk
             Website (Bulk) http://www.bulkclub.co.uk

Nearest train station Vauxhall Cross
Nearest tube Vauxhall
Car parking Ample side-street parking
A–Z ref. P77/6J
Nearest landmark Vauxhall Bridge

Membership details Temporary membership on night

Opening hours	Friday: 'Bamboozled': 22.00–06.00/'Used': 22.00–04.00
	Saturday: 22.00–05.00
Admission charges	Friday: 'Bamboozled': £5 Before 24.00 and £7 after/'Used':
	£6
	Saturday: £6 guests/£4 members

Regular entertainment Friday: 'Bamboozled' (every second Friday of the month)/'Used' (last Friday of the month)
Saturday: 'Bulk 2000'

The 600 capacity Viaduct is a private hire club, which means that the club is hired out to different promoters. There are only three gay nights per month at this establishment. 'Bamboozled' is hosted by the popular Millie Mopp, with resident DJs Rob C and The Mix Mistress. Late night dance club with not-too-high an admission price. 'Bulk 2000' is a club for the *big* boys and their admirers. There's a stripper on each week. Phone the 'Bulk' infoline for more details on the club and its membership facilities. 'Used' is Suzie Krueger's newest cruise night for boys and girls—a six hour set of the best house and underground dance music available. No dress code.

Village Soho

81 Wardour Street
Soho
London
W1V 3TG   Telephone 0171 434 0302

Nearest train station Charing Cross (ten minutes)
Nearest tube Piccadilly
Car parking No
A–Z ref. P61/6G
Nearest landmark Old Compton Street

Membership details None required
Opening hours   Monday–Saturday: 11.30–23.00
                         Sunday: 12.00–22.30
Admission charges None
Food available Served up until 17.00

A stylish and trendy establishment that was at one time the flagship of Soho's gay scene. That was then. Now it attracts the tea-time crowd of professional gents. As the evening goes on, the music gets louder and the crowd gets younger. Situated on the corner of Old Compton Street/Wardour Street.

The Way Out Club @ Charlies

9 Crosswall
London
EC3 2JY   Telephone 0171 488 1766 (Charlies)/0181 363 0948 (infoline–24
                 hour messaging)
                 E-mail Wayoutclub@wayout-publishing.com
                 Website http://www.wayout-publishing.com

Nearest train station Tower Gateway DLR
Nearest tube Tower Hill

Car parking Difficult at all times
A–Z ref. P63/7F
Nearest landmark Tower Hill Tube (Crosswall is off Minories)

Membership details £15 per year entitles holders to a £2 discount off admission (enquire at door)
Opening hours   Saturday: 21.00–04.00
                       (Every Saturday only)
Admission charges   Guests £8/members £6
Food available Full food menu available all night
Regular entertainment Excellent cabaret extravaganza with The Way Out Girls and guests
Every two months is the 'Fetish Fashion Night Catwalk'
Regular talent search and 'Blind Date'

Billed as 'A Celebration Of Diversity for Boys, Girls and Inbetweenies', your hosts Vikki Lee and Steffan have been welcoming everyone to The Way Out Club in person for the past six years. An extremely popular venue for TVs/TSs/CDs and their admirers particularly those who would like to meet and get to know transgendered people (know what I'm saying?). However, having said that, with the friendly and lively atmosphere the clientele is a complete mix with no attitude, all coming together to enjoy what is an extremely good night. The Way Out Girls are the regular cabaret, well known for their TV appearances and Spice Girls impersonations in the *Spiceworld*   movie. There are two giant video screens, one in the restaurant and one on the dance floor showing continuous tranny films and shows. In addition to this, the slide projector shows stills of the people in the club. For people not willing to get on the number 49 bus in full drag, there are ample changing facilities at the club as well as a taxi service from the door. The music is happy handbag and camp, ensuring the dance floor is always full. For newcomers to the scene, have a word with Vikki or Steffan on the door and they will do their utmost to welcome you to the club and if necessary, introduce you around. Full disabled access too.

West Five
Popes Lane
Ealing
London
W5   Telephone 0181 579 3266

Nearest train station Ealing Broadway (15 minute walk)
Nearest tube South Ealing
Car parking Ample side-street parking
A–Z ref. P72/3D
Nearest landmark South Ealing Tube (Popes Lane is the B4491)

Membership details None required
Opening hours   Monday–Tuesday: 18.00–23.00
                       Wednesday–Thursday: 18.00–24.00
                       Friday–Saturday: 18.00–01.00
                       Sunday: 13.00–22.30
Admission charges None
Food available Sunday lunch for £5
Regular entertainment Tuesday: Singles night

Wednesday: Quiz night (£100 outright winner each week)
Thursday: Stripper
Friday–Saturday: Cabaret/'Open Mike In The Piano Bar'

A large, exclusively gay pub situated around the corner from South Ealing Tube Station. It is comprised of Streisand's Piano Bar, a lounge bar: Manhattan Cabaret Lounge and a pool and games room, with three pool tables, darts, pinball, etc.

The White Hart

51–57 The Hale
Tottenham
London
N17 9JZ   Telephone 0181 808 5049

Nearest train station Tottenham Hale
Nearest tube Tottenham Hale
Car parking Limited side-street parking
A–Z ref. P31/3G
Nearest landmark Blockbuster Video

Membership details None required
Opening hours   Monday–Friday: 12.00–01.00
                         Saturday: 12.00–02.00
                         Sunday: 12.00–24.00
Admission charges   Monday–Thursday: Free
                         Friday–Saturday: £2 after 01.00
                         Sunday: Free
Food available At any time of the day
Regular entertainment Monday: Bingo
Tuesday: Cabaret/DJ
Wednesday: Karaoke/DJ
Thursday: Quiz/bingo
Friday–Sunday: Cabaret/DJ

Very popular mixed gay and straight venue where entertainment is doled out in The Lee Paris Variety Bar. Quieter lounge downstairs with adjoining pool room. Over the weekends this place can get heaving.

The White Swan/BJs

556 Commercial Road
London
E14 7JD   Telephone 0171 780 9870

Nearest train station None
Nearest tube DLR/Limehouse
Car parking Side-street parking
A–Z ref. P64/6A
Nearest landmark Limehouse DLR on Commercial Road

Membership details None required
Opening hours   Monday: 21.00–01.00
                         Tuesday–Thursday: 21.00–02.00
                         Friday–Saturday: 21.00–03.00
                         Sunday: 17.30–24.00
Admission charges   Monday–Thursday: Free

Friday: £3 after 22.00
Saturday: £3.50 after 22.00
Sunday: Free
Food available Yes
Regular entertainment Monday: 'Men Seeking Men'/occasional stripper
Tuesday: 'The Late, Late Cabaret Show'
Wednesday: 'Amateur Strip Night' (men only)
Thursday: Cabaret
Friday: DJ/stripper
Saturday: 'Handbag Disco'
Sunday: 'Joe Purvis' Original Sunday Tea Dance' (High-Tea-High Camp)

Adjoining BJs, The White Swan is a treasure chest of talent of all ages from all parts of the East End. The venue itself is split into two part; a large bar with plenty of seating, and a large cabaret room with a well-used stage. Wednesday is strictly men-only and at other times all are welcome. Situated close to Sailors Sauna (572–574 Commercial Road), so in between pints you can pop in and . . .

The Woolwich Infant
9 Plumstead Road
Woolwich
London
SE18 7BZ   Telephone 0181 854 3712

Nearest train station Woolwich Arsenal

the
ultimate
GAY
guide

Tell us what you think

Ultimate Guides
PO Box 64
Manchester
M7 4NZ

email
ugg@ic24.net

(or you can use the form at
the back of this book)

Dome
bar   café

VIBRANT
PRE-CLUB
VENUE
OPEN
MON-SAT 10AM-1AM
SUN 10AM-MIDNIGHT

Food available from10am
till late

LIVE & KICKING

57-59 Old Compton Street,
London, W1
Tel: 0171 287 0770

Nearest tube None
Car parking Outside pub (after 19.00)/local car parks
A–Z ref. P83/4F
Nearest landmark Near Beresford Square/close to Woolich Arsenal Mainline

Membership details None required
Opening hours   Monday–Wednesday: 13.00–23.00
                     Thursday–Saturday: 13.00–02.00
                     Sunday: 16.00–24.00
                     Note: No entry after 22.00, except at the manager's
                     discretion.
Admission charges None
Food available Lunch-time snacks and full roast dinner on Sundays
Regular entertainment Monday–Tuesday: Mixed gay social night
Wednesday: Disco
Thursday: Karaoke
Friday: Cabaret and disco
Saturday: Disco request night/occasional karaoke
Sunday: Cabaret and disco

Exclusively gay after 19.00 (mixed prior to this) The Infant is a safe and friendly public house which provides for the needs of its clientele, whom the management prefer to call their friends. It has a reputation for being clean, friendly and has an atmosphere so often missing in public houses these days. Although female dominated (which is probably due to the fact that it is run by two ladies) it more than welcomes men, TVs, TSs and so on and a good party atmosphere is usually always to be had. No-one is ever left on their own and all efforts are made to introduce new customers to the existing crowd, therefore making this venue the ideal starting place for the newcomer to the gay scene. The Garden (in summer) is used to celebrate birthdays, blessings and any other excuse where a good piss-up is involved.

The Yard

57 Rupert Street
Soho
London
W1V 7HN   Telephone 0171 437 2652

Nearest train station Charing Cross
Nearest tube Piccadilly Circus/Tottenham Court Road
Car parking No
A–Z ref. P61/7H
Nearest landmark Windmill Theatre

Membership details None required
Opening hours   Monday–Saturday: 12.00–23.00
                     Sunday: Closed
Admission charges None
Food available Bar snacks: 12.00–17.00
Situated just one street away from its sister pub The Village. The Yard has bars on two floors with a balcony overlooking the courtyard and when the sun shines, the patio bar is filled with a stylish, professional and trendy crowd. Not the place for disco dollies, but a great place for hanging out, chilling and chatting.

ENGLAND

Crossroads Tavern
4 High Street
Alfreton
Derbyshire   Telephone 01773 834 699

Nearest train station Alfreton
Car parking Ample street parking

Membership details None required
Opening hours   Monday–Wednesday: Closed (available for private hire)
                       Thursday: 19.00–23.00
                       Friday–Saturday: 12.00–16.00/19.00–23.00
                       Sunday: 19.00–22.30
Admission charges None
Food available Friday and Saturday lunch

At the time of going to print this bar intended to set up as a predominant venue for TVs/TSs/CDs and their admirers. There are ample changing facilities and make-up areas available for those who require them, and for groups travelling to the venue a separate party room if required can be organised free of charge. The bar itself is a friendly venue divided into two rooms; the large disco area (no seating) and a smaller bar with a relaxing atmosphere. Clientele are mixed: a gay and accepting straight crowd. There is a large bi element and a good local TV/TS crowd. For details regarding the TV/TS nights please phone the venue direct.

Blues Club/Pinkies Bar
211–213 Stamford Street
Ashton under Lyne
Lancashire
OL6 7QB   Telephone 0161 330 3212

Nearest train station Ashton Charlestown
Car parking Main road parking after 18.00/side streets and public car park at rear of club (ensure valuables are out of sight)
A–Z ref. P92/2A
Nearest landmark Yates Wine Lodge

Membership details None required
Opening hours   (Pinkies)
                       Monday–Saturday: 12.30–23.00
                       Sunday: 19.00–23.00 (90% gay)
                       (Blues)
                       Monday–Friday: 22.30–02.00
                       Saturday: 22.00–02.00
                       Sunday: Closed
Admission charges Free up to 22.30 (Pinkies Bar)
                     Various charges up to £4 on normal occasions (Blues Club)

Pinkies and Blues have been in the same ownership for well over 19 years. An extremely well-established 'fun bar' with its (Bar Show) format copied all over the country. With the competition from nearby Manchester (7 miles), this venue cannot operate as an exclusive gay pub/club, however, the camp atmosphere and lively entertaining staff do more than enough to attract a large local gay following and gay-friendly straight crowd. The in-house team of drag artists perform their brilliant, constantly changing routines on the bar at various times throughout the evening. Entertaining the customers is the priority of this venue. There are more 'one-liners' from the bar staff to put a stand-up-comic to shame and a brilliant atmosphere to boot. There is a DJ playing downstairs every night and then continuing upstairs in the club. Sundays in Pinkies (with Blues not open) tends to be more for a gay audience, with various cabaret and drag shows. If you are looking for an entertaining local night out, rather than the hedonistic club scene of nearby Manchester, then you can do a lot worse than trying out this venue.

The Saracen's Head

5 Rickfords Hill
Aylesbury
Buckinghamshire
HP20 2RT   Telephone 01296 421 528

Nearest train station Aylesbury (five minutes)
Car parking Limited side-street parking
Nearest landmark Safeways Supermarket

Membership details None required
Opening hours   Monday–Thursday: 17.30–23.00
                        Friday–Saturday: 12.00–23.00
                        Sunday: 12.00–22.30
Admission charges None during the weekand a nominal charge over the
                     weekend when cabaret is staged

Food available No
Regular entertainment Monday–Tuesday: Free pool
Wednesday: Disco/'Take Your Pick'
Thursday: Cheap drinks/quiz/'Games Night'
Friday–Saturday: Disco/karaoke and cabaret
Sunday: 'Games Night': quiz/bingo

Situated just off the ringroad by Safeways Supermarket. The Saracen's Head is Aylesbury's only gay pub, which opened in 1996. It is a friendly mixed (gay and lesbian) bar. There is usually something happening in the evenings to keep you entertained and more notably over the weekends when the venue is packed to capacity.

Baker Street (formerly known as Charlies Bar)

46 Sheffield Road
Barnsley
Yorkshire
S70   Telephone 01226 280 258

Nearest train station Barnsley (ten minutes)
Car parking Ample side-street parking
A–Z ref. P23/1H
Nearest landmark Follow signs to A61 (Sheffield Road)

Membership details None required
Opening hours   Tuesday: 19.00–23.00
                      Thursday: 19.00–24.00
                      Sunday: 19.00–22.30
Admission charges   None
Regular entertainment Tuesday: Karaoke
Thursday: Drag cabaret
Sunday: Karaoke

Mixed gay and straight bar. Predominantly gay on Tuesdays, Thursdays and Sundays. Used as a pre-'Powder Puff' meeting place every second Tuesday.

Powder Puff @ Regents Park

12A Regent Street
Barnsley
South Yorkshire Telephone 01226 240 040

Nearest train station Barnsley Metro (five minutes)
Car parking Street parking (nothing on-site)
A–Z ref. P13/5G
Nearest landmark Town Hall

Membership details None required
Opening hours   Tuesday: 22.00–02.00 (second Tuesday of the month only)
Admission charges   £3/£2 with flyers available from local gay pubs/free
                      admission to revellers on organised coach trips (see below)
Food available Yes–food bar
Regular entertainment Monthly cabaret and/or stripper
Monthly cheap drink promos

Regents Park is the massive, normally straight, 1,800 capacity, fully air-conditioned venue. Now over one year old and well-established as a 'must-go' monthly night out. Boasting no less than five bars and featuring guest jocks and live PAs. The boys and girls of Barnsley and its surrounding districts are well and truly spoiled. Monthly cheap drink promotions are: pints at a drunktastic £1.25; bottled beers at two for the price of one (just like Sainsbury's) and selected shorts at only £1. Just make sure that you have booked Wednesday off work. Admission to the club on this night is strictly for gays and lesbians only. Straight friends of gays will be made welcome although they will not be admitted without a gay person being present. If you experience difficulty in gaining admission, tell the doorman that you saw the listing in this guide. If you are intending to travel a distance to Regents Park it is recommended that you phone the venue beforehand to make arrangements for guaranteed entry (contact Hugh). If your local pub or club organises a coach trip to 'Powder Puff' then all the occupants of the coach are guaranteed free entry. Again, phone Hugh for further details. Regular coach trips are already in hand at The Vine in Doncaster and The Polar Bear in Hull. See separate listings for departure times and arrangements.

Sh–Out @ The Exeter Inn

Litchdon Street
Barnstaple
North Devon   Telephone 01271 321 709

Nearest train station Barnstaple (two minutes)
Car parking Car parks in surrounding area

Membership details None required
Opening hours   Wednesday: 20.00–23.00
                      (Wednesday evenings only)
Admission charges None

Coming together in the front bar of The Exeter Inn is this regular weekly gathering of Barnstaple's and surrounding districts'gay and lesbian community. Well, it's better than nothing. It may be wise to phone the Exeter switchboard, who will be able to advise on other contact groups in the area and possibly hook you up with other newcomers, in order that you have someone to go in with.

The Bath Tap

19 St James' Parade
Bath
BA1 1UL   Telephone 01225 404 344
                 Website http://www.bathtap.co.uk/bathtap

Nearest train station Bath (two minutes)
Car parking Two minutes away
A–Z ref. P106/3A
Nearest landmark Opposite McDonalds

Membership details None required
Opening hours   (Pub)
                      Monday–Saturday: 12.00–23.00
                      Sunday: 12.00–22.30
                      (Club)
                      Friday–Saturday: 22.00–02.00
Admission charges Saturday: £2 after 22.00
Food available No
Regular entertainment Monday: Karaoke
Tuesday: Students night/cheap drinks
Wednesday: Quiz night
Thursday: 'Booze Cruz'/ drinks promos on the hour every hour
Friday: Occasional stripper
Saturday: Pre-club party night/'Crazy Fruit': hard house sounds in Club Eros
Sunday: Chill out day

The Bath Tap is now Bath's only exclusively gay pub/club. Extremely well managed and developing the city centre venue into what promises to be an excellent night out. The premises are split over three levels. The ground floor is the club–Club Eros (possibly due to be changed to Whirlpool). The first floor is the main bar with a separate sound system and yet still, very much dance-orientated. The second floor, again has its own bar and sound system, is more relaxed and is used mainly by the older customers and as a general chill out room to rest those weary, tired rattling old bones. The Bath Tap is used by the entire spectrum of Bath's gay community. Weekly meetings in the upstairs bar for LGB, Gay Mens Health Project and the Aled Richards Trust, amongst others who use the premises for their regular meetings.

Clarence Hotel

13 St John Street
Bedford
MK42 0AH   Telephone 01234 352 781

Nearest train station Bedford (five minutes)
Car parking Large facility at venue
Nearest landmark Telecom House

Membership details None required
Opening hours   Monday–Saturday: 12.00–23.00
                       Sunday: 12.00–22.30
Admission charges None
Food available Full menu and snacks available at lunch-times (not weekends).
Sunday roast available too
Regular entertainment Monday–Tuesday: Resident DJ
Wednesday–Thursday: Disco
Friday: Disco/cabaret/last Friday of the month: TUF
Saturday: Cabaret
Sunday: 'The Pussycat Club'/cabaret

The Clarence Hotel operates its own cabaret venue where, on the last Friday of
the month, it runs the TUF night (Transsexual, Uniform, Fetish). A pub with a
club atmosphere, being both cruisy and social. TVs are especially welcome, as are
well-behaved straights (usually friends of gays). The dress code is 'wear what
you dare' and with its own private car park you can avoid the stares from the
pensioners on the bus! Accommodation is available although it is wise to phone
beforehand to make arrangements.

Angels

131 Hurst Street
Birmingham
B5 6SE   Telephone 0121 244 2626

Nearest train station New Street
Car parking Ample side-street parking
A–Z ref. P74/4A
Nearest landmark Hippodrome Theatre

Membership details None required
Opening hours   Monday–Saturday: 12.00–23.00
                       Sunday: 12.00–22.30
Admission charges None
Food available Full menu available during the day
Bright and modern cafe-bar right in the heart of the gay village. By day, it is an
ideal venue to chill out and watch everything go by. By night, it transforms (as
if by magic) into a trendy, packed pre-club meeting place. Discount tickets to
most gay venues can be obtained from here, in particular; free admission
vouchers to Subway City on Thursday by purchasing a drink over the value of
£1.50 (ask the barman for a voucher).

The Fountain Inn

102 Wrentham Street
Birmingham
B5 6QL   Telephone 0121 622 1452

Nearest train station New Street (ten minutes)
Car parking Outside venue
A–Z ref. P74/5A
Nearest landmark The Nightingale

Membership details None required
Opening hours   Monday–Friday: 19.00–Close
                         Saturday–Sunday: 13.00–Close
Admission charges None
Food available No
Birmingham's premier leather, uniform and denim gay bar, hosting one bears
night (every third Friday) and two (MSC) leather nights (first and third Sunday)
per month. Predominantly men-only, with real ale and cask-conditioned beer.
Hotel accommodation available too (see 'Accommodation' listing).

The Fox

17 Lower Essex Street
Birmingham
B5   Telephone 0121 622 1210

Nearest train station New Street
Car parking Ample Side-street parking/local car parks
A–Z ref. P74/4A
Nearest landmark Off Sherlock Street

Membership details None required
Opening hours   Monday–Friday: 18.00–23.00
                         Saturday: 19.00–23.00
                         Sunday: 12.00–15.00/19.00–22.30
Admission charges None
Food available Yes
Mixed gay bar, particularly popular with women.

Gough Arms

Upper Gough Street
Edgbaston
Birmingham
B1   Telephone 0121 643 3774

Nearest train station New Street
Car parking Ample side-street parking/local car park
A–Z ref. P73/4H
Nearest landmark Holloway Circus
Opening hours   Monday–Saturday: 12.00–23.00
                         Sunday: 12.00–22.30
Admission charges None
Regular entertainment Tuesday: 'Fanny Golightly' (women only)

Wednesday: 'Killer Pool'
Thursday: Occasional quiz night
Friday: Disco
Saturday: Disco (alternate Saturdays)
Sunday: 'Singalong' (drunken)

The Gough Arms is a gay-friendly bar, although it is now gaining a good reputation as a women's bar. The (new at time of going to print) women-only night on Tuesday in the upstairs room is gaining an increasing crowd. The Gough is not a trendy bar, however it is extremely friendly (staffed by gays, what else would you expect?) and sociable. During the day it is used by the local factory workers. The night sees a complete U-turn and all the gay stops are pulled out.

The Jester
Holloway Circus
Birmingham
B1 1EG   Telephone 0121 643 0155

Nearest train station New Street
Car parking NCP opposite/limited street parking
A–Z ref. P73/4H
Nearest landmark Top of Hurst Street

Membership details None required
Opening hours   Monday–Saturday: 12.00–23.00
                        Sunday: 12.00–22.30
Admission charges None
Food available Snacks available lunch-times

Probably Birmingham's longest running gay bar. A social cruisy atmosphere helped along by the circular bar set in the centre of the room. Community-type pub, with lots of regulars. Popular with the older male although some of the younger guys will pub-hop through here.

Missing (formerly the Australian Bar)
48 Bromsgrove Street (corner of Hurst Street)
Birmingham   Telephone 0121 622 4256

Nearest train station New Street
Car parking Ample side-street parking
A–Z ref. P74/4A
Nearest landmark Hippodrome Theatre

Membership details None required
Opening hours   Monday–Saturday: 10.30–23.00
                        Sunday: 12.00–22.30
Admission charges None
Food available Full menu available in the on-site Alexander Restaurant
Regular entertainment Monday–Tuesday: Resident DJ
Wednesday: Drag cabaret and stripper
Thursday: Disco/quiz night

Friday–Saturday: Disco

At the time of writing, the bar was undergoing a complete £100,000 refurbishment programme, with plans to make the venue a complete entertainment centre for the gay community. A better sound and lighting system will be installed as well as complete stage equipment. A late licence has been applied for, however, the new opening times have not yet been confirmed (these can be gained by phoning the venue direct).

The Nightingale

Essex House Kent Street
Birmingham
B5 6RD   Telephone 0121 622 1718/0121 622 2192 (infolne)

Nearest train station Birmingham New Street
Car parking Ample street parking
A–Z ref. P74/5A
Nearest landmark Hippodrome Theatre/Hurst Street

Membership details None required (it was previously required for you to be a member for 48 hours prior to first admission but now this is no longer the case)

Opening hours   Monday: Closed (available for private hire)
                         Tuesday–Wednesday: 22.00–02.00
                         Thursday: Closed (available for private hire)
                         Friday: 21.00–03.00
                         Saturday: 21.00–03.30
                         Sunday: 12.00–24.00 ('Sundisential')
                         Sunday: 09.00–24.00 ('Scream')
Admission charges   Tuesday–Wednesday: £2
                         Friday: £3 before 01.00/£5 after
                         Saturday: £5 before 23.00/£7 after
                         Sunday: £3

Food available Restaurant on site
Regular entertainment Tuesday: Stripper/Hi Nrg and dance
Wednesday: Chart dance/house
Friday: 'Bubble': dance/chart
Saturday: 'Camp Nation': cheesy chart, etc.
Sunday: 'Sundisaential': 12.00–24.00 (guest DJs)/'Scream': 09.00– 24.00 Simon Harris

The Nightingale is a massive club complex with five bars, two discos, restaurant/cafe bar and games room. Spread out over three floors and with a capacity for around 1,000-plus homos. It will be celebrating it's 30th Birthday in May 1999 as a gay venue from its roots on Camp Hill to it's present location, so keep a space free for what will be a massive party. All three floors are open on Friday, Saturday and Sunday. During the rest of the week it is only open on the first and second floor.

Partners Bar

Albany House 27–31 Hurst Street
Birmingham
B5 4BD   Telephone 0121 622 4710
                E-mail: partners.bar@virgin.net
                Website http://www.welcome.to/partners

Nearest train station New Street (two minutes)
Nearest Car parking Side streets around venue/Arcadian car park
A–Z ref. P74/4A
Nearest landmark Hippodrome Theatre (next door)

Membership details None required
Opening hours   Monday–Saturday: 01.00–23.00
                       Sunday: 01.00–22.30
Admission charges None
Food available Sunday lunch only
Regular entertainment Monday: DJ
Tuesday: Stripper
Wednesday: DJ
Thursday: Karaoke
Friday: Drag cabaret/DJ
Saturday: DJ
Sunday: Star cabaret night

Situated next to The Hippodrome Theatre this is an excellent cabaret bar catering for gay, lesbian, TV and friends. One of the oldest bars in the gay village. This cellar room has one large bar and a well used stage. A reputation for fun and friendliness, and where anything goes, any night of the week. There is a pool table and gaming machines. Happy hour is from 17.00 daily to get you in the party spirit early in addition to regular drink promotions.

Route Two (formerly Route 66)

139–147 Hurst Street
Birmingham
B5 6JD   Telephone 0121 622 3366

Nearest train station New Street
Car parking Loads of side-street parking
A–Z ref. P74/4A
Nearest landmark Hippodrome Theatre

Membership details None required
Opening hours   Monday–Saturday: 19.00–02.00
                       Sunday: 12.00–22.30
Admission charges Nominal charge over the weekend
Food available Restaurant on premises is open until 01.45 (checkout their very popular 9" hot dog for not much moolah)
Regular entertainment Monday: Regular cabaret/entertainments
Tuesday: Cabaret
Thursday: 'Splash–Studs in Suds'
Friday: Cabaret
Saturday: Top PAs/disco

Route Two (three bars/two dance floors/one restaurant) ranks amongst the biggest gay bars in the country. A young and trendy energetic crowd dance on the invisible dance floors. The music is loud and the atmosphere is charged. Weekends (obviously) are packed, however, the weekdays tend to be more of a social, but never the less, popular gay outing. Hostess Miss Billie keeps everyone in order.

Subway City

27 Water Street
Old Snow Hill
Birmingham
B3 1HL   Telephone 0121 233 0310

Nearest train station New Street (taxi required)
Car parking Street parking
A–Z ref. P73/2H
Nearest landmark Constitution Hill

Membership details Subway City is a private members club. Members can sign in up to five guests; any more will require prior arrangement. Either complete the application form at the door (48 hours before admission) or phone the venue to join. For visitors from out of town, phone in advance in order to put your name on the guest list

Opening hours   Thursday: 22.00–02.00
                         Saturday: 22.00–09.00 (all-nighter)
Admission charges Thursday: £2 members/£3 guests
                         Saturday: Before 23.00: £2 members/£3 guests; before
                         24.00: £4 members/£6 guests; after
                         24.00: £6 members/£8 guests

Food available Restaurant on premises
Regular entertainment Thursday: Cheap drinks/very busy
Saturday: 'Blue': guest DJs from Trade/Galaxy/Subway City, etc.

Subway City is not predominantly gay, except for Thursday and Saturday. At other times it is hired out to various promoters (some of whom may operate a gay night, so it is wise to keep an eye on the gay press for details). It is however a private members club (see above information on membership). On Thursday and Saturday a member with four or more guests will receive free admission. Coach trips to Subway City are organised by many gay bars around the Midlands; more notably: The Phoenix, Cheltenham (last Saturday of the month) and the Queen and Crumpet, Hanley, Stoke on Trent (first Saturday of the month). Phone the respective venues for further details. 'Blue' is the Saturday night entertainment and if you like Trade, you'll *love* this. This night started off as a monthly event and, due to its popularity, became a weekly bash closing at 09.00 rather than the previous 06.00. (Admission prices may increase during 1999.) Keep an eye out for Bill Gavan's new development opposite The Nightingale!

Village Inn

152 Hurst Street
Birmingham
B5 6RY   Telephone 0121 622 4742

Nearest train station New Street
Car parking Limited street parking/NCP close by
A–Z ref. P74/4A
Nearest landmark Hippodrome Theatre

Membership details None required
Opening hours   Monday–Saturday: 13.00–23.00
                         Sunday: 12.00–22.30
Admission charges None

Food available No

Exclusively gay venue in the heart of the gay village. There is nothing pretentious about this place. If you want a good drink in cosy surroundings at the right price with gay people (predominantly male orientated) then this is where you go. Limited accommodation available too (advance booking required).

The Wonder Bar
30 Ladywell Walk
Birmingham
B5   Telephone 0121 622 4321

Nearest train station New Street
Car parking Side-street parking
A–Z ref. P74/4A
Nearest landmark Hippodrome Theatre

Membership details None required
Opening hours   Monday–Thursday: 17.00–01.00
                         Friday–Saturday: 17.00–02.00
                         Sunday: 17.00–22.30
Admission charges None
Food available Light bar snacks available

A DJ six nights of the week and Philly Stine introducing the very busy karaoke session on Wednesdays and Sundays are a big part of the success of this venue. Happy hours run from 19.00 to 22.00 during the week and from 19.00 to 20.00 over the weekend and ensure that the bar gets busy earlier on as punters bar-crawl ready for a night on the town. This unpretentious and fun venue is on two floors; the upstairs disco and the downstairs quieter bar. The crowd are a mixed bunch of young gay and lesbian.

Wood Loft/Steel Works
18 Kent Street
Birmingham
B5 6RD   Telephone 0121 622 6717

Nearest train station New Street
Car parking Side streets/local car park
A–Z ref. P74/5A
Nearest landmark Hurst Street

Membership details Not required
Opening hours   Monday–Thursday: 17.00–23.00
                         Friday–Saturday: 12.00–23.00
                         Sunday: 12.00–22.30
Admission charges None
Food available Yes

One of Birmingham's newest venues (open since October 1998) operating two distinct venues in one: The Wood Loft, which is the cosy and camp top floor bar; and the industrial and open- plan Steelworks.

Cest La Vie

11–15 Market Street
Blackburn
Lancashire
BB2 2DE   Telephone 01254 691 877

Nearest train station Blackburn
Car parking Ample street parking
Nearest landmark Cathedral

Membership details None required
Opening hours   Sunday: 21.00–Late (Sunday nights only)
Admission charges £1 before 21.30/£2 before 22.00/£3 before 22.30/no
                            admission after 22.30
Food available Free buffet on the gallery

Very busy gay night in this usually straight club. Free buffet available, but be quick: all the best stuff goes quite early on and latecomers are usually left with the lettuce garnish. Downstairs is the main disco room, whilst upstairs is the gallery bar with comfortable seating and a few dark corners.

Basils On The Strand

9 The Strand
Blackpool
Lancashire
FY1   Telephone 01253 294 109
                Website http://www.in-the-pink.com

Nearest train station Blackpool North
Car parking Limited Street parking/local car parks
A–Z ref. P12/4A
Nearest landmark Talbot Square

Membership details None required
Opening hours   Monday–Saturday: 12.30–00.30
                            Sunday: 12.30–15.00/19.00–22.30
Admission charges None except for monthly charity events (nominal charge)
Food available Snacks only

Popular local, exclusively gay bar. Used as a meeting place prior to going to Flamingo's. This place opened in 1991 and quickly became a popular bar with the young crowd. Situated on two floors with three bars and a small dance floor. There is a pool table upstairs with a more relaxed atmosphere. Thursday nights get extremely busy due to the cabaret and cheap drink bar promotions. Throughout the season and also over weekends, the bar is packed out to capacity. Happy hour is every day from 12.00–20.00 and a once-a-month charity event (Sunday) keeps the bar open till late.

Cow Bar

Church Street
Blackpool
Lancashire
FY1 1PT   Telephone 01253 757931

Nearest train station Blackpool North
Car parking Street parking
A–Z ref. P12/4A+4B
Nearest landmark Railway Station/Talbot Road

Membership details None required
Opening hours   Monday–Saturday: 12.00–23.30
                         Sunday: 12.00–14.00/18.00–22.30
Admission charges   None
Food available Full menu 12.00–19.00 every day
Regular entertainment Thursday: Quiz night
Friday–Saturday: Dance DJ
Sunday: Drag DJ (camp)

The Cow Bar is a large, mixed gay venue (integrating mixed gay and straight at weekends) and is the newest addition to Blackpool's ever expanding gay scene. It is a bright, cosmopolitan, modern bar, which caters for all tastes and needs. There is a games room, bar area, dance floor and seating arena. Situated on the corner of Cookson Street and Church Street, you really can't miss it. It's a large building with a 'striking' yellow and purple decor and inside it's pretty similar. If you are high on some substance or another you may well get the feeling of being inside a cartoon! Cheap drinks are available on a regular basis and occasional cabaret makes the Cow Bar a popular venue, particularly with the ladies.

Flamingo's
174–176 Talbot Road
Blackpool
Lancashire
FY1 3AZ   Telephone 01253 624 901
                 Website http://www.in-the-pink.com

Nearest train station Blackpool North
Car parking Large P&D close by
A–Z ref. P12/3B
Nearest landmark Railway Station/North Pier (venue at top of Talbot Road)

Membership details None required but available for reduced (or free) admission (enquire at venue)
Opening hours   Monday–Saturday: 22.00–02.00
                         Sunday: 21.00–24.00
Admission charges   Monday–Thursday: £2
                      Friday: £3
                      Saturday: £4.50
                      Sunday: £2
Food available Cafe area on premises
Regular entertainment Monday: 'Retro Night'
Tuesday: Super drink promos (free admission to members plus one guest)
Thursday: 'Pop Pickers Paradise' (free admission to members)
Friday: Top cabaret (see press for details of line-up)
Saturday: All four levels open

Blackpool's only gay club. Consisting of six bars and two dance floors over four levels it is not hard to see why this very modern club is popular with all the gay people who visit (and live) in Blackpool. Loads of cruisy corridors, brilliant DJs, gorgeous bar staff, cafe, Clone Zone shop and an outlet of BPM records. The jewel in the crown of the Basil Newby empire, which also includes Basils On The Strand, Pepes, Funny Girls to name a few. There's limited car parking space at the club, however, there are two large public car parks just around the corner. Situated next door to The Flying Handbag (another ITP venue) Flamingo's is in easy reach of the motorway network.

The Flying Handbag

172–174 Talbot Road
Blackpool
FY1 3AZ   Telephone 01253 625 522
                   Website http://www.in-the-pink.com

Nearest train station Blackpool North
Car parking Several P&D close by (free in the evening)
A–Z ref. P12/3B
Nearest landmark Blackpool North Railway Station

Membership details None required
Opening hours   Monday–Saturday: 11.00–23.00
                         Sunday: 12.00–22.30
Admission charges None
Food available No
Regular entertainment Monday: Cabaret
Tuesday: Quiz night/DJ
Wednesday: Bingo
Friday: Karaoke/cabaret
Saturday: Resident DJ
Sunday: 'Funday': male stripper (lunch)/drag cabaret (evening)

This pub is next door to the Flamingo's club and was formerly The Kings Head. Since it was taken over by ITP, it has become one of the most popular gay bars around. The manager, Bill Kershaw has brought a new meaning to the word camp . . . with an extensive entertainment policy, cheap drinks and even an annual 'Christmas Party'. Nothing unusual in that you may say, but this Christmas party takes place in the middle of July (!!), with all the decorations, trees and even snow. This event usually coincides with the Blackpool annual 'Fiesta Fiesta' bank holiday Pride weekend. Regular once-a-month Sunday charity events, with a late night bar extension (nominal entrance fee to charity).

Lucy's Bar

9–11 Talbot Road
Blackpool
FY1 1LB   Telephone 01253 293 204   Fax 01253 622 502

Nearest train station Blackpool North
Car parking Side-street parking/local car parks
A–Z ref. P12/4A
Nearest landmark North Pier

Membership details

Available but not required: £5 per year (June-July) which entitles holder to free entry at all times (apply at bar)

Opening hours	Monday–Saturday: 20.00–02.00
	Sunday: 20.00–22.30
Admission charges	Monday–Thursday: Free
	Friday–Saturday: Free for members/£1 guests
	Sunday: Free (except for charity events)

Food available Bar snacks available 22.00–02.00
Regular entertainment Monday: Drink promos/DJ Frostie (Natalie)
Tuesday: 'Hitman and Her' Karaoke (prizes)
Thursday: Drink promos/'Open The Box'
Monday–Thursday: 23.00–02.00: cheap drinks
(Regular bar shows/DJ–male and female–every night)

This bar has a reputation for being *just* a girl's bar, which is quite untrue. Although the girls do tend to use Lucy's bar above any other in Blackpool, it does in fact offer a warm welcome to all members of the gay community, particularly TVs and TSs (and their admirers). The bar is situated on Talbot Square, opposite the Town Hall and there is another basement bar (underneath Rumours Fun Pub). There is one long bar, a pool table (always busy) and a small dance floor. Cheap drinks are a regular feature, as are the live DJs and cabaret. During the summer season, the bar is heaving and there seems to be a constant 'party' atmosphere (must be the sea air). Lucy's bar is well-known by all in Blackpool. It is one of the oldest gay bars in the country having opened over thirty years ago (Lucy herself died over three years ago–the woman behind the bar is Linda . . . *not* Lucy).

The Church Hotel

174 Crook Street
Bolton
Lancashire
BL3 6AS   Telephone 01204 521 856

Nearest train station Bolton (opposite venue)
Car parking Ample street parking
A–Z ref. P38/1B
Nearest landmark Railway station

Membership details	None required
Opening hours	Monday–Wednesday: 16.00–23.00
	Thursday: 16.00–01.00
	Friday–Saturday: 14.00–02.00
	Sunday: 12.00–22.30

Admission charges None
Food available Bar snacks available
Regular entertainment Wednesday: Karaoke
Thursday–Saturday: Disco
Sunday: Cabaret/DJ

Situated opposite the railway station, this is a very friendly mixed gay bar, comprising of two rooms: the lounge bar with pool table and the disco bar where all the entertainment happens. Regular cheap drink promotions and extended happy hours available.

The Star and Garter

11 Bow Street
Bolton
Lancashire
BL1 2EQ   Telephone 01204 361 113

Nearest train station Bolton (five minutes)
Car parking Local car parks
A–Z ref. P24/6B
Nearest landmark Bolton Market Hall

Membership details None required
Opening hours   Monday–Wednesday: 17.00–23.00
                         Thursday–Saturday: 12.00–23.00
                         Sunday: 12.00–22.30
Admission charges None
                     Intimate gay bar

The King's Head

2 Emery Lane
Boston
Lincolnshire
PE21 8QA   Telephone 01205 362 926

Nearest train station Lincoln
Car parking Limited on street/NCP 150 metres
Nearest landmark Lincoln Railway Station (about 500 yards)

Membership details None required
Opening hours   Monday–Thursday: 11.00–23.00
                         Friday–Saturday: 11.00–24.00
                         Sunday: 12.00–16.00/19.00–24.00
Admission charges None
Food available Full menu available lunch-times and evenings

'Dorothys On Sunday'–exclusively gay and gay guests on Sunday evenings only. The regular entertainment every other week consists of a male stripper or drag cabaret. For the rest of the week the King's Head is a mixed establishment with Fridays having a female stripper and Saturdays a karaoke or disco. The King's is a trouble-free establishment with all forms of travel facilities within only a stone's throw of the venue.

Bakers Arms

77 Commercial Road
Bournemouth
Dorset
BH2 5RT   Telephone 01202 555 506

Nearest train station Bournemouth (two miles)
Car parking Limited street parking/local car park
A–Z ref. P57/4G
Nearest landmark C&A department store

Membership details None required
Opening hours   Monday–Saturday: 11.00–23.00
                       Sunday: 12.00–22.30
Admission charges None
Food available Lunch-times 11.30–15.00 full menu/evening bar snacks

The Bakers Arms is a mixed gay and straight venue with TVs welcome, situated more or less opposite C&A. A warm and friendly pub suiting all tastes and ages. Regular cabaret and karaoke throughout the week.

The Queens Hall Hotel
14 Queens Road
Westbourne
Bournemouth
BH2 6BE   Telephone   01202 764 416

Nearest train station Bournemouth (two miles)
Car parking On-site
A–Z ref. P57/4F
Nearest landmark Queens Gardens

Membership details None required
Opening hours   Monday–Saturday: 12.00–23.00
                       Sunday: 12.00–22.30
Admission charges None
Food available Light snacks only
Regular entertainment Tuesday: Quiz night
Wednesday: Pool night–competition
Saturday: DJ/cabaret
Sunday: Stripper/cabaret

Bournemouth's oldest, extremely busy gay pub. Consisting of three bars, two of which are mixed gay and the other mixed gay and straight. A ten minute walk from the town centre and clubs.

Triangle Club
29 The Triangle
Bournemouth
Dorset
BH2 5SE   Telephone   01202 297 607

Nearest train station Bournemouth
Car parking Street parking/NCP (very safe)
A–Z ref. P57/4G
Nearest landmark The Triangle

Membership details Not necessary. Membership requires an annual fee (apply at venue)
Opening hours   Monday–Thursday: 21.30–02.00
                       Friday: 21.00–02.00
                       Saturday: 21.30–02.00
                       Sunday: Closed
Admission charges Monday–Thursday: £1 members/£2 guests
                     Friday–Saturday: £1.50 members/£2.50 guests before 23.00;
                     £2 members/£4 guests after 23.00

Regular entertainment Friday: Leather night/cabaret (usually stripper)
Saturday: Cabaret

The Triangle club, with a capacity of around 600, is now in its 10th successful year. The top lounge bar has now been completely refurbished with full air-conditioning installed. The basement disco bar is lively and friendly, playing a selection of handbag and current dance classics. The atmosphere in general is dance orientated, with plenty of room to cruise and be cruised. Weekly Friday night venue for Bournemouth Leather: 21.30–23.00.

The X-Change Wine Bar

4 The Triangle
Bournemouth
Dorset
BH2 5RY   Telephone 01202 294 321

Nearest train station Bournemouth
Car parking Opposite venue
A–Z ref. P57/4G
Nearest landmark Avenue Shopping Centre/Triangle (well signposted)

Membership details None required
Opening hours   Monday–Saturday: 12.00–01.00
                         Sunday: 12.00–23.00
Admission charges None
Food available Bar snacks and sandwiches
Regular entertainment Monday: DJ
Tuesday: Bingo/quiz night
Wednesday: Cabaret
Thursday: 80s disco
Friday: Disco/girls night
Saturday: Disco
Sunday: Social night

A lively community-based wine bar catering for a majority lesbian, gay, TV and gay-friendly straight crowd. The X-Change is a young venue, both very friendly and welcoming. The long bar leads to the stage at the far end and everywhere in between there is ample comfortable seating and standing room. On bank holidays all the stops are pulled out and it's just one non- stop party. Cheap drinks, themed weekends, cabaret and everything else that goes with having a good time.

Jesters Fun Bar

14 St Thomas Road
Bradford
BD1   Telephone 01274 741 520

Nearest train station Forster Square
Car parking Ample side-street/local car parks
A–Z ref. P58/3A
Nearest landmark Westgate (St Thomas' School)

Membership details None required
Opening hours   Monday–Wednesday: 12.00–23.00
                         Thursday: 12.00–24.00

Friday–Saturday: 12.00–01.00
Sunday: 12.00–22.30

Admission charges   None
Food available   No
Regular entertainment   Monday: Cheap drinks
Tuesday: 'Killer Pool' with cash prizes: (free coach to Red Raw every first
Tuesday at 22.35)
Wednesday: Free pool all night
Thursday: 70s and 80s disco
Friday: Disco: late bar till 01.00
Saturday: Disco: late bar till 01.00

The management duo (Jane and Poppy), the billiard table and the free pool go
some way to ensure that this venue has a very strong female presence. Situated
off Westgate, just a stone's throw from The Sun, this 100% gay establishment,
that looks somewhat similar to a working men's club, is a treat for the ladies.
Happy hour is Monday–Friday, 17.00–19.00. You'll find friendly bar staff and a
huge video screen over the dance floor . . . . Excellent.

Sackville Lounge/S29 Club

29 Sackville Street
Bradford
Yorkshire
BD1 2AJ   Telephone   01274 740 644

Nearest train station   Forster Square
Car parking   Side-street parking/local car parks
A–Z ref.   P58/3A
Nearest landmark   Sunwinn House department store

Membership details   48 hours advance membership required before first
admission. This can be done in two ways: either phone the above number and
ask that your membership be left at the door or send your name, address, date
of birth and signature to the club address (remember, if you cannot receive mail
at home then state so on your application, and mention also that you do not
want your name on any mailing list)
Opening hours   Monday–Tuesday: 21.00–02.00 (Sackville Lounge only)
                         Wednesday–Saturday: 21.00–03.00
                         Sunday: 21.30–24.00
                         (Licensed till 02.00–soft drinks till 03.00)
Admission charges   Monday–Tuesday: Free (pub only)
                         Wednesday: Free (pub and club)
                         Thursday: £1 before 24.00/£2 after
                         Friday: £2 before 24.00/£3 after
                         Saturday: £3 before 24.00/£4 after
                         Sunday: Free (pub only)
                         Free admission to club Thursday–Saturday before 22.30/
                         guests of members £1 extra
Food available   Snackville Restaurant on premises
Regular entertainment   Monday: 'Monday Chill Out'/drink promos
Wednesday: DJ (S29)
Thursday: DJ (S29)/cabaret

Friday–Saturday: DJ (S29)
Sunday: Cabaret

Members are able to sign in guests on the night and they are encouraged to join the venue. The reasoning for the membership is that priority to gay customers can be given over our straight friends on busy nights. The venue is a bright modern establishment catering for a predominantly young mixed gay, bi and lesbian crowd. Sister venue to the Sun Hotel.

The Sun Hotel
124 Sunbridge Road
Bradford
West Yorkshire
BD1 2ND   Telephone   01274 737 722

Nearest train station Bradford Interchange
Car parking Outside venue
A–Z ref. P57/3D
Nearest landmark Alhambra Theatre

Membership details None required
Opening hours   Monday–Thursday: 11.00–23.00
                         Friday–Saturday: 11.00–23.30
                         Sunday: 12.00–22.30
Admission charges   None
Food available
Lunch-times only (snacks)
Regular entertainment Monday: Free pool/free buffet/cheap drinks
Tuesday: Student night/drink promos
Wednesday: Fun quiz at 21.30
Thursday: DJ/cabaret
Friday: 'The Weekend Starts Here' disco/'Bears Night' on third Friday of the month
Saturday: Disco party
Sunday: 'Sexy Sundays': guest DJs

Sister venue to The Sackville Lounge, opening during the day and offering a wider range of entertainment. As both venues are situated only 100 yards apart it is quite acceptable to flit between the two if there is no one in here that takes your fancy.

The Bedford Tavern
30 Western Street
Brighton
BN1 2PG   Telephone   01273 739495

Nearest train station Brighton Mainline
Car parking Outside the venue/side-street parking
A–Z ref. P28/5B
Nearest landmark Three blocks west of Montpelier Road on the border of Brighton and Hove

Membership details None required
Opening hours   Monday–Saturday: 10.30–23.00
                         Sunday: 12.00–22.30

Admission charges   None
Food available   Mariners Kitchen seafood restaurant at venue. Open
Wednesday–Saturday: 19.30–21.15 (last orders) and lunch-times Sunday

Over 200 years old The Bedford Tavern is full of charm and character and is
known as the country pub in the heart of town (complete with resident ghost!). A
straight-friendly, intimate pub where gays and straights get on well together
(60/40–gay/straight). The venue itself is known as a trouble-free zone. The
Bedford hosts monthly themed events, which are usually a good excuse to dress
up (fancy dress optional) and have a party.

The Black Horse
112 Church Street
Brighton
BN1 1UD   Telephone   01273 606 864

Nearest train station   Brighton
Car parking   On-street parking
A–Z ref.   P28/4D
Nearest landmark   Clock Tower/St Paul's Church

Membership details   None required
Opening hours   Monday–Saturday: 11.00–23.00
                        Sunday: 12.00–15.00/19.00–22.30
Admission charges   None
Food available   Full menu: 12.00–15.00 (except Sunday)
Regular entertainment   Tuesday: Karaoke (evening)
Wednesday: Piano bar (evening)
Sunday: Cabaret (afternoon)/karaoke (evening)

Known locally as 'The Pink Pony', The Black Horse is a very friendly bar catering
for all tastes (mixed gay and straight; TVs welcome). Karaoke nights are very
popular. Same gay ownership for over twelve years and popular with students
and the young crowd. Close to the city centre making this venue an excellent
pre-club bar. The pool room attracts the girls.

The Bulldog Tavern
31 St James' Street
Brighton
BN1   Telephone   01273 684 097

Nearest train station   Brighton Mainline (ten minutes)
Car parking   On-street parking/local car parks
A–Z ref.   P29/6F
Nearest landmark   Sealife Centre on Marine Parade (St James runs behind–
venue at top)

Membership details   None required
Opening hours   Monday–Saturday: 11.00–23.00
                        Sunday: 12.00–22.30
Admission charges   None
Food available   No

Spread over two floors. The main bar is an olde worlde stylee pubee, popular predominantly with Brighton's men, although women and TVs/TSs are welcome. The modern upstairs disco room is only open on a Saturday night, hosting a popular retro disco club night. Sunday is cheap drinks all day (the day-long happy hour) with additional happy hours through the week from 15.00–19.00.

Club Revenge

32–34 Old Steine
Brighton
BN1 1EL   Telephone 01273 606 064
                 Website http://www.revenge.co.uk

Nearest train station Brighton (ten minute walk)
Car parking Limited street parking/local car parks
A–Z ref. P29/5E
Nearest landmark Bus Station/Palace Pier

Membership details Available but not necessary at £3 (entitles the holder to reduced admission and further benefits)

Opening hours	Monday–Thursday: 22.30–02.00
	Friday–Saturday: 22.00–02.00
	Sunday: Closed
Admission charges	Monday: £1 members/£2.50 non-members
	Tuesday: Free members/£2 non-members
	Wednesday–Thursday: £1 members/£2.50 non-members
	Friday: £2.50 members/£4.50 non-members
	Saturday: £4 members/£6 non-members

Food available Food venue on premises
Regular entertainment Monday: 'Man Trap': Strippers
Tuesday: 'Dance Division'
Wednesday: 'Fun House': cabaret/fun and games
Thursday: 'D.I.S.C.O.': cabaret/strippers
Friday: 'Lollipop'
Saturday: 'Choice Choonz': Revenge club night

The venue's name goes before them. A well established gay nightclub that probably has the best sound system in the country (Turbo Sound–I don't know what it is but it sounds bloody good!). The atmosphere is always buzzing with the punters out strictly for a good time. The two dance floors are always packed with hot sweaty bodies .... Mmmm, lovely. On two floors–handbag and commercial pop on the upper and club anthems, classics and techno on the lower. Checkout the website for information on upcoming events.

Doctor Brightons

16–17 Kings Road
Brighton
BN1 1NE   Telephone 01273 328 765

Nearest train station Brighton Mainline
Car parking Outside venue (free after 18.00 voucher before)/many NCPs nearby
A–Z ref. P28/5C
Nearest landmark Opposite Palace Pier

Membership details None required
Opening hours   Monday–Saturday: 11.00–23.00
                     Sunday: 12.00–22.30
                     (Out of season hours may reduce during the day)
Admission charges None
Food available No

A friendly mixed gay and straight pub (with a club atmosphere) on the prime position of Brighton's sea front. This bar is used most nights as a pre-club meeting place for all the club nights (gay and straight) going on around the area. Although not exclusively gay, Doctor Brightons is trying to break the mould of pigeon-holing people into categories, stating that their venue is about diversity and that it makes no difference what your sexuality is nor the colour of your skin–everyone is welcome, as long as they enjoy themselves and other people's company. A resident DJ is on every night with two DJs on a Sunday from 16.00–19.00 and 20.00–22.30. On Monday through to Thursday (from 18.00) there is a cheap spirits bar with spirit and a splash for a quid. An ideal venue for people venturing out on to the scene for the first time. You will be able to look around and socialise without feeling like a fish out of water.

Legends Bar/Schwartz Bar

The New Europe Hotel
31–32 Marine Parade
Brighton
BN2   Telephone 01273 624 462

Nearest train station Brighton
Car parking Street parking/local car parks
A–Z ref. P29/6F
Nearest landmark Sealife Centre

Membership details None, but there is a dress code for Schwartz Bar
Regular entertainment (Schwartz Bar)
Friday: Leather, rubber, uniform, industrial and denim
Saturday: Leather, rubber, uniform, industrial and denim

The bar is situated in the basement of the hotel as well as in the hotel itself and access between the two is totally acceptable. Reminiscent of Trades Hotel in Blackpool, the bars are extremely cruisy to say the least. Popular with non-residents. The dress code exists but is not that particularly strict. Legends Bar is open to all and attracts the local boys and girls throughout the week and stages regular karaoke and cabaret. Accommodation also available (see hotel listings).

The Marlborough

4 Princes Street
Brighton
BN2   Telephone 01273 570 028

Nearest train station Brighton Mainline
Car parking Side-street parking
A–Z ref. P29/5E
Nearest landmark Opposite Royal Pavilion

Membership details None required

Opening hours   Monday–Saturday: 19.00–23.00
                      Sunday: 12.00–22.30
Admission charges None
Food available Full bar menu Monday–Friday: 12.00–14.30 and full Sunday
lunch 12.00–15.30

A mixed gay venue with a 50 seat, fully-working theatre on the premises, used
throughout the Brighton festival by various groups and at other times by charity
organisations (Pride, etc.). With two bar rooms, the first being the theatre bar
(wood panelled with leather upholstery)–popular with the students and theatre
goers. The main bar is a mixed gay space. It was formerly a men-only
leather-type bar but now, at times, there can be more women than men. The
Marlborough is not a scene pub although the clientele are mainly young, gay and
sociable.

The Oriental
5–6 Montpelier Road
Brighton
BN1 2LQ   Telephone 01273 728 808

Nearest train station Brighton Main
Car parking Montpelier Road/limited street parking
A–Z ref. P28/5C
Nearest landmark West Pier (four blocks west of the pier)

Membership details None required
Opening hours   Monday–Thursday: 12.00–15.00/19.00–23.00
                      Friday–Saturday: 12.00–23.00
                      Sunday: 12.00–22.30
Admission charges None
Food available No
Regular entertainment Monday: Easy listening
Tuesday: Karaoke
Wednesday: 'The Dave Lynn Show'
Thursday: Quiz night
Friday: 'Music Hall'/cabaret
Saturday–Sunday: Cabaret

Mixed gay, straight and TV/TS bar. The Oriental is a well-established lively
venue with a full programme of entertainment through the week to keep you
amused. The straight element know that it's a predominantly gay bar and go in
because of the friendly and fun atmosphere.

Queen's Arms
7 George Street
Brighton
BN2 1RH   Telephone 01273 696 873

Nearest train station Brighton Central
Car parking Back of pub/Safeways car park (free after 19.00)
A–Z ref. P29/5E
Nearest landmark Safeways Supermarket

Membership details None required
Opening hours   Monday–Saturday: 11.00–23.00

Sunday: 12.00–22.30

Admission charges None
Food available Snacks available at lunch-times

Known as the QA to the locals, this traditionally styled bar should be known as a karaoke bar, as that will be the main sort of entertainment running through the week. Weekends in the main bar see a top London cabaret and regular stripper. This is a social and cruisy venue catering for a mixed gay crowd with the odd smattering of (curious and friendly) straights.

Queen's Head

10 Steine Street
Brighton
BN2 1TE   Telephone 01273 602 939

Nearest train station Brighton Central (ten minutes)
Car parking Difficult, but Sainsburys close by, also various NCPs
A–Z ref. P29/6E
Nearest landmark Sealife Centre

Membership details None required
Opening hours   Monday–Saturday: 12.00–23.00
                         Sunday: 12.00–22.30
Admission charges   None
Food available Full menu lunch-times only
Regular entertainment Wednesday–Saturday: Disco
Occasional cabaret

Everyone is welcome at this social venue: frocks, leather, denim, feathers, etc., and as a general rule, it works well. Attracting a more local crowd, the atmosphere is friendly and amiable.

Ruby's Bar (formerly Marilyns)

43 Providence Place
Brighton
BN1   Telephone 01273 620 630

Nearest train station Brighton Mainline
Car parking Directly opposite (multi-storey)
A–Z ref. P29/3E
Nearest landmark Multi-storey car park on London Road

Membership details None required
Opening hours   Monday–Saturday: 11.00–24.00
                         Sunday: 12.00–23.30
                         (No admission after 22.00 on Sunday and 23.00 every other
                         day)
Admission charges   None
Food available Full menu available with lunch-time/evening snacks also available
Regular entertainment Wednesday: Karaoke 21.00–24.00
Friday: Pre-'Fresh' party night

This split-level pub/club offers a great atmosphere to the predominantly mixed gay, straight and TV clientele. On Wednesday the popular karaoke is staged whereas Friday and Saturday sees the stage well-used for cabaret, live music and the disco session. It should be noted that in February of 1999, new owners took over the venue. Ruby's will stay a gay venue although there may be some changes to the entertainment schedule.

Wildfruit @ Paradox

78 West Street
Brighton
BN1   Telephone 01273 327 083

Nearest train station Brighton Central
Car parking Limited street parking/local NCP close by
A–Z ref. P28/5D
Nearest landmark The Brighton Centre

Membership details None required
Opening hours   Monday: 22.00–02.00
                       (First Monday of the month)
Admission charges £4–6 (concessions available)
Food available Food area at venue

This monthly event is billed as 'The South's Biggest Gay and Lesbian Party!' Hosting entertainments such as top PAs, theme parties and top shows. Huge–1,500-plus capacity–venue, pretty much nearly always full for this top event. It is recommended that you arrive early, otherwise you'll be queueing for ages. The dress code is anything goes, from outrageous to really outrageous.

Zanzibar

129–130 St James Street
Brighton
BN2   Telephone 01273 622 100

Nearest train station Brighton (taxi required)
Car parking Side-street parking/local car park
A–Z ref. P29/6F
Nearest landmark Behind Marine Parade

Membership details None required
Opening hours   Monday–Thursday: 17.00–01.00
                       Friday–Saturday: 17.00–02.00
                       Sunday: 17.00–22.30
Admission charges None
Food available Yes

Same family as the London 'Kudos' group, operating the same 'Crush Bar' theme, whereby when a featured artist appears on the large video screen, drinks are dead cheap (hence the crush!). A predominantly young, hip and trendy crowd and *the* place to meet up prior to Wildfruit.

Castro's

72–73 Old Market Street
Bristol
BS2   Telephone 0117 922 6969

Nearest train station Bristol Templemeads
Car parking Street parking/local car park
A–Z ref. P70/3A
Nearest landmark Evening Post Building

Membership details Members only–you can obtain free full membership by sending in your full name and address, date of birth and signature. If you cannot receive mail at home, enclose a note saying that you will collect it at the door (identification required to do this). Also, if you cannot receive mail, ask that your name will not be put on to a mailing list. Alternatively, you can join at the door

Opening hours	Monday: 21.00–02.00
	Tuesday: 20.00–Late
	Wednesday–Thursday: 21.00–02.30
	Friday–Saturday: 21.30–02.00
	Sunday: 15.00–Late
	Sunday: 19.00–02.00 ('Sundaze' Bar till 22.30)
Admission charges	Monday–Thursday: Free
	Friday: £3
	Saturday: £4
	Sunday: Free
	Sunday: 'Sundaze': £2 (by purchasing raffle)

Food available Light bar snacks
Regular entertainment Thursday: Cheap drinks/promos
Friday: 'Yum Yums' (hard house disco)
Saturday: First of the month: 'Hanky Panky'; second of the month: 'Revenge' (all-nighter:
22.00–10.00)
Sunday: Chill out/cheap drinks/'Sundaze': hard house weekly dance night (brilliant!)

Castro's is a members-only club and free membership must be obtained prior to entering the club. If you look 'dodgy' you may be told that you will have to wait 48 hours. However, if you tell them that you saw the listing in this guide they may let you in on the night. Castro's is on three levels. In the basement there is a games room with skittle lane, pool table and gaming machines. On the ground floor there is the disco bar and the first floor is the quieter lounge. The venue is quite cruisy and a lot can be made of the various nooks and crannies around the building (ooh-er!). *Note*:Since the recent closure of Just and Lakota, Castro's has become one of the major club nights in Bristol. Sunday dance club is extremely busy. The Friday night dance club 'Yum Yums' may go through some changes during the coming year.

Club Loco
84 Hepburn Road
Stokes Croft
Bristol
BS1 3QY

Nearest train station Bristol Templemeads
Car parking Street parking (limited on club night)
A–Z ref. P70/2A

Nearest landmark Hepburn Road is off A38 Stokes Croft

Membership details None required
Opening hours   Infamous @ Club Loco: First Saturday of month. 22.00–
                       04.00
                       Heresey @ Club Loco: First Sunday of month. 04.00–10.00
Admission charges
                       £5 for either event
                       Concessions available (identification required)
                       £8 joint ticket for Infamous and Heresey
Food available No

No big prices. No big names. No dress policy. No attitude. Mixed (gay and straight) top all- nighter each and every 'first weekend of the month'. It is wise to get in here early as the queues do tend to be quite long (and that's an understatement). Unfortunately, precise information on these club nights could not be confirmed, as the previously published info line numbers are no longer available and the telephone number to Club Loco is ex-directory! The night starts with Infamous and then switches to Heresey, so it is a continuous twelve-hour long bash. The last report regarding Infamous and Heresey stated that at 02.00 they were operating a strict one-out and one-in policy (unconfirmed). For visitors to Bristol, it may be wise to contact the local switchboard to see what advice they give on the club.

The Elephant
20 St Nicholas Street
Bristol
BS1 1UB   Telephone 0117 949 9901

Nearest train station Bristol Templemeads
Car parking Street parking
A–Z ref. P69/4F
Nearest landmark Tourist Information Office

Membership details None required
Opening hours   Monday–Saturday: 12.00–23.00
                       Sunday: 14.00–22.30
Admission charges None
Food available No
Regular entertainment Monday–Tuesday: Social night
Wednesday: DJ
Thursday: Cabaret (evening)
Friday: Karaoke (very busy)
Saturday: Disco
Sunday: Cabaret (afternoon)

Established for well over thirty years, this could be one of the city's longest running gay bars. A friendly, sociable place popular with the lesbian community.

The Griffin
41 Colston Street
Bristol
BS1 5AP   Telephone 0117 927 2421

Nearest train station Bristol Temple Meads
Car parking On-street after 18.00/meters and multi-storey
A–Z ref. P69/4F
Nearest landmark Colston House

Membership details None required
Opening hours   Monday–Friday: 15.00–23.00
                       Saturday: 12.00–23.00
                       Sunday: 12.00–22.30
Admission charges None
Food available No
Regular entertainment Thursday: TV/TS/CD

The Griffin is a small, intimate traditional-style pub housed in an unusual wedge-shaped building. It is very much a community bar and is used by many local gay groups as a meeting place. TVs are always welcome and tend to meet on Thursday evenings. Friday and Saturday finds The Griffin packed wall-to-wall with hunky bear types and the atmosphere becomes a little more cruisy than during the midweek social nights. The Griffin caters for all of the gay community, but with particular attention to the leather, rubber and uniform element, even more so on the first and third Friday of the month, when the MSC Severn Link meet in the bar.

The Old Castle Green
44 Gloucester Lane
St Phillips
Bristol
BS2   Telephone 0117 955 0925

Nearest train station Bristol Templemeads
Car parking Plenty of street parking after 18.00
A–Z ref. P70/3B
Nearest landmark Palace (Gin Palace) Hotel

Membership details None required
Opening hours   Monday–Tuesday: 11.30–14.30/17.00–23.00
                       Wednesday–Friday: 11.30–23.00
                       Saturday: 19.00–23.00
                       Sunday: 13.00–23.00
Admission charges None
Food available Monday–Friday: 13.00–16.00 and Sunday lunches: 13.00–16.00
(bookings advised)

Medium-sized pub, just off West Street in the Old Market and only ten minutes' walk from the centre of Bristol. Although it is not exclusively gay it is gay-owned with a majority gay clientele. When I asked him about the age range he said 'middle-aged, you know . . . about thrityish' (middle-aged . . . thirtyish?). The venue is well placed within easy reach of all the other gay venues giving you ample opportunity to flit between them all to find someone that takes your fancy. It does not have an extensive entertainment policy although the friendly atmosphere (Bristol lads are lovely) more than makes up for it.

The Pineapple

37 St Georges Road
Bristol
BS1 5UU   Telephone 0117 907 1162

Nearest train station Bristol Templemeads (ten minute walk)
Car parking Outside venue
A–Z ref. P69/4D
Nearest landmark Council offices

Membership details None required
Opening hours   Monday–Saturday: 12.00–23.00
                         Sunday: 12.00–22.30
Admission charges   None
Food available No
Regular entertainment Monday: Karaoke
Wednesday: Stripper
Friday: (every first Friday of the month) Party night
Saturday: Party night
Sunday: Occasional cabaret

The Pineapple is a typical friendly gay pub, full of fun and energy. Men, women and TVs are all welcome. A varied music policy, from camp to hard house. Sky TV and Happy Hour from 17.00–20.00 every day. The perfect place to come and relax after work. Excellent beer prices.

Push

53 Old Market Street
Bristol
BS2 0ER   Telephone 0117 921 0362
                 E-mail chclub@aol.com

Nearest train station Bristol Templemeads (ten minutes)
Car parking Street parking
A–Z ref. P70/3B
Nearest landmark Evening News Roundabout

Membership details None required
Opening hours   Monday–Saturday: 11.00–24.00
                         Sunday: 12.00–11.30
Admission charges None
Food available Full bar menu available all day every day (particularly popular during lunch)

Situated right slap-bang in the centre of Bristol's gay village, Push is the new kid on the gay scene block. Old (very old) and traditional, the owners aim to make it into a place where you can walk in and feel instantly at home (a bit like the *Cheers* bar off the telly, only without that ugly bird who takes the drinks orders). Although the premises takes in four levels, the bar is only on the ground floor, with plans to expand further over the coming years. There will be karaoke, cabaret, etc., however, at the present time there were no firm dates for these.

The Queens Shilling

9 Frogmore Street
Bristol
BS1 5NA   Telephone 0117 926 4342

Nearest train station Bristol Templemeads
Car parking Street parking
A–Z ref. P69/4E
Nearest landmark Ice Rink

Membership details None required
Opening hours   Monday: 21.00–02.00
                        Tuesday–Saturday: 19.00–02.00
                        Sunday: 17.00–22.30
Admission charges Monday–Wednesday: Free
                        Thursday: £1 after 22.00
                        Friday–Saturday: £2 after 22.00
                        Sunday: Free
Food available Light bar snacks
Regular entertainment Monday: 'CRAP' (Chart Retro And Pop)/cheap drinks
Tuesday: Cheap drinks/karaoke
Wednesday: Disco (club anthems)
Thursday: Stripper/disco
Friday: Disco/occasional PA
Saturday: Disco/'Weekend Party Night'
Sunday: Cabaret

Attracts the younger disco (-ish) crowd of gay boyz and bender babes, being one of the most popular venues for Bristol's student community. This large and extremely lively venue celebrates it's 7th birthday in May 1999 (big party planned). Although the venue is on one level, it is divided into three different parts; the further back you go–the more louder and livelier it becomes. The Queens is a community-based pub, with no attitude and a friendly atmosphere always. For visitors to the area, the bar staff are always well informed of what is happening in the city and will be pleased to help you any way they can.

Roosters

46 West Street
Old Market
Bristol
BS2 0BH   Telephone 0117 914 0049

Nearest train station Bristol Templemeads
Car parking Ample street parking or factory car parks
A–Z ref. P70/3B
Nearest landmark Sofa Project/A420

Membership details None required
Opening hours   Monday–Saturday: 16.00–02.00
                        Sunday: 16.00–23.30
Admission charges None to pub
                        £3–4 (various) to club depending on attraction
Food available Yes
Regular entertainment Monday: DJ/video quiz

Tuesday–Saturday: DJ
Saturday: (club) 'Respect': weekly spin-off from the popular monthly bash/
(pub) happy handbag/drag DJ/a jolly good time
Sunday: Prize karaoke

Having opened its doors in November 1998, this large, 350 capacity chic, comfortable bar and hi-tech dance club has quickly become an integral part of Bristol's ever increasing gay scene. The layout of the venue enables you to choose either to stay in the large late licence bar or move on upstairs to the club. Both options enable you to drink and dance into the early hours. The atmosphere throughout is friendly and welcoming where young meets old(er), leather meets feathers and straight(-ish) meets gay. All combine to make a fun and fluffy party spirit. The two dancefloors are always packed and the chill out room upstairs provides a welcome respite for the weary. Regular women-only nights in the upstairs club will soon become a permanent feature (details at the time of going to press were sketchy). Situated close to Castro and The Cottage Health Club (gay sauna–see separate Sauna listing.)

Garden Bar

133 St James Street
Burnley
Lancashire
BB11   Telephone 01282 414 895

Nearest train station Burnley
Car parking Ample side-street parking
Nearest landmark Marks and Spencer (practically next door)

Membership details None required
Opening hours   Monday–Saturday: 11.00–23.00
                       Sunday: 12.00–17.00/19.00–22.30
Admission charges None
Food available No

Mixed gay and straight bar (gay-run). More of a local drinking bar than a trendy gay bar. Predominantly gay on a Thursday and a Sunday when a disco and cabaret are held. Because of the lack of gay venues in this part of the world, this venue has been listed to offer the gay person at least one place to go.

Dot Cottons @ The Junction

Clifton Road
Cambridge
CB1 4GX   Telephone 01223 511 511 (Box office)
               Website http://www.junction.co.uk/(Dot Cottons): http://
               www.dccc.demon.co.uk

Nearest train station Cambridge (five minutes)
Car parking On-site (The Junction is in the middle of a Park & Ride car park!)
A–Z ref. P29/1F
Nearest landmark A1307 Hills Road to Park and Ride

Membership details 10% discount on up to 'two tickets per member' scheme in advance only for club nights (phone for further details)
Opening hours   Saturday: 22.00–03.00
                       (Last Saturday of the month only)

Admission charges   £6 advance/£7 on door
                      Advance tickets can be purchased at The Junction
Food available Cafe open in venue

The Dot Cotton Club is The Junction's longest running mixed gay and straight club night with a capacity of 1,000. Each 'Dot' features regular DJs Chris G and Lee plus guests. Hostess (with the mostess) and door whore Felicity Flappes keeps everyone in order. There is always a top live PA (check out the website for up-to-date info). The regional heats of Mr Gay UK are very nearly always held here. This venue is always busy, always loud and always a great night out.

The Five Bells
126–128 Newmarket Road
Cambridge
CB5 8HE   Telephone   01223 314 019

Nearest train station Cambridge
Car parking Street parking (limited during the day)
A–Z ref. P21/2E
Nearest landmark Cambridge Regional College

Membership details None required
Opening hours   Monday–Tuesday: 19.00–23.00
                      Wednesday–Friday: 12.00–14.00/19.00–23.00
                      Sunday: 12.00–22.30
Admission charges None
Food available Sunday lunch: 12.00–16.00

Very friendly mixed gay pub with occasional discos, pool competitions and quiz nights. Comprising of two bar areas, one with background music, the other much louder.

The Town and Gown
Northampton Street
Pound Hill
Cambridge
CB3 0AE   Telephone   01223 353 791

Nearest train station Cambridge
Car parking Street parking (limited during the day)
A–Z ref. P20/1B
Nearest landmark St John's College

Membership details None required
Opening hours   Monday–Tuesday: 18.00–23.00
                      Wednesday–Saturday: 12.00–14.30/18.00–23.00
                      Sunday: 12.00–22.30
Admission charges None
Food available No

Well-established gay pub with regular promotions and events and cabaret over the weekend. More of a local than a clubby bar.

Secrets

12B New Road
Chatham
Kent
ME4 4QR   Telephone 01634 832 433

Nearest train station Chatham (five minutes)
Car parking Ample street parking
A–Z ref. P17/3D
Nearest landmark George Hotel

Membership details
Required–on the first Wednesday in September a birthday party is held when free memberships are given out; otherwise, it will cost £5 per year
Opening hours   Thursday–Saturday: 20.00–02.00
                        Sunday: 19.00–24.00
Admission charges Thursday–Saturday: Free before 22.00
                        £3 before 23.00/£5 after
Food available Light snacks
Regular entertainment Thursday–Friday: DJ
Saturday: 'Dance Zone' (DJ Joe/Lady Dee, etc.)
Sunday: 'Carnival Karaoke' till 23.00/DJ after

Members-only club with regular entertainment. Non-members can join on the night or be signed in as a guest. The venue itself is on one level and is extremely lively, friendly and fun. There are regular PAs, cheap drinks, pool table and so on. The clientele are a good mix of lesbian, gay and gay-friendly straights, who are out for the fun atmosphere. Newcomers to the scene in Chatham or surrounding areas can phone Maxine on the above number and she will do her best to introduce you around.

Army and Navy

138 Parkway
Chelmsford
Essex   Telephone 01245 354 155

Nearest train station Chelmsford (£2 in taxi or about a ten minute walk)
Car parking Own car park at venue
Nearest landmark Army and Navy Roundabout

Membership details None required
Opening hours   Wednesday: 19.00–23.00
                        Sunday: 19.00–22.30
Admission charges None
Food available No
Regular entertainment Wednesday: DJ
Sunday: DJ/Occasional cabaret

Predominantly gay on two days of the week, in this otherwise straightish pub. Being more of a local pub in an area not renowned for the abundance of gay bar space, I suppose it is better than nothing.

Bar Icon

20 High Street
Cheltenham
Gloucestershire
GL50 1DZ   Telephone 01242 260 706
                 E-mail Bar_icon@yahoo.com

Nearest train station Cheltenham Spa
Car parking Car park and street parking
A–Z ref. P5/5F
Nearest landmark Junction of London Road and Bath Road/Memorial Gardens
(freedom flag indicates the venue)

Membership details Free membership available–phone or write enclosing name
and address, date of birth and signature (if you cannot receive mail at home
state this on the application)

Opening hours   Monday–Wednesday: 20.00–24.00
                        Thursday–Saturday: 20.00–02.00
                        Sunday: 20.00–01.00
Admission charges   Monday–Wednesday: Free
                        Thursday: £2 after 22.00
                        Friday–Saturday: £3 after 22.00/£4 after 23.00
                        Sunday: Free before 22.00/£2 after
                        (Guests may be admitted for £1 extra)
Food available Saturday nights only
Regular entertainment Monday–Tuesday: Chill Out
Wednesday: Social evening
Thursday: 70s and 80s night/Karaoke
Friday: Students night twice a month/cheap drinks
Saturday: Dance anthems
Sunday: Drinks served till 01.00/karaoke

Bar Icon is a large venue spread over three floors. The entertainment and cabaret
programme changes quite regularly and details are advertised well in advance in
the free gay press.

Handbag @ The Racecourse (formerly The Racecourse Disco)

Betting Hall Suite
Prestbury Race Course
Cheltenham
Gloucestershire Telephone 01452 529 417 (The Phoenix for enquiries)

Nearest train station Cheltenham Spa
Car parking Car parking at venue
A–Z ref. P6/1B
Nearest landmark Prestbury Racecourse (A435)

Membership details None required
Opening hours   Saturday: 21.30–02.00
                        (Monthly disco every second Saturday of the month)
Admission charges   £3.50 advance tickets/£4.50 on the door
                        Advance tickets can be purchased from either The
                        Leckhampton Inn or The Phoenix (see listings)
Food available Buffet included in admission price

Shuttle buses go from The Leckhampton Inn and The Phoenix at 23.15 and 23.45 and also from Stroud Bus Station (phone Phoenix for times). After The Racecourse Disco (as it was formerly known) closed down, the Phoenix took over the running of the venue, renamed it to The Handbag and kept this fabulous monthly venture open. The music policy is camp handbag and classic club anthems. Easy to find as the racecourse is well signposted. At the racecourse you will find pink handbag signs directing you to The Betting Hall suite. There's a pre-club get together at The Phoenix and The Leckhampton. The clientele are young party animals and there are a lot of people who do not go out on the gay scene who tend to use this place as a meeting place (!).

The Phoenix Inn

36 Andover Road
Cheltenham
Gloucestershire
GL50 2TS   Telephone   01242 529 417

Nearest train station Cheltenham
Car parking Ample street parking
A–Z ref. P15/1E
Nearest landmark Tivoli Centre

Membership details None required
Opening hours   Monday–Friday: 12.00–14.00/18.00–24.00
                         Saturday: 11.00–14.30/19.00–24.00
                         Sunday: 12.00–22.30
                         (Doors close at 23.00)
Admission charges   None
Food available Sherbets Restaurant open during the day as a cafe. Breakfasts available on Saturday morning
Regular entertainment Monday: Quiz night
Tuesday: Bingo every second and fourth of the month
Wednesday: Raffle (cash rollover)
Thursday: Karaoke
Friday: Stripper every second and fourth of the month
Saturday: Coach to Subway City last Saturday of the month
Sunday: Cabaret

At the time of going to print The Phoenix was due for a major refurbishment and the venue may close for the duration. Plans are to transform the venue into a bright modern cosmopolitan establishment for the gay community. The monthly gay night at The Racecourse will still continue and any further information that you may require can be directed to the above telephone number. Bed and breakfast accommodation is available at the venue and again, further details can be obtained on the above number.

The Pride Of Leckhampton Inn

33 Shurdington Road
Cheltenham
Gloucestershire
GL53 0HY   Telephone   01242 527 763

Nearest train station Cheltenham (taxi required from here)
Car parking At venue

A–Z ref. P14/5C
Nearest landmark On main road A46 from Bath

Membership details None required
Opening hours   Monday–Friday: 18.00–23.00
                             Saturday: 12.00–15.00/18.00–23.00
                             Sunday: 12.00–15.00/18.00–22.30
Admission charges None
Food available No
Regular entertainment Tuesday: Competition night
Thursday: Quiz night
Sunday: 'Gay-oki Karaoke' (compered by drag kings–The Blues Sisters.

Traditional pub, known locally as 'The Lekkie', where everyone, gay, bi, TV or
straight will receive the same courteous and friendly welcome. Total attitude-
free zone which makes for an enjoyable time. With three bars and a pool table it is
as popular with the girls as it is with the boys. In conjunction with the Phoenix, a
shuttle bus is in operation once a month to ferry passengers to The Racecourse
Disco (leaving both venues every 20 minutes or so). See separate listing for Pink
Handbag at The Racecourse.

FAB @ Alchemy
20–24 City Road
Chester
CH1 3AE   Telephone 01244 314 794/07801 065 061 (infoline)

Nearest train station Chester (200 metres)
Car parking Ample street parking
A–Z ref. P8/3A
Nearest landmark Chester Railway Station

Membership details Required–non-members can join on the night for £5 (take
with you a passport photo and membership can be completed, otherwise you
have up to 30 days to bring in the photo)
Opening hours   Friday: 22.00–02.00
                             (Friday nights only)
Admission charges £5 (includes membership on first visit)
Food available Snacks only

One night a week popular gay club night (look for the freedom flag). The larger
room is the main dance arena and cabaret stage hosted by the resident hostess

Suited
& Booted (West End)

Escort Agency
0171 224 3312

stunning, educated guys with great personalities and friendly attitude.
One call to us and we make all the arrangements.
Portfolio available for viewing by appointment or sent to you by email.
Or simply choose from our web site:
http://www.sandb.demon.co.uk
Call Mark or Paul on:
0171 224 3312
for further details and friendly advice.

Doreen Kum Kwik. The smaller room acts as a chill out room. Drag queens serve behind the bar and rollerblade around the floor. There is a nice little 'quiet' area behind the dance floor and foyer where you can take your new found friend for a little chat (or tongue-twister). This venue does get extremely busy, due to the lack of clubs serving the North Wales coast. It is well frequented by the girlz who also use the Liverpool Arms (see listing) as a pre-club meeting space. A note regarding membership: your details are held on the computer but there is *no way* that the list is used for mailshots, etc. Usual free gay press available. After club hours the 'Chester Walls' can get extremely busy, particularly in the summer (see cruising listing).

Liverpool Arms

79 Northgate Street
Chester
CH1 2HQ   Telephone 01244 312 805 (Bar)/01244 310 232 (Office)

Nearest train station Chester (one mile)
Car parking Local (250 metres) but do not park outside residents' flats/houses
A–Z ref. P7/3G
Nearest landmark Northgate Bridge/Chester Bus Station (one minute walk)

Membership details None required
Opening hours   Monday–Saturday: 11.00–23.00
                              Sunday: 12.00–22.30
Admission charges None
Food available No, though food may be purchased from the sandwich shop opposite and eaten in the pub (no fish and chips though)
Regular entertainment Wednesday: Cabaret/DJ
Thursday–Saturday: DJ
Sunday: Drag cabaret

Being situated in the ideal position underneath 'Chester Walls' makes the Liverpool Arms the ideal venue for a spot of welcome relief in between cruising (see listing). Consisting of two rooms, the larger one being loud and busy, the second, more relaxed and 'snug'. Friday nights are extremely busy as The Liverpool Arms is used as a pre-'Alchemy' meeting place. Apart from the weekly club night at Alchemy, the Liverpool Arms is the only gay bar in Chester, and with this being the case you can be sure that it will be busy on most nights. Regular cheap drinks with an all day spirits doubles bar (using main brands). The clientele is mixed gay and lesbian with an age range across the board, making this a good place for the people of Chester and surrounding areas to come in and make new friends. Car parking can be a bit of a bind and it is wise not to park in front of the residential flats at the bottom of the road in order to avoid nasty notes (or worse) on your car. The area around the bus station offers ample car parking spaces. *Note*: There is news of a new gay bar, The Amsterdam, opening in Chester very shortly. It is deemed to be a fun bar with bar shows, cabaret and such like. Unfortunately at this time there are no further details.

The Basement @ The Bluebell Inn

Cavendish Street
Chesterfield
Derbyshire   Telephone 01246 201 849

Nearest train station Chesterfield

Car parking Local car parking
A–Z ref. P13/2A
Nearest landmark YMCA

Membership details None required
Opening hours   Wednesday: 20.00–23.00
                       (Wednesday night only)
Admission charges None
Food available No

If nothing else, this venue offers you a change of scenery and disco one night per week with the opportunity of cheap drinks in the happy hours 20.00–22.00. Entrance to The Basement is through the normally straight bar The Bluebell.

Club X-Cell

11 Lordsmill Street
Chesterfield
Derbyshire   Telephone 01246 222 550

Nearest train station Chesterfield (quarter of a mile)
Car parking Street parking and local car park
A–Z ref. P138/3B
Nearest landmark Crooked Spire

Membership details Not necessary, but available (enquire at door or Marsdens Bar)
Opening hours   Monday–Tuesday: Closed
                       Wednesday–Saturday: 22.00–02.00
                       Sunday: Closed
Admission charges Wednesday: £3/£1.50 Concessions
                       Thursday–Saturday: Various (depending on event)
Food available Light snacks available
Regular entertainment Wednesday: 'Gay Club Night'
Thursday: 'Mixed Retro Night'
Friday–Saturday: Dance club cight–promotional dance club events

Run by the team at Marsdens. Concessions to the club are given to Marsdens customers. Wednesday is the only exclusively gay night at this venue; the rest of the time it is mixed gay and straight. The weekends are organised by up and coming dance clubs on promotion and the admission can vary from £5–10 depending on the organiser. The venue is a young trendy place with 15k sound and light system and lots of steel and industrial fittings. The main room is a large open-plan dance arena with exhibitionistic dancers in cages and a quieter chill out area with comfortable seating and the like. Even though the venue attracts the straight element over the weekend, they are all open-minded without attitude and everyone seems to get along just fine.

Marsdens Bar

13 Marsden Street
Chesterfield
Derbyshire
S40 1JY   Telephone 01246 232 618

Nearest train station Chesterfield (quarter of a mile)
Car parking Street parking and local car parks

A–Z ref. P138/2A
Nearest landmark Crooked Spire

Membership details None required
Opening hours   Monday–Saturday: 20.00–23.00
                       Sunday: 12.00–15.00/20.00–22.30
Admission charges None
Food available Snacks available in the evenings
Regular entertainment Monday: Social night/cheap drinks (20.00–21.00)
Tuesday: Quiz night
Wednesday: Male stripper
Thursday: Karaoke (busy)
Friday–Saturday: DJ
Sunday: Cabaret (upstairs)
(Happy hour is Monday–Friday 20.00–21.00)

Easy-going, friendly mixed gay bar with TVs more than welcome. A trendy, youngish crowd. Varied music policy from fun music to the latest club sounds. It is a modern bar with pool table and dance floor, with an additional upstairs disco room open on Sundays. The downstairs bar area is dived into two separate areas and can become quite cruisy. Sister club X-Cell opened in April 1998 and obviously Marsdens is the official feeder bar for the club. Concessions to Club X-Cell are given to Marsdens customers (ask at bar for details).

The Old Feathers

26 Lordsmill Street
Chesterfield
Derbyshire   Telephone 01246 232 018

Nearest train station Chesterfield (ten minute walk)
Car parking On-site car park
Nearest landmark Markham House/Kwik Fit (opposite)

Membership details None required
Opening hours   Monday–Friday: 12.00–14.00/19.00–23.00
                       Saturday: 19.00–23.00
                       Sunday: 19.00–22.30
Admission charges None
Food available Full menu available lunch and evenings
Regular entertainment Monday: Disco/cheap drinks/pub quiz
Tuesday: Social night
Wednesday: Drag disco/pre-club cheap drinks
Thursday: Disco
Friday: 'Big Moll Drag' DJ/cabaret/'Friday Frolics'
Saturday: 'Sleaze Night' cabaret/'Big Moll Disco' 70s-90s
Sunday: Disco
(Karaoke evenings planned for summer 1999)

This is a very camp establishment, loads of drag queens, TVs, TSs (and admirers), with cabaret and entertaining the punters high on the agenda. The horseshoe-shaped bar breaks up the room, enabling you to cruise around trying to entice nice young men into your clutches. Winners of the many 'games' hosted by the DJ could end up with pints of ale or a bar dash (pull a pint and then a spirit as many times as you can within a couple of minutes). There is always a good friendly atmosphere; a predominantly young crowd all intent on enjoying themselves and in this place it would be exceedingly hard not to.

The Bush Inn
16 The Hornet
Chichester
West Sussex
PO19 4JG   Telephone 01243 782 939

Nearest train station Chichester (three-quarters of a mile)
Car parking On site car park (18 spaces)/NCP 180 metres
Nearest landmark Chichester Railway Station

Membership details None required
Opening hours   Monday–Saturday: 10.30–23.30
                         Sunday: 12.00–22.30
Admission charges   None, except for published cabaret nights
Food available Full menu available at lunch-time
Regular entertainment Monday: Free pool all day
Thursday: Disco
Friday: Disco/karaoke once a month
Saturday: Disco
Sunday: Free pool 12.00–17.00

The Bush Inn is a well-established pub and has been for well over 18 years in the city centre at the eastern end of the shopping centre. A large pub with two bars, one a lounge bar and the other with a pool table, both flowing freely on disco nights, which take place every week. Popular with the whole of the gay community: gay, bi, lesbian, TV and TS. Accommodation available also.

Fox and Hounds
Bentley Road
Little Bromley
Colchester
Essex
CO11 2PL   Telephone 01206 397 415

Nearest train station Manningtree
Car parking Large on-site facility

Membership details Can be arranged on the night (offers reduced admission)
Opening hours   Monday–Tuesday: Closed
                         Wednesday: 19.00–24.00
                         Thursday: 20.00–24.00
                         Friday–Saturday: 20.00–02.00
                         Sunday: 12.00–15.00/20.00–22.30
Admission charges   Friday–Saturday: £3/£2 Members
                      (Free at other times)
Food available Full Sunday lunch available plus evening snacks
Regular entertainment Monday–Tuesday: Closed
Wednesday: Disco/free prize draw
Thursday: 'Girls Night Out' (women only)/otherwise special events

Friday: Cabaret/disco with late bar
Saturday: Disco with late bar
Sunday: Social evening

A gay pub/club with straights escorted by their gay friends. TVs are welcome and popularise the bar on Wednesdays. Although the pub is set in a rural location situated off the A120, five miles out of Colchester, it is very far from having a rural attitude, making it an ideal out-of-town experience without you being bored stiff.

McGuigans Bar

Swanswell Street
Coventry
CV1 5FZ   Telephone 01203 222 536

Nearest train station Coventry (just over a mile)
Car parking Outside venue
A–Z ref. P116/4C
Nearest landmark Coventry and Warwick Hospital

Membership details None required
Opening hours   Monday–Tuesday: 11.00–23.00
                    Wednesday–Thursday: 11.00–02.00
                    Friday–Saturday: 11.00–03.00
                    Sunday: 12.00–22.30
Admission charges   Monday–Tuesday: Free
                    Wednesday–Thursday: £1
                    Friday–Saturday: £3 after 23.00
                    Sunday: Free
Regular entertainment Wednesday: Disco
Thursday: Karaoke
Friday–Saturday: Disco
Sunday: Chill out

McGuigans has been established as a popular mixed gay venue for the past ten years. A lesbian pool team is based here.

Rainbows

88 Short Street
Parkside
Coventry
CV1 2LW   Telephone 01203 551 738

Nearest train station Coventry (five minute walk)
Car parking On-site for approximately 100 cars
A–Z ref. P116/5C
Nearest landmark Universal Technological Park at rear of venue

Membership details None required
Opening hours   Monday–Wednesday: 18.00–23.00
                    Thursday–Saturday: 12.00–02.00
                    Sunday: 12.00–15.00/19.00–22.30
Admission charges   Monday–Thursday: No charge
                    Friday–Saturday: £3 after 21.30
                    Sunday: No charge

Food available Full menu and snacks at all times
Regular entertainment First Thursday: Karaoke/'Pink Pound Weekly'
Second Thursday: 'Purr-Vert' student night
Friday: DJ/cabaret/'Bears Night' every last Friday
Saturday: Club night

Coventry's venue catering for an all mixed gay clientele with a welcome to their straight family and friends, all fetishes, transvestites, transsexuals, etc. Very friendly and sociable venue on two levels: the ground floor is the bar and chill out area and upstairs is the nightclub and bar. The summer months see the opening of the courtyard garden with loads of seating for those hot summer nights and warm spring evenings. Recently voted into third place in 'The Midlands Best Gay Bar' Awards (*Zone* Magazine). Monthly group meetings in the upstairs bar for Mesmen, Coventry Friend, and The Police Liaison Group. Leather nights planned for the future.

The Park
42 Wistaton Road
Crewe
Cheshire
CW2 7RE   Telephone 01270 662677

Nearest train station Crewe Central (five minute walk)
Car parking Rear of venue

Membership details None required
Opening hours Monday–Saturday: 19.30–Late
Sunday: 19.30–22.30
Admission charges None
Food available No (except for free buffet on Wednesday night events)

Social and intimate, true gay bar near to the centre of Crewe comprising three bars on two levels. The top level is used only as a meeting space for gay groups and for special occasions. The bar is popular with TVs/TSs and their admirers with ample changing facilities/make-up room, etc. TV/TS groups (and other gay groups) are welcome to utilise the meeting rooms free of charge. The venue itself is a melting pot for the Cheshire gay community including a fair proportion of bisexuals and curious straights. The large bar area is likened to your living room (that is if you have a load of drunks round your house every night) meaning that it's cosy and friendly. The separate games room with dartboard and pool table is popular with the lesbians (why is that?). Cabaret is booked for every other Wednesday, and to make the evening more like a house party, a free buffet is laid on.

Curzons
23–25 Curzon Street
Derby
DE1 1LH   Telephone 01332 363 739

Nearest train station Derby (two miles)
Car parking Ample street parking
A–Z ref. P12/4B

Nearest landmark St Werburgh's Church

Membership details 48 hours notice required (either apply by post or phone first and arrange to collect your membership at the door)

Opening hours   Monday: Closed (available for private hire)
                       Tuesday: 22.00–02.00
                       Wednesday: Closed (available for private hire)
                       Thursday–Saturday: 22.00–04.00
                       Sunday: 21.00–01.00

Admission charges   Tuesday–Thursday: Free before 23.30/approximately £1 after
                       Friday– Saturday: £4 (approximately)
                       Sunday: Free
                       Reduced admission for students with valid NUS card/with club pass stamped at Freddies Bar

Food available Restaurant in venue

Regular entertainment Monday: Fetish night once a month (phone for details)
Tuesday: Cabaret (every second Tuesday of the month)/cheap drinks/retro disco
Thursday: Disco (commercial)
Friday: Cabaret (usually drag)
Saturday: Disco (commercial, garage and house with DJ Paul Andrews–ex-Tin Tins)
Sunday: '100% Camp' with stripper and cabaret/free supper (watch out for those pesky
students!)

Curzons is the sister venue to Freddie's Bar. The club pass is available at Freddies Bar and works like this: when you buy a drink at Freddies you will get your pass stamped at the bar and each stamp is worth 50p off the admission price to Curzons. The club itself is a fair-sized venue catering for the gay community, so you will get all types and all ages going in. Quite a cruisy venue, with loads of dark nooks and crannies to explore.

Freddies Bar

101 Curzon Street
Derby
DE1 1LH   Telephone 01332 204 290

Nearest train station Derby (two miles)
Car parking Ample street parking
A–Z ref. P12/4B
Nearest landmark St Werburgh's Church

Membership details None required
Opening hours   Monday–Thursday: 19.00–23.00
                       Friday–Saturday: 12.00–16.00/19.00–23.00
                       Sunday: 12.00–16.00/17.00–22.30

Admission charges None
Food available No

Freddies Bar is the feeder bar to its sister venue, Curzons. A bright continental styled bar on one large level divided by stages into three different areas. The music is loud to get you in the mood for a night on the town. All ages and types including a fair few TVs and TSs, who seem to be more prominent on Mondays and Tuesdays. Again, like Curzons, this can be a cruisy type of venue. Occasional cabaret and entertainment is staged, although the concentration is more on the music, drinking and just having a jolly good time. Don't forget to collect your stamps from the bar to allow you reduced admission to Curzon's.

Feeling Fruity @ The Warehouse
Northbridge
Marshgate
Doncaster   Telephone 01302 322 199/0468 021 315 (infoline)

Nearest train station Doncaster (three minute walk)
Car parking Ample parking outside venue
A–Z ref. P32/5C
Nearest landmark Carnhills Motor Company on the Northbridge

Membership details None required on Friday but required on Saturday: phone beforehand and ask for membership to be left at the desk. Otherwise a member can sign in up to three guests (you can wait outside and ask a member to sign you in, but the desk staff cannot arrange this–you have to do it yourself)
Opening hours   Friday: 22.00–02.30
                       Feeling Fruity (Friday night is gay night only)
                       Saturday: 23.00–06.00
Admission charges Friday: £4/£6 when cabaret is on

Millennium
NOTTING HILL
ESCORTS AND MASSEURS

We offer a selection of exceptional young and friendly escorts and masseurs. Available to visit your home/hotel or come and visit our spacious and discreet Notting Hill Gate premises.

Open daily 12.00 noon till late
Vacancies for suitable guys

Tel: 0171 727 3387
Website: www.nottinghill93.freeserve.co.uk
Email: millennium@nottinghill93.freeserve.co.uk

Saturday: £5 members/£7 guests

Food available No

A free ride to The Warehouse leaves The Vine (see separate listing) every Friday at 23.15. This is a 700 capacity venue. You must take your own drinks. This means that you can nip down to Sainsburys and buy a load of cheap wine and get pissed for next to nothing. If spirits are your bag then the same applies. The warehouse can provide all glasses, mixers and ice in order that you don't look like a cheap common slut swigging from the bottle. The house party atmosphere does a lot to make this place a good venue to spend your Fridays. On Saturdays some extra rules apply; you still need to bring your own booze but it is a predominantly straight night, so the straight rule of no jeans/trainers and smart(-ish) dress apply (fashion trainers may be acceptable). If the doorman gives you a hard time tell him that you saw the listing in this guide . . . better still, try and become a member. The music on Saturday is excellent, stating off with commercial house and club anthems and progressing through to hard house as the evening goes on. The crowd are young and trendy on both nights. On Friday the dress code is a lot more relaxed and the music tends to be Hi Nrg to club classics and anthems. Despite sound of the name, The Warehouse is a smart club and the bonus of BYOB and the party atmosphere makes it even better.

The Vine

2 Kelham Street
Balby
Doncaster
South Yorkshire
DN1 3RE   Telephone 01302 364 096

Nearest train station Doncaster
Car parking Rear of venue
A–Z ref. P46/2C
Nearest landmark Balby Industrial estate/Kelham Bank

Membership details None required
Opening hours   Monday: 19.00–23.00
                         Tuesday–Wednesday: 20.00–23.00
                         Thursday–Saturday: 19.30–23.00
                         Sunday: 19.30–22.30
Admission charges None
Food available No
Regular entertainment Thursday: Disco
Friday: Disco/Ride to Feeling Fruity @ The Warehouse
Saturday: Disco
Sunday: Disco/stripper

Exclusively mixed gay bar. Free ride to Doncaster Warehouse leaving The Vine at 23.15 every Friday. Remember to bring your own bottle to The Warehouse not to The Vine.

Boxes on Tuesday

Boxes Nightclub
37–39 Commercial Road
The Quay
Exeter
EX2   Telephone 01392 259 292
                Website http://www.visitweb.com/wbb

Nearest train station Exeter
Car parking Free parking close by
A–Z ref. P9/1H
Nearest landmark The Quay (signposted)

Membership details None required
Opening hours   Tuesday: 21.00–01.00
Admission charges   £3 before 22.00/NUS £2
                      £4 after/NUS £3

Food available No

Once a week venue for gay people and friends. Boxes on Tuesday has run in various guises and under different names every week for more than 17 years, possibly making it one of the longest running discos for gays in the area. For over two years, Boxes on Tuesday has been co-promoted by DJ Alan, who has widened the music policy of playing the best of today as well as some of the favourite club classics. Boxes is a friendly club which has recently seen many alterations including new sound system, lighting and dance floor. There is a good atmosphere and regular patrons attend from across the South-West, as well as from further afield. Admission is moderately priced in addition to drinks promotions every week.

Liberty's @ Bart's Tavern

53 Bartholomew Street West
Exeter
Devon
EX4 3AJ   Telephone 01392 275 623/01392 664 367 (infoline)

Nearest train station Central Station
Car parking Side-street parking
A–Z ref. P9/1H
Nearest landmark Picture House cinema/close to the sex shop

Membership details None required
Opening hours   (Liberty)
                      Monday–Saturday: 11.00–01.00
                      Sunday: 12.00–22.30
                      (Bart's)
                      Monday: 20.00–23.00 (women only)
                      Wednesday & Saturday: 21.00–01.00
Admission charges   Monday: £1 waged/50p unwaged (women's night)
                      Wednesday & Saturday: Free before 22.00/£3 after/£2
                      concessions

Food available Full menu available

Bart's Tavern is the upstairs club at Liberty's and is exclusively gay on Monday, Wednesday and Saturday evenings. The downstairs cafe bar is gay-friendly at all times. On Monday evenings there is a women-only night in Barts: 'Women Take Liberty's' (the only night with an admission charge to cover expenses). New faces are always welcome and more details can be obtained by contacting the venue. The venue is lively and busy. The bar staff are friendly and accommodating (and noticeably good). Complete age range on gay nights.

Northbridge Inn
11 St David's Hill
Exeter
Devon
EX4 3RJ   Telephone 01392 252 535

Nearest train station Exeter St David's
Car parking Local car park/street parking
A–Z ref. P3/5G
Nearest landmark Railway Station/Technical College

Membership details None required
Opening hours   Monday–Saturday: 19.00–23.00
                         Sunday: 12.00–15.00 (closed evenings)
Admission charges None
Food available Full menu and traditional Sunday lunch

At the time of going to print this venue was being taken over by a new landlord. Future changes will be taking place, however, there were no definite plans at the current time.

The Queens Vaults Central
8 Gandy Street
Exeter
EX4 3LS   Telephone 01392 426 416

Nearest train station Exeter St David's
Car parking Ample street parking
A–Z ref. P4/6A
Nearest landmark Central Library

Membership details None required
Opening hours   Monday–Saturday: 12.00–23.30
                         Sunday: 18.00–22.30
Admission charges None except for occasional cabaret nights (nominal charges)
Food available Lunch-times till 15.00
Regular entertainment Tuesday: Karaoke
Sunday: Cabaret

The Queens Vaults is a massive underground venue (hence the name) catering for a mixed gay and no-attitude straight crowd. Throughout the week there are regular drinks promotions and what seems like a continuous happy hour. There is no regular scheduled entertainment, except for the busy karaoke on a Tuesday evening and top cabaret on a Sunday. Pool table too.

The Cellar

33 Shortheath Road
Farnham
Surrey
GU9 8SH   Telephone 01252 715 844

Nearest train station Farnham
Car parking Street parking (residential area–park with care)

Membership details None required
Opening hours   Friday: 22.00–01.30 (Weekly)
                         Saturday: 21.00–03.00 (Last Saturday of the month only)
Admission charges   Phone for details (nominal)
Food available Free buffet

The Cellar is a unique place for the gay and bi community of Farnham and surrounding areas. It is not a commercial venue, it is more of a house party in order to provide the gay community with some sort of space in an area which does not otherwise cater for the communtiy at all. Friday nights is a chill out night whereby the free gay press is made available, opportunity to chat and meet new people (particularly those new to the area or just coming out), with background music and the pool table. The once a month party get-together is well attended and further details of this event can be gained by phoning the above number for directions and details. The venue is strictly run by gays for gays. Volunteers get together each month in order to organise the event (more are required so if you are interested please give them a call). The Cellar has been running for about 24 years and still maintains the same friendly atmosphere. It is also worth noting that the GAGS (Guildford Area Gay Society) meets in the area on a Wednesday. For more information on this group phone 01252 370 809.

Dick Van Dykes

63 North Quay
Great Yarmouth
Norfolk
NR30 1JB   Telephone 01493 332 783

Nearest train station Great Yarmouth
Car parking Side-street parking (limited during the day)
Nearest landmark Avonbridge House/The Harbour

Membership details None required
Opening hours   Monday–Tuesday: 19.00–23.00
                         Wednesday–Saturday: 20.00–02.00
                         Sunday: 12.00–15.00/19.00–22.30
Admission charges   Monday–Thursday: Free
                         Friday–Saturday: Free before 23.00/£2 after
                         Sunday: Free
Food available Light snacks

Gay bar with a welcome late licence. Plenty of entertainment from midweek onwards, such as karaoke on Thursday and discos over the weekend. A friendly and welcoming venue, popular with all ages and types.

Kings Wine Bar

42 King Street
Great Yarmouth
Norfolk
NR30 2PN   Telephone 01493 855 374

Nearest train station Great Yarmouth (15 minutes away)
Car parking Front and rear of the venue

Membership details Free club membership for cheap drinks: apply at bar
Opening hours   Monday: 11.00–18.00/20.00–24.00
                       Tuesday–Friday: 11.00–24.00
                       Saturday: 11.00–18.00/20.00–24.00
                       Sunday: 20.00–23.30
Admission charges None
Food available Full menu all day

Mixed gay and straight venue with an extremely keen drinks policy and regular drinks promotion evenings. The atmosphere in the front bar is relaxed and homely and ther's a disco each weekend in the back bar. Although there are two bars (apparently one is for the straights and the other is for the gays) it is becoming more of a mixed venue where everyone mixes together (quite right too).

Club I-Dentity

18–20 Prospect Place
Hastings
East Sussex
TN34 1LN   Telephone 01424 722 240

Nearest train station Hastings Central
Car parking Ample street parking on adjacent roads
Nearest landmark White Rock Theatre (venue situated behind)

Membership details Runs from November-October with a maximum fee of £5, reducing by the quarter
Opening hours   Monday-Wednesday: Closed
                       Thursday-Saturday: 19.30–23.00
                       Sunday: 19.30–22.30
Admission charges £2 guests and non-members (cabaret evenings only)/no
                     charge to members
Food available No

I-Dentity is a small private members (but guests welcome) club, providing a relaxed yet stimulating atmosphere for the gay community in and around Hastings to drink and socialise. The club hosts weekly live acts and has experimented successfully with other performances including drag and karaoke. It produces a monthly newsletter informing members of future events and news about the club and other members.

Club Impulse @ Docs Nightclub

Aubrey Street
Hereford
HR4 0BU   Telephone 01432 262 037

Nearest train station Hereford (one mile)
Car parking Ample street parking
Nearest landmark Green Dragon Hotel

Membership details None required
Opening hours   Wednesday: 21.00–01.00 (Every third Wednesday of the
                     month only)
Admission charges £2 before 22.00/£3 after
Food available No

Situated behind the Green Dragon Hotel on Broad Street. Profits from this popular monthly night go back into helping Hereford's gay community. Pre-club meeting place is The Saracens Head (see separate listing). Club Impulse is an exclusive gay night organised by Hereford's Gay Men's Health Project and all of the gay community are welcome, in addition to TVs/TSs and gay-friendly straight guests. The atmosphere is friendly and welcoming, especially to newcomers to Hereford's gay scene and Bob will be on hand to help you with any questions or concerns that you may have. During late 1999 the night may be changing to the last Thursday of the month. Information on any future changes can be gained by phoning the above number (Gay Men's Health Project). In addition to Gay Men's Health Project there is also Hereford and Worcester Switchboard available for advice on any gay matters. Phone them at any time on 01432 275 700 (answerphone at un-manned times). Alternatively, you can write to PO Box 178, Hereford, HR4 0XU. There is also a drop-in centre at 27A St Owens Street, Hereford (phone 0374 977 817) where you can collect the free gay press and have a coffee and a chat (very friendly).

The Saracen's Head
1 St Martins Street
Hereford
HR2 7RD   Telephone 01432 275 480

Nearest train station Hereford
Car parking Large car park at rear
Nearest landmark Old River Bridge

Membership details None required
Opening hours   Wednesday: 19.00–01.00 (Every third Wednesday of the
                     month only)
                     Saturday–Sunday: 19.00–Late
Admission charges None
Food available Sandwiches, rolls, etc. (hot snacks on request) and cream teas
served during the summer

Although the weekly gay get-together takes place in the back bar over the weekends, as does the pre-'Club Impulse' @ Docs Nightclub (see separate listing) once a month every third Wednesday, this bar is an open house to all at all times. It is a safe and friendly venue with hosts Erica and Des. The Saracen's is an old-fashioned, traditional pub offering an exceptionally warm welcome to all, particularly the new faces. The back bar contains the pool table, games, etc. and the free gay press. If you would like to be introduced around, phone Erica beforehand, who will only be too pleased to assist you.

The Skinners Arms

Totteridge Road
High Wycombe
Buckinghamshire
HP13 6HR   Telephone 01494 522 038

Nearest train station High Wycombe
Car parking Ample street parking

Membership details None required
Opening hours   Monday–Thursday: 19.00–23.00
                       Friday–Saturday: 19.00–01.00
                       Sunday: 12.00–23.00
Admission charges £3 (approximately) when cabaret is staged
Food available Traditional Sunday lunch (£3 approximately)

The Skinners is a friendly and welcoming community-based lesbian and gay pub. A young bar with an average age range of 18–35. Most weekends there are cabaret and disco nights taking place in the adjoining function room. Each fortnight there are 'Women for Women' groups and social meetings and 'Icebreakers' for men taking place at the venue. Committee meetings by the Gay Men's Health Project take place here and any information regarding these groups can be found on the well-stocked notice-board or by phoning the venue direct. This place is more of a social venue rather than a clubby bar. New people are more than welcome and every effort will be made to introduce you to regular members.

Star of Brunswick

32 Brunswick Street West
Hove
BN3 1EL   Telephone 01273 771 355

Nearest train station Hove
Car parking Street parking
A–Z ref. P28/5B
Nearest landmark Dudley Hotel

Membership details None required
Opening hours   (Vats Club)
                       Monday: Closed
                       Tuesday–Saturday: 23.00–01.00
                       Sunday: 19.00–22.30
                       (Pub)
                       Monday–Friday: 12.00– 23.00
                       Saturday: 11.00–23.00
                       Sunday: 12.00–22.30
Admission charges   Tuesday–Thursday: Free
                       Friday: £2 before 23.00 (from pub)/£3 after
                       Saturday: £2 before 23.00 (from pub)/£3 after
                       Sunday: Free
                       (Admission to pub free at all times)
Food available Full menu available till 20.00 and bar snacks after 20.00
Regular entertainment Monday: Social in pub
Tuesday: 'Sounds of the 80s'

Wednesday: 'Undiscovered 70s'
Friday–Saturday: DJ (club)
Sunday: Cabaret/retro disco (70s-90s)

The Star is not an exclusively gay venue but it is extremely gay-friendly, both in the bar and in the club (Vats). Entrance to the club can be gained through the bar, entitling you to a discount on the door admission charge. Otherwise access to the club is from the street. The traditionally styled bar has a complete age range from 18 to 80, with the newly installed bar billiards table (which is always in use), real ale and the ('. . . I remember when it was all just green fields') regulars. However, the club is more for the younger generation (some that like to dabble) and the atmosphere is lively and welcoming.

The Greyhound Hotel
16 Manchester Road
Huddersfield
West Yorkshire
HD1   Telephone 01484 420 742

Nearest train station Huddersfield
Car parking Street parking

Membership details None required
Opening hours   Monday–Saturday: 19.00–late
                       Sunday: 19.00–22.30
Admission charges None
Food available No

The only exclusively gay bar in Huddersfield. The Queens Hotel and Market Tavern advertise themselves as 'gay-friendly', although I personally don't think there are enough gays in the area to go around, and for visitors it would be better to go and patronise a predominantly gay venue. Entertainment consists of cabaret and karaoke on Tuesday evenings and further cabaret over the weekend.

The Polar Bear
229 Spring Bank
Hull
HU3 1LR   Telephone 01482 323 959

Nearest train station Paragon
Car parking On-site
Nearest landmark Jacksons Bakery

Membership details None required
Opening hours   Monday–Saturday: 11.00–23.00
                       Sunday: 12.00–22.30
Admission charges None
Food available No
Regular entertainment Wednesday: Cabaret
Thursday: Social evening
Friday: Karaoke/pre-Silhouette party night
Saturday: Live bands/pre-Silhouette party night

Sunday: Free jukebox/pool competition

The Polar Bear is a mixed gay and straight venue. The front bar is used as a meeting place prior to going to the Silhouette Club over the weekend, and discounted tickets to this event are available from behind the bar. It is an extremely friendly and social place, where gay and straight mix together comfortably. Pool, darts and gay press available.

Pride Disco @ Silhouette Club

Park Street
Hull
Humberside
HU1   Telephone 01482 443 333 (manned switchboard from 19.00 to 21.00 and
             answerphone at other times)

Nearest train station Hull
Car parking Plenty of street parking
Nearest landmark Technical College (annexe)

Membership details None required
Opening hours   Friday: 23.00–03.00 (Every Friday only)
Admission charges Friday: £1 with ticket available from local gay bars/£3 on
                          the door
Food available No

Pride Disco is organised and promoted by Humberside friend. A popular weekly disco for lesbians, gays and TVs/TSs. Profits from this evening go into maintaining the switchboard and other facilities for the gay community. A very busy night with a varied music policy with guest DJs from all over the country. Humberside Friend/Switchboard will be pleased to offer support to newcomers to the scene, both lesbian and gay. Give them a ring on the above number or write to the following address: Humberside Friend, c/o CVS, Analby Road, Hull.

The Vauxhall Tavern

1 Hessle Road
Hull
Humberside
HU3   Telephone 01482 320 340

Nearest train station Hull
Car parking Ample street parking
Nearest landmark Alexander Hotel

Membership details None required
Opening hours   Monday–Tuesday: 11.00–15.00/18.30–23.00
                          Wednesday: 18.30–23.00
                          Thursday–Saturday: 11.00–15.00/18.30–23.00
                          Sunday: 11.00–15.00/18.30–22.30
Admission charges None
Food available No

The Vauxhall is a cruisy locals' bar. There's a pool room in the back and discos are held over most weekends. Tickets to the Silhouette Club (see separate listing) are available from behind the bar.

Hob In The Well

Littleport Street
Kings Lynn
PE30 1PP   Telephone 01553 774 404

Nearest train station Kings Lynn (150 metres)
Car parking On-site
Nearest landmark City Walls

Membership details None required
Opening hours   Monday–Wednesday: Closed
                         Thursday–Saturday: 20.30–23.00
                         Sunday: 20.30–22.30
Admission charges None
Food available No

A traditional, intimate and social riverside pub built onto the historic town wall of Kings Lynn. A local bar with cheap drinks prices. There is no regular scheduled entertainment.

The Navigation

Penny Street
Bridge Wharf
Lancaster
Lancashire   Telephone 01524 849 484

Nearest train station Lancaster (five minutes)
Car parking Adjacent (Thurman Street)
Nearest landmark Thurman Street car park

Membership details None required
Opening hours   Monday–Saturday: 10.00–23.00 (summer)/19.00–23.00
                         (winter)
                         Sunday: 10.00–22.30 (summer)/19.00–22.30 (winter)
Admission charges   None
Food available Snacks in summer only

Friendly, gay-run, continental style wine bar with canal-side gardens and large conservatory. Not the place for the disco dolly but ideal for a relaxing evening in a friendly and welcoming environment. Checkout the camper than camp toilets (cherubs and chandeliers? Please).

Out on Wednesday @ The Warehouse

49 North Road
Lancaster
Lancashire   Telephone 01524 390 24

Nearest train station Lancaster
Car parking Ample side-street parking
Nearest landmark Waring and Gillow

Membership details None required
Opening hours   Wednesday: 22.00–02.00 (First Wednesday of the month
                         only)

Admission charges   £2 before 23.00/£3 after
NUS concessions available
Discounted admission with flyers
Food available Light bar snacks

Large monthly gay night that has been running in total for a period of nearly five years. A strict door policy is in operation, ensuring that only those wanted to be let in will be let in. If you have that 'dodgy' look about you, then tell the doorman that you saw the venue listed in this guide and mention the club night name to him (that should do the trick). Because of the nearby university there will be a lot of students and a largely young clientele–mixed lesbian and gay. Music policy is happy house and the huge dance floor is very nearly always heaving.

The Cockpit
Swinegate
Leeds
LS1

Nearest train station Leeds
Car parking Large car park by station
A–Z ref. P67/3D
Nearest landmark Railway station/Queens Court
Opening hours   Thursday: 22.00–02.00
Admission charges £2 before 23.00/£3 after
Regular entertainment Thursday: Poptastic

Very cheap drinks, usually on selected bottles and beers–£1. For full details regarding Poptastic, see Poptastic @ The Mutz Nutz, Manchester.

The New Penny
57–59 Call Lane
Leeds
Yorkshire
LS1 7BT   Telephone 0113 243 8055

Nearest train station Leeds Central
Car parking NCP by railway station (free in evening)
A–Z ref. P67/3D
Nearest landmark Railway station

Membership details None required
Opening hours   Monday–Friday: 13.00–23.00
Saturday: 12.00–16.00/19.00–23.00
Sunday: 13.30–22.30
Admission charges None
Regular entertainment Monday: Quiz night
Thursday: Male stripper
Sunday: Drag/cabaret (lunch-time and evenings)

Leeds' longest established gay-owned and -run pub. A cruisy and social atmosphere with a mixed gay and straight clientele. Thursday night at this venue is very busy because of the regular male stripper. Holding court most nights is the much loved–her words–Vicki Graham who keeps back the baying audience with a quick wit and firm hand (ooh-er). *Note*: At the time of going to press there were rumours that The New Penny was in the process of selling up. It was not certain whether or not it would continue trading as a gay venue.

Old Red Lion
2 Meadow Lane
Leeds
LS11 5BJ   Telephone 0113 242 6779

Nearest train station Leeds
Car parking Loads of parking areas
A–Z ref. P67/4D
Nearest landmark Leeds Station (one minute)

Membership details None required
Opening hours   Monday–Thursday: 11.00–15.00/19.00–23.00
                         Friday: Saturday: 11.00–23.00
                         Sunday: 12.00–15.00/19.00–22.30
Admission charges None

Mixed gay and straight(-ish) Victorian pub. Close to all other venues, so it is nice to pop in for a change.

Queens Court
Lower Briggate
Leeds
LS1 6NA   Telephone 0113 245 9449

Nearest train station Leeds Central (two minute walk)
Car parking Large P&D by station
A–Z ref. P67/3D
Nearest landmark Leeds Central Station

Membership details Available but not necessary–take along two passport photos for membership card (£5 per year entitles you to reduced admission charges)
Opening hours   (Bar)
                         Monday–Saturday: 11.00–23.00
                         Sunday: 12.00–22.30
                         (Club)
                         Monday–Thursday: 23.00– 02.00
                         Friday: 22.30–02.00
                         Saturday: 22.30–03.00 (Bars close 02.00)
                         Sunday: Closed
Admission charges (Club)
                         Monday: £1 members/£2 guests
                         Tuesday: Free/after 24.00 £1 members/£2 guests
                         Wednesday: Free
                         Thursday: £2 members/£3 guests
                         Friday–Saturday: £4 members/£5 guests
Food available Restaurant open Monday–Friday: 12.00–15.00/17.00–19.00; Saturday: 12.00–19.00 and Sunday: 12.00–15.00
Regular entertainment Monday: 'Carry On Camping' (retro camp tunes) and 'Pink Pound Night'

Tuesday: 'Bonnie la Blue Show' (cabaret/strippers/etc.)
Wednesday: 'Play Skool' (best of old school house)/cheap drinks
Thursday: '70s Disco Fever'
Friday: 'Club Tropicana' (80s classics)
Saturday: Nu Nrg and house
Sunday: DJ D-Tox ('The Ultimate Come Down')

One of Leeds' most popular gay bars. The downstairs bar is a long narrow room with trolling areas either side. Always very busy and during the summer it opens out on to the huge courtyard. The club upstairs is a mirror image of the bar downstairs, except for the seating, and the bar is in a different place, and there is a dance floor, but the walls are in the same place.

Red Raw @ Nato
Boar Lane
Leeds
LS1   Telephone 08701 200 600/08701 242 542

Nearest train station Leeds
Car parking Local car park (by station)
A–Z ref. P67/3D
Nearest landmark C&A (Nato is underneath)/Boar Lane is pretty much opposite the railway station

Membership details Not necessary but available (phone or apply at venue for details)
Opening hours   Tuesday: 22.00–04.00 (First Tuesday of the month only)
Admission charges   Members £5/ guests £6/coach travellers £8
                      (Flyers available in gay press for discounted entry before 23.00)
Food available Food area at venue

This massive once-a-monther took over from the huge and successful Confettis and is now as big as it ever was, with punters travelling from as far away as Newcastle and Manchester. The club is split up into separate rooms. The 'main' Raw Room plays hard house and club anthems and also features top Pas. The 'Red' Room plays retro and camp classics from the 70s and 80s. The VIP Leopard Room is ideal for a chill out and a chat (and talent spotting). Coach pick-ups are available from the Bay Horse (Exhibition Square, York) at 21.30 and the Vauxhall, Hull at 22.00. Double check with the venues direct to ensure that the coach trip is running.

The Crown/Leicester Place
24 Dryden Street
Leicester   Telephone 0116 251 0785

Nearest train station Leicester (ten minutes)
Car parking Car park in Lee Circle/side-street parking
A–Z ref. P28/1C
Nearest landmark Situated off Lee Circle

Membership details None required
Opening hours   Monday–Tuesday: 19.30–23.00
                      Wednesday: 19.30–02.00
                      Thursday: 21.30–02.00

Friday: 22.00–04.00
Saturday: 19.30–02.30

The deal with Leicester Place, which takes in both The Crown Bar and Streetlife Disco, is that you get down to The Crown between 19.30–23.00 and start to get some in without having to pay an admission charge. Then, after chucking out, the bar becomes the lounge for Streetlife which runs from 23.30–02.30.

Dolly's Dover Castle
34 Dover Street
Leicester
LE1 6PT   Telephone   0116 222 8826

Nearest train station Leicester
Car parking Large adjacent car park
A–Z ref. P28/2C
Nearest landmark Leicester Station (three minutes)

Membership details None required
Opening hours   Monday–Thursday: 12.00–15.00/19.00–23.00
                         Friday–Saturday: 12.00–23.00
                         Sunday: 12.00–22.30
Admission charges None
Food available No
Regular entertainment DJ/disco seven nights per week

Old, traditional, popular gay pub with regular and camp entertainment. The venue is due for a major refurbishment during the Summer. Keep an eye on the gay press for details of expected changes.

Junction 21
13 Midland Street
Leicester
LE1   Telephone   0966 233 521 ('Hotdog' infoline)/0116 251 9333 ('Juicy
             Fruits' infoline)

Nearest train station Leicester
Car parking Ample street parking
A–Z ref. P28/1C
Nearest landmark Leicester Mercury (newspaper) Building (venue situated behind)

Membership details Available for 'Hotdog' (phone in advance or enquire at the door)
Opening hours   'Hotdog': Saturday: 22.00–03.00 ('Hotdog' is a weekly
                         Saturday nighter only)
                         'Juicy Fruits': Sunday: 22.00–03.00 ('Juicy Fruits' is a
                         monthly event happening every third
                         Sunday)
Admission charges 'Hotdog': £8–10/NUS concessions (depending on
                     membership and time)
                     'Juicy Fruits': £5 Charity donation

'Hotdog' is a hugely popular mixed gay and straight night taking place at this usually straight venue. With three rooms: bangin' house, disco and ambient chill out. 'Juicy Fruits'is staged in association with Leicester Aids Trust. Although it is predominantly a gay dance night, the percentage is more like a 60/40 mix for the gays. The music has a slightly harder edge than 'Hotdog', with guest DJs such as Steve Thomas from Trade. Both are good nights in the Leicestershire gay calendar but just remember to book the Monday off work.

The Pineapple

27 Burleys Way
Leicester   Telephone 0116 262 3384

Nearest train station Leicester
Car parking Ample side-street parking
A–Z ref. P20/6B
Nearest landmark Bus station

Membership details None required but available–£5 per year entitles you to reduced drink prices on Friday and lots of other discounts (apply at the door)
Opening hours   Monday–Thursday: 19.00–01.00
                         Friday–Saturday: 19.00–02.00
                         Sunday: 19.00–22.30
Admission charges Monday–Thursday: Free
                         Friday–Saturday: Free before 23.00/£1 after
                         Sunday: Free
Food available Sunday lunch
Regular entertainment Friday: Cabaret
Sunday: Stripper

Popular lesbian and gay bar with a welcome late licence. Large L-shaped room split into three different areas; the bar, sofa lounge and the main disco space at the back. Entertainment during the week is limited, except for cabaret on Friday evenings and a stripper on Sunday.

Birdcage @ Squares

95 Canwick Road
Lincoln
LN5 8HE   Telephone 01522 522 825

Nearest train station Lincoln Central (five minutes)
Car parking Across the road at Office World
A–Z ref. P11/5F
Nearest landmark Office World on Canwick Road

Membership details Optional at £3 per year–members receive reduced admission fees (appy at door)
Opening hours   Tuesday: 20.00–23.00
                         Friday: 20.00–01.00
                         Sunday: 20.00–22.30
                         (No entry after 23.00)
Admission charges Tuesday: Free
                         Friday: £1.50 before 20.30/£3 after

Sunday: Free
Food available No
Regular entertainment Tuesday: Social night/bingo
Friday: Birdcage disco/monthly cabaret
Sunday: Social

As Birdcage is the only venue catering for lesbians and gays in Lincoln, it comes as no surprise that the Friday night disco as well as the social nights pulls them all in from far and wide. Although 'gay and lesbian' on the above nights, 'Squares' plays host to 'straight' nights on the remainder. By mentioning the name 'Birdcage' either by phone or on the door ensures the doorman knows that you are well aware that it is a gay night. The spacious downstairs bar contains a separate games room area with snooker table, dartboard and pool tables. The large upstairs stage and disco is only open on the Friday and access between the two is acceptable until 22.00. With an 'all ages welcome' policy you will be assured of a friendly and welcoming environment. Bed and breakfast accommodation is available at a local gay run guest-house (phone 01522 820 576 for details).

Curzon Club

8 Temple Lane
Liverpool
L2   Telephone 0151 236 5160

Nearest train station Moorfields
Car parking Street parking
A–Z ref. P66/2B
Nearest landmark Moorfields (venue opposite off Dale Street/Victoria Street)

Membership details None required
Opening hours   Monday–Saturday: 12.00–02.00
                        Sunday: Closed
Admission charges   Monday–Thursday: Free
                        Friday: £2
                        Saturday: £3
Food available Bar snacks available
Regular entertainment Monday: Stripper/cabaret
Wednesday: Drag cabaret
Friday–Saturday: Disco in club

Long-established, large gay pub and club venue, with three bars and two dance floors. Busy at weekends with commercial sounds. The upstairs club is only open on Friday and Saturday evenings. Music on the top floor is Hi Nrg with house and garage on the ground floor.

G-Bar

1–7 Eberle Street
Liverpool
L2   Telephone 0151 258 1230

Nearest train station Moorfields
Car parking Street parking

Best in the North West

Three floors of overwhelming atmosphere

A bar to suit every known tastebud

Love lounge
Temple Room
Basement dance floor
Top American sound system
Monthly theme nights
weekly camp entertainments

Saturday, basement, wall to wall Women ONLY

And unforgettably,

THE LATE ONE:
Mixed heavy dance nights
with the infamous Jimmy Jay on the decks,
3am - 6am Friday
4am - 9 am Saturday

Cheap drinks, Friendly Staff, Great Night!
G-Bar
1-7 Eberle Street, Liverpool L2
Tel: 0151 258 1230

A–Z ref. P66/2B
Nearest landmark Moorfields Station/off Dale Street

Membership details
Available for 'The Late One'–membership entitles holder to reduced admission (for further information contact Tracy Edwards at the above address)

Opening hours	Thursday: 21.00–02.00
	Friday: 21.00–02.00/03.00–06.00 ('The Late One')
	Saturday: 22.00–02.00/04.00–09.00 ('The Late One')
	Sunday: 17.00–Late
Admission charges	Thursday: Free before 22.30/£2 after
	Friday: £2 before 23.00/£3 after/£5 'The Late One'
	Saturday: £2–3/£7 'The Late One' (members £5)
	Sunday: Free before 21.00/£2 after

Regular entertainment Thursday: 'Lavinia' (drag hostess)/cheap drinks
Friday: 'Alterantive Medicine': (80s, indie and pop)
Friday: 'The Late One' (mixed dance club)
Saturday: 'Women Only' in the basement (men as guests)/rest of club open to all
Saturday: 'The Late One' (mixed dance club)
Sunday: Karaoke/cheap drink promos

G-Bar is a gay venue and hosts events for the gay community, with monthly themed nights and weekly camp entertainments. It is an extremely friendly and popular venue and even the doormen have gained recognition for being friendly and helpful. Well-laid out over three floors, the top floor is the Love Lounge with comfy couches, fire, lights and soft music (prrr). The first floor is the Temple Room: gothic, medieval surroundings with unique style and grace, plus a top American sound system and a bar to suit every tastebud known to man. The ground floor is the basement dance area with futuristic surroundings, large dance floor, cloakroom, enquiry desk and real live goldfish. 'Women Only' in the basement is an exclusive night for women and male guests only. Cheap drinks, wall-to-wall women and a free lollypop. The rest of the venue is open to all. 'The Late One' is a very busy, mixed, heavy dance night with the infamous Jimmy Jay mixing the decks and pumping up the atmosphere to lift the roof. Be early or expect to queue. Although the dance club is mixed gay-straight, the doormen will ask if you are aware it is a gay venue. If you do experience problems gaining admission, then tell them you saw the listing in this guide (better still get a membership). Bear in mind that the bar will serve only soft drinks.

Garlands

8–10 Eberle Street
Liverpool
L2   Telephone 0151 236 3307 (infoline)

Nearest train station Moorfields/Lime Street
Car parking Side-street parking
A–Z ref. P66/2B
Nearest landmark Dale Street/Moorfields Station

Membership details None required

Opening hours	Friday: 22.30–04.00
	Saturday: 22.30–04.30

Busy gay club with two bars and two dance floors. Mixed gay and lesbian with a fair smattering of TVs/TSs. Open only at weekends. On other nights the venue is hired out for separate promotions.

Lisbon

35 Victoria Street
Liverpool
L1 6BG   Telephone 0151 231 6831

Nearest train station Lime Street
Car parking Limited on street/Stanley Street/Victoria Street
A–Z ref. P66/2B
Nearest landmark Old Haymarket

Membership details None
Opening hours   Monday–Saturday: 12.00–23.00
                          Sunday: 19.00–22.30
Admission charges None

Mixed gay and straight basement bar with TVs welcome. Regular discos, usually on Monday and Wednesday, and getting extremely busy on a Sunday. Popular with the students.

Masquerade Bar

10 Cumberland Street
Liverpool
L2   Telephone 0151 236 7786

Nearest train station Moorfields
Car parking Street parking
A–Z ref. P66/2B
Nearest landmark Moorfields Station/off Dale Street

Membership details None required
Opening hours   Monday–Saturday: 12.00–23.00
                          Sunday: 11.00–22.30
Admission charges None
Food available Good bar meals served all day
Regular entertainment Monday: Chill out night
Tuesday: Karaoke
Wednesday: Disco
Friday: Retro Disco/drag cabaret
Saturday: Disco
Sunday: Disco/drag cabaret (very busy)

Masquerades is a basement bar with two bars and always with something going on to keep you entertained during the evening. Cheap drinks and trebles bar. Young lively mixed gay crowd.

Metz

Baker House
Rainford Gardens
Cavern Quarter
Liverpool
L2 6PT　　　　　Telephone　0151 227 2282
　　　　　　　　Website　http://www.metz.co.uk

Nearest train station　Moorfields
Car parking　Side-street parking (easy in evening)
A–Z ref.　P66/2B
Nearest landmark　Off Whitechapel opposite Wade Smith

Membership details　None required
Opening hours　　　　Monday–Friday: 12.00–23.00
　　　　　　　　　　　Saturday–Sunday: 11.00–24.00
Admission charges　None
Food available　Full menu lunch and evenings

Cafe-bar restaurant with a bohemian atmosphere, where all are welcome, providing they treat other customers with the appropriate respect, regardless of sex, age, colour and sexual preference. The excellent menu is Eastern European and food is served all day from 12.00, seven days a week. Situated opposite Wade Smith. Checkout their sister venue, Metz in Manchester.

Pacos Bar

25 Stanley Street
Liverpool
L1 6AA　　　　　Telephone　0151 236 9737

Nearest train station　Moorfields
Car parking　Victoria Street (around corner from venue)
A–Z ref.　P66/2B
Nearest landmark　Moorfields Station

Membership details　None required
Opening hours　　　　Monday–Saturday: 12.15–23.00
　　　　　　　　　　　Sunday: 19.00–22.30
Admission charges　None
Food available　No

Pacos is a small, sociable and intimate bar on two levels, situated off Dale Street and close to most of the other gay venues. Comprising two bars (one on each floor), the upstairs bar being open only on Friday and Saturday evenings. The oldest gay bar in Liverpool (established over 25 years ago) and still under the same ownership. Offering a friendly atmosphere with cheap drinks and a doubles bar all the time. Catering for all age groups, everyone is welcome—gay and straight.

Poptastic @ The Escape

41–45 Paradise Street
Liverpool
L1

Nearest train station Liverpool Central
Car parking Side-street parking/local car park
A–Z ref. P66/3B
Nearest landmark Hanover Flyover (B5339)–Paradise Street runs beneath it
Opening hours   Friday: 22.30–02.00
Admission charges   £3/£2 members

Cheap drink prices–usually £1.50 for bottles and beers. For further details of Poptastic, see the Poptastic @ The Mutz Nutz, Manchester listing.

Inkerman Arms

52 Inkerman Street
Luton
Bedfordshire
LU1 1JB   Telephone 01582 450 389

Nearest train station Luton (quarter of a mile)
Car parking Side roads around venue
A–Z ref. P13/6H
Nearest landmark Galaxy Complex

Membership details None required
Opening hours   Monday–Saturday: 12.00–23.00
                       Sunday: 12.00–22.30
Admission charges None
Food available Sandwiches and light snacks available

Mixed gay bar with TVs welcome. Cruisy, intimate and sociable atmosphere. Two years old in May 1999, this quite popular bar is a favourite with the locals. Every weekend there is a disco with cabaret entertainment.

Shirley's Temple

1 Liverpool Road
Luton
Bedfordshire
LU1 1RS   Telephone 01582 725 491

Nearest train station Luton
Car parking On-road parking
A–Z ref. P13/6H
Nearest landmark City centre/Galaxy Centre

Membership details None required
Opening hours   Monday–Friday: 16.00–23.00
                       Saturday: 14.00–23.00
                       Sunday: 14.00–22.30
Admission charges None

This popular, 100 capacity venue has been open for at least 16 years as a homo hangout, with occasional cabaret through the week and a regular stripper on Sunday evenings.

Bar Med

109 Princess Street
Manchester
M1 6JD   Telephone 0161 200 1800   Fax 0161 200 1801

Nearest train station Piccadilly/Oxford Road (two minute walk)
Car parking Side-street parking and local NCP or meters (daytime)
A–Z ref. P87/5E
Nearest landmark Chorlton Street Bus Station

Membership details None required
Opening hours   Monday–Wednesday: 11.30–12.00
                         Thursday–Saturday: 11.30–02.00
                         Sunday: 12.00–22.30
                         (Bar Med is licensed till 02.00 seven days per week. A bar
                         extension will be used for charity events and during busy
                         periods)
Admission charges None except for scheduled charity events
Food available Extensive Mediterranean menu available from opening until
one hour before bars close (there are designated no-smoking areas in the
restaurant)
Regular entertainment No scheduled entertainment as yet although DJ will be
downstairs seven nights per week

Opening its doors in May 1999, Bar Med is the latest cafe-bar to join the ever
expanding gay village. It is not an exclusively gay *or* straight venue, although
the integration of both will ensure the atmosphere will be flamboyant,
light-hearted and fun. Bar Med is a supertrendy cosmopolitan establishment
replacing 'attitude' with 'Northern hospitality'. Even the door staff–male and
female–welcome you on arrival and bid you 'goodnight' on departure (could this
be a first?). Consisting of two large open-plan floors, the ground floor being the
main bar and staged dining area and the lower ground housing the DJ box and
dance floor. The decor is modern and contemporary (*à la Changing Rooms* and
House Style) using the freedom flag colours in all their glory (although I'm sure
this was unintentional). The Abingdon Street entrance (behind The New Union)
will in all probability be used as the 'gay' entrance, leading you directly to the DJ
and dance floor and it is at this entrance that all the gay press and literature is
stored.

Café Hollywood

First Floor
Phoenix Shopping Centre (entrance at rear of Hollywood Showbar–Hart Street)
Manchester
M1   Telephone 0161 236 5253

Nearest train station Piccadilly
Car parking Ample side-street parking (daytime meters or P&D)
A–Z ref. P87/5E
Nearest landmark Chorlton Street Bus Station
Opening hours   Monday–Wednesday: 10.00–04.00
                         Thursday–Sunday: 10.00–04.00 (Monday morning)

Café Hollywood occupies the first floor of the Phoenix Shopping centre. A large,
bright, airy room with large screen TV. The food is appetising home-cooked fare,

not over priced and certainly not fancy, but extremely welcome after a hard night's pubbing and clubbing, as well as a welcome break during the day from the hustle and bustle of the city. What makes this place so special (apart from being the only cafe listed in this guide) is the fact that a few months after opening, Manchester Police in liaison with the City Council granted Cafe Hollywood a continuous 24 hour trading licence. This was done in order to reduce the number of gay men cruising the canal late at night, providing us with a safer environment. The idea has paid off handsomely. The Phoenix Shopping Centre and particularly Café Hollywood is an absolute man fest. Not only whilst the clubs are open, but all the way through to the early hours. The Rainbow Cars taxi rank is housed in this building, so even whilst you are waiting for a cab you can either enjoy a coffee and sandwich or cruise the corridors. Unlike most 'chill out' venues, there is no admission charge. Your privacy (if required) is totally respected and the cafe provides you with a friendly space to get acquainted with any new found friend that you have met in the clubs during the evening. The daytime is no different. The same safe environment, without the rush to get rid of you once you have spent your money. As with any gay venue . . . if you don't use it, you will lose it, and losing Café Hollywood would be a great loss for Manchester.

Chains

4–6 Whitworth Street
Manchester
M1 3QW   Telephone 0161 236 4566

Nearest train station Manchester Piccadilly
Car parking NCP adjoining premises (free after 18.00)
A–Z ref. P87/5E
Nearest landmark Whitworth Street NCP/U.M.I.S.T.

Membership details Available for reduced admission but not necessary (enquire at the venue for further details)

Opening hours	Monday–Tuesday: 22.30–02.00
	Wednesday: Closed
	Thursday: 22.30–02.00
	Friday: 22.30–02.30
	Saturday: 22.00–03.00
	Sunday: 22.00–01.00
Admission charges	Monday–Tuesday: Free
	Wednesday: Closed
	Thursday: Free
	Friday: £3
	Saturday: £4
	Sunday: Free

Food available Snacks and hot drinks available in Café Confidential (in-house cafe)

Situated next door to Follies, Chains is a men-only bar for predominantly (although not necessarily) the leathers, rubbers, denims, combats, skins and uniform fraternity. Situated just a two minute drunken stagger away from the gay village, this club offers an extremely relaxed atmosphere where you can do what you like without anybody tut-tutting. There is no strict dress code, although on one of their regular party nights they may insist on some specialist item of clothing. After negotiating the stairway down (which is quite difficult if you have had a skinful) you will enter the large cavernous (former Rockies) basement that is Chains. The first bar is used as a meeting and mingling place, away from the dance floor and the delights that await you in other areas of the club. Attached to this on a higher level is the games room with pool tables and ample seating. Going through the corridor (past the toilets) takes you to the large expanse of dance area. From here (by the side of the dance floor) there is a small and dark passageway that will lead you to Café Confidential–walking through takes you to yet another bar. Subdued lighting, plenty of seating, another pool table and the ahem! er . . . videos being shown. Continuing around the bar will bring you to the corridor which houses another set of toilets. Further on down, you'll come to the 'shop' selling magazines, videos and such like and around this area there's another set of toilets–that's three so far. Chains is an excellent venue for the man who does not like standing in the same space all night. There is ample opportunity to cruise around the myriad of corridors and bars without having to backtrack on yourself. Cafe Confidential is a chill out space, so even if you have been somewhere else you can pop into here for a quick one (or a drink!). Phone the venue for the monthly dates of 'Boot Crew' @ Chains which equals no attitude, no camp, no trainers.

Churchills

37 Chorlton Street
Manchester
M1

Nearest train station Piccadilly
Car parking Ample street parking/local car parks during the day
A–Z ref. P87/5E
Nearest landmark Chorlton Street Bus Station

Membership details None required
Opening hours   Monday–Wednesday: 12.00–23.00
                      Thursday–Saturday: 12.00–02.00
                      Sunday: 12.00–22.30
Admission charges None (except for charity events occasional Sundays)

Churchills is a small but lively pub with a great party atmosphere. It does tend to get quite busy during the evening and getting to the bar is near-imposible. From Thursday onwards the place is jam packed with people taking advantage of the extended opening hours.

Cruz 101

101 Princess Street (entrance on Major Street)
Manchester
M1 6DD   Telephone 0161 950 0101   Fax 0161 237 3412
                E-mail cruz@cruz101.com
                Website http://www.cruz101.com

Nearest train station Piccadilly
Car parking Plenty of side-street parking or an adjacent car park if you are early
A–Z ref. P87/5E
Nearest landmark Chorlton Street Bus Station

Membership details Required—must be obtained 48 hours prior to first admission and immediate membership will be granted only at the manager's discretion (mention this guide if you have difficulty). Either complete the application form at the door or apply by e-mail (there is a small membership fee of approximately £3 which is renewable each year—you will be issued with a swipe card which must be produced on each visit)

Opening hours Monday: 22.00–02.00
       Tuesday: Closed
       Wednesday: 22.00–02.00 (Sub 101 Basement only)
       Thursday–Saturday: 22.00–02.00
       Sunday: Closed

Admission charges Monday: £3
       Wednesday: £2
       Thursday: £2 (Free to students with NUS identification card)
       Friday: £3
       Saturday: £5

Food available Yes

Regular entertainment Monday: 'Disco Inferno': extremely busy 70s/80s night (main floor)/90s in Sub 101

Wednesday: 'Sub-Version' in Sub 101/selected drinks £1 (upstairs closed)

Thursday: 'Vibeology': busy dance night (Sub101 closed)

Friday: 'Friday Experience' including 'Cruz 'n' Cop': a busy dance night. Both floors open most weeks ('Cruz 'n' Cop' labels issued at door)/'Dusty's' (women only) every first and third Friday of the month in the Sub 101 basement (separate entrance—membership to Cruz not necessary)

Saturday: 'Malestrom': Completely open, occasional PAs (arrive early or queue)

Very busy, trouble-free club attracting the younger end of the market, although the complete age range is still very much in evidence. The downstairs bar (Sub 101) is a very cruisy area, with dimmed lights and with a little passage that runs behind one of the bars making for an ideal snogging area, although anything more will get you thrown out. Mondays, Fridays and Saturdays still enjoy a huge crowd (a few gay-friendly straights included) and the atmosphere is totally buzzin' and cheap drink promotions are very nearly always to be found. The club itself is a large expanse of floor space, enabling you to either dance or cruise, depending on what mood you are in. Women's night at 'Dusty's' every other Friday in Sub 101—with pre- club meeting at Vanilla—is a trouble-free friendly night. If you need to be 'introduced' tell the brilliant Janice (door girl) that it's your first time and she will ensure that you get to meet other people to show you around.

Hollywood Showbar

105–07 Princess Street (entrance on Bloom Street)
Manchester
M1 6DD Telephone 0161 236 6151

Nearest train station Piccadilly
Car parking Ample side-street parking
A–Z ref. P87/5E
Nearest landmark Chorlton Street Bus Station

364   The Ultimate Gay Guide

Membership details Free gay membership–membership cards must be produced on entry (apply at door or by phone)

Opening hours   Monday–Saturday: 19.00–02.00
                       Sunday: 19.00–22.30

Admission charges   Free to members with card at all times (except scheduled charity events)/£1 to members who forget their card/£2 to members' gay guests (price includes membership)

Food available At all times–see separate listing for Café Hollywood

Regular entertainment Monday: DJ/male stripper (men only)
Tuesday: Closed
Wednesday: National Concord (TV/TS–privately hired)
Wednesday: Open to all after 11.00
Thursday: Cabaret night
Friday–Saturday: DJ/bar cabaret
Sunday: DJ (afternoons through to the evening)/alternate Sundays: charity events (late bar till 01.00)

If you have never been onto the Manchester gay scene before, then this bar is thoroughly recommended as your first foray. Not only is it as exclusively gay as you can get (due to the strict gay-only membership and extremely gay-friendly door policy) but it is also a friendly and welcoming establishment with a community spirit. More importantly, it is a safe venue. The brilliant door staff will ensure that the venue stays totally 'attitude-free'. They are not aggressive but they will ensure that you are who you say you are. If you do experience difficulty in gaining admission, tell them that you saw the listing in this guide. Drinks prices are probably the best in town and so too are the outrageous, friendly and entertaining bar staff. The venue itself is a large open-plan room on two levels. The main floor with DJ stage and large screen TV, and the unique 'stage-bar' is very nearly always packed. The upper raised level with ample seating (for those tired old bones) gives you the vantage point of 'surveying the talent'. Regular charity nights see an enhanced party atmosphere. Token door charges on these nights go straight to the charity concerned. Membership to the Showbar is free and it is expected that you bring your card with you. If you don't, you can expect to pay a small admission fee. *Author's note*: There are only a couple of establishments in this guide that I would commit myself to recommending and the Hollywood Showbar is one of them. Operating a bar where a gay man, lesbian TV or TS can feel 100% safe is fast becoming rare. Their commitment to the gay village as a whole is second to none and they deserve the patronage of the community.

Manto

44 Canal Street
Manchester
M1 3WD   Telephone 0161 236 2667

Nearest train station Piccadilly
Car parking NCP opposite/street parking after 18.00
A–Z ref. P87/5E
Nearest landmark Chorlton Street Bus Station

Membership details None required, although Paradise Factory membership offers reduced admission to the Breakfast Club (see Paradise Factory listing for details)

Opening hours   (Manto)
                    Monday–Thursday: 11.00–24.00
                    Friday–Saturday: 11.00–01.00
                    Saturday: 02.30–06.00 (Breakfast Club–last Saturday of the
                    month sees the Breakfast Club open from 02.30 to 08.00
                    (Sarasota Restaurant)
                    Monday–Thursday: 12.00–24.00
                    Friday–Saturday: 12.00–01.00
                    Sunday: 12.00–22.30
Admission charges   Saturday: £5 (Breakfast Club only)
Food available Dine in style in Sarasota, the new rooftop restaurant.
Alternatively, Manto serves a huge range of delicatessan type food from 11.00
until closing time in the mezzanine
Regular entertainment Manto features top Manchester DJs seven nights per
week
Saturday: The Breakfast Club

Manto was the original trendy bar in Manchester, setting the standard that all
the other bars were to follow. Underwent a massive refurbishment programme in
1998, to add yet another floor/restaurant and larger balconies. All this will
ensure that Manto may once again win 'Café-Bar of the Year'. The official
pre-Paradise venue; Friday and Saturday nights see the venue absolutely packed
with people, spilling out onto the street, and getting a drink at the bar after 22.30
is very nearly imposible. The Breakfast Club is the meeting place of all the club
trendies who realise that 02.30 is still too early to go home. The new restaurant,
Sarasota, easily seats up to 60 people. In the summer the roof can fully retract, in
order that the pigeons from the Town Hall can come across and shit on you.

Metz

Amazon House
Canal Street
Manchester
M1 3PJ   Telephone 0161 237 9852
               Website http://www.metz.co.uk

Nearest train station Piccadilly
Car parking Large NCP close by/limited street parking
A–Z ref. P87/5E
Nearest landmark Chorlton Street Bus Station

Membership details None required
Opening hours   Monday–Wednesday: 12.00–23.00
                       Thursday–Saturday: 12.00–02.00
                       Sunday: 12.00–22.30
Admission charges None
Food available Extensive menu available

Restaurant cafe-bar set in the centre of Manchester's gay village. A bohemian
atmosphere, where all are welcome, providing they treat other customers with
the appropriate respect, regardless of their sex, age, colour or sexual preference.
The extensive menu is Eastern European and is served all day from 12.00, seven
days a week. Also busy with punters just coming in for a drink and there's no
thumping loud music, so you can actually hear the person that you are talking to.

The New Union

111 Princess Street/corner of Canal Street
Manchester
M1 6JB   Telephone 0161 228 1492

Nearest train station Piccadilly
Car parking Side-street parking (Canal Street is pedestrianised)
A–Z ref. P87/5E
Nearest landmark Chorlton Street Bus Station

Membership details None required
Opening hours   Monday–Saturday: 11.00–01.30
                         Sunday: 12.00–22.30
Admission charges   Friday–Saturday: £2 after 23.00
                      (Drinks prices increase slightly after 23.00)
Regular entertainment Monday: Stage show/DJ
Tuesday: Cabaret/DJ
Wednesday: Stage show/DJ
Thursday: 'Karaoke with Roxy Hart' (be early–extremely popular)/DJ
Friday: DJ
Saturday: Disco (very busy)
Sunday: Stage show and DJ all day
Food available Lunch-times only

One of the most popular bars in Manchester and one for a complete mixed age
group. Every night of the week the place is almost full to capacity. If you do not
arrive early enough over the weekend then expect to queue for quite a while
(usually subsides by 23.30). During the summer months, the outside street is
very nearly always packed with outside drinking (as is the whole of Canal Street)
and a brilliant Ibiza-style atmosphere. Most nights during the week, your
hostess will be the fabulous Roxy Hart, who is probably the envy of all the gay
pubs in Manchester (my words, not hers) if not the world (her words, not mine . .
.). The entrance is via Canal Street. The layout is as follows: A small bar room on
your left as you enter is used for, a) sitting down before you fall down, or, b) for
chatting where the music isn't so loud. Carrying on takes you to the bar in
another quieter area of the pub with seating area on the raised level and
following the corridor around will lead you to the toilets and another bar. This
bar by the gents' toilet seems to be a gathering point for single gay men and tends
to be the quieter of all the three bars. You will now be in the main room, where
lesbians and the few gay-friendly straights congregate by the stage and seating
area to the right of the dance floor. The rest of the open-plan room is just full of
men! The raised level in the main room by the third bar is used generally as a
meeting area as well as a vantage point for men on the pull. With three large bars
and a dance floor, most people will stay here rather than going on to a club. An
excellent place for the newcomer to the scene as you will be able to get lost in the
crowds. On most Sundays (in rotation with the other Manchester bars) there is a
charity event which means that the bar will stay open late with a nominal charge
for charity. Hotel accommodation is also available (nearly always full, so book
early–see separate 'Accommodation' listings).

New York, New York/Ballans

98 Bloom Street
Manchester
M1 3LY   Telephone 0161 236 6556

Nearest train station Piccadilly
Car parking Side-street parking
A–Z ref. P87/5E
Nearest landmark Chorlton Street Bus Station

Membership details None required
Opening hours   (New York, New York)
                         Monday–Saturday: 20.00–02.00
                         Sunday: 15.00–22.30
                         (Ballans)
                         Monday–Sunday: 12.00–23.00
Admission charges Monday–Thursday: £1 after 22.30 (except Tuesday which
                         is free)
                         Friday–Saturday: £1 between 22.00–23.00/£2 after
                         Sunday: Free
Food available Yes
Regular entertainment Monday–WednesdayCabaret
Thursday–Saturday: DJ
Sunday: Drag cabaret (afternoon)/DJ (evenings)
And a drag DJ every night (usually Kampari)

One of the original gay bars in Manchester. Now extensively modernised,
providing an open- plan floor space, extended bar and well-used cabaret stage.
The huge neon 'Statue of 'Liberty'' on the outside wall (unfortunately no longer
utilised) was a source of much controversy when it was first unveiled with the
statue's limp wrist moving up and down. Packed at weekends, with a smattering
of gay-friendly straights. Sunday afternoons are a favourite with the Manchester
gays. An open mike, camp tunes and a weekly appearance by Roxy Hart with
Kampari assures you of a fab drunken time. Ballans of Bloom Street, the New
York's sister bar, situated next door with a separate entrance, is a more quiet
affair. A bright modern place with scope to relax and chat without the loud
thumping music. The upstairs club (The Bronx), home of many a gay experience,
is no longer open on a regular basis, although it can be hired out for private
functions.

Paddys Goose

29 Bloom Street
Manchester
M1 3JE   Telephone 0161 236 1246

Nearest train station Piccadilly
Car parking Opposite (800 space P&D daytime only)/limited on street in
evenings
A–Z ref. P87/5E
Nearest landmark Chorlton Street Bus Station opposite

Membership details None required
Opening hours   Monday–Saturday: 11.00–23.00
                         Sunday: 11.00–22.30

Admission charges   None
Food available   Value-for-money full menu available lunch-times and evenings

Paddys Goose is a small venue that has been established on the scene for many years. Comfortable olde worlde interior, catering for a wide variety of tastes with a heavy TV/CD profile on Wednesday and Saturday evenings. Food is served through the day, offering an excellent steak menu.–great value for money. Situated at the top end of the gay village, close to Chorlton Street Bus Station, it is one of only a few pubs that offers complete wheelchair access. A traditional venue with scope to chat and socialise without the heavy thumping music. The age range is decidedly mixed and the clientele is across the board.

Paradise Factory

112–116 Princess Street
Manchester
M1 3WD   Telephone   0161 228 2966 (Head office)/0161 273 5422

Nearest train station   Oxford Street/Piccadilly
Car parking   Street parking outside venue
A–Z ref.   P87/6E
Nearest landmark   Bank of Scotland on Princess Street

Membership details   Available at £10 but not necessary (a good status symbol though!)–members are entitled to reduced admission to Paradise and The Breakfast Club at Manto and will also receive discounts at selected stores throughout Manchester, including Aspecto Clothing, Häagen Dasz and numerous restaurants (phone the above head office number to apply)

Opening hours   Monday–Tuesday: 22.00–02.00
                         Wednesday–Thursday: (depending on production)
                         Friday–Saturday: 22.30–03.00
                         Sunday: (depending on production)
Admission charges   Monday–Tuesday: £3
                         Wednesday–Thursday: various
                         Friday: £3 guests/£2 members
                         Saturday: £6 before 23.00 for guests and members/£8 after
                         23.00 for guests
                         Sunday: (depending on production)
Food available   Snacks available in the evening
Regular entertainment   Monday: 'The Monday Club': A *ménage à trois* of music styles over three floors/up-front house and garage in Level 1/'Cheesy As You Like It' with Sticker Vicar from Galaxy 102 in Level 2/'Funky Disco' with Dave Pearce from Funkademia in Level 3
Tuesday: 'Release': Manchester's biggest student night/happy house in Level 1/soul, hip hop and big beat in Level 2/'Party Loft' with Sy Frater in Level 3
Wednesday–Thursday: Various productions each week
Friday: 'Vanity': gay night. Club anthems/classics with Adrian C and Thaddeous in Level 1/70s, 80s and disco with Sy Frater in Level 2/'Funky Cheese House' with Dave Booth and Huey in Level 3
Saturday: 'Club Paradiso': gay night with an all-star line-up of some of the best known DJs in the country. The last Saturday of the month brings in guest DJs from Heaven, Trade and DTPM/hard house with Little Miss Natalie, Adrian C, Mike Allan, Richard Cobey in Level 1/handbag house with Sista Marta and

Stuart Robinson in Level 2/stomping house anthems with Robbie and guests in
Level 3
Sunday: Various productions each week

Paradise Factory is spread over three floors: Level 1, Level 2 and Level 3. Paradise
Factory is probably the most famous gay club outside London. What was once
the home of Factory Records, now caters for a young, 'trendy' market. The music
policy on the vast expanse of Level 1 provides some of the most up-front music in
the land. Resident DJs Little Miss Natalie, Adrian C and Richard Cobey are
amongst some of the biggest names in the world. Level 2 supplies a more relaxed
atmosphere, with seating, stage shows and character DJs including the
(in)famous Sista Marta and Lady Lola. Level 3 offers club anthems and dance
classics, provided by local DJs. There's plenty of seating and opportunity to
socialise at the far end by the stairs. Clientele are a good no-attitude combination
of mixed gay, bisexual and straight. Everyone who enters Paradise knows it is a
predominantly gay venue. There is never any trouble and everyone who is there
is there for a good time. Friday and Saturday sees Paradise packed to the rafters
(literally), probably making it the best place in Manchester or indeed the
North-West. Either arrive early or expect to queue. Cloakroom and toilet
facilities are in the basement. The long winding corridor offers the weary a quiet
place to chill and/or cruise (whatever is your bent). An excellent place to
cruise—up and down the levels—and a brilliant, friendly atmosphere. Well and
truly recommended. See listing for sister venue Manto and details of The
Breakfast Club.

Poptastic @ The Mutz Nutz

Corner of Bloom Street/Princess Street (entrance to The Mutz Nutz is on Princess
Street)
Manchester
M1   Telephone 0161 236 3995

Nearest train station Piccadilly or Oxford Road
Car parking Ample side-street parking
A–Z ref. P87/5E
Nearest landmark Chorlton Street Bus Station/New York, New York (gay bar)

Membership details Although membership is not absolutely necessary it is a
good status symbol and entitles you to various concessions to the venues and
other events. Membership runs from September to August and costs a measly
£5 per year. Apart from door discounts on regular Poptastic nights there are
also further reductions on various other special events they do (Mardi Gras,
NYE, etc.)—phone or write to the address below for a form and further
information

Opening hours	Tuesday: 23.00–02.00
	Saturday: 22.30–03.00
Admission charges	Tuesday: £3.50/£3 members
	Saturday: £5/£4 members

Poptastic is the birthplace of the infamous 'shagtags'—that little piece of paper
that can mean the difference between you meeting the man (or woman) of your
dreams or going home alone. You are given a numbered sticker upon arrival at
the club and, after having it slapped on your brand new Ralph Lauren shirt, you
then spend the rest of the night wondering if any one is going to leave you a

message, inviting you to spend the rest of the night with them (as if you could be that cheap!). Alternatively, you could be the hunter and do some writing yourself. Whichever way you look at it, it's a brilliant way of breaking the ice for the newcomer to the scene. Music policy is indie, hip Brit and trash disco. The venues are usually split up into two rooms–the main room being for the indie and the other, always called the Kitsch Bitch Lounge, is more cheesy chart/retro. Poptasic is run as a gay night. The punters are usually young with no attitude, intent on a good night out and partying. The straight element that go in do so because of the music and atmosphere; they know it's a gay night and being approached is not a problem to them (Hey! it is the millennium). The Poptastic crew (Over The Edge Promotions) also promote the monthly fetish night 'Hellfire' taking place on the first Friday of every month at The Music Box, Oxford Road, Manchester. Admission is £5 for members and £7 for non-members (different membership to Poptastic) and advance tickets. Open to all with a penchant for dressing up in all that's kinky i.e. skinheads, leather, rubber, uniform, boots, industrial or sport kit. At least one item of the aforementioned clothing or style is required (designer name tags and swooshy, swishy fashions are strongly discouraged, as are Muir caps, and it's doubtful you will see a cloney moustache). The clientele, men and women (dicks and clits) are young and hedonistic, knowing what they want and that this will be the place to get it! Advance tickets can be purchased from Clone Zone or Rembrandt or by phoning the HQ number at the bottom of the page. In addition to the progressive house music, there will also be stage shows of a fetishistic kind i.e. Fist/Block/Erotic Workshops/Roiffey Workshops/Dungeon Scenes/etc. As if all that wasn't enough, another new night is being planned as we speak. 'Skint' is planned to take place at The Roadhouse on Newton Street, Manchester, every third Saturday. No details (at all) are available at the moment, except for the fact that it will be a night for gays and straights (large skinhead fraternity) without attitude (except the right one)! No prejudice will be tolerated. Music will be ska, northern soul perhaps! and reggae, as well as progressive house for the twinks. Details on all of the above nights are available from the Poptastic Head Office address below.

Poptastic
Over The Edge Promotions
Suite 225, Ducie House
Ducie Street
Manchester
M1 2JW   Telephone 0161 236 6264   Fax 0161 281 6431
                Website http://www.poptastic.co.uk
                See the following listings for further details of Poptastic club nights:
                Poptastic @ The Polo Lounge, Glasgow
                Poptastic @ The City Hall, Sheffield
                Poptastic @ The Cockpit, Leeds

It must be noted that Poptastic has changed its venues many times in the past two years, so if you are preparing to travel a fair distance it may be wise to phone them (or the venue, where available) to check if the event is still running.

Prague Five

40 Chorlton Street
Manchester
M1 3HW   Telephone 0161 236 9033

Nearest train station Piccadilly
Car parking Local car parks/street parking difficult after 22.00
A–Z ref. P87/5E
Nearest landmark Chorlton Bus Station/Canal Street

Membership details Pilot scheme in progress, phone for further details
Opening hours   Monday–Wednesday: 11.30–23.00
                         Thursday–Saturday: 11.30–02.00
                         Sunday: 12.00–22.30
Admission charges None (except for scheduled events)
Food available Excellent full menu available throughout the day until close

A vast cafe-bar with an extensive menu, well-stocked bars and a loose Czech theme, which almost transforms itself into a nightclub on Thursday, Friday and Saturday nights. A state-of- the-art sound system pumping out the best of Manchester house/garage. Catering mainly to a young and trendy mixed crowd, the venue is packed out to capacity over the weekends, so it is advisable to arrive early or end up joining the massive queue winding its way down Canal Street. The cavernous industrial interior and selective door policy makes Prague Five one of Manchester's over-subscribed weekend nights out. Prague Five is definitely not an exclusively gay venue. Popular with the student fraternity of Manchester, there are more straight(-ish) couples than gays and it's something that makes you particularly aware of your surroundings. However, if you are more into the music and drinking scene than copping off, then this may be the place for you.

Rembrandt Hotel

33 Sackville Street
Manchester
M1 3LZ   Telephone 0161 236 1311

Nearest train station Piccadilly
Car parking Ample street parking and local car parks
A–Z ref. P87/5E
Nearest landmark Chorlton Street Bus Station

Membership details None required
Opening hours   Monday–Wednesday: 11.00–23.00
                         Thursday–Saturday: 11.00–01.00
                         Sunday: 11.00–22.30
Admission charges None
Food available Full bar menu available at lunch-times (with vegetarian food available). Very busy, with excellent value-for-money food (listed in most good food guides)

Gay-owned for over 17 years by the same proprietors, this is a popular bar with the leather, denim and skinhead crowd, although saying that, nearly everyone pops in here on their trawl around the bars. The Rembrandt is used as a pre-Chains venue most nights. Very popular as a lunch-time spot due to the value-for-money food. It is also the birthplace of Manchester's Mardi Gras, when some six or seven years ago a paste table was erected outside the doors selling wares in order to raise money for people suffering with HIV/AIDS. The venue itself is laid out over two floors. The large modern downstairs bar is a general meeting place mix of open-plan layout and seating. The upstairs accommodates the large and airy restaurant, as well as offering a quieter area to sit and chat. As a contrast to most of the other venues, there is no dance floor, although taped music is played, providing an atmosphere aimed at the social rather than the 'clubby'. There is hotel accommodation available (see 'Accommodation' listings), but ideally situated in the heart of the gay village as it is, it does tend to be full over the weekends, so early booking is advised.

The Thompson Arms

Sackville Street
Manchester
M1　　　　　　Telephone　0161 237 5919

Nearest train station　Piccadilly
Car parking　Street parking (car park in day opposite)
A–Z ref.　P87/5E
Nearest landmark　Chorlton Street Bus Station (opposite)

Membership details　None required
Opening hours　　　Monday–Thursday: 17.00–23.00
　　　　　　　　　　Friday–Saturday: 18.00–02.00
　　　　　　　　　　Sunday: 17.30–22.30
Admission charges　None
Food available　No
Regular entertainment　Tuesday: 'Voyeurs' gay rock night/doubles bar
Wednesday: Live music
Thursday: Disco
Friday–Saturday: Disco: chart, dance and Hi Nrg/doubles bar

This was formerly known as Central Park (the old home of Danceteria) and has now reverted back to the original name of The Thompsons Arms. Recently refurbished, transforming the dingy old Central Park into a bright modern pub/club. The clientele here tends to be more of a mixed gay and friendly straight crowd. Just one open-plan room, with a large seating area on the one side and standing areas opposite.

Vanilla

Richmond Street
Manchester
M1　　　　　　Telephone　0161 236 3966

Nearest train station　Piccadilly
Car parking　Side-street parking (difficult over weekend)
A–Z ref.　P87/5E
Nearest landmark　McTucky Takeaway on Sackville Street (opposite Rembrandt)

Membership details　None required

Opening hours   Monday–Friday: 12.00–02.00
                      Saturday: 13.00–02.00
                      Sunday: 13.00–22.30
Admission charges   None except 'Licked': bank holiday charity events for BP
                      Women and Children
Food available Extensive value-for-money menu available from 12.00–20.00,
including the now infamous
'Spotted Clit and Custard' (£2.50)
Regular entertainment Tuesday: 'Dyke-U-Like': singles night (very busy and
you do not have to be single to mingle)
Wednesday: Tarot card readings
Thursday: Dance night
Friday: 'Chic & Glam': chart/pre-Dusty's every first and third Friday of the
month
Saturday: 'Vanilla Essence': up-front music with resident Sara Furey (very
busy)
Sunday: 'Vanilla Sundaes' (a nice relaxing day)

Vanilla, the North-West's seven day a week space for women is situated just off
the main drag in Manchester's gay village. The venue is not even a year old but
already attracts regular visitors from as far away as Sheffield and Liverpool. The
venue is a bright, friendly, modern contemporary bar, always busy and
particularly more so on Friday, when it is used as the pre- 'Dusty's' meeting place
(see Cruz 101 listing) and the monthly Black Angel event at Follies. Tuesday's
singles night is heaving. On arrival you will be given 'Traffic Lights' with the
explanation that Red = Attached/Amber = Maybe/Green = Single. This is not a
serious night and the emphasis is on fun and meeting new friends. It is however
extremely busy and an early entrance is advised. *Note*: Although Vanilla is a
women's bar, men are indeed welcome as guests.

Velvet

Canal Street
Manchester
M1 3DE   Telephone 0161 236 9003

Nearest train station Piccadilly
Car parking Side-streets and car park near by
A–Z ref. P87/2E
Nearest landmark Chorlton Street Bus Station

Membership details None required
Opening hours   Monday–Wednesday: 12.00–23.00
                      Thursday–Friday: 12.00–01.00
                      Saturday: 12.00–01.30
                      Sunday: 12.00–23.00
Admission charges None
Food available Excellent menu available (value-for-money)

One of the more trendy and elegant mixed venues along Canal Street. A
basement-style bar, attracting the more beautiful people in our community.
Sunday tends to get really busy with people trying to have a relaxing afternoon.
Minimalist décor and no loud thumping music, plus pavement seating to watch
the lads go by.

Via Fossa

28–30 Canal Street
Manchester
M1 3EZ   Telephone 0161 236 6523

Nearest train station Piccadilly (one mile)
Car parking Ample side-street parking
A–Z ref. P87/5E
Nearest landmark Chorlton Street Bus Station

Membership details None required
Opening hours   Monday–Wednesday: 11.00–24.00
                         Thursday: 11.00–01.00
                         Friday–Saturday: 11.00–02.00
                         Sunday: 12.00–22.30
Admission charges None (except for scheduled charity events)
Food available Excellent full menu till 22.00 and snacks all day till close

Via Fossa is a large labyrinth of a bar, catering for all of the lesbian and gay community and their friends. There are four bars over five levels, with equal amounts of standing and seating space. The layout of the bars and sound system allows for couples to retreat to a secluded area or for groups to see and be seen. The floor areas can be viewed from above, either from the balconies or from the 'pulpit'. The atmosphere is lively, yet relaxed and casual. The decor is unbelievable–gothic and (mostly) original. There's loads of room to cruise and be cruised in a brilliant atmosphere. During the summer months, the doors in the main bar are fully opened onto the packed street, providing a continental-style atmosphere. Via Fossa is more of a meeting and drinking place than a cabaret bar, hence no regular entertainment or cabaret is provided.

The Yard/Ten Nightclub

61 Westgate
Mansfield
Nottinghamshire
NE18 1RU   Telephone 01623 622 230

Nearest train station Mansfield
Car parking Rear of club
Nearest landmark

Membership details None required
Opening hours   Monday: 21.30–02.30
                         (Last Monday of the month only)
Admission charges Monday: £2 before 23.00/£3 after
Food available Snacks available in the evening

Last Monday of the month event. Exclusively lesbian, gay and TV. This monthly event has been in operation for well over eight years and is as popular as ever. Drinks are at pub prices with regular cheap drink promotions.

Cassady's

41–45 Grange Road
Middlesborough
TS1 5AU   Telephone 01642 221 241

Nearest train station Middlesborough
Car parking Behind venue

Membership details None required
Opening hours Monday–Saturday: 19.00–23.00
Sunday: 19.00–22.30
Admission charges None
Food available No
Regular entertainment Wednesday–Saturday: DJ/disco
Sunday: Karaoke (evenings)

Cassady's is a large gay pub on two levels with three bars and a dance floor. It is mainly a disco pub, but there are quiet areas and a pool room too. Happy hour runs every day from 19.00 to 20.00. The atmosphere at Cassady's is cruisy(-ish) and dance orientated.

The Monastery (formerly The Bull)

15 Watling Street
Fenny Stratford
Bletchley
Milton Keynes   Telephone 01908 373 018/01908 373 005

Nearest train station Milton Keynes
Car parking Ample side-street parking
Nearest landmark Camponile Hotel (300 yards from venue)

Membership details You do not have to be a member to obtain admission, however, membership–which costs £5 per year–gives you and your guests priority admission over non-members and concessions (application forms are available at the door or by post to the above address)
Opening hours Monday–Thursday: 20.00–24.00
Friday–Saturday: 20.00–02.00
Sunday: 18.00–22.30
Admission charges None except for cabaret nights
Food available Light bar snacks
Regular entertainment Monday: Chill out and social
Tuesday: Karaoke night
Wednesday: 'Killer Pool'
Thursday: 'Timewarp' (60s/70s/80s/disco)/cheap drinks
Friday: Disco (house and classic handbag)
Saturday: House and pop disco/top cabaret

The first full-time gay nightclub for Milton Keynes; catering for all ages and both sexes. Large one-floor venue with always something going on. Popular and very friendly late night drinking den for the gay and gay-friendly community. Weekends tend to get rather busy and it is advisable that you turn up early or take your chances with the queue.

The Barking Dog

Marlborough Crescent
Newcastle upon Tyne
Tyne and Wear
NE1   Telephone 0191 221 0775

Nearest train station Newcastle (two minutes)

Car parking Side-street parking
A–Z ref. P60/3B
Nearest landmark Bus station by Newcastle BR

Membership details None required
Opening hours   Monday–Saturday: 11.00–23.00
                     Sunday: 12.00–22.30

A friendly bar situated in the heart of the city's gay area. During the daytime it is mixed gay and straight. The downstairs bar attracts more of the gay/straight crowd, whilst upstairs is more of a wine bar. Upstairs bar is open from 20.00.

The Courtyard/Heavens Above

2 Scotswood Road
Newcastle upon Tyne
Tyne and Wear
NE4 7JB   Telephone 0191 232 2037 (Courtyard)/0191 261 0488 (Heavens
                 Above)

Nearest train station Newcastle
Car parking Large car park nearby
A–Z ref. P60/3B
Nearest landmark Centre For Life Building

Membership details None required
Opening hours   (Courtyard)
                     Monday–Thursday: 17.00–23.30
                     Friday–Saturday: 12.00–23.00
                     Sunday: 12.00–22.30
                     (Heavens Above)
                     Monday–Saturday: 19.30–23.00
                     Sunday: 12.00–22.30
Admission charges None
Food available No
Regular entertainment Monday & Saturday: Cabaret with Greta LaMore in The Courtyard
Sunday: Chill out and socialise in The Courtyard

The Courtyard is a traditional, sociable (and cruisy) pub on the ground floor, where people come more for a chat (and troll) rather than to shout above the music. The clientele is a very mixed bunch and it seems that this venue is a melting pot for all the 'types' (leather, bears, muscle, etc.) on the gay scene. Upstairs–Heavens Above is exactly the opposite: a modern bar where louder dance music fills the air and a younger, trendy crowd of boys and girls enjoy the cheap drinks and dance on the spot. There is a separate entrance to Heavens Above situated on Churchill Street, around the corner from The Courtyard.

Powerhouse

Alfred Wilson House
Waterloo Street
Newcastle upon Tyne
NE1 4DE   Telephone 0191 261 8874
                 Website http://www.power-house.co.uk

Nearest train station Newcastle Central

Gold Liberty Travel

GAY RUN and INDEPENDENT
ABTA BONDED AGENTS

Short breaks, Package Holidays,
European, USA & Worldwide Flights

Call
+44 (0)191 245 0757
Fax
+44 (0)191 245 0737
email
mailus@gold-liberty.co.uk
web
www.gold-liberty.co.uk

Gold Liberty Travel
2 West Road
Newcastle upon Tyne
NE4 9HB
England

Now in our 5th year of arranging Business Travel
and Holidays for the UK gay community

Car parking Side-street/local car parks
A–Z ref. P60/3B
Nearest landmark Centre For Life Building/bus station

Membership details None required
Opening hours   Monday: 22.00–02.00
                       Tuesday–Wednesday: 23.00–02.00
                       Thursday: 22.00–02.00
                       Friday–Saturday: 22.30–03.00
                       Sunday: Closed
Admission charges   Monday: £2
                       Tuesday–Wednesday: Free
                       Thursday: £3
                       Friday: £4
                       Saturday: £5
Food available Yes
Regular entertainment Monday: 'Sweet Peach'/top cabaret
Tuesday–Wednesday: Disco chill out (entrance through Village Bar)
Thursday: 'Cruze': strippers/'Super Singles Shagtags'/cabaret
Friday: 'Rendezvous' (retro revival)
Saturday: 'Thrust': (putting the house into powerhouse)

Open six nights and gay for six of those nights. Powerhouse is a large, 600 capacity nightclub with a h-u-g-e dance floor. Thursday is a busy singles night (or–less politely–a cruise night) with shagtags given out by the Sisters of Syphilis, who keep everyone in order. Every night from then on gets busier until the end of the weekend. Sister venue, The Village Bar, next door, is open from 12.00 each day and used as an access to the club on Tuesday and Wednesday nights. There's no charge to the pub, which also stages karaoke (Friday) and cabaret (usually a stripper, on Sunday) with additional entertainments throughout the week.

Rockies
78 Scotswood Road
Newcastle upon Tyne
Tyne and Wear
NE4 7JH   Telephone 0191 232 6536

Nearest train station Newcastle
Car parking Car park at rear of venue
A–Z ref. P60/3B
Nearest landmark Telewest Arena/Centre For Life Building

Membership details None required
Opening hours   Monday–Saturday: 19.30–23.00
                       Sunday: 19.30–22.30
Admission charges None
Food available Bar snacks available
Regular entertainment Monday–Tuesday: Social
Wednesday: DJ/games ('Open Your Box'/'Play Your Cards Right', etc.)
Thursday: Karaoke
Friday: 'Men Only': stripper/retro camp classics (70s and 80s)
Saturday: 'Men Only': DJ

Sunday: Stripper/DJ

Friendly, busy pub on three large, raised levels. Ample seating and 'quiet' areas, with loads of red Chesterfields dotted around. It is a unique mixed bar where everyone seems to get along just fine, particularly over the weekend when there are female strippers (tits oot for the lads), which makes it an ideal place for the newcomer to have a gander around without being too obvious. Everyone is made welcome here–male, female and TVs/TSs, and a good time will be had by all (honest).

Rumours @ The Frog and Nightgown
3–5 Waterloo Street
Newcastle upon Tyne
NE1   Telephone 0191 232 2014

Nearest train station Newcastle
Car parking Street parking
A–Z ref. P60/3B
Nearest landmark Centre For Life Building

Membership details None required
Opening hours   Friday–Sunday: 19.00–23.00
Admission charges None
Food available No

Rumours is above The Frog and Nightgown, with a separate entrance through the main door leading upstairs. A mixed gay and lesbian venue, with a pleasant atmosphere and cheap drinks. More suitable for relaxing and socialising rather than trolling and bopping. There is no regular scheduled entertainment except for the drag cabaret every Sunday.

Pinkys @ Sands Ridge Hotel
Headland Road
Newquay
Cornwall
TR7 1HN   Telephone 01637 872 089

Nearest train station Newquay (ten minute walk)
Car parking Ample street parking
Nearest landmark Fistral Beach/Golf Course

Membership details None required
Opening hours   Friday–Saturday: 20.00–Late
Admission charges £2.50
Food available Light bar snacks available

In an area decidedly lacking any sort of gay meeting place, Pinkys takes place in the basement bar of the hotel. Don't expect a 20,000 watt sound and lighting systems, nor trendy, cosmopolitan decor. What you can expect is a friendly and welcoming atmosphere; a place where you are allowed to enjoy yourself and just have fun. There is no dress code, no age limit and never, ever, any problems. Accommodation is available from £15 per person per night, including breakfast. Phone the hotel for further details. The entrance to the 'club' is through the hotel front door, which should be well lit and signposted.

The Castle

1 Spittalfields (off Ketts Hill)
Norwich
NR1 4EY   Telephone 01603 768 886

Nearest train station Norwich (half a mile)
Car parking Car park at venue and street parking.
A–Z ref. P25/2F
Nearest landmark Ketts Hill roundabout

Membership details None required
Opening hours   Monday–Friday: 14.00–23.00
                         Saturday–Sunday: 12.00–late
Admission charges None
Food available Full bar snack menu available

Regular entertainment at The Castle includes discos, pop quizzes, occasional cabaret and karaoke. The front bar has a relaxed atmosphere for socialising and the rear bar is the opposite: loud dance music, lights and a party atmosphere. At the time of going to print, the bar is undergoing a refurbishment programme to the back bar to double its present size. Keep an eye out for later opening hours.

The Lord Raglan

30 Bishop Bridge Road
Norwich
NR1 4ET   Telephone 01603 623 304

Nearest train station Norwich (ten minutes)
Car parking Outside venue
A–Z ref. P25/2f
Nearest landmark Norwich Cathedral/Ketts Hill roundabout

Membership details None required
Opening hours   Monday–Saturday: 12.00–14.00/19.00–23.00
                         Sunday: 12.00–15.00/19.00–22.30
Admission charges None
Food available No
Regular entertainment No regular scheduled entertainment

Traditional style and very friendly gay bar with a (mostly) male clientele, although lesbians and TVs are more than welcome. There are monthly theme nights (Rocky Horror/construction/etc.) and a weekly free raffle (bottle of spirit for the winner). The Lord Raglan is a local's local, catering for all ages and types, not really for the trendy disco dolly. Offering B&B accommodation too (see 'Accommodation' listings). Popular beer garden throughout summer.

K2 Club

39 Sheep Street
Northampton
NN1 2NE   Telephone 01604 622 822

Nearest train station Northampton
Car parking Ample street parking

A–Z ref. P14/3B
Nearest landmark Job Centre

Membership details None required
Opening hours   Monday: Closed
                      Tuesday–Wednesday: 20.00–01.00
                      Thursday: 20.00–02.00
                      Friday–Saturday: 20.00–03.00
                      Sunday: 19.00–Late
Admission charges   Tuesday–Thursday: Free
                      Friday–Saturday: £3 after 22.00

Food available No
Regular entertainment Tuesday: Male stripper every other week
Wednesday: Social
Thursday: DJ
Friday: DJ: 'Cilla's Cottage'
Saturday: DJ: 'Queen Bee's Hive'
Sunday: Karaoke (19.00–late)

Being Northampton's only gay venue it's not hard to imagine how busy this place gets most evenings and particularly over the weekend. Although the crowd is a predominantly young gay and lesbian set, there are also a few of the older generation (thirty-something!) propping up the bar.

The Admiral Duncan

74 Lower Parliament Street
Nottingham
NG1 1EH   Telephone 0115 950 2727

Nearest train station Nottingham Midland
Car parking Limited street parking on Lower Parliament Street and surrounding areas
A–Z ref. P37/4H
Nearest landmark Palais Nightclub/end of Victoria Centre

Membership details
Members and bona fide only (£2 fee payable 24 hours in advance by phone or in person–up to four guests allowed per member
Opening hours   Monday–Tuesday: 20.00–24.00 (Lounge only)
                      Wednesday–Saturday: 20.00–02.00
                      Sunday: 20.00–24.00
Admission charges   Monday–Wednesday: Free
                      Thursday: £1.50 Guests/£1 members
                      Friday: £2 Guests/£1 members
                      Saturday: £3 Guests/£2 members
                      Sunday: Free

Food available Light snacks available

Nottingham's only dedicated late night venue for gay people, straight guests and TVs. Predominantly gay-men-venue, with cheap drink promotions on Thursday and a stripper on Sunday. In a previous life, this was a normal local pub which was converted into a late night drink and dance club, by ripping out all the seating, dimming the lights and having a late night licence. Popular venue for visitors from the surrounding areas (Stoke on Trent, etc.)

The Forest Tavern

257 Mansfield Road
Nottingham
NG1 3FT   Telephone 0115 947 5650

Nearest train station Nottingham
Car parking Limited street parking
A–Z ref. P37/2F
Nearest landmark Arboretum

Membership details None required
Opening hours   Monday–Tuesday: 16.00–23.00
                         Wednesday–Saturday: 12.00–23.00
                         Sunday: 12.00–22.30
Admission charges None
Food available
Full international menu and snacks (tapas, etc.), coffee and cappuccino
Regular entertainment No regular scheduled entertainment

One of the more gay-friendly venues in Nottingham—part of the Tynemille Group, just outside of the city centre. A continentally styled cafe bar, with influences from Belgium and Germany. A refreshing, social atmosphere, catering for a trendy, young mixed crowd who know what's hot and what's not. Over 60 continental bottled beers, in addition to a good range of real and cask-conditioned ales, most with their own badged glass (don't go nicking them (they're counted!).

Forester's Arms

18 St Anne's Street
Nottingham
NG1 3LX   Telephone 0115 958 0432

Nearest train station Nottingham Central
Car parking Own car park at venue
A–Z ref. P37/4G
Nearest landmark Victoria Centre

Membership details None required
Opening hours   Monday–Saturday: 11.00–23.30 (Last orders 23.00)
                         Sunday: 12.00–23.00 (Last orders 22.30)
Admission charges None
Food available No
Regular entertainment Monday: Monday chill out
Tuesday: Karaoke
Thursday: 60s Disco/cabaret
Friday–Sunday: 90s Disco/DJ
Regular cheap drink promotions throughout the week

The Forester's will be going through a transformation over the next few months to change the face of the venue into a more young and dynamic pre-club bar, but still maintaining the traditions of a pub for their older clientele. Situated only twenty minutes from MGM (the club, not the studio). A mixed lesbian and gay gathering, not defining themselves to any one 'type' as all 'types' are in and all are welcome. Not to be confused with the Forester's Inn on Huntingdon Street.

Forester's Inn

183 Huntingdon Street
Nottingham
NG1 3NL   Telephone   0115 941 9679

Nearest train station Nottingham
Car parking Victoria Centre/St Marks Street/street parking
A–Z ref. P37/3G
Nearest landmark Victoria Centre

Membership details None required
Opening hours   Monday–Saturday: 10.30–23.00
                        Sunday: 12.00–22.30
Admission charges   None
Food available Full menu and snacks available lunch-times and 18.00–21.00
Regular entertainment Thursday: Quiz night
Friday–Sunday: Disco

Mixed gay and straight clientele during the day; predominantly gay in the
evening. A fair sized venue with three bars and pool room. Not to be confused
with The Forester's Arms on St Anne's Street.

The Lord Roberts

24 Broad Street
Hockley
Nottingham
NG1 3AN   Telephone   0115 941 4886

Nearest train station Nottingham
Car parking Ample street parking
A–Z ref. P37/4H
Nearest landmark Bus station/Victoria Centre

Membership details None required
Opening hours   Monday–Saturday: 11.45–23.00
                        Sunday: 12.00–22.30
Admission charges   None
Food available Full restuarant facilities
Lunch-times only/bar menu

The Lord Roberts is a theatrically themed gay-*friendly* pub in the centre of
Nottingham. There is no regular entertainment although cabaret and karaoke are
organised on an ad hoc basis.

The Mill

27 Woolpack Lane
Hockley
Nottingham
NG1 1GA   Telephone   01159 644 941/07970 175 311(infoline)

Nearest train station Nottingham
Car parking Ample local car parks
A–Z ref. P37/5H

Nearest landmark Ice Stadium/Bowling Alley

Membership details None required
Opening hours   Monday–Saturday: 17.00–24.00 (last admission 23.00)
                       Sunday: 18.00–23.00
Admission charges Wednesday: £1 'Pink Pounder'
                       Sunday: £2
                       Free at all other times
Food available Lunch-times/Sunday lunch: 12.00–15.00
Regular entertainment Monday: Pre-club venue for Revolution @ MGM and Ten @ The Yard
Tuesday: 'Dyke's Delight': women only upstairs (monthly)/cheap drinks
Wednesday: 'Pink Pound Night' (almost all drinks £1)
Thursday: 'Entertainment and Extravaganza'; live entertainment Friday: 'Dancing Queen': retro night–70s, 80s and 90s dance
Saturday: 'Candyland': resident's night commercial dance
Sunday: 'Wild Sundaes': live DJ from 19.00 (house and techno)

Two floors of pumping new sound. A totally refurbished, stylish, cosmopolitan bar and lively pre-club drinking venue. Happy hours every day from 17.00–20.00. For details of the monthly women-only night in the upstairs bar, phone the venue direct for dates and times.

Revolution @ MGM
Greyfriar Gate
Nottingham
NG1   Telephone 0115 958 0555

Nearest train station Nottingham
Car parking Local car parks
A–Z ref. P37/6G
Nearest landmark Bus station/Maid Marion Way (A6008)

Membership details Available at the door, but not essential
Opening hours   21.30–02.30
                       (First Monday of the month only)

Revolution @ MGM is one of the biggest monthly dates in the gay clubbing calendar, with music courtesy of Peter Martine and guests. At the time of going to print, MGM was due to close down for a major refit, so future details of Revolution were not available. There was no doubt however, that the club night will continue after the refurbishment, although the re- opening date was still sketchy. Keep an eye on the gay press for updates.

Iguana
171 Union Street
Oldham
Lancashire
OL1 1TD   Telephone 0161 652 5662

Nearest train station Mumps (one minute)
Car parking Outside venue (no charge)

A–Z ref. P64/3D
Nearest landmark Mumps Bridge

Membership details £5 per year–entitles free admission over weekends
Opening hours   Monday: Closed
                      Tuesday–Saturday: 22.00–02.00
                      Sunday: 21.00–24.00
Admission charges Tuesday–Thursday: Free
                      Friday–Saturday: £2/Members free
                      Sunday: Free
Food available Yes–simple freezer-to-microwave dishes
Regular entertainment Tuesday: Disco
Wednesday: Karaoke
Thursday: Cabaret
Friday–Saturday: Disco
Sunday: Drag DJ

Iguana is a small and intimate basement club. The three owners are all from a theatrical background and this is reflected in the club's atmosphere. Particularly recommended for newcomers to the gay scene. Mixed gay and straight, friendly clientele.

The Coven

Oxpens Road
Oxford
OX1   Telephone 01865 242 770

Nearest train station Oxford
Car parking Limited street parking
A–Z ref. P15/3D
Nearest landmark College of Further Education/coach and lorry park

Membership details None required
Opening hours   Friday: 22.00–03.00
                      (Every Friday night only)
Admission charges £4

'Loveshack' is a busy gay and lesbian night happening every Friday. The Coven is a large venue popular with the student fraternity. Cheap drinks each week with occasional PAs and cabaret once a month. Music tends to be happy handbag with classic club anthems thrown in for good measure. Phone the infoline above for further details.

The Jolly Farmers

20 Paradise Street
Oxford
OX1 1LD   Telephone 01865 793 759

Nearest train station Oxford (five minutes)
Car parking Westgate Shopping Centre
A–Z ref. P15/2D
Nearest landmark Westgate Shopping Centre

Membership details None required
Opening hours   Monday–Saturday: 12.00–23.00
                       Sunday: 12.30–22.30
Admission charges None
Food available Full menu and snacks available lunch-times (including vegetarian)
Regular entertainment No regular scheduled entertainment, except for monthly quiz nights and occasional cabaret evenings

The Jolly Farmers is a late 16th Century public house (close to Westgate Shopping Centre), full of character (and characters). The building consists of low beamed ceilings, open fireplace and snugs with a designated no-smoking area. Warmer weather sees the opening of the enclosed beer garden. The clientele during the day is decidedly mixed gay and straight, whereas the evening is predominantly gay. Not a cruisy place, more of a sociable drink kind'a place.

Royal Bleinheim
13 St Ebbes Street
Oxford
OX1 1PT   Telephone 01865 248 280

Nearest train station Oxford
Car parking Multi-storey close by (Oxford is not car-friendly)
A–Z ref. P15/2E
Nearest landmark British Home Stores/Westgate Shopping Centre

Membership details None required
Opening hours   Monday–Saturday: 12.00–23.00
                       Sunday: 12.00–22.30
Admission charges None
Food available Lunch-times: 12.00–15.00
Regular entertainment No regular scheduled entertainment

Recently refurbished under the new ownership, The Royal is a large comfortable open-plan split-level venue. A traditional establishment, popular with students from Oxford and Brooks, it occasionally hosts the relevant party nights. The daytime trade sees a mix of straight and gay (shoppers, business and the like), whilst the evening is predominantly gay and lesbian. This is a pub that doesn't pretend to be a 'bar'. The welcome, not only from the staff but also the customers, is friendly and social (guaranteed!) and they will take the time to make a new face welcome. Music comes courtesy of a well-stocked and -used jukebox and although there is no scheduled entertainment policy, there will be the occasional cabaret act or drag show booked. Flyers to The Coven (see separate listing) are distributed when available, and current information regarding the local scene, etc. is posted up on the notice-board. For fans of real ale there is always at least one cask of well-maintained brew on offer.

The Acadamy
Broadway
Peterborough
PE1 1RS   Telephone 01733 349 528/01733 882 901

Nearest train station Peterborough
Car parking Local car parking/limited side-street parking
A–Z ref. P12/3A
Nearest landmark Peterborough Library

Membership details None required
Opening hours   Tuesday: 19.00–01.00 (Tuesday night only)
Admission charges £2

Opening its doors in March 1998, The 500 capacity Academy has established itself as one of the East of England's biggest gay nights. It is always packed to the rafters, so an early admission is advised. With DJ Pete Martine (of Revolution fame) at the decks, cheap admission for six hours of clubbing along with the (very) cheap drinks, it's one of the very best ways to spend a Tuesday evening.

The Bridge
London Road
Peterborough
Cambridgeshire   Telephone   01733 312 192

Nearest train station Peterborough
Car parking Car parking behind venue
A–Z ref. P20/5A
Nearest landmark Football ground (one minute)

Membership details None required
Opening hours   Monday: 12.00–14.00/19.00–23.00
                       Tuesday: 12.00–14.00/Closed in the evening
                       Wednesday–Saturday: 12.00–14.00/19.00–23.00
                       Sunday: 12.00–15.00/19.00–22.30
                       (During the winter season the bar opens only in the
                       evenings)
Admission charges None
Food available No
Regular entertainment Disco each weekend and occasional cabaret

Known locally as Jimmies, this is a popular mixed gay and lesbian venue with cruisy overtones. Mixed ages from young to old, although the younger element tend to congregate more in here during the weekend when the discos are on.

The Clarence
31 Clarence Place
Stonehouse
Plymouth
PL1 3JP   Telephone   01752 603 827

Nearest train station Plymouth
Car parking Street parking outside venue
A–Z ref. P21/3F
Nearest landmark R. N. Hospital

Membership details None required

Opening hours	Monday–Saturday: 10.00–23.00
	Sunday: 12.00–22.30

Admission charges None
Food available Snacks only at lunch-times
Regular entertainment No regular scheduled entertainment

Large capacity pub catering for a gay, lesbian and well-behaved straight clientele. Set in a Victorian facade (Brass and Beams). The Clarence offers a lovely atmosphere and a warm welcome to all newcomers. At the time of writing The Clarence were working on a regular women only night and the formation of a pub pool team. For updated information on these events please phone the venue direct.

The Swallow
59 Breton Side
Plymouth
Devon
PL4   Telephone 01752 251 760

Nearest train station Plymouth (one mile)
Car parking Council car park next door (free after 18.30)
Nearest landmark Plymouth Bus Station

Membership details None required
Opening hours   Monday–Saturday: 11.00–23.00
                          Sunday: 12.00–22.30
Admission charges None
Food available Lunch-time snacks
Regular entertainment No regular scheduled entertainment

The Swallow is a gay-run, straight-friendly gay pub. A recently refurbished traditional venue catering for the town's younger gay element, although all ages will be made welcome. Although there is no regular scheduled entertainment, there is a monthly karaoke session and the occasional cabaret evening. Separate pool room.

Martha's/1 Above
227 Commercial Road
Portsmouth
Hampshire
PO1 4BS   Telephone 01705 852 951   Fax 01705 366 554

Nearest train station Portsmouth/Southsea
Car parking Limited on-street
Nearest landmark McDonalds

Membership details Not required, but available at £10 per year (entitles the holder to reduced and priority admission–apply at venue)
Opening hours   (Martha's)
                          Monday–Saturday: 11.00–23.00
                          Sunday: 12.00–22.30
                          (1 Above)
                          Monday–Saturday: 22.00–02.00
                          Sunday: Closed
Admission charges (1 Above)

Monday–Wednesday: Free
Thursday: £2 members/£3 guests
Friday–Saturday: £3 members/£4 guests

Food available Monday–Saturday: 12.00–20.00 and Sunday: 12.00–15.00
Regular entertainment Monday: '70s/80s Night' (1 Above)
Tuesday: Cheap drinks & cabaret in the (Martha's)
Wednesday: 'Code': monthly strict dress code night–skin, rubber, denim, etc.
(1 Above)
Thursday: Stripper–alternate male and female (1 Above)
Friday: Regular cabaret (1 Above)
Saturday: Disco: busy (1 Above)
Sunday: Karaoke (Martha's)
Cheap drinks every Monday to Thursday from 20.00

Situated in the town centre, Martha's pub tends to get a good mix of gay and straight (especially at lunch-times) with a friendly and acceptable attitude. The evenings see a change to a predominant mixed gay clientele. The club (1 Above) situated at the back of Martha's, has largely a mix of gays and lesbians and is friendly and welcoming to all newcomers. It operates non-stop dance and chart sounds on Thursdays and Saturdays. Martha's and 1 Above are drug-free zones, so if you take them, take them somewhere else.

The Old Vic

104 St Paul's Road
Portsmouth
Hampshire
PO5 4AQ   Telephone 01705 297 013

Nearest train station Portsmouth (five minute walk)
Car parking Ample street parking
Nearest landmark Guildhall

Membership details None required
Opening hours   Monday–Saturday: 11.00–23.30
                         Sunday: 11.00–22.30
Admission charges   None
Food available Home-cooked food: lunch-times only (dinner parties catered for)
Regular entertainment Monday: Pool competitions
Tuesday: Happy hour all evening
Wednesday: Quiz night
Thursday: Karaoke
Friday–Saturday: DJ/Disco
Sunday: DJ/cabaret (18.00)

A very friendly gay bar presided over by the fabulous landlady Roisine (pronounced Roshine). At the time of writing, she was trying to organise Portsmouth's first Gay Pride to take place on the 10 July 1999. This is one of those extra special bars where nothing will be too much trouble and she puts herself out to ensure that you enjoy your evening. Although it is a predominantly gay bar, there are a few straights in who are usually friends of gays and come in because they enjoy the atmosphere. A good mix of men and women with a pool room and a separate function room which is used for parties, blessings, etc. A meeting place for most gay groups in the area and if you require any information on any local group then this bar should be your starting point.

The Granby

120 London Road
Reading
Berkshire   Telephone   0118 935 2537

Nearest train station Reading
Car parking Car park at venue
Nearest landmark Cemetery Junction

Membership details None required
Opening hours   Monday–Thursday: 19.00–24.00
                         Friday–Saturday: 19.00–02.00
                         Sunday: 19.00–23.30
Admission charges   Monday–Thursday: No admission
                         Friday–Saturday: £2 after 22.00
                         Sunday: No admission
Food available No

Mixed gay and straight friendly bar with regular disco and cabaret over the weekend. It is quite popular with women although there are no specific meeting nights.

The Wynford Arms

110 Kings Road
Reading
Berkshire
RG1 3BY   Telephone   0118 958 9814

Nearest train station Reading
Car parking On-road
Nearest landmark Kwik Fit (next door)

Membership details None required
Opening hours   Monday–Saturday: 12.00–23.00
                         Sunday: 12.00–22.30
Admission charges None
Food available No, although you are welcome to take in your own sandwiches, etc.
Regular entertainment Cabaret on Tuesday is the only scheduled entertainment

The Wynford is a traditional gay, predominantly male venue. Split into two rooms: the large, comfortable lounge with stage and the smaller bar room. A friendly relaxed atmosphere; this venue is more for the serious drinker than the disco bunny.

The Stage Door

31 Baille Street
Rochdale
Lancashire
OL16 1JA   Telephone   01706 718 340

Nearest train station Rochdale

Car parking Ample street parking
A–Z ref. P19/4H
Nearest landmark Rochdale Bus Station (practically next door)

Membership details None required
Opening hours   Monday–Saturday: 11.00–23.00
                         Sunday: 11.00–22.30
                         (A late 01.00 licence has been applied for, however, this
                         was not confirmed at the time of going to print–phone for
                         further details)
Admission charges None, except for charity events (nominal charge)
Food available Lunch-times only
Regular entertainment Monday: Karaoke
Tuesday: DJ
Wednesday: 'Talent Night' (winner has 'spot' on Friday night)
Thursday: Krystle (drag DJ)
Friday: Krystle (drag DJ)/'Talent Night' winner spot
Saturday–Sunday: Krystle (drag DJ)

The latest, much needed gay bar to hit Rochdale for a long, long time opened in
December 1998 and has already opened another venue in Blackburn. The Stage
Door is a lively, fun-packed bar, with velvet drapes, chandeliers and everything
that goes with it, concentrating heavily on cabaret and entertaining the punters.
At the beginning of the week there is plenty of seating to rest your sassy old
behinds, however, from Thursday these are removed to accommodate the disco
and dance floor. Because of the fun and no-attitude atmosphere, there is a
mixture of 'types'–from lads from the local rugby team to TVs and TSs and
everyone in between. A separate pool room and quieter area is always open. The
Blackburn venue was not open at the time of going to print, however, I have been
informed that it will be at the Old Wheatsheaf Hotel (re-named Stage Door) on
Mincing Lane (phone 01254 674 761). This new venue will run on the same lines
as the Rochdale Stage Door. A late 01.00 licence has been applied for. For further
information phone the venue direct.

The Ship Inn
347 High Street
Rochester
Kent
ME1 1DA   Telephone 01634 844 264

Nearest train station Chatham and Rochester
Car parking Own car park at rear of venue
Nearest landmark Synagogue opposite or bike shop next door

Membership details None required
Opening hours   Monday–Saturday: 11.00–23.00
                         Sunday: 12.00–22.30
Admission charges None
Food available Yes
Regular entertainment Monday–Wednesday: Social
Thursday–Saturday: Disco
Sunday: Live jazz (popular)/disco evening

The Ship is divided up into three rooms. There are two predominantly gay bars and one mixed bar. The entrance to the gay bars is on Ship Lane. It can be described as a 'traditional' venue, and even though there are discos in the latter part of the week, there is no dance floor. The punters use the ample floor space as the dance area. Being the only gay venue in this part of Kent, the age range and clientele is totally across the board and everyone seems to fit in well. A tourist trap during the summer with loads of students and attractions such as The Naval Dockyard Museum (sailors?) and the Cathedral.

Spritzers

Redbourne Road
Redbourne
St Albans
Hertfordshire
AL3 6RP   Telephone   01582 794 053

Nearest train station St Albans
Car parking On-site

Membership details None required
Opening hours   Monday: Closed
                         Tuesday–Thursday: 19.00–24.00
                         Friday: 19.00–02.00
                         Saturday: 19.00–04.00
                         Sunday: 19.00–24.00
Admission charges Friday and Saturday: 21.00–22.30: £2/£3 after
Food available No

An exclusively gay, bi and lesbian club (TVs welcome), situated in the heart of the countryside, with a friendly and regular clientele. At the weekend it turns into a dance club with London DJs a regular feature. With two bars and a stage, it hosts regular cabarets and entertainments. Verulam MSC is the last Thursday of the month at 21.00–PO Box 158, St Albans AL2 3UQ.

The Duke Of York

34 York Road
Salisbury
Wiltshire   Telephone   01722 324 092

Nearest train station Salisbury
Car parking Ample street parking
Nearest landmark Salisbury Cathedral (two minutes)

Membership details None required
Opening hours   Monday–Saturday: 18.00–23.00
                         Sunday: 12.00–22.30
Admission charges None
Food available No

The Duke of York is a local gay venue with a young friendly mixed crowd. There is no regular scheduled entertainment although most Sundays offer pool and games' competitions.

Bar-Celona

387 Attercliffe Road
Sheffield
South Yorkshire
S9   Telephone 0114 244 1492

Nearest train station Sheffield
Car parking Ample side-street parking
A–Z ref. P88/6A
Nearest landmark Sheffield Arena/A6178 is Attercliffe Road

Membership details None required
Opening hours   Monday–Saturday: 20.30–23.00
                         Sunday: 20.30–22.30
Admission charges None
Food available No
Regular entertainment Thursday: DJ
Friday: DJ Ken and Barbie/stripper
Saturday: DJ Steven/pre-Planet party
Sunday: DJ Ken and Barbie/stripper

Situated close to The Planet (see separate listing), about five minutes from the town centre by taxi, Bar-Celona is a large split-level European style bar. Bright and lively, with a good friendly atmosphere. Boys, girls and everyone in between will be made welcome. In the latter part of the week you can catch the campest drag DJs you are ever likely to see, namely Ken and Barbie. It should be obvious, without explanation, what happens! Themed evenings could be Ken and Barbie goes Cruising, or Ken and Barbie try for a baby . . . . You get the gist? During the summer the rooftop garden opens up, adding yet another floor for you to troll around on. See listing for Men's Bar, which occupies the same building as Bar-Celona.

Club Xes (formerly The Norfolk Arms)

195 Carlisle Street
Sheffield
South Yorkshire
S4 7LT   Telephone 0114 275 2469

Nearest train station Sheffield (Meadowhall)
Car parking Side-street parking(Carlisle Street)
A–Z ref. P87/6G
Nearest landmark Norfolk Bridge

Membership details None required
Opening hours   Monday–Thursday: 21.00–01.30
                         Friday–Saturday: 20.00–02.30
                         Sunday: 20.00–22.30
Admission charges None
Food available Yes
Regular entertainment Monday–Thursday: Resident DJ
Friday: Every first Friday of the month: 'Sheffield Bears' (cuddly, hairy types)/every second
Friday: 'Transvestite Night'/every third Friday: 'Leather Night'/every fourth Friday: 'Kitty La

Camp' (un-missable drag DJ)
Saturday: 'Club Night'
Sunday: Stripper/resident DJ

A good alternative to the scene in Sheffield, offering a lively and friendly atmosphere for a complete age group and mixture of people. Situated about five minutes (by car) from the town centre, Club Xes offers a vast variety of music to tantalise those dancing feet during the week. If this isn't your 'cup of tea' then why not relax in the quieter lounge area–instead of cavorting around showing your rhythmic moods, let your mouth do all the working.

The Cossack

45 Howard Street
Sheffield
South Yorkshire
S1 2LW   Telephone 0114 281 2654

Nearest train station Sheffield
Car parking Limited street parking
A–Z ref. P99/3F
Nearest landmark Railway station

Membership details None required
Opening hours   Monday–Saturday: 12.00–23.00
                       Sunday: 12.00–22.30
Admission charges None
Food available Yes

Traditional, city-centred, *extremely* gay-friendly pub. This place used to be Sheffield's longest running homo hangout, and even now–although mixed–is an alternative choice for the girls of the town and a drinking den for the boys.

Luxury Voodoo

The Unit
Milton Street
Sheffield
S1   Telephone 0114 258 0470
                Website http://members.xoom.com/xloungers/

Nearest train station Sheffield
Car parking Ample street parking/local car parks
A–Z ref. P99/3E
Nearest landmark Off A61 (Hanover Way)/close to Devonshire Green

Membership details Not necessary, but phone the above number to join the mailing list for advance party info and club entry discounts
Opening hours   Wednesday: 21.00–02.30 (Monthly–second Wednesday of the month only)
                       Phone for dates (may be changing)
Admission charges Members £3.50/guests £4

Hosted by Spoof and X-Loungers, this is an extremely popular monthly night out in Sheffield. The X-Loungers collective is a group of artists who stage events and club nights in Sheffield and around the country. They endeavour to reduce prejudice and bigotry by producing events and publishing material that 'x-pounds' their views. In short: it doesn't matter whether you are black, white, gay, straight or a bit of both, or if you cannot help dressing as a girl. This night is for you. The music is funky and hard, drinks are cheap and the entertainment is non-stop. *This is strictly a prejudice-free zone!*

Men's Bar

Washford Road (off Attercliffe Road)
Sheffield
S9   Telephone 0114 244 1492
            E-mail planetangel@compuserve.com

Nearest train station Sheffield
Car parking Ample side-street parking
A–Z ref. P88/6A
Nearest landmark Sheffield Arena (five minutes)/A6178 is Attercliffe Road

Membership details None required
Opening hours   Monday–Saturday: 20.30–23.30
                         Sunday: 20.30–22.30
Admission charges None

Men's Bar, as the name suggests, is strictly men-only. Due to open in June 1999, it will be a cruisy dress-code bar, for lovers of leather, rubber, uniform, industrial, denim, sports kit, skins, etc. Although it occupies the same building as Bar-Celona, it will have a separate entrance situated on Washford Street. Still heavily under construction, the theme will be 'prison style' (whereby you can recreate your favourite scenes from Jeff Stryker videos or '*Cell Block H*!) with strippers keeping you entertained every Friday, Saturday and Sunday. Keep an eye out in the gay press for precise opening dates. Sounds fab! Remember to obtain your concessions from the bar to give you reduced entry to Planet. *Note*: The Attercliffe area is fast becoming a gay village in itself, with Bronx Sauna, Planet Nightclub, Bar-Celona and now Men's bar. With ample parking available, there will soon be no need to travel from the city centre to Attercliffe.

Planet

429 Effingham Road
Sheffield
South Yorkshire
S9   Telephone 0114 244 9033
            E-mail planetangel@compuserve.com

Nearest train station Sheffield
Car parking Two car parks available
A–Z ref. P88/6A
Nearest landmark Sheffield Arena/B6073

Membership details None required
Opening hours   Thursday: 22.30–02.00
                         Friday: 22.30–03.30
                         Saturday: 22.30–04.00 (Bar closes at 02.00)

	Sunday: 22.00–01.00 (Doors close at 23.00)
Admission charges	Thursday: £3 (Free before23.00)
	Friday: £5
	Saturday: £7
	Sunday: £3
	(Remember to get your concessions from Bar-Celona and Men's Bar for reduced admission to the club before 22.30 Concessions not available for Sunday or after 22.30)

Food available Bistro on premises
Regular entertainment Thursday: Disco DJ Tony (requests)/drinks promotions
Friday: DJ Stuart (camp–the music, not Stuart)/top entertainment last Friday of the month
Saturday: Disco: DJ Stuart (camp) and Tony (harder)/late licence
Sunday: DJ/stripper/late licence (extremely busy)

The Planet is a large, exclusively gay (straight friends welcome) club that gets very busy and can get very hot and sweaty! Spread out over two floors, the main room is the dance area, with seating either side of the dance floor for those who can't keep up with the pace. Women usually hang around by the stage whilst the men (or blokes ... well it is Sheffield!) take advantage of the circuit, from downstairs to the quieter upstairs Globe Bar, used as a general chill out area, to cruise around. The balcony provides the opportunity to 'select' your target and move in. Pre-Planet party is at the popular Bar-Celona (see separate listing). The Planet is a very mixed club and because of the area students do tend to populate the bar on a Thursday, taking advantage of the regular cheap drink promotions. Now in its third successful year, The Planet has plans to totally refurbish the venue during 1999 (watch this space). See listings for Bronx Sauna, Bar-Celona and Men's Bar also.

Poptastic @ The City Hall
Barkers Pool
Sheffield
S1

Nearest train station Sheffield
Car parking NCP/street parking (quite difficult as the evening draws on)
A–Z ref. P99/2E
Nearest landmark Behind Town Hall/City Hall is a landmark in itself
Opening hours   10.30–02.30
                      Last Friday of the month
Admission charges   £5/£4 members or advance ticket

The latest Poptastic night, close to Sheffield University, thus attracting all those yummy students. Cheap drinks with selected bottles at £1.50. For further details of Poptastic see the lsiting for Poptastic @ The Mutz Nutz, Manchester.

The Rutland Arms
86 Brown Street
Sheffield
S1   Telephone 0114 272 9003

Nearest train station Sheffield (two minute walk)
Car parking Side of venue
A–Z ref. P99/3F

Nearest landmark New Centre for Popular Music (looks like four pickled onions gone mad)

Membership details None required
Opening hours   Monday–Friday: 11.00–23.00
                               Saturday: 12.00–16.00/19.00–23.00
                               Sunday: 12.00–15.00/19.00–22.30
Admission charges None
Food available Monday–Friday 12.00–19.00 and Saturday–Sunday 12.00–14.30
Regular entertainment No scheduled entertainment

Extremely gay-friendly mixed bar. No camp canoodlings, no Karaoke or cabaret (eh?): just a good pint. The Rutland Arms is a Victorian Grade 2 listed building. Voted 'CAMRA Pub of the Month for January' and forever in the 'Beer Guides' for the quality of the ale they serve, with a minimum of at least five different 'real ales' always available. Due to their location in the middle of the 'recording industry' studios, the clientele are often known (or soon to be known) celebrities. Although it is not a gay bar, The Rutland does offer a courteous welcome to all (especially to those who do like their beer) and if the friendliness of the pub is anything like the friendliness extended to me by the manager (I was in hysterics) then you are in for a treat. Accommodation is also available (phone beforehand for booking details), in addition to a function room available for hire. Award-winning beer garden is open during the summer.

Club Greyhound
Colnbrook By-Pass
Colnbrook
Slough
Berkshire
SL3 0EH   Telephone 01753 684 920

Nearest train station Slough
Nearest tube Hounslow
Car parking On-site
Nearest landmark BP Garage (on corner)

Membership details None required
Opening hours   Monday–Friday: 12.00–15.00/19.00–02.00
                               Friday: 12.00–02.00
                               Saturday: 12.00–03.00
                               Sunday: 12.00–14.00/19.00–24.00
                               (Winter season: bar closed in mornings)
Admission charges Monday–Thursday: £2 after 23.00 (free with UB40)
                               Friday: £3: 21.00–23.00/£4 after
                               Saturday: £4: 21.00–23.00/£5 after
                               Sunday: £2 after 21.00
                               (Friday–Sunday: half-price admission with UB40–positive
                               identification required)
                               (Free admission before 21.00 Friday–Sunday)
Food available Full menu and snacks available lunch and evenings
Regular entertainment Monday: DJ/Karaoke (alternate Mondays)
Tuesday: DJ garage and house
Wednesday: DJ (disco, trash and handbag)

Thursday: DJ/cabaret
Friday: DJ
Saturday: DJ/PA/cabaret
Sunday: DJ/stripper

Club Greyhound is situated on the A4 (Junction 5 off the M4), two miles from Heathrow Airport and stands in four acres of grounds, complete with beer garden, swimming pool (summer) and BBQ facilities. Mixed gay with TVs welcome and no attitude. The bar caters for a predominantly male clientele. Based on one floor, it can be described as a traditional venue with the addition of a huge dance area. The atmosphere can be cruisy, as well as being sociable and friendly. The large beer garden opens up in the summer when there are regular BBQ parties. Ideally placed by Heathrow Airport, whereby there is a possibility that all the fresh meat could troll in before hitting the streets of London.

The Atlantic Queen
Bugle Street
Southampton
Hampshire
SO14 0BE   Telephone 01703 229 146

Nearest train station Southampton Central (five minutes)
Car parking Outside venue (street parking)
A–Z ref. P40/2B
Nearest landmark Isle of Wight Ferry Terminal–opposite is Bugle Street/Royal Pier (closed)

Membership details None required
Opening hours   Monday–Saturday: 12.00–23.00
                       Sunday: 12.00–22.30
Admission charges None
Food available Sunday lunch-times 12.00–15.30 and then snacks available lunch-times through the week
Regular entertainment Monday: Quiz night
Tuesday: Cheap drinks
Wednesday: Games night
Thursday: Themed night
Friday: Cabaret
Saturday: Occasional cabaret
Sunday: 'Sunday Gold': A day full of fun (cabaret/stripper/etc.)

A mixed gay and lesbian venue, with cabaret and entertainment high on the agenda. A large, open-plan long bar with the stage able to be viewed from anywhere in the room. It also has a 'telephone exchange' facility whereby, in order to break the ice with someone you fancy, you can 'call' their table or area and speak (drool) over the phone (whilst seductively licking your lips!). The Atlantic is a fun venue; a major strength being the diversity of age and 'type', all of whom are made to feel very welcome. Newcomers to the scene (whatever age) are encouraged to phone the bar beforehand, in order that you are not left entirely on your own, thus giving you the opportunity to meet new people. This also applies to TVs who would like a non-discriminatory venue to socialise in. Full disabled access to the venue.

The Edge

Compton Walk
Southampton
SO140BH   Telephone 01703 366 163

Nearest train station Southampton Central
Car parking On-site car park
A–Z ref. P30/6C
Nearest landmark Fire Station/Charlotte Place roundabout

Membership details
Free membership scheme in operation (enquire at the bar)–a regular newsletter is produced and posted to all members. Note: If you are unable to receive post at home remember to tick the box advising of such
Opening hours

> Monday–Saturday: 12.00–02.00
> Sunday: 12.00–22.30

Admission charges None
Food available The Loft is a restaurant and snack bar, serving a full menu 19.00–22.00 daily and Sunday lunch 12.00–17.00
Regular entertainment Monday: Social
Tuesday: Karaoke (alternate with DJ Kevin)/gay and lesbian youth groups meet in The Loft (all welcome)
Wednesday: Drink promotions
Thursday: Varied cabaret (drag/strippers/etc.)
Friday–Saturday: Disco night
Sunday: Sunday lunch (booking advised but not necessary)

A busy and popular three-in-one venue. The Edge is a lively open-plan pub for a mixed gay and lesbian clientele. With pool table, gaming machines and soft furnishings. The bar can get quite cruisy over the weekends (boys and girls!), although it must be said that it is not a 'cruise bar'. The Loft is a comfortable and relaxing chill out area incorporating the restaurant, cocktail bar and snack bar. Homely furnishings and the place to chat in a quieter environment. The local youth groups (gay and lesbian) meet up here on Tuesday evenings, in order to make newcomers to the scene feel welcome. The Box is a large open-plan dance area, playing a selection of everything–from house to handbag. What makes the place so popular apart from the friendliness et al., is the fact that there is no admission charge whatsoever. The Edge complex is an exceptionally friendly venue, particularly to those who are new to the scene, who are encouraged to ask the bar staff/management for further details regarding the gay scene in Southampton. The staff are pleasant and will try to do their utmost to ensure your evening goes well.

The Magnum Club

113 St Mary's Road
Southampton
SO14 0AN   Telephone 01703 335 049

Nearest train station Southampton Central
Car parking Limited street parking (residential area–be careful of obstruction)
A–Z ref. P30/5C
Nearest landmark Fire station

Membership details Available but not necessary at £10 year/£7 NUS (identification required). The benefits are reduced or free admission

Opening hours	Monday–Thursday: 22.00–02.00
	Friday–Saturday: 21.30–03.00
	Sunday: Closed
Admission charges	Monday–Tuesday: Free
	Wednesday–Thursday: £1 Guests/members free
	Friday: £3 Guests before 23.00/£2 members before 23.00; £4 guests after/£3 members after
	Saturday: £4 Guests before 23.00/£3 members before 23.00; £5 guests after/£4 members after

Food available Light snacks available, Friday and Saturday only
Regular entertainment Monday–Tuesday: 'Pink Pounder' (cheap drinks)
Wednesday: Karaoke/drink promos
Thursday: Disco/women only
Friday: Disco/stripper–men only
Saturday: Disco

Laid out over three floors. The ground floor is the main arena, with DJ, stage and dance floor. Continuing up the stairs on your right (at reception) takes you to the chill out zone and wine bar; a quieter area in which to wind down and relax. Continuing across the landing up a further flight of stairs you will come to another dance area. The age range and clientele is decidedly mixed (lesbian and gay). This place is particularly popular with the student fraternity, especially on the cheap drink nights.

The Smuggler's Arms

114 Bernard Street
Southampton
Hampshire
SO14 3DZ   Telephone 01703 399 144

Nearest train station Southampton Central
Car parking Council car park free after 18.00/P&D before
A–Z ref. P40/2C
Nearest landmark Queensway

Membership details	None required
Opening hours	Monday–Saturday: 12.00–23.00
	Sunday: 12.00–22.30
Admission charges	None

Food available No
Regular entertainment Wednesday: Quiz night/'Last Chance Lottery'
Thursday: Karaoke (alternate Thursdays)
Friday: Disco
Saturday: Disco/'Last Chance Lottery'
Sunday: Stripper/bingo in the afternoon

Large open-plan bar room with regular discos each weekend. A friendly no-attitude and welcoming pub, with a mixed clientele of lesbian and gay and an age range across the board. Newly refurbished and cosy.

The Strand

Canal Walk
Southampton
Hampshire   Telephone 01703 630 372

Nearest train station Southampton
Car parking Side-street parking
A–Z ref. P40/2C
Nearest landmark Queensway

Membership details None required
Opening hours   Monday–Saturday: 12.00–16.00/19.00–23.00
                         Sunday: Closed
Admission charges None
Food available No

Probably Southampton's original gay pub. Friendly and welcoming, it is described as a local pub rather than a trendy bar. There is no regular scheduled entertainment; just a good place to have a drink and a chat.

The Victoria

51–53 Northam Road
Southampton
SO14 0PD   Telephone 01703 333 963/01703 225 511 (Red Ribbon)
                  Website http://www.gaysouthampton.ml.com

Nearest train station Southampton (15 minute walk)
Car parking Outside venue
A–Z ref. P30/6D
Nearest landmark Southampton Institute/Six Dials

Membership details None required
Opening hours   Monday–Thursday: 18.30–23.00
                         Friday–Saturday: 12.00–23.00
                         Sunday: 12.00–22.30
Admission charges None
Food available No (new management take-over–so subject to change)
Regular entertainment Monday: Social
Tuesday: Quiz night/bingo/etc./'Gay Bikers' is every first Tuesday
Wednesday: Social
Thursday: Social/health project group meeting (all welcome)
Friday & Sunday: Cabaret

The Victoria is a community pub and as you would expect, it caters for the entire gay spectrum. Hosts a myriad of group meetings i.e. Gay Bikers, Switchboard, Leather and Rubber, etc. For more information on any groups either call in for available literature or phone. The Vic' is also home to The Red Ribbon Centre, a drop-in centre for people affected by HIV and AIDS, with its own separate entrance and telephone line (see above). Definitely a fun pub, comprising two bars; the top one being intimate whilst the ground floor one is cruisy and social (or is that the other way around?). The good thing about community pubs is that the friendliness, welcome and overall atmosphere is genuine and they are always a good place for the newcomer to ask their questions and gain advice on the gay scene. Excellent.

The Cliff Hotel

48 Hamlet Road
Southend on Sea
Essex
SS1 1HH   Telephone 01702 344 466

Nearest train station Southend Central (five minute walk)
Car parking Ample street parking
Nearest landmark Odeon Cinema

Membership details None required
Opening hours   Monday–Saturday: 12.00–23.30
                                 Sunday: 12.00–22.30
Admission charges None
Food available No
Regular entertainment No regular scheduled entertainment

The Cliff is a mixed gay and lesbian community-based venue, which means that there is probably some sort of charity event happening each week. A traditional venue—all brass and wood, with a friendly and welcoming staff. A pool table is available and well used for the regular competitions (usually on a Thursday). The last Saturday of the month is extremely busy when the pub is used as a warm-up bar for Campus (gay disco) and the pub hosts it's own regular disco on a Sunday evening. All information on the local and surrounding gay scene, available literature and the gay press can be picked up from here.

Hellbent @ Underworld

New York Nightclub Complex
Coronation Walk
Southport   Telephone 01704 500 466 (Venue)/0151 327 2424 (infoline)   Fax
                                 0151 708 8371 (Boyz Behaving Badly)

Nearest train station Southport
Car parking Ample street parking
Nearest landmark Close to the promenade/ Prince of Wales Hotel

Membership details None required
Opening hours   Saturday: 22.00–02.00 (Weekly Saturday night only)
                                 (May be transferring over to a Friday night—contact above
                                 number for info and keep an eye on the gay press)
Admission charges £3

Hellbent @ Underworld is a weekly gay night in one of the North-West's largest seaside resorts, run and promoted by Boyz Behaving Badly. Underworld is a basement club with a capacity for 250. Drink promotions are at every event, with occasional cabaret and theme nights too. The music policy is varied, from gay classics to chart dance and stretching to a bit of the hard stuff. The free gay press is also available. *Note*: It should be noted that Boyz Behaving Badly promote a number of 'Hellbent' gay nights around the North-Wales coast, however, at the time of writing they were re-negotiating with venue proprietors in Llandudno and Rhyll and nothing concrete has been confirmed. For up to date information on these events, phone Ian on the above infoline number.

The New Inn

95 Wellington Road South
Stockport
Lancashire
SK4   Telephone 0161 480 4063

Nearest train station Stockport
Car parking Side-street parking
A–Z ref. P131/3H
Nearest landmark Town Hall

Membership details None required
Opening hours   Monday–Wednesday: 19.00–23.00
                               Thursday–Saturday: 12.00–15.00/19.00–23.00
                               Sunday: 12.00–22.30
Admission charges None
Food available No

A large relaxed and friendly gay bar, with a mixed age clientele, but in the main they are young and local. Not a clubby-type place but a local where you can go in for a quick pint and chat. Occasional entertainment in the form of karaoke and cabaret.

The Club

14 Hillcrest Street (rear of Bucknall New Road)
Hanley
Stoke-on-Trent
Staffordshire
ST1 2AA   Telephone 01782 201 829   Fax 01782 201 827

Nearest train station Stoke-on-Trent (three miles)
Car parking At rear of venue (Huntsbach Street Car Park)
A–Z ref. P34/1C
Nearest landmark Large blue footbridge on Bucknall New Road

Membership details Membership is required and is also free (complete form at venue, remembering to tick the box if you do not wish to receive mail-shots)– guests of members will be accepted
Opening hours   Monday–Tuesday: 21.30–02.00
                               Sunday: 21.00–24.30
                               (Club is open Wednesday, Friday and Saturday)
Admission charges Wednesday: Apply at venue
                               Thursday: Free
                               Friday: Apply at venue
                               Saturday: £4 members/£5 guests
Food available Light bar snacks
Regular entertainment Monday: 'Dogz Bollox' (cheap drinks)
Wednesday: DJ (Club)/cabaret alternate weeks
Thursday: Karaoke (pub)
Friday: DJ (Club)/stripper (Pub)/last Friday of the month: male and female strippers
Saturday: Club night (very busy)
Sunday: 'Karaoke in The Diamond Mine'

The Club is divided into two parts: Ruby's Diamond Mine and The Club. The Diamond Mine is adjacent The Club, with a separate entrance and is a pre-club venue in addition to hosting the early evening entertainments. The club itself is a large venue on different levels, with a huge dance floor and staging areas. With the lack of gay venues in Stoke on Trent this place gets rather busy at all times, along with The Club's sister venue, The Three Tuns (see separate listing).

The Queen and Crumpet
5 Hope Street
Hanley
Stoke-on-Trent
Staffordshire   Telephone 01782 289 925

Nearest train station Stoke-on-Trent (taxi required from here)
Car parking Ample side-street parking
A–Z ref. P34/1B
Nearest landmark Tesco

Membership details None required
Opening hours   Monday–Friday: 19.00–23.00
                     Saturday: 13.00–16.00/19.00–23.00
                     Sunday: 13.00–22.30
Admission charges None
Food available No

Popular mixed gay pub with drag DJs. One large open-plan room with discos running over the weekend and occasional cabaret. There's an organised coach to Subway City the first Saturday of the month (£7 inclusive of club entry). Phone the venue direct for further details.

The Three Tuns
9 Bucknall New Road
Hanley
Stoke-on-Trent
Staffordshire
ST1   Telephone 01782 769 293

Nearest train station Stoke on Trent (taxi required from here)
Car parking Street parking and large car park behind venue
A–Z ref. P34/1C
Nearest landmark Blue footbridge on Bucknall New Road

Membership details None required
Opening hours   Monday–Friday: 19.00–23.00
                     Saturday: 17.00–23.00
                     Sunday: 17.00–22.30
Admission charges None
Food available No

The Three Tuns is the sister venue to The Club. A large dimly lit venue, with Ruby doing the honours most nights on the decks. On Friday, Jackie Dogz (lesbian DJ) takes her turn on the decks, encouraging a more female audience into the place.

The Cricketer's Arms
14 Emlyn Square
Swindon
Wiltshire
SM1   Telephone 01793 523 780

Nearest train station Swindon
Car parking Ample street parking
A–Z ref. P11/3F
Nearest landmark Railway Museum/Brunel Market

Membership details None required
Opening hours   Monday–Friday: 19.00–23.00
                         Saturday: 12.00–16.00/19.00–23.00
                         Sunday: 12.00–16.00/19.00–22.30
Admission charges No charge at any time
Food available Full Sunday lunch 12.00–15.00 (approximately £3.50) and bar snacks available over the weekend lunch-time hours
Regular entertainment Saturday: Cabaret/'Grab a Bag' (cash jackpot)
Sunday: Cabaret evenings

The Cricketer's Arms, situated close to the British Rail station, is a lively and popular bar, with an age range that goes right across the board. Very nearly exclusively gay, with a good mix of lesbians and gays. The adjoining pool room is popular (especially with the ladies) and there are regular cheap drink promos along with happy hours between 19.00 and 21.00 each evening. See separate listing for the Cricketer's Arms sister venue London Street.

London Street
Unit 1 London Street
Railway Village
Swindon
Wiltshire
SN1   Telephone 01793 523 780 (Cricketer's Arms)

Nearest train station Swindon
Car parking Ample street parking
A–Z ref. P11/3F
Nearest landmark Railway Museum

Membership details Strictly members and bona fide guests only–membership is £15 per year and can be obtained at The Cricketer's Arms or by post to The Cricketer's Arms address (see separate listing and phone for further details)
Opening hours   Monday–Wednesday: Closed
                         Thursday–Saturday: 22.00–01.30
                         Sunday: Closed
Admission charges   Thursday: Free
                      Friday–Saturday: £2 members/£3.50 guests
Food available Bar snacks available
Regular entertainment Thursday: Second Thursday of every month: 'Dyke's Delight' (women-only night)/fourth
Thursday: 'Sleaze Pit' (Men-only night)
Saturday: Second Staurday of every month: 'Shagtagz!'

Modern, bright and vibrant. The aluminium dance floor, the stainless steel bar, the metal tables around the pillars, in contrast to the purple and blues of the decor makes this an ideal place for the trendy ones amongst you. The once-a-month bashes for the lads see the lights on the lowest setting, a male stripper cavorting around and cheap drinks to help you get in the mood. The ladies 'do' is just as good. The fact that no men are in should be reason enough to go. There is no sign outside the venue, and as everyone meets up at The Cricketers Arms, it may be best to ask at the bar for directions, or just follow the crowd. Remember, it is a members-only bar, so phone the above number for further details or enquire at the Cricketer's Arms bar.

Embassy Club

Spinning School Lane
Tamworth
Staffordshire01827 587 72 (Embassy infoline)/01827 537 92 (BJs telephone)

Nearest train station Tamworth
Car parking Three large car parks at venue
Nearest landmark Ritz Bingo Hall

Membership details None required
Opening hours   ('Legs Up Lucy')
                      Thursday: 21.00–02.00 (Every Thursday only)
Admission charges Thursday: £2.50 before 22.00
                      £3.50 after 22.00
                      (Poundsaver tickets from BJs)
Food available Light bar snacks

Popular weekly gay disco for a majority-gay crowd and few gay-friendly straights. Selective door policy, so if you experience any problem, say that you saw the listing in this guide. The evening has a fun, party atmosphere, helped along by the cheap drinks (£1 per pint of bitter, lager or cider or per glass of wine) The music is a broad mix of Hi Nrg through to club classics. Pre-club meeting place is the adjoining BJs (10.00–15.00/17.00–23.00) and discount vouchers (£1) for the club can be obtained from here free of charge either from the DJ or the bar. Through the week BJs is the only gay friendly bar in the area (well worth a visit).

The Meadfoot Inn

7 Meadfoot Lane
Torquay
Devon
TQ1 2BW   Telephone 01803 297 112
                   E-mail pbrocklehurst@btconnect.com

Nearest train station Torquay
Car parking Terrace car park/on-street in evenings
Nearest landmark Clock Tower in the harbour

Membership details None required
Opening hours   Monday–Saturday: 12.00–16.00/19.00–23.00
                      Sunday: 12.00–15.00/19.00–22.30

Admission charges None
Food available Full menu 12.00–15.00/19.00–20.30

The Meadfoot Inn is a small and friendly gay pub, whose clientele consist mainly of gay men from Torquay and the surrounding area. However, being a popular seaside resort, they also see visitors from not only other parts of the country but from all over the world. The venue has been in the same ownership for well over nine years and is completely gay-owned and staffed. Popular bar over the weekends, with a very wide age range from between 18 and 80. Although predominantly gay men, lesbians and TVs are made extremely welcome. Situated above the harbour, close to all of the gay hotels and clubs (see separate listings).

Rocky's
Rock Cottage
Rock Road
Torquay   Telephone 01803 292 279   Fax 01803 200 442

Nearest train station Torquay (one mile)
Car parking NCP 130 metres/difficult to park on street
Nearest landmark GPO Roundabout

Membership details Temporary membership required (application by post or at the venue)
Opening hours   Monday–Saturday: 21.30–02.00
                       Sunday: Closed
Admission charges £2 (Temporary membership)/£3 after 24.00
Food available Restaurant open 20.00–24.00
Regular entertainment Thursday: Karaoke
Friday–Saturday: 'Camp': Camp tunes and antics
Sunday: Disco till 23.00

A busy venue, particularly during the weekends and summer months. The venue is well laid out over four floors. The top floor, comprises a gallery bar overlooking the dance floor, going down to the dance area and disco bar. Stairs down lead to the food bar and the quieter chill out area (closed Monday to Wednesday), and further down still, in the basement, are the toilets and corridor (surprisingly busy down here!). For visitors to Torquay, free admission passes (or discounted tickets) are available from most of the gay hotels in the area (see 'Accommodation' listings). Rocky's mainly attracts the younger end of the market, although a complete age range is in evidence.

Bar Zeus (formerly The Dolphin)
6 Lower Warrengate
Wakefield
West Yorkshire
WF1 1SA   Telephone 01924 201 705

Nearest train station Wakefield Kirkgate/Westgate
Car parking Small, on-site/large car park down the road (two minutes)
A–Z ref. P33/1H
Nearest landmark Wakefield Cathedral

Membership details None
Opening hours   Monday–Saturday: 11.00–24.00
                       Sunday: 12.00–15.00/19.00–22.30

	(Dance licence till 24.00 and a drinks licence extension in progress)

Admission charges   Saturday: £1 after 21.00 (this is a charity donation rather than a door charge)

No charge at all other times

Food available From light bar snacks to full bar menu: 11.30–19.00, daily (possibly extending hours later in the year), plus full Sunday lunch: 12.00–17.00

Regular entertainment Monday: Student night (cheap drinks)

Tuesday: Drag DJ/karaoke/bingo

Wednesday: 'Wine and Dine'

Thursday: Drag DJ/top stripper/very cruisy!

Friday: Drag DJ/drag cabaret/'Northern Girls' TV and TS Night

Saturday: Drag DJ

Sunday: Sunday party night disco with DJ Jools

Large-capacity dance/cabaret pub, occupying one of the oldest public houses in Wakefield, situated on the quieter side of the city centre, at the bottom of the Cathedral precinct. The door policy is extremely liberal, believing that all people, gay and straight, male and female, able and disabled can come together to enjoy themselves. The atmosphere is local and communal, with a broad age range, background and taste every night of the week. Leather clones, students, mature lesbian couples and everyone else in between. Bar Zeus hosts a weekly Deaf Gay and Lesbian group (Sunday), with one member of the bar staff trained in sign language in order that all are made welcome. On the first Tuesday of the month, a coach link to Red Raw (Leeds) is arranged. The extensive refurbishment in the summer of 1998 gave the added benefits of a new sound and lighting system and full air-conditioning and made the venue wheelchair accessible (including the toilets). Popular with the women of Wakefield and surrounding districts on a Sunday.

The Golden Lion

41 Birchills Street
Walsall
West Midlands
WS2 8NG   Telephone 01922 610 977

Nearest train station ten minute walk
Car parking CCTV monitors at venue and roadside
A–Z ref. P33/1G
Nearest landmark Fire station

Membership details Available but not necessary (enquire at bar)
Opening hours   Monday: 20.30–24.00

Tuesday–Thursday: 20.30–02.00

Wednesday: 20.30–24.00

Friday: 19.30–02.00

Saturday: 13.00–02.00

Sunday: 13.00–24.00

Admission charges   Monday–Thursday: Free

Friday: Members free before 23.00/guests £1; members £1 after 23.00/guests £2

Saturday: £2 guests before 23.00/£3 after
Members £1 before 23.00/£2 after
Sunday: None
No admission charges to guests or members before 21.00 at
any time

Food available Hot and cold snacks
Regular entertainment No scheduled regular entertainment, however, this does not mean that there is never any. All forthcoming events are well advertised in *Boyz* or on the premises

The Golden Lion is Walsall's only gay venue (combined pub and club), with late night drinking and socialising even at the beginning of the week. On warm nights (and all through the summer) the doors to the garden are opened up and because of the interesting way the fencing has been erected, a delightful little secluded cruising area on the premises has been created (of course everyone is going to deny that it's a cruising area, and would prefer to call it a . . . erm . . . 'patio'). This enables you to walk from the club through the 'garden', through the pub and around again without having to backtrack on yourself. A very popular pub, even if it wasn't the only one in the area. Sundays are particularly busy as are any of the late night openings.

The Flag
87–89 Meadow Street
Weston-super-Mare
Somerset   Telephone 01934 635 021

Nearest train station Weston-super-Mare
Car parking Ample street parking
Nearest landmark Tesco (two minute walk)

Membership details None required
Opening hours   Monday–Saturday: 12.00–23.00
Sunday: 12.00–22.30
Admission charges None
Food available Bar snacks available
Regular entertainment Monday: Quiz night/bingo
Tuesday: Social
Friday: Karaoke (first Friday of the month)
Saturday: 'Men Only In Dungeon' (last Saturday of the month–uniform/combats/etc.)

Exclusive gay and lesbian traditional venue. All ages. All types. The last Saturday of the month event is for men only in the dungeon, although women are still welcome to use the main bar. The venue is more of a local's bar, with cheap drinks, a friendly atmosphere and a good place to unwind without the loud music.

The Amazon
72–73 Darlington Street
Wolverhampton
WV1 4LY   Telephone 01902 424 112

Nearest train station Wolverhampton (half a mile)
Car parking Back of premises
A–Z ref. P29/1G
Nearest landmark Mander House Building (large block with blue neon sign)

Membership details Available at a cost of £1 (join at door or by post) with members benefiting from reduced door entry. *Note*: If you are unable to receive post at home, then please tell the person completing the membership (your card will then be left at reception)

Opening hours	Thursday–Saturday: 22.00–02.00
	Sunday: To be announced
Admission charges	Thursday: Free to members/guests £1 (approximately)
	Friday: £3 members/£4 guests
	Saturday: £3 members/£4 guests
	Sunday: To be announced

Food available Bar snacks plus a burger van outside at rear of venue
Regular entertainment Thursday: R&B(-ish) 'Chill Zone'/students night
Friday: 70s and 80s Hi Nrg classics
Saturday: Handbag and house (very busy night)
Sunday: Watch this space

The only gay club in Wolverhampton, catering for the complete gay community. It celebrated its first birthday in February 1999. The entrance to the club is on Clarence Street (the rear of Darlington Street). Spread over two floors, the ground floor being the main dance arena with a pool room and separate chill out area. The music is nothing too heavy, just the delightful handbag, camp tunes and dance anthems that we all love. Upstairs you can play Tarzan and Jane, chasing each other in and out of all the jungle 'thingies'. The Amazon–although all are welcome–is predominantly a young club with a good half-and-half of lesbians and gays. Meet up with your friends at The Greyhound (see separate listing) prior to going to the club as that is the main pre-club party bar.

The Greyhound
14 Bond Street
Wolverhampton
West Midlands
WV2 4AS   Telephone 01902 420 916

Nearest train station Wolverhampton (ten minute walk)
Car parking Ample parking outside club in evenings (no charge)
A–Z ref. P29/2H
Nearest landmark St John's Square Church

Membership details	None required
Opening hours	Monday–Friday: 12.00–14.00/19.00–23.00
	Saturday: 19.00–23.00
	Sunday: 19.00–22.30
Admission charges	None

Food available Bar snacks available
Regular entertainment No regular scheduled cabaret, etc.

Wolverhampton's well established, 170 capacity gay venue, now in its 17th successful year. The Greyhound is a large venue with four distinct 'areas'. Busy most nights of the week, with a predominantly male clientele, the customers during lunch-times being a mix of gay and straight. The Greyhound is a pre-Amazon (see separate listing) feeder bar from Thursdays onwards. It cannot be described as a 'cruise' bar, since it consists of mainly couples and friends socialising. All in all: a welcoming venue, under the management of Steve and Kevin. Leather/bears/uniform/industrial especially welcome.

The White Hart

66 Worcester Street
Wolverhampton
WV2 4LQ   Telephone 01902 421 701

Nearest train station Wolverhampton (five minute walk)
Car parking Pitt Street, side of the pub
A–Z ref. P29/H2
Nearest landmark The Fox Hotel

Membership details None required
Opening hours   Monday–Friday: 10.00–16.00/19.00–23.00
                         Saturday: 10.00–23.00
                         Sunday: 14.00–22.30
Admission charges None
Food available Full menu at lunch-time and hot baguettes in the evenings
Regular entertainment No regular scheduled entertainment, though the occasional cabaret is well advertised in advance

The White Hart is a trendy, exclusively gay venue. Very cruisy and intimate (am I mixing my metaphors here?) and popular with the girls as well as the boys of the town. There is also a weekly coach arranged to take you to Subway City each Saturday evening with plans to extend the coach trips to other gay venues throughout the Midlands.

Goodfellows Bar

50 Lowes Moor
Worcester
WR1 2SG   Telephone 01905 724 460

Nearest train station Worcester
Car parking Side-street parking

Membership details None required
Opening hours   Monday–Saturday: 12.00–23.00
                         Sunday: 13.30–22.30
Admission charges None
Food available Bar snacks available

Popular local bar (particularly with the ladies), with regular entertainment during the week, such as discos (most weekends) and cabaret. Busy during the day and extremely busy in the evenings. Pool and darts always available.

The Steam Packet

51 Stanley Street
Workington
Cumbria
CA14 2JG   Telephone 01900 621 86

Nearest train station Workington (500 yards)
Car parking Plenty–one on-site, the other across the road
Nearest landmark The Quayside

Membership details None required
Opening hours   Monday–Friday: 12.30–17.30/19.30–23.00
                       Saturday: 12.00–23.00
                       Sunday: 12.00–22.30
Admission charges   Sunday–Friday: Free
                       Saturday: Free before 21.30/£1 after
                       (Token increase if cabaret is scheduled)
Food available Full bar snacks menu
Regular entertainment Saturday: Disco
Sunday: 'Recovery!'
Summer: BBQ parties

The Steam Packet is the only gay bar in Cumbria and will obviously be busy. The summer months particularly so, with the influx of tourists to this beautiful part of the world. The popular Saturday night disco attracts a lot of people trying to get in before 21.30, so they have an extra £1 to spend at the bar! Even though it is a friendly and welcoming gay pub, it is extremely straight-friendly, ensuring the mix is just right. Apart from the main bar area with dance floor, there is also a pool room and an additional late night snack bar open on Saturday nights (you'll need it!). Bed and Breakfast accommodation is also available (at very competitive rates), though this is usually fully booked during the summer, so an early booking is advised.

Bay Horse and Buddys Bar
54 Gillygate
York
YO3 7EO   Telephone 01904 627 679

Nearest train station York
Car parking At rear of pub (large car park)
Nearest landmark York Minster

Membership details None required
Opening hours   Monday–Saturday: 11.00–23.00
                       Sunday: 12.00–22.30
Admission charges None
Food available Lunch-times only–full menu and snacks
Regular entertainment Monday: Karaoke
Tuesday: Quiz
Wednesday: Disco (70s and 80s)
Thursday: 'Strictly Boozing'/Social
Friday: Disco and stripper
Saturday: Disco
Sunday: Drag/cabaret/disco

York's newest, predominantly gay city centre venue. Hosting a well planned entertainments policy, which doesn't include the tired old bingo and quiz nights (well . . . except on Tuesday!). Split into a lounge bar (Bay Horse) and an even larger dance bar (Buddys). On one level, the atmosphere can be either lively dance or quiet and social. A coach is in operation to Red Raw in Leeds on the first

Tuesday of every month (however, the quiz night is so popular that most people want to stay at the bar). As there are seven 'Bay Horse' pubs in York, please make sure that you go to the right one! For out-of-towners, there is bed and breakfast accommodation on site (pre-booking advised as they usually do not accept bookings after 18.00: see 'Accommodation' listings for details). *Note*: Despite what some listings state, The York Arms and The White Horse are no longer gay venues, in fact, the proprietors are reported to be quite rude to prospective guests. The Bay Horse and Buddys Bar is the only gay venue in York.

SCOTLAND

Club 2000

62 Shiprow
Aberdeen   Telephone 01224 596 999

Nearest train station Aberdeen
Car parking Ample street parking
Nearest landmark Market Street

Membership details None required
Opening hours   Monday–Saturday: 21.00–02.00
                         Sunday: Closed
Admission charges Monday–Thursday: Free
                         Friday–Saturday: £2 after 23.00
Regular entertainment Friday: Drag cabaret
Saturday: DJ

Since the closure of Castro, Club 2000 has now become Aberdeen's only gay venue. A small and intimate place with late-night drinking.

Bar 'XS'

St Andrews Lane (Behind Liberty Nightclub)
Dundee
DD1 2HB   Telephone 01382 200 660

Nearest train station Tay Bridge
Car parking Street parking
Nearest landmark Bus station

Membership details None required
Opening hours   Monday–Saturday: 20.00–24.00
                         Sunday: 20.00–23.00
Admission charges None
Food available No

Opened over two years ago to offer the gay community a plush, intimate and alternative environment. Bar 'XS' has everything to offer the discerning customer, from coffee to Cointreau. An ideal place to unwind or, should the mood take you, get psyched up for a night on the tiles. Occasional quiz nights (and bingo) are offered to keep you entertained. See Liberty Nightclub listing.

Charlies Bar (formerly Deva's)

75 Seagate
Dundee
DD1 2EH   Telephone   01382 226 840

Nearest train station Dundee (ten minute walk)
Car parking Around the corner from venue (Gellatly Street)
Nearest landmark Behind Marks and Spencers/Cathedral

Membership details None required
Opening hours   Monday–Saturday: 11.00–24.00
                                    Sunday: 12.30–22.30 (may revert back to 18.00–22.30 after
                                    trial period)
Admission charges None
Food available No

Pretty much a local, predominantly male-orientated gay bar with the obligatory pool table and video jukebox. A large bar with a separate lounge area. Due for refurbishment in 1999, so above details may change (perhaps the name will change . . . again!).

Liberty Nightclub

124 Seagate
Dundee
DD1 2HB   Telephone   01382 200 660

Nearest train station Tay Bridge
Car parking On-street parking
Nearest landmark Bus station (venue opposite)

Membership details None required
Opening hours   Monday–Tuesday: Closed
                                    Wednesday–Sunday: 23.00–02.30
                                    Bank holidays: Open till 03.30
Admission charges Wednesday–Thursday: £2
                                    Friday: £3 before 24.00/£4 after
                                    Saturday: £4 before 24.00/£5 after
                                    Sunday: £2
Food available No

Now nearly three years old, Liberty Nightclub is an established venue catering for the gay community and their friends in North-East Scotland. Karaoke on a Wednesday evening and lively friendly disco all other nights. See listing for sister pub, Bar 'XS'.

CC Blooms

23–24 Greenside Place
Edinburgh
EH1 3AA   Telephone   0131 556 9331

Nearest train station Waverley
Car parking Limited street parking
A–Z ref. P3/1G

Nearest landmark Playhouse Theatre

Membership details None required
Opening hours   Monday–Friday: 19.00–03.00
                       Saturday–Sunday: 14.00–03.00
Food available On request
Regular entertainment Monday: DJ from 22.30
Tuesday: 60s through to the 80s night
Wednesday: DJ from 23.00
Thursday: Karaoke/DJ
Friday–Saturday: DJ from 22.30
Sunday: Stripper/karaoke

Situated next to The Playhouse, CC Blooms is a large ground floor bar and basement disco. Through the week this venue can fill up nicely. The basement disco is packed at the weekend.

The Claremont Bar

133–135 East Claremont Street
Edinburgh
EH7 4JN   Telephone 0131 556 5662   Fax 0131 558 3539
                 E-mail Robin@scifipub99.freeserve.co.uk

Nearest train station Waverley
Car parking Ample street parking
A–Z ref. P15/1H
Nearest landmark Bus station

Membership details None required
Opening hours   Monday–Thursday: 11.00–12.30
                       Friday–Saturday: 11.00–01.00
                       Sunday: 12.30–24.00
Admission charges None
Food available Full menu–value for money home-cooked food (the food area is on the first floor although food can be eaten in all parts of the venue)
Regular entertainment Monday: 'Chill Out Night'
Tuesday: Social
Wednesday: Quiz: 'Liam's Bumping House Party'
Friday: Stripper (once a month)
Saturday: every first Saturday of the month: women only (whole venue)/every third of the month: Hi Nrg mixed night/last of the month: men only (whole venue) and MSC meets

The Claremont is one of the newest venues on the Edinburgh scene, describing themselves as straight-friendly. The atmosphere is friendly without the labels of gay or straight. Wednesday night has become one of the busiest nights of the week with non-stop entertainment–a cross between *Noel's House Party* and *It's A Knockout*. As it is only one of three 'Sci-Fi' pubs in the United Kingdom, the decor as you may have guessed is devoted to a massive amount of cult TV memorabilia (*Star Trek/Space 1999/Logans Run*, etc.). The venue is on two floors divided by a mezzanine in order that you can quite easily cruise around and mingle.

French Connection

87–89 Rose Street Lane North
Edinburgh
EH2 3DT   Telephone 0131 225 7651

Nearest train station Waverley (five minutes)
Car parking Castle Street (two minutes)
A–Z ref. P15/3F
Nearest landmark Albert Memorial

Membership details None required
Opening hours   Monday–Saturday: 12.00–01.00
                         Sunday: 13.00–01.00
Admission charges None
Food available No

Small, friendly family-run establishment, catering for a mixed gay and straight clientele. Friendly and lively atmosphere with karaoke during the week. Cheap bar prices and a welcome late licence.

Joy @ Wilkie House

207 The Cowgate
Edinburgh
EH1   Telephone 0131 467 2551 (infoline)
             Website (Joy) http://freespace.virgin.net/alanjoy.dj/joyhome.htm

Nearest train station Waverley
Car parking Anywhere in the city centre
A–Z ref. P15/4H
Nearest landmark Library/Law Courts

Membership details Membership is free upon application entitling you to discounted door charges and regular newsletters. Send your name, address (including postcode) and two passport photos to Joy, PO Box 13456, Edinburgh, EH6 8YA. All information is strictly confidential and is used solely for Joy-associated events (enclose SAE where possible)
Opening hours   22.00–03.00
                         Once a month event (usually fourth Saturday). *Note*: Dates may change (always call the infoline
Admission charges £6 before 23.00/£7 after (members); £8 before 23.00/£9 after (non-members)
                     (The prices may change for special nights and guest DJs)
Food available No

Joy is advertised as a gay club, aiming to provide a safe and enjoyable atmosphere for gay people and their friends. No-attitude straights are welcome and always return because of the brilliant party atmosphere. Wilkie House has two distinct dance rooms. In the back room, DJs Trendy Wendy and Sally Findlay play a mixture of cool house, club classics and school disco tunes for a bit of light relief. In the main hall, DJs Alan and Maggie Joy go for a full-on, hard, fast sound. Wilkie House is a large functional venue rather than a purpose-built club. As long as the sound and lighting system works, everyone is happy. It is a club where people can really let their hair down and no one cares. Some people get really dressed up, others don't. The atmosphere is very special, most people come here to dance and socialise rather than for posing or cruising. The music policy is hardhouse/techno and the dance floor is always packed with sweaty half-naked bodies (male and female) ... excellent! Alan Joy promotes other dance nights throughout Edinburgh and Glasgow. Keep an eye on the gay press for details. Alternatively, a membership to Joy will keep you informed of future dates. Resident DJs are all those mentioned above. A dress code that insists you wear only whatever you feel comfortable in!

Mingin' @ Studio 24

Calton Road
Edinburgh
EH1   Telephone 0131 467 2551
                 E-mail its.mingin@virgin.net
                 Website http://www.freespace.virgin.net/alanjoy.dj/mingin.htm

Nearest train station Waverley
Car parking Street parking (difficult)
A–Z ref. P15/2H
Nearest landmark St James Centre

Membership details None required
Opening hours   22.30–03.00
                       (Once a month event–*always* phone the above number to
                       confirm dates)
Admission charges £5

Hosted by Alan Joy, you can rest assured that the music will be tops, the atmosphere will be electric and the people will be stripping off before the end of the night. The original concept for Mingin' was to bring top notch DJs to Edinburgh every month. However, it soon became clear that this meant there was no consistency to the club from one month to the next. Following a new (and successful) strategy, local DJ Brian Dempster was brought in to play the first half of the night. His music starts out quite mellow but by the time he's finishing his set, he is racing along and has the crowd eating out of his hand. For the second half, Alan Joy takes over, playing a much darker, dirtier, sexier, trancier style than his usual sets at Joy (see separate listing).

Newtown Bar/Intense Cellar Bar

26B Dublin Street
Edinburgh
EH1 6NN   Telephone 0131 538 7775

Nearest train station Waverley
Car parking Street parking/local car park
A–Z ref. P15/1H
Nearest landmark National Portrait Gallery

Membership details None required
Opening hours   (Newtown Bar)
                       Monday–Thursday: 12.00–01.00
                       Friday–Saturday: 12.00–02.00
                       Sunday: 12.30–01.00

(Intense Cellar Bar)
Monday–Wednesday: Closed
Thursday: 21.00–01.00
Friday–Saturday: 21.00–02.00
Sunday: 21.00–01.00

Admission charges   None
Food available No
Regular entertainment Thursday: 'Mixed Gay Disco' in Intense Cellar Bar
Friday–Saurday: 'Men Only' in Intense Cellar Bar
Sunday: 'Mixed Gay Disco' in Intense Cellar Bar

A popular venue for a mixed gay and lesbian clientele of all ages. The evenings
see the bar extend to the basement disco (Intense) and what with the free
admission, is an ideal place for late night drinking. The basement bar used to
have a dress code of rubber and leather etc., however, the policy has now
changed and it is open to all.

Shebang @ Wilkie House

207 The Cowgate
Edinburgh
EH1   Telephone   0131 557 4656 (24 hour eventline)/0131 556 4843
                 (bookings/office)

Nearest train station Waverley
Car parking Anywhere in the city centre
A–Z ref. P15/4H
Nearest landmark Library/Law Courts

Membership details Available for discounted admission on all Taste Promotions
events but not necessary (phone for membership application)
Opening hours   Saturday (Monthly–near beginning of the month): 23.00–
                       03.00 (phone event line for further dates)
Admission charges   £8 members/£10 non-members
Food available No

Taste Productions presented its feminine side by breaking new ground in the
mixed clubbing scene with an all woman DJ line-up for the latest Saturday night
in Edinburgh. Shebang started its monthly night in March 1999, aiming at the
straight/gay mix of clubbers who have made Taste such a success on Sundays
(The Honeycombe–see separate listing). But, there is a difference–the all woman
DJ line up, every night, every month. Gail Sellars and Jaqui Morrison will be
resident with their own blend of garage, progressing to happy and hard house
for an all-in night of great dance music. Future guest DJs at Shebang will be
women who have been booked solely because of their talent. The door policy
will encourage an atmosphere where clubbers can mix in an environment free
from hassle and bad attitudes. A membership policy will also be in operation. See
further listings for Taste Productions: Taste @ The Honeycombe, Edinburgh and
Fruitfly @The Arches, Glasgow.

Stag and Turret

1–7 Montrose Terrace
Abbeyhill
Edinburgh
EH7 5DJ   Telephone 0131 478 7231

Nearest train station Waverley
Car parking Rear of venue/limited on street
A–Z ref. P15/2K
Nearest landmark Junction A1 (Regent Road) and B1350 (London Road)

Membership details None required
Opening hours   Monday–Saturday: 11.00–01.00
                         Sunday: 12.30–01.00
Admission charges   None
Food available No
Regular entertainment Wednesday: Karaoke

An old traditional bar set with a Scottish theme. Popular with the women of Edinburgh and holds a weekly women-only night in the pool room (where else?). Weekly karaoke on a Wednesday is the only regular scheduled entertainment.

Tackno @ Club Mercado

33–39 Market Street
Edinburgh
EH1   Telephone 0131 226 4224 (infoline)/0131 558 1755

Nearest train station Waverley
Car parking Local NCP/limited street parking
A–Z ref. P15/3H
Nearest landmark Waverley Station

Membership details Available, but not necessary (entitles holder to reduced admission and mailshots of future events)
Opening hours   Sunday: 23.00–04.00 (Every last Sunday of the month only)
Admission charges   £6/£4 if you dress up (?)/£3 members
                         (Subject to change in 1999)

DJ Trendy Wendy of Joy fame hosts this very crowded and mixed monthly club night. Totally funky gay night in a tacky club (what more could you want?). Checkout the leopard-skin decor (you don't see that in Terrence Conran's . . . or do you?)

Taste @ The Honeycombe

36 Blair Street
Edinburgh
EH1 1QR   Telephone 0131 557 4656 (24 hour eventline)/0131 556 4843
               (bookings/office)

Nearest train station Waverley
Car parking Limited street parking/local car park
A–Z ref. P15/3H
Nearest landmark Waverley Station

Membership details Members-only club with temporary passes available (see below)
Opening hours   Sunday: 23.00–03.00 (Sunday nights each week only)
Admission charges   £6 members/£8 guests

Long running mixed gay and straight weekly dance night. Totally buzzin' atmosphere and probably one of the best weekend nights out North of the border (unless you don't like dancing). Arrive early or expect to queue for simply a . . . g . . . e . . . s. Two discos, four DJs–one great party night. DJs Fisher and Price in the main room (hard house) and Martin Valentine and Stuart Barrie in the garage room. See further listings for Taste Productions' dance club nights: Shebang @ Wilkie House, Edinburgh and Fruitfly @ The Arches, Glasgow.

Bennetts
90 Glassford Street
Glasgow
G1 1UR   Telephone 0141 552 5761

Nearest train station Queen Street/Argyle Street
Nearest tube Buchanan Street
Car parking Outside venue and side streets (no problem)
A–Z ref. P83/4G
Nearest landmark Argyle Street Station

Membership details None required
Opening hours   Monday–Tuesday: Closed
                         Wednesday–Sunday: 23.00–03.30
Admission charges   Wednesday: £3
                         Thursday: £3.50
                         Friday: £4
                         Saturday: £6
                         Sunday: £3
Food available No–but an extensive 'menu' of nuts and crisps are available from behind the bar!
Regular entertainment Wednesday: DJ Sarah/cheap drinks
Thursday: DJ Shawn (upstairs)/DJ Annie (downstairs)/cheap drinks
Friday: DJ Karen Dunbar (upstairs)/DJ Grant Duff (downstairs)/drink promos
Friday: Every first Friday of the month: 'Girls On Top' (women only with donations at door to Women's Library)
Saturday: DJ Grant Duff (upstairs)/DJ Sarah (downstairs)/drink promos
Sunday: DJ Jon Frazer/cheap drinks

Bennetts is Glasgow's longest running gay nightclub, in operation since 1981 and still thriving. The addition of a new floor to the venue in the summer of 1998 has made Bennetts the biggest. Having had an extensive list of now-established acts (Wet Wet Wet, Sister Sledge and Take That–who?), they still continue to have weekly PAs from chart acts and up-and- coming bands. Nightly drinks promotions and the obviously popular Sunday drinks night, where all beers and spirits are only £1.25 (subject to change). All this, in addition to probably the best DJs in Scotland, i.e. Karen Dunbar, Sara Martinella, John Fraser and Grant Duff. It all combines to make Bennetts a *pure, dead brilliant* place to go. For the single person venturing to Bennetts on his own, it can prove worthwhile to stand in the passage on the way to the toilets (I've said too much as it is!).

Court Bar
69 Hutcheson Street
Glasgow
G1 1SH   Telephone 0141 552 2463

Nearest train station Queen Street
Nearest tube St Enoch Square

Car parking Ample free street parking all evening
A–Z ref. P83/4G
Nearest landmark George Square

Membership details None required
Opening hours   Monday–Saturday: 08.00–24.00
                     Sunday: 12.30–24.00
Admission charges None
Food available Breakfast 08.00–11.00/snacks available

Situated in the heart of the Merchant City and close to most of the other gay bars in Glasgow, the Court Bar is a small, friendly pub where you are guaranteed excellent service at all times. The music is predominantly 60s, 70s and 80s, played at a level that allows for conversation while you are standing in the bar or seated with your friends. The Court Bar has a breakfast licence, enabling you to roll in from the clubs on a weekday morning in order to get something hot inside of you. The complete gay press is available, as are discounted tickets to the local gay clubs.

Delmonicas

68 Virginia Street
Glasgow
G1   Telephone 0141 552 4803
                  Website http://www.pololounge.co.uk

Nearest train station Argyle Street/Queen Street
Nearest tube St Enoch
Car parking Limited street parking
A–Z ref. P83/4G
Nearest landmark Argyle Street Station

Membership details None required
Opening hours   Monday–Sunday: 12.00–24.00
Admission charges None
Food available No, but sister venue Café Latte is next door
Regular entertainment Monday: Cheap drinks–continuous happy hour
Tuesday: 'Killer Pool' competitions
Wednesday: Cocktail night (cheap cocktails)
Thursday: Quiz with rollover jackpot
Friday: DJ Andy
Saturday: DJ Tom
Sunday: Karaoke (very busy)/drinks £1.25 all day

Delmonicas is a large, modern, stylish bar, attracting a young and vibrant clientele all creating and enjoying a great atmosphere. During the day it is an ideal place to relax with a coffee, whereas the evenings can get extremely busy. The large main room has ample seating and an excellent sound system, pumping out the best in popular music. Delmonicas is a young bar, popular with the student fraternity, with an average age range of 18–25. Free passes to their sister venue The Polo Lounge are given out at the bar on Friday and Saturday after 23.00. Happy hours are between 17.00–19.00 and 21.00–22.00 (with all pints and spirits with mix £1.25). Ideally situated between Delmonicas and The Polo Lounge is Café Latte, Glasgow's only award-winning cafe, open daily from 11.00 to 24.00. Loads of special offers are available each week; i.e. Monday: two pizzas for the price of one; Tuesday: two diners eat for half-price; Wednesday: 20% off food all night; and so on. For further information call the cafe direct on 0141 553 2553.

Fruitfly @ The Arches

Midland Street
Glasgow
G1   Telephone   0131 557 4656 (eventline)/0131 556 4843 (bookings/
                       office)

Nearest train station Glasgow Central
Nearest tube St Enoch
Car parking Ample side-street parking
A–Z ref. P83/4F
Nearest landmark Railway station (the venue is in the station arches)

Membership details Available, but not necessary (membership entitles you to discounted admission and priority admission–phone for application)
Opening hours   Saturday: 23.00–04.00 (Third Saturday of the month only)
Admission charges £8 members/£10 guests
Food available No

Fruitfly is the newest night to hit Glasgow. Organised by the promoters of the popular and very successful Taste @ The Honeycombe (Edinburgh), Fruitfly takes place on the third Saturday of the month at The Arches having opened on Saturday 20th March and every third Saturday since. Based on the idea that a straight crowd loves a gay night out–hence the name Fruitfly. The door policy will encourage an atmosphere where clubbers can mix in an environment free from hassles and bad attitudes–where in clubbing terms, sexuality is not an issue. Resident DJs are Fisher and Price, Martin Valentine and Stuart Barrie with a music policy of garage through to uplifting and hard house. See other Taste listings: Shebang @ Wilkie House, Edinburgh and Taste @ The Honeycombe, Edinburgh. The Arches will also be playing host to Trade (Yep, that one) on the first Saturday of every month. Phone the venue direct for all relevant details.

The Polo Lounge

84 Wilson Street
Glasgow
G1 1UZ   Telephone 0141 553 1221
                     Website http://www.pololounge.co.uk

Nearest train station Queen St/Glasgow Central
Nearest tube Buchanan Street
Car parking On-street
A–Z ref. P83/4G
Nearest landmark City Hall/Bennetts/Candleriggs

Membership details None required
Opening hours   Monday–Thursday: 12.00–01.00
                       Friday–Sunday: 12.00–03.00
Admission charges Monday–Thursday: Free (except for special events)
                       Friday–Sunday: Free before 23.00/£5 after

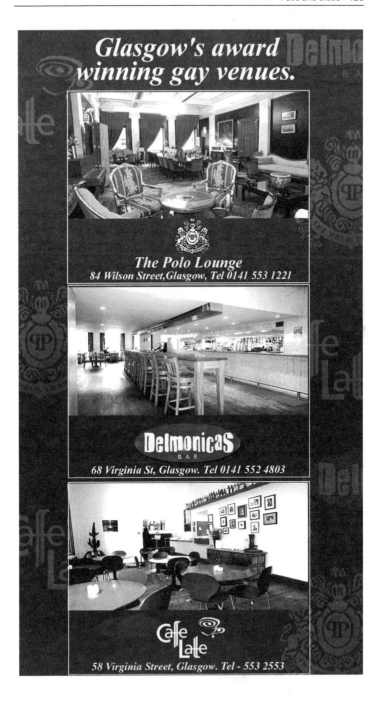

Food available No, but Café Latte in Virginia Street is a sister venue
Regular entertainment Tuesday: Pianist and guests in the Piano Lounge
Friday: 'Twisted Elegance' (indie, dance and 90s in the club room)
Camp 'Classics' in the Trophy Room
Saturday: 'Wonderland' (dance and chart in the club room)/'Fab Trash' in the
Trophy Room
Sunday: Live jazz, 16.00–18.00, in the Piano Lounge/every first Sunday of the
month:
Poptastic (Manchester's finest Indie gay club–see Poptastic, Manchester
listing); second
Sunday: 'Sanctuary' (credible sounds in the Polo Club); third Sunday: 'Vixen'
(women only in the Polo Club); fourth Sunday: 'Poor White Trash' (the best of
the worst . . .)

The Polo Lounge opened in November 1996. It comprises three bars and two
dance floors, spread over three levels and is deemed to be the largest capacity gay
bar and club in Scotland. Housed in the former headquarters of the Scottish Legal
Life Assurance Society, situated in the Merchant City area of Glasgow, the
building took over one year to rebuild, completely restoring and refurbishing all
the original marblework and tiling in addition to sourcing all of the original
antique furniture and fittings. The Polo Lounge has been voted 'Best Pub and
Club' of 1997 and 1998 by gay publication *Boyz* in addition to another leading
national newspaper describing it as being 'The most gorgeous gay bar in the
world'. The venue as a whole tends to attract a slightly cooler crowd but
endeavours to appeal to as wide a range of people as possible and to keep it
accessible to all.

Poptastic @ The Polo Lounge

84 Wilson Street
Glasgow
G1 1UZ
Opening hours   Sunday: 22.30–03.00 (First Sunday of the month only)
Admission charges   Free before 23.00/£5 after
                      (This night is extremely busy, with entry is on a first-come,
                      first-served basis and early arrival is advised)
                      For full details of Poptastic at this venue and others see the
                      listings for Poptastic @ The Mutz Nutz, Manchester. For
                      full details of The Polo Lounge, see previous listing.

Sadie Frosts

8–10 West George Street
Glasgow
G2 1DR   Telephone 0141 332 8005

Nearest train station Queen Street
Nearest tube Buchanan Street
Car parking Outside venue
A–Z ref. P83/3E
Nearest landmark George Square

Membership details None required
Opening hours   Monday–Saturday: 12.00–24.00
                      Sunday: 13.00–22.30

Admission charges   None
Food available   Full menu at lunch-times: 12.00–19.00
Regular entertainment   Monday: Chill out
Wednesday: DJ/games/quiz
Thursday: Karaoke
Friday–Saturday: DJ/disco
Sunday: DJ/karaoke/cheap drinks all day

Mixed gay and lesbian venue with a handful of 'no-attitude' gay-friendly straights. Regular happy hours every day from 17.00 to 19.00 and 21.00 to 22.00 and all day Sunday. Consisting of the main bar/disco which is lively and sociable and the Blue Room (pool and games, etc.). Sadie's tends to be more than popular with the ladies and was once the home of 'Sapphos', an exclusive women-only bar–now the women tend to meet in the main bar. Discounted tickets available to their sister venue, Bennetts (see separate listing).

W A L E S

Boar's Head
Queens Road
Aberystwyth
Dyfed
SY23 2HT   Telephone   01970 626 106

Nearest train station   Aberystwyth (five minutes)
Car parking   On-site

Membership details   None required
Opening hours   Monday–Saturday: 12.00–14.00/19.00–01.00
Sunday: Closed
Monday–Saturday: 12.00–01.00 (in-season)
Sunday: Closed
Admission charges   £2 on some nights
Food available   Full menu available lunch-times/limited menu in the evening

Lively mixed bar, especially on Friday and Saturdays when it is predominantly gay.

Atlantica Bar/Wow Nightclub
Bute Terrace
Cardiff
CF1 2FE   Telephone   01222 384 902

Nearest train station   Cardiff Central
Car parking   On-site at rear of venue
A–Z ref.   P30/4B
Nearest landmark   Cardiff International Arena

Membership details   Not necessary for admission although a membership scheme will become operational in the forthcoming year (apply at venue for further details)

Warm spacious and colourfully decorated cafe bar with cabaret venue and sister nightclub.

Hot and cold food served every day till late
Exclusive, top cabaret you won't see anywhere else
Happy hour 7 days a week 5pm till 7pm ... plus drinks promotions throughout the week
Covered beer garden featuring one of the worlds largest rainbow flags

With the friendliest and sexiest collection of definitely up-for-it boyz and girlz you'll meet anywhere.

**The best and most outrageous entertainment
7 nights a week...
hosted by Cardiff's most glamourous drag queen**

Monday   Karaoke night

Tuesday   Enter Cardiff's most outrageous Quiz night

Wednesday Join Doctor Beverly Ballcrusher, for top entertainment and drinks promotions + Miss Kitty and a male stripper in nightclub

Thursday   Gameshow hosted by Miss Kitty, party night in nightclub

Friday   Top cabaret night with Miss Kitty and Dr. Beverley Ballcrusher, Fusion with DJ's Andre and Sharon O'Love in nightclub

Saturday   Party night with Miss Kitty and Dr. Bev, dancing till late with DJ's Krys R and laon in nightclub

Sunday   Join Miss Kitty for top cabaret

**Café bar open 11am till 11pm Mon-Sat and open 11am till 10.30pm Sunday
Nightclub open 10pm till 2am Wed-Sat
Opposite the C.I.A in Bute Terrace, Cardiff. Freephone 0808 1002192**

Voted best café bar and best nightclub in the GAY WALES FAIRY awards ...
Read all about it at www.gaywales.co.uk

Opening hours   (Atlantica Café Bar)
Monday–Saturday: 12.00–23.00
Sunday: 12.00–22.30
(Wow)
Monday–Tuesday: Closed: Available for private hire
Wednesday–Saturday: 22.00–03.00
Sunday: Closed

Admission charges   (Wow)
Wednesday: £3/Students £2
Thursday: £2
Friday: £3 before 23.00/£4 after
Saturday: £5

Food available Extensive menu and snacks available

Regular entertainment (Atlantica)
Monday: 'Maim That Tune' (karaoke)
Tuesday: 'Revival' 70s-90s/quiz night
Wednesday: 'Doctor's Orders'with Dr Beverley Ballcrusher/'Fun and Games'/
cheap drinks
(very busy)
Thursday: 'Fun and Games' with Miss Kitty and Dr. Beverley
Friday: 'Weekend Begins Here' with Miss Kitty and Dr. Beverley
Saturday: 'Warm-Up in Atlantica'
Sunday: 'Cabaret Showcase'/Sunday lunch for under a fiver.
(Wow)
Monday–Tuesday: Closed
Wednesday: Stripper/cheap drinks
Thursday: 'Poptartz' with Shaggy Tags
Friday: 'Fusion' with guest DJs (upfront house)
Saturday: Themed evenings with resident DJs

The Atlantica is a very modern bar. Throughout the day it creates the perfect atmosphere for lunch-time diners and drinkers and then at 17.00 everyday, 'the pink pound(-ish) zone' starts. This sets the tone for the evening; the lights are dimmed, the lighting rig goes on and the music goes up! All drinks are cheap until 20.00 and then the entertainment starts . . . . Clientele are young, mixed lesbian and gay with a penchant for fun and nothing will stand in their way. Wow Nightclub is vibrant, young, wild, modern, stimulating, exhilarating and so on. Exclusively gay and set to become one of the largest gay venues in the country when they open a further floor and triple their capacity.

Club X

35–39 Charles Street
Cardiff   Telephone 01222 400 876
                   Website http://www.gaywales.co.uk/clubx

Nearest train station Cardiff Queen Street
Car parking Street parking and local car parks
A–Z ref. P30/4B
Nearest landmark International Arena/Cardiff Cathedral

Membership details None required
Opening hours   Wednesday: 22.00–02.00

Friday: 22.00–03.00
Saturday: 22.00–04.00
Admission charges   Wednesday: £1 students with NUS card/£2.50 all other
Friday: £2 (subject to change in 1999)
Saturday: £5
Food available New ultra-modern cafe-bar under construction and opening summer 1999
Regular entertainment Wednesday: 'Tradespotting': student night in association with Cardiff NUS/cheap drinks
Friday: 'The Ibiza Experience': top monthly foam party every first Friday of the month/'Rubbertonic': strict dress code of leather, rubber, PVC, uniform, underwear and TV every second Friday/'The Comedy Zone': top stand-up in room 1 and upliftin' house in room 2 every third Friday/and 'The World Of UV': Ultra Violet Party (see it–believe it–dress appropriately) every fourth Friday
Saturday: Top DJs playing the best in cutting edge and commercal dance/once-a-month 'Shag
Tag' disco

Club X is the largest gay club in Wales and is 100% gay with two floors, three bars and two separate dance floors catering for a mixed age '*up for it*' lesbian and gay crowd.

Exit Bar
48 Charles Street
Cardiff
CF1 4EF   Telephone 01222 640 102

Nearest train station Cardiff Queen Street
Car parking Street parking/local car parks
A–Z ref. P30/3B
Nearest landmark Queen Street Station

Membership details None required
Opening hours   Monday–Saturday: 18.00–02.00
Sunday: 18.00–24.00
Admission charges   Monday–Wednesday: £1.50
Thursday: £1
Friday–Sunday: £1.50 (£2 after 23.00 Friday–Saturday)

Popular gay bar and club situated on the main gay street in Cardiff, attracting a positively young mixed gay crowd.

Kings Cross
Mill Lane
The Hayes (Cardiff's Cafe Quarter)
Cardiff
CF1 1FF   Telephone 01222 649 891

Nearest train station Cardiff Central (three minutes)
Car parking Opposite venue
A–Z ref. P30/4A
Nearest landmark Marriots Hotel (opposite)

Membership details None required

Opening hours	Monday–Thursday: 11.00–23.00
	Friday–Saturday: 11.00–24.30
	Sunday: 12.00–22.30

Admission charges None
Food available Full menu available lunch-times and evenings until 19.00

Kings Cross is the oldest establishment on Cardiff's gay scene, which has recently undergone a half-million pound face-lift. It has still retained its down to earth atmosphere and is still the choice of the younger end of the market. At the time of going to print I was informed of a management change and that details regarding the venue may be changing.

The Park @ Talardy Park Hotel

St Asaph
North Wales   Telephone 01745 584 957

Nearest train station Rhyll or Prestatyn (transport required from here)
Car parking On-site
Nearest landmark St Asaph Junction off A55

Membership details None required
Opening hours   Saturday: 21.00–02.00 (Every other Saturday only–phone
                      for next date)
Admission charges £4

Gay disco every other Saturday. Situated in the large purpose-built function room at the rear of Talardy Park Hotel. Due to the limited number of gay venues in this part of the country, this bi-monthly event does get quite busy with a mixed gay, fun-loving crowd.

Café Klone

63–64 High Street
Swansea
SA1 1LN   Telephone 01792 413 355

Nearest train station Swansea
Car parking Own car park at rear
A–Z ref. P43/2G
Nearest landmark Cardiff Railway Station

Membership details None required
Opening hours   Monday–Saturday: 11.00–02.00
                      Sunday: 12.00–01.00
Admission charges None
Food available Top-notch home-cooked food. Baguettes baked on the premises with a choice of over 30 fillings (£1.20) and served from 11.00–19.00

Café Klone is the newest mixed gay cafe-bar to add to Swansea's limited scene. It is a young trendy, cosmopolitan and up-market venue. As the evening progresses, the music gets louder and the cafe-bar transforms into more of a club.

Weekly entertainment consists of a resident DJ most nights, cabaret on Wednesday and a stripper on Friday (that's the up-market bit!). Dress code is smart-casual, with no blue denim or track suits. Smart trainers acceptable.

The Waterside/H2O

18 Anchor Court
Victoria Quay
The Marina
Swansea   Telephone 01792 648 555
                 E-mail gaywaterside@compuserve.com
                 Website http://www.gaywales.co.uk

Nearest train station Swansea (not close to venue)
Car parking Ample side-street parking
A–Z ref. P43/4G
Nearest landmark Leisure Centre (venue behind)/follow signs for Maritime Industrial Museum

Membership details None required
Opening hours   (Waterside)
                     Monday–Saturday: 12.00–23.00
                     Sunday: 12.00–22.30
                     (H2O)
                     Monday–Tuesday: Closed
                     Wednesday–Saturday: 22.00–02.00
Admission charges (H2O)
                     Wednesday: Free
                     Thursday: £2
                     Friday–Saturday: £3
Food available Full menu available 12.00–18.00 (separate restaurant)

Swansea's gay scene was seriously flagging and in dire need of rejuvenation. Now, thanks to Bass they have two new trendy venues, The Waterside/H2O and Café Klone (see separate listing). The Waterside, takes up the ground floor of this three-storey venue and is a trendy young bar, decked out in freedom colours, including a wall with the freedom flag compiled out of coloured fluorescent tubes, to ensure that straights know that it is no longer a hetro establishment. The second floor will become the comfortable chill out zone with restaurant and the third floor is H2O a 650 capacity club (the entire building has a capacity for 1,300 people). It is an exclusively gay venue, with gay men, lesbians, bis and TVs/TSs welcome. It has to be noted that it is a strict drugs-free zone (including poppers)–so be warned.

the ultimate guide to
Saunas

Introduction

Gay saunas are similar to cruising grounds in two respects. You go there to have sex, and you go there to have sex with no strings attached. The difference with a sauna, compared to a cruising ground is the fact that there is no risk element. Gone are the 'is he or isn't he?' doubts that you may have been thinking on Hampstead Heath or some such place. It's definite. He is. This makes for a relaxing evening and you can enjoy a bit of ... erm, relaxation, without the fear of being caught or, of approaching someone who you think 'is' but turns out, 'isn't'.

Saunas, I believe are very much underrated. They are not used as often as they should be and it is all down to the fact that there are far too many misnomers. The people who tend to knock them have either, a) never been to a sauna in their lives. Or, b) they have been once and perhaps on a quiet night. Even the most popular club has an off night, but it never stops you from returning.

You may see signs posted up in some saunas stating that 'sexual advances to other people will not be tolerated'. Yeah right! Everyone knows that 'it' goes on and if 'it' didn't go on then the place would be empty. Don't make the mistake of sitting there twiddling your thumbs. I'm sure the police would rather 'it' went on in saunas than on cruising grounds.

With the danger of homophobic attacks happening in notorious cruising grounds, the only safe options would either be not to go out at all, or, to frequent your local sauna. The second option seems to me the best bet and they seem to be attracting the usual cruising circuit crowd. You could also make an exceptionally good evening for yourself by starting off at the sauna, obtaining a pass-out after you have 'relaxed', going to the pubs and clubs and then finishing off at the sauna again. All without any risk whatsoever.

If you have never been to a sauna before, you may be feeling a great deal of trepidation as to what actually goes on. It's no mystery, and once you have been, there is going to be no doubt at all that you *will* return. The following is a list of 10 things you didn't know about gay saunas:

1. It is very rare for a gay sauna to be raided by the police. I am sure undercover police are at times present in saunas (either working, or not, if you know what I mean) so are undercover journalists (!) and undercover judges.
2. The size of the towel you are given upon entry is larger than a face cloth. In fact it is bath towel size. It is true that some places will charge you for a dry towel in exchange for your wet towel.
3. Gay saunas are not full of fat, sad, lonely, ugly people. On the contrary, you will find that the people who are not present on the gay pub and club scene usually use the sauna scene as an outlet for their activities. Perhaps it is because they are married or, they might be concerned that they would be recognised in a gay pub/club.
4. It is not expected that you take part in group sex in a dark room or other place (of course, you do have the option of joining in if you want to).
5. If you do look under 18 years of age you will be expected to show proven identification.
6. It is extremely unlikely that there will be a hidden camera filming your exploits.
7. Private rest rooms are not necessarily there for resting privately!
8. A considerable amount of straight-ish clubbers pop into the sauna after their mates have gone home on a Saturday night.
9. The shower area is a good place to pick up a bit of trade.
10. It is not true that 50p coins are superglued to the floor.

There are rules which apply to most, if not all, saunas. For example, alcohol is never served or indeed available (you may be able to purchase a glass of wine with a meal but that will be all). Smoking will not be permitted in any area except in a designated room. You will not be allowed to take drinks, cans or food into wet areas.

Picking up in a sauna is easy peasy. A look, smile, wink, a 'follow me' signal, 'accidentally' having your foot or arm 'touched' whilst you are sitting next to someone in the sauna cabin or steam room, . . . the list goes on. However, if you are *not* interested then make it known and move away. There should be no embarrassment if you get the 'knock back', like cruising grounds, move on and try with someone else. Don't harass the person who said 'no'and you certainly shouldn't be offended if you get the knock back. It happens everywhere and it is a fact of life that no matter how beautiful you are there is always someone who may be after a different 'type'.

Gay saunas, for some reason, are usually situated in residential areas. It is worth ensuring, after arriving and then parking, that your car is not blocking someone's drive, doorway or other place that will cause concern to the local residents. I would strongly recommend that you actually park away from the sauna and walk the short distance to the premises.

Additionally, it should be made clear that gay saunas have all the facilities of a health club and that sex should not necessarily be the purpose of your visit. The use of a gay sauna enables the pink pound to stay in the pink coffers and you are able to relax more fully than you would using a straight establishment.

Licensed and regulated saunas are the 'safest' kind of saunas to visit. It may at first seem strange that you have to offer your correct name and address but this is for your own protection. The form that you (usually) complete will specifically ensure that you know the sauna is for gay men, and that you are aware of the rules and regulations of the sauna.

Once you have completed, and read the rules on the form and your positive identification (driving licence, passport, etc.,) has been checked, then a membership card will be produced using a code from your details. Your application form will then be destroyed in front of you. This is only done once and should remove any concern (particularly for married men) that your name and address will be held on some sort of retrieval system in a gay venue.

The other benefits are that licensed and regulated saunas do have to apply to strict health, safety and fire regulations (again for your own safety). The biggest benefit is that licensed saunas do not get raided by the police, and they are more open with their 'facilities'.

All in all, the sauna is another venue in the gay inventory not used as often as it should be, probably because there are too many scare stories going around as to what has happened to a friend of a friend ... If you like no-strings fun then use the sauna along with limited use of the cruising grounds, add a little pub and club scene (just to socialise) and you will have everything that you could possibly wish for.

British Sauna Listings

LONDON

Aquarius Sauna

14 Gleneagle Road
Streatham
London
SW16 6AB   Telephone 0181 769 6998

Nearest train station Streatham BR Thameslink
Nearest tube None
Car parking Plenty off-street parking
A–Z ref. P109/5H
Nearest landmark Safeways/Ice Rink

Membership details None required
Opening hours   Monday–Thursday: 12.00–24.00
                         Friday: 12.00–08.00 (all night)
                         Saturday: 08.00–08.00 (continuous)
                         Sunday: 08.00–24.00
Admission charges   £6 before 15.00/£10 any other time
                         Concessions available (UB40/NUS: positive identification
                         required)
                         Mondays only: two for the price of one
Food available Light snacks and refreshments. Complimentary squash
Facilities Ground floor: Wet area, sauna cabin, large steam room. First floor: TV
lounge and snack bar. Second floor: two large communal rest areas (one dim
and one dark). Third floor: Communal rest room and video lounge (subtly lit).

Chariots Roman Spa

Chariots House
Fairchild Street
London
EC2A 3NS   Telephone 0171 247 5333
                  Website http://www.gayuk.cc

Nearest train station Liverpool Street
Nearest tube Liverpool Street
Car parking Limited at venue/on-street after 18.00
A–Z ref. P62/4E
Nearest landmark Majestic Wine Warehouse

Membership details None required
Opening hours   Sunday–Thursday: 12.00–24.00

CHARIOTS I

Chariots Spa & Bar, Chariots House
Fairchild Street London EC2A 3NS 0171-247 5333

England's BIGGEST and FRIENDLIEST Sauna
20,000 sq. feet of Hedonistic decadent Roman Decor! This really is the finest
club of its kind plus a fabulous bar/restaurant & beer garden

2 x 30-man steam rooms	2 x 20-man sauna cabins	Fabulous heated pool
A host of private rooms	2 large hot bubbly Jacuzzis	Large fully-equipped gym
Genuine qualified massage	Huge screen TV with lounge	Complimentary tea & fruit juice bar
High powered sunbeds	300 locker changing room	Complimentary towels & toiletries

Opening Times   Fri & Sat: 12noon - 9am (all night)

Mon to Thurs: 12noon - midnight   Sun: 12noon - midnight+

CHARIOTS II

Open 7 days a week
Mon-Thurs: 12 noon till 12 midnight
Weekends: Fri 12 noon till Sun midnight
Admission £10

Winter Warmers: £5 b4 4pm Mon-Thurs
Sundays: The Chill Out Party,
24 hours of Chill out music & fun
Tuesday: BARE, For big boyz & bear cubs

(rear of) 292 Streatham High Rd. SW16
T: 0181 696 0929

CHARIOTS III

FARRINGDON   Directly opposite Farringdon tube station

**visit us at
www.gayuk.cc**

Large Sauna ★ Large Steam Room ★ Rest Rooms
FREE Refreshments (complimentary Tea & Fruit Juice Bar)
Snack Bar ★ TV Lounge ★ High Powered Sun Shower
Complimentary Towel & Toiletries
Open 7 days a week Mon-Thurs10am to 10pm
Weekend Friday - Saturday
10am to 9am (All night)
Sunday 10am to 10pm

57 COWCROSS STREET LONDON EC1   T: 0171 251 5553

Friday–Staurday: 12.00–09.00 (all night)

Admission charges   £12 at all times

Concessions available (NUS/UB40: photo identification required)

Food available   Snack bar. Free refreshments at the coffee bar (tea, coffee and cold drinks)

Facilities   Ground floor: Reception area. A door on the right leads to the huge changing rooms (with 300 lockers), shower room, toilets and vanity area (complimentary hair gel and body moisturiser). Follow the changing rooms through to the extremely well-equipped gym; pass the mirrors (the lighting is definitely not flattering so, unless you want a complex on how you look to others, don't look at yourself) to the stairwell. Straight ahead, up the first few steps, an entrance leads to a series of small private rest rooms. Continuing up the stairs takes you to the . . . First floor: Where lies the main wet area dominated by a swimming pool (at body temperature) with ample seating all around. The room to your left is the (large screen) TV and video room; the entrance to your right leads you past a small Jacuzzi to the saunas and steam rooms (two of each). At the end of the passageway are the showers and toilets. Follow the passage around and you will be back in the main wet area. The coffee bar (serving complimentary drinks), cigarette vending machine, water cooler and an additional small Jacuzzi are situated at this top end. The stairwell next to the coffee bar will lead you back down to the reception entrance (by the coke machine – that's cola, not the other!) and return you to the changing rooms. If you continue up the stairs past the wet area, you will be led to another series of private rest rooms, there is no through passage so you will have to return the way you came up. This passage is notoriously busy, with more action in the passage than in the rest rooms.

Smoking is allowed anywhere throughout the complex except in the passageway, housing the sauna and steam rooms. Additional dry towels are available at the reception. Free phone taxi service is available at the public pay phone situated by the reception side entrance. See listing for Chariots' sister venues 'Chariots 2' (Streatham) and 'Chariots 3' (Farringdon). Checkout the Chariots Bar which is attached to the sauna.

Chariots 2

(Rear of) 292 Streatham High Road
Streatham
London
SW16   Telephone   0171 247 5333 (Main info line)/0181 696 0929 (venue)
               Website   http://www.gayuk.cc

Nearest train station   Streatham
Nearest tube   None
Car parking   Ample street parking
A–Z ref.   P109/4J
Nearest landmark   The Manor Arms pub (opposite)

Membership details   None required
Opening hours   Monday–Thursday: 12.00–24.00
                          Friday–Sunday: 12.00–24.00 Sunday (continuous 72 hours!)

Admission charges Monday–Thursday: £5 before 16.00

Friday–Sunday: £10 at all times

Food available Free refreshments. Snacks available too

Facilities 150-locker changing room, two saunas, luxury steam room, two Jacuzzis, TV lounge (smoking), (the all-important) private rest rooms and high powered sunbed too.

The second of the 'Chariots' empire, comprising 8,000 square feet of 'Roman Splendour'. Every Tuesday is Bears Night. Every Saturday there is a chill out party (midnight Saturday until midnight Sunday).Wednesday is 'Naturist Night'. Towels are not necessary although you will not look out of place if you choose to wear one. Checkout the website and listings for Chariots 1 (Fairchild Street) and Chariots 3 (Farringdon).

Chariots 3

57 Cowcross Street

Farringdon

London

EC1   Telephone 0171 247 5333 (Main info line)/0171 251 5553 (venue)

Website http://www.gayuk.cc

Nearest train station Farringdon

Nearest tube Farringdon

Car parking Limited street parking

A–Z ref. P62/5B

Nearest landmark Farringdon Tube (opposite)

Membership details None required

Opening hours   Sunday–Thursday: 11.00–23.00

Friday–Saturday: 11.00–09.00 (all night)

Admission charges £12 at all times

Food available Free refreshments. Snacks available

Facilities Extremely large sauna, large Turkish steam room, relaxing TV lounge and bar area (smoking), luxury changing rooms and showers and high powered fast-tan unit

Chariots 3, or Chariots Farringdon as it is known, is the latest sauna to be included on the growing list of Chariot acquisitions. Perfectly situated close to Trade; you will be in no doubt whatsoever as to the type of person who may frequent this place (phwoor!). 4,000 square feet of sheer opulence (. . . their words) the venue boasts great facilities. Unfortunately, on this venue there was no mention of 'rest' facilities, however, if the venue bears any resemblance to Chariots 1 and 2, there should be no doubt that rest rooms are available. It is ideally situated opposite Farringdon tube and BR lines, making it a perfect 'stop' for city workers during the day and clubbers in the evening.

Covent Garden Health Spa

29 Endell Street

Covent Garden

London

WC2H 9BA   Telephone 0171 836 2236

Nearest train station Charing Cross

Nearest tube Covent Garden

Car parking 24 hour multi-storey car park on Shelton Street/Drury Lane
A–Z ref. P61/6J

Membership details	None required
Opening hours	Monday–Sunday: 11.00–23.00
	(every second Saturday of the month, 23.00–03.30, is women only: see below)
Admission charges	£13.50
	50% discount for NUS/UB40 card holders (identification required)

Food available Hot and cold food. Light snacks and refreshments
Facilities Includes large sauna cabin, solarium, huge Jacuzzi, steam room and even a barber shop where manicures and pedicures can be gained. The only sauna in the UK to be granted a drinks license.

A luxurious sauna set in the heart of London. 'Flirt' is a women-only night operating every second Saturday of the month from 23.00 to 03.30 (phone for prices and up to date details). Unfortunately, for some reason, this sauna was 'unable' to furnish me with complete details regarding the layout of the venue. It is advisable to phone them with any further questions that you may have.

The Health Club
800 Lea Bridge Road
Walthamstow
London
E17   Telephone 0181 556 8082

Nearest train station Walthamstow Central (ten minute walk)
Nearest tube Walthamstow Central
Car parking Around venue
A–Z ref. P32/5E
Nearest landmark Bakers Arms (straight pub) on corner

Membership details	None required
Opening hours	Monday–Sunday: 13.00–24.00
Admission charges	£10 – stay as long as you like
	Concessions available (UB40/NUS) positive identification required

Food available Snacks and refreshments available
Facilities Ground floor: Discreet entry, reception, steam room, Jacuzzi and sauna cabin. First floor: Communal and private rest areas.
3,000 square feet of leisure and pleasure spread out over two floors.

HPS 156 (Holland Park Sauna)
156 Shepherd's Bush Centre
London
W12 8PP   Telephone 0181 743 3264

Nearest train station Shepherd's Bush
Nearest tube Shepherd's Bush

Car parking Extremely limited, though NCP close by
A–Z ref. P75/2F
Nearest landmark Boots, in the Shopping Centre

Membership details None required
Opening hours   Monday–Sunday: 11.30–23.30
Admission charges   £12
                       £ 9 concessions (UB40/NUS/etc., positive identification
                       required)
                       £5 sunbed per half-hour
Food available Light snacks available
Facilities Ground floor: Reception area, snack bar serving simple sandwiches, hot and cold drinks, changing rooms, seating areas, solarium and toilet facilities. Mezzanine floor: Large communal rest room, approximately eight private rest rooms and TV room (non-smoking). Basement: two shower areas, Jacuzzi, cold plunge pool, large steam room, gymnasium (moderately equipped), two sauna cabins (one large, one small), massage parlour and dark room.

Conveniently situated inside Shepherd's Bush Shopping/Concord Centre, just opposite the Shepherd's Bush tube station. A few doors down from Argos and opposite Iceland and Boots. The entrance is discreet with 'HPS 156' painted on both sides of the glass doors. Popular with both a gay and bi clientele. The venue is clean and welcoming. Staff are friendly and bi(lingual). So, while the missus is doing the weekly shop around Sainsburys, why not pop in here for a bit? Holland Park sauna has been established for over 18 years, and is probably one of London's biggest sauna complexes.

The Locker Room
8 Cleaver Street
Kennington
London
SE11   Telephone 0171 582 6288

Nearest train station Waterloo
Nearest tube Kennington
Car parking Meters (extremely limited in evening)
A–Z ref. P78/5A

Membership details None required
Opening hours   Monday–Thursday: 11.00–24.00
                       Friday–Saturday: 11.00–04.00
                       Sunday: 11.00–24.00
Admission charges   £10/£6 before 13.00
                       £7 concessions for UB40/NUS/under 25s (identification
                       required)/£6 before 13.00
                       Two guys share a locker after 20.00: pay one admission
Facilities Includes steam room, sauna cabin, luxury lounge, relaxation rooms, video room.

Situated close to Waterloo station, at the junction of Kennington Lane and Kennington Road, this attitude-free compact sauna is situated on two flooors. Apologies for the lack of descriptive information on this venue.

Pacific 33

33 Hornsey Road
Holloway
London
N7   Telephone 0171 609 8133/0171 609 8011

Nearest train station Finsbury Park/Drayton Park
Nearest tube Holloway Road (one minute)
Car parking Easier after 18.30; limited street parking prior
A–Z ref. P46/4A
Nearest landmark Holloway Road Tube Station

Membership details None required
Opening hours   Monday–Thursday: 11.00–23.00
                       Friday–Saturday: Open from Friday 11.00 continuously,
                       through to Sunday 23.00
Admission charges   £10
                       Concessions (UB40/NUS): Monday–Friday only (positive
                       identification required)
Food available Free light snacks and refreshments. Tea, coffee and cold drinks
Facilities Ground floor: From the reception there is the TV lounge (smoking),
the bar area where all of the refreshments are laid out (all free). Changing rooms
and two sets of toilets. Continuing through you will come to the wet area
comprising of a large sauna, showers and large steam room. Down the corridor
are the communal relaxation rooms. The first one being dimly lit and the

Twenty years' tradition of warm
and friendly atmosphere for all ages

Bright 'n' Beautiful Sauna Club

9 St. Margaret's Place   T **01273 328330**
Brighton Sussex BN1 2FD   F **01273 385793**

Right in the heart of Brighton Near Churchill Square

NORTH LONDON
Steam Sauna   **PACIFIC 33**

ADMISSION £10   Monday to Thursday open 11am-11pm

ALL WEEKEND   Less than one minute from Holloway Road tube,
                         2 stops from Kings Cross
from Friday 11am   Very near to North London University
through to Sunday 11pm   UB40 & Student conc. Mon-Fri
                         pacific033@hotmail.com

33 Hornsey Road N7   ☎ 0171 609 8133   0171 609 8011

second absolutely black (I guess it's so that you will not be disturbed by the light whilst you are trying to relax!).

This venue may be small in comparison to other well-known establishments throughout London, but as we all know, size isn't everything. The friendliness and hospitality, particularly to newcomers to the sauna scene, more than makes up for it. Testament to this is that people return time and time again. A particularly busy little sauna situated close to North London University (and all the students!) with plenty of darkened cruising areas around the venue. All in all, a venue worth visiting if you want no attitude and a carefree and friendly time. You will return!

Pleasuredrome Central

125 Alaska Street
Waterloo
London
SE1 8XE   Telephone 0171 633 9194
                        Website http://www.pleasuredrome.co.uk

Nearest train station Waterloo
Nearest tube Waterloo
Car parking Extremely limited
A–Z ref. P78/1A
Nearest landmark Waterloo Station

Membership details None required
Opening hours   24 hours every day of the year – including Christmas and
                        New Year
Admission charges   £10 All facilities
                        £4 Sunbed
Food available Only self-service complimentary refreshments, biscuits and fruit
Facilities Ground floor: Reception leads through to the changing rooms. You are given two towels, additional dry towels are available at a charge of around 50p. The vanity area offers a complete range of complimentary toiletries, shaving equipment, hair preps, etc. To your right (from reception) is the wet area passageway housing the first sauna cabin and a single shower room opposite. Go through the shower 'tunnel' to an open area with seating. This is situated next to the second sauna cabin. Continuing through the passageway will take you to an amply sized, subtly lit, steam room. Return back to the changing rooms and make your way up the metal stairway to . . . the first floor, which is one huge communal relaxation area, combining rest beds along one side of the wall, and cafe seating along the other. Complete range of the free gay press is available. The addition of 11 private rest rooms and an additional steam room have added to the quality of this popular place and more rest rooms are planned for the future.

Smoking is not allowed anywhere on the premises except for the area in the changing rooms by the reception. Situated (literally) within the arches supporting the train lines of Waterloo. Every now and again you can hear the 'whoosh' of the train going by. Taxi service is available by booking at reception, alternatively, there is a pay phone in the changing room to make your own arrangements. There is a sign on the wall by the sauna stating that public sex in Great Britain is illegal, etc. (yawn!) but this is obviously ignored. Don't fall into the trap of sitting around thinking that no one is going to break the law.

Pleasuredrome North

278 Caledonian road
London
N1   Telephone 01761 607 0063
                         Website http://www.pleasuredrome.co.uk

Nearest train station Kings Cross
Nearest tube Kings Cross
Car parking Extremely limited
A–Z ref. P61/2J
Nearest landmark Swimming pool on Caledonian Road (walking distance)

Membership details None required
Opening hours   Monday–Thursday: 12.00–04.00
                       Friday: 12.00–08.00 (all night)
                       Saturday: 08.00–08.00 (all night)
                       Sunday: 08.00–04.00
Admission charges   £8 at all times
                       £6 UB40/NUS (proof required)
                       Free re-entry on same day
                       Free entry to Pleasuredrome Central between 23.00 and
                       06.00 on the same day (ask for token)
                       Pleasurecard benefits (ask for details)
Food available No, but complimentary refreshments available
Facilities Changing area, refreshment and TV lounge, large three-room sauna (hot to warm), plunge pool and showers, communal rest areas, large steam room and further rest areas

A smaller venue than its sister sauna at Waterloo, though the same friendly welcome applies. This is a busy little place, popular with students and clubbers from nearby Central Station. Well laid out and air-conditioned over two levels. Smoking is allowed upstairs but not downstairs. Pleasurecard benefits include discounted admission to either of the saunas in addition to discounts on various other venues and items. The card is free although you do have to complete an application form.

Sailors Sauna

574 Commercial Road
London
E14 7JD   Telephone 0171 791 2808

Nearest train station DLR/Limehouse (sauna is situated next to the station)
Nearest tube Bank, then 2 stops on DLR
Car parking Side-streets free after 17.30(-ish)
A–Z ref. P64/6A
Nearest landmark The Railway Tavern pub

Membership details None required
Opening hours   Monday–Tuesday: 12.00–24.00
                       Wednesday: 12.00–06.00 (all night)

Thursday: 12.00–24.00
Friday: 12.00-Sunday: 24.00 (continuous)
Admission charges   £10
Monday–Thursday: 12.00–14.00: £5
Wednesday only: £5 after 24.00

Food available   Hot and cold snacks. Light refreshments

Facilities   Cellar: Video lounge (non-smoking), closet rooms (make of that what you will) and large communal and private rest rooms. Spacious locker room too. Ground floor: Cinema TV lounge showing the latest blockbuster films (not ballbuster films!), second TV lounge, snack bar (smoking), arcade games, additional locker space, toilets and showers and the new 14 foot combined Jacuzzi and pool. This is the smoking floor. First floor: Sunbed (high powered), large sauna and steam room. High powered 'His and His' showers (you will know what I mean when you see them), a large darkened communal rest area and 11 private rest rooms, two of which have . . . erm . . . ventilation grills! Second floor: Secluded roof garden and seating areas.

A superb luxurious sauna, celebrating its second birthday in August 1999, set out on four floors, occupying three buildings on Commercial Road. The whole of the first floor is dedicated to 11 private rest rooms, cruising area and one large communal rest room. Despite the immense refurbishment programme and expansion of the premises, Sailors has not increased any of its prices. In fact, the early hour daytime rate has been lowered. The venue is situated close to The White Swan (see 'Pub and Club' listings). So try and get a pass-out between shags so that you can have a pint (to wash your mouth out!).

LONDON'S PREMIER SAUNA

574 Commercial Road
E14 7JD

☎

0171 791 2808

Outlines   from Absolute press

A delightful collection of monographs detailing the loves and lives of some of the most prolific gay and lesbian creative artists of this century.

Titles in the series:
David Hockney
Benjamin Britten
Bessie Smith
We are Michael Field
Federico Garcia Lorca
Arthur Rimbaud
k.d. lang
Armistead Maupain
Tallulah Bankhead

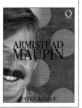

Star Steam Sauna

38 Lavender Hill
Battersea
London
SW11 5RL   Telephone 0171 924 2269

Nearest train station Clapham Junction BR (Victoria, three minutes)
Nearest tube Clapham Junction (10–15 minute walk)
Car parking Street parking
A–Z ref. P92/4C
Nearest landmark Clapham Common (north side)

Membership details None required
Opening hours   Monday–Sunday: 11.00–24.00
Admission charges   £11
                      £7.50 concessions (UB40/NUS: positive identification
                      required)
Food available Complimentary hot and cold drinks, biscuits, etc.
Facilities Ground floor: Reception area leads through to the changing rooms
and solarium. Refreshment area situated here. The summer months sees the sun
terrace open, decked with sun loungers. Where better to top up your tan than
in South–West London? Lower ground floor: Additional locker space, two
shower areas, TV Lounge (smoking) steam room, sauna cabin and six private
rest rooms.

Established for well over 16 years. Star Steam Sauna is in the infamous district of
Clapham within walking distance of the notorious common. Don't get waylaid
by strangers, make your way directly to the sauna. Here you will find everything
quite sufficient for your needs. There have been lots of good reports from various
quarters regarding Star Steam. The main ones being that although it is a compact
little sauna it is very nearly always busy with a good bunch of guys, none of
whom are willing just to sit around looking pretty. The addition of the new
'lockable' private rest rooms add to the quality of the venue.

Steaming @ 309

309 New Cross Road
London
SE14 6AS   Telephone 0181 694 0606/0181 694 0316

Nearest train station Charing Cross
Nearest tube Charing Cross/New Cross Gate
Car parking Very limited although side-street parking may be found
A–Z ref. P79/7J
Nearest landmark New Cross Gate tube station (one minute walk from here)

Membership details None required
Opening hours   Monday–Thursday: 11.00–23.00
                      Friday–Sunday: 11.00–23.00 Sunday (continuously)
Admission charges   £10
                      Concessions Monday–Friday only (NUS/UB40:
                      identification required)
                      £5 under 25s (positive identification required)
Food available Free refreshments

Facilities Ground floor: From the reception you carry on through to the changing rooms and the two sets of toilets. Basement: The wet area, consisting of two sets of showers, two 20-man steam rooms and one 20-man sauna cabin. Continuing through will lead you to the darkened TV room and the ever so dark communal rest room.

Small, intimate sauna easily accessible by tube. Situated next to Goldsmiths Art College (students!), the clientele are a young amiable crowd.

ENGLAND

Greenhouse Health Club

56 Sheffield Road
Barnsley
Yorkshire
S70 1HS   Telephone 01226 731 305
               Website http://www.gay-sauna.com

Nearest train station Barnsley
Car parking Backstreet parking (quite safe)
A–Z ref. P23/1H
Nearest landmark Alhambra Centre (100 yards)

Membership details £1 on first visit – no personal details expected except first name. Membership card with number issued
Opening hours   Monday–Thursday: 11.00–23.00
                      Friday–Saturday: 11.00–02.00
                      Sunday: 12.00–23.00
Admission charges £9
Food available Hot and cold snacks, refreshments
Facilities Ground floor: Reception, through to changing rooms, refreshment bar, diner, TV lounge (smoking), sauna, showers, sunbed room and toilets. Basement: Communal darkrooms (rest areas), Jacuzzi, steam room, toilets and showers. First floor: Communal and private rest rooms.

As with all Greenhouse venues you can expect the staff to be friendly and welcoming. You can also expect the facilities to be top class, not too posh, but just right. Emphasis is placed on 'relaxation' and the facilities here are no exception. Well laid out over three floors, with stairs either end of the building which means that you can quite comfortably cruise around to your heart's content. 'Bears Night' is every second Saturday of the month. This is not an exclusive night and you will not be excluded admission if you are not big and bulky. The venue is easy to find on the Sheffield Road. However, if you do experience problems give the venue a call and they will be only too pleased to help. Checkout the website for their new Darlaston venue in addition to their other venues around the country.

Looking Glass

Unit 5
Kent House
Gooch Street North
Birmingham
B5 Telephone 0121 666 7529
Website http://www.birmingham.co.uk/lookingglass

Nearest train station Birmingham New Street (five minute walk)
Car parking Own car park and plenty of street parking (free after 19.00) P&D
A–Z ref. P74/5A
Nearest landmark The Hippodrome

Membership details £2 on first visit (membership card and number issued). No personal details are recorded or kept
Opening hours   Monday–Thursday: 12.00–23.00
                      Friday: 12.00–06.00 (all night)
                      Saturday: 12.00–06.00 (all night)
                      Sunday: 13.00–23.00
Admission charges   £8
                      £5 concessions (UB40/NUS: proof required)
                      £5 Express, fast-tan cabin (for six minutes)
Food available Hot and cold meals. Snacks and refreshments available too
Facilities Ground floor: Reception and large cafe-style dining area, changing area, toilets and showers, full-sized gym (free weights and multi-gym), steam room, Jacuzzi and express, fast-tan cabin. First floor: TV lounge (smoking) and rest rooms.

Centrally located and close to the Nightingale (gay club), this smart, friendly and clean sauna is aimed exclusively at gay and bisexual men. Remember that there is a Gooch Street and a Gooch Street *North*: don't make the mistake of driving up and down the wrong one. During the day the car park at the venue will be full so street parking at the meters will be your next alternative. Parking during the evening poses no problems.

Spartan Health Club

127 George Road
Erdington
Birmingham
B23 7SH   Telephone 0121 382 3345

Nearest train station Gravelly Hill (ten minute walk)
Car parking Ample street parking
A–Z ref. P60/2D
Nearest landmark MEB opposite

Membership details £2 payable on first entry (lasts one year)
VIP and Gold Card membership available (phone for details)
Opening hours   Monday–Saturday: 11.00–23.00
                      Sunday: 13.00–22.00
Admission charges   11.00–18.00: £8
                      18.00–23.00: £6
                      £1 discount on production of Bears Club Card

Half-price to Birmingham venue staff (staff card required)
Concessions for NUS/UB40 (photo identification required)
Food available Hot and cold snacks, refreshments
Facilities Ground floor: Reception area, locker room, showers, sauna cabin and steam room. Basement: TV Lounge with satellite (non-smoking) cruisy corridor. First floor: Good sized gym, TV lounge (non-smoking) rest rooms (private and communal), toilet facilities and fast-tan stand up sun cabin.

Occupying a three storey building, the Spartan Health Club is a friendly and welcoming establishment. Because of its location it does get quite busy with men from all over the Midlands and beyond. Smoking is not allowed anywhere in the building except for an area set aside in reception. Directions to the sauna are straightforward; it is approximately two minutes from Spaghetti Junction. Exit Junction 6 off the M6 (North to South), take the first left at the island and you should be on Slade Road. The third-left is George Road. It's opposite Brookvale Reservoir.

The G. S. Club (formerly The Galaxy Sauna Club)

25–27 Springfield Road
Blackpool
FY1 1QW   Telephone 01253 294 610

Nearest train station Blackpool North
Car parking Side-street/'pay and display' local car parks
A–Z ref. P12/3A
Nearest landmark Metropole Hotel/North Pier

Membership details £3 payable on first visit (identification required)
Opening hours   Monday–Friday: 12.00–24.00
                         Saturday: 12.00–04.00
                         Sunday: 12.00–24.00
Admission charges £9 at all times
Food available Excellent café area. Hot and cold food, snacks and refreshments
Facilities Basement: Changing rooms, lockers and toilets. Ground floor: The wet area consisting of huge steam room (15-man), large sauna, Jacuzzi and cold splash. Extremely comfortable and hospitable restaurant serving freshly prepared hot and cold food. There is also a tastefully decorated smokers lounge complete with leather Chesterfields and other homely furnishings.
First Floor: The first floor has the non-smoking lounge, gay cinema with raised levels, several corridors with both private (five) and communal rest rooms (About three-quarters of the first floor is dedicated to cruising and relaxing!) What more could we ask for?

Situated opposite the Butlins Metropole Hotel (more or less opposite the North Pier.) The G. S. Club is a spacious and well-equipped sauna with all the usual facilities in a clean, friendly and welcoming environment. The wet area is confined to the ground floor with pine surrounds, subtle lighting and plants everywhere. At the moment there are no specialist nights on a regular basis (i.e. Bears Night) although these are organised once in a while and are advertised well in advance in the gay press. Pass-outs are available, however, fresh towels will be charged for. There is also the Gay UK shop on the premises with the usual free gay press available.

The Spa Sauna

121 Poole Road
Westbourne
Bournemouth
Dorset
BH4 9BG   Telephone   01202 757 591

Nearest train station Branksome
Car parking Street parking or local car parks
A–Z ref. P57/4E
Nearest landmark Venue is situated between Barclays Bank and Midland Bank
and directly opposite the Anglo World Language School

Membership details None required
Opening hours   Monday–Sunday: 01.00–21.00
Admission charges   £9 Unlimited stay
                       Concessions for NUS/UB40 (positive identification required)
Food available No, but complimentary refreshments available
Facilities Includes two sauna cabins, a steam room and two communal
relaxation areas.

This exclusively men-only sauna, established in 1994, caters mainly for the local
clientele with increasing trade during the tourist season. The Spa is a small but
friendly establishment spread out over two floors, welcoming all. Bear in mind
that Poole Road (A35) carries on alongside Wessex Way (A338), after you hit the
large roundabout (it is best to aim for Westbourne).

Rimmers Sauna

Simes Street
Bradford
BD1   Telephone   01274 742 444

Nearest train station Bradford Forster Square (two minutes)
Car parking Private (shared) car park at front of building
A–Z ref. P58/3A
Nearest landmark Rawson Market (venue situated opposite)

Membership details None required although membership is available at £30 per
year to benefit from reduced admission and private room hire
Opening hours   Monday–Friday: 14.00–24.00
                       Saturday: 14.00–10.00 (all-nighter)
                       Sunday: 14.00–22.00
                       (Overnight stays on request)
Admission charges   £10
                       £25 per hour for hire of private room with *en suite* facilities
                       and video/£15 per hour for hire of private room with
                       shower
Food available Light snacks and soft drinks
Facilities Large sauna, Jacuzzi, subtly lit crash room with video, communal
rest room and video lounge.
Private rooms are available for hire (see above for rates). Smoking is permitted
in all areas.

Having opened in March 1999 this is Bradford's newest and only exclusively gay
sauna complex. The layout of the venue is all on one large level. On your first

visit the discreet entrance may be a little difficult to find, so; go up the side steps on the left of the building on Simes Street, then right off Westgate (opposite Rawson Market). The sauna is situated above an establishment that cannot be named (think curry!), in what used to be an old church.

Bright 'n' Beautiful

9 St Margarets Place
Brighton
BN1   Telephone 01273 328 330

Nearest train station Brighton Central
Car parking Cannon Place car park nearby (hotel car park can be used at times)
A–Z ref. P28/5D
Nearest landmark Metropol Hotel

Membership details Available (enquire at reception)
Opening hours   Monday–Saturday: 12.00–22.00
                         Sunday: 12.00–20.00
Admission charges   Members £8 before 18.00/£9.50 guests; members £6 after/
                         guests £7 after
Facilities The usual, including sauna and steam room.

Located in a small street behind the Metropol Hotel (next to the hotel car park) the sauna utilises two floors. The upper floor is completely dedicated to relaxing, either in the TV lounge or in one of the many private cubicles, with dimmer switches! An extremely active sauna popular with the mature gentleman, although a whole range of mixed ages is always in evidence.

Bristol Gardens Health Spa

24–26 Bristol Gardens
Brighton
East Sussex
BN2 5JR   Telephone 01273 698 904   Fax 01273 626 661
                 E-mail bghs@dircon.co.uk
                 Website http://www.bghs.dircon.co.uk

Nearest train station Brighton Central
Car parking On-street parking (no problem)
A–Z ref. P30/6A
Nearest landmark North-west of Brighton Marina/behind Sussex Square

Twenty years' tradition of warm
and friendly atmosphere for all ages

Bright 'n' Beautiful Sauna Club

9 St. Margaret's Place   T **01273 328330**
Brighton Sussex BN1 2FD   F **01273 385793**

Right in the heart of Brighton Near Churchill Square

Membership details None required
Opening hours Monday–Friday: 12.00–22.30
Saturday–Sunday: 12.00–17.45
Saturday–Sunday: 17.45–22.30 (male and female couples only)
Admission charges £12 per person/£20 per male with female couple only
Food available Refreshments available at all times
Facilities Basement: two large saunas, two large steam rooms, four hot tubs, a Jacuzzi, cold plunge shower and swimming pool plus showers, toilets, etc. Clean towels are provided changed upon request. Ground floor: Warm dry changing rooms with lockers and hair-drying facilities. TV lounge, main lounge, conservatory and mini-gym. First floor: ten rest rooms, lounge, massage room, sunbed room and toilets. Second floor: Indoor and outdoor solarium.

Bristol Gardens Health Spa is a very deceptive building. Whilst on the outside it looks like a two-storey building, on the inside it is a four-storey premises covering 7,000 square feet of space. It has a mixed client base and a very gay-friendly attitude. Their aim is to be a modern version of the Roman Baths; a place to meet, relax and enjoy life. They try deliberately not to be 'over the top' and you will be under no pressure to be part of 'any' scene. They believe that you have the right to your own space and that anyone invading that space should be told to desist. A lot of the gay clients have told them that they enjoy the 'no pressure' attitude that is encouraged. Situated to the east of the pier, just above the marina. On-street parking no problem. Easy access by taxi or bus or even on foot from the town centre (about one and a quarter miles). From the Pavilion go straight down Edward Street, past the hospital, turn left into Church Place, and then first-right into Bristol Gardens. The sauna is about 100 yards on the right.

Denmark Oasis Sauna
75–76 Grand Parade
Brighton
BN2 2JA   Telephone 01273 689 966

Nearest train station Brighton (five minute walk)
Car parking Street voucher parking/local car parks
A–Z ref. P29/5E
Nearest landmark Palace Pier/venue opposite Royal Pavilion

Membership details None required
Opening hours Sunday–Thursday: 12.00–22.00
Friday–Saturday: 12.00–04.00
(Weekend opening hours may be extended to all-nighters)
Admission charges £11
Season tickets available at £90 for ten admissions, which can be used at either of the Denmark Saunas
Food available Coffee shop serving light snacks (hot and cold) and refreshments
Facilities Ground floor: Reception, coffee shop (smoking is allowed in a designated area of the coffee shop only – it is not allowed in any other part of the venue), eight rest rooms (one of these is designated as a 'family room' – it's big! – and stand-up fast-tan cabin). Basement: 28 foot swimming pool, two sauna cabins (one of which can hold over 30 people and is extremely subtly

lit!), whirlpool and steam room. There are two changing areas, three more rest rooms and very large shower block. There are two massage rooms housed within the building (appointment advised) and future plans include all-inclusive cabaret nights with complimentary wine and beer, etc.

Sister venue to The Denmark in Hove, opening it's doors for the first time in April 1999, so slight changes to the above listing, particularly the opening hours may be inevitable. As with the Denmark in Hove, the premises are spotlessly clean with the Oasis sporting a fabulous Egyptian theme running throughout.

Fitness Camp Sauna
90 St James Street
Brighton
BN2   Telephone 01273 674 455

Nearest train station Brighton Central
Car parking Limited street parking/pay and display car park
A–Z ref. P29/5E
Nearest landmark Public toilets

Membership details None required
Opening hours   Monday–Thursday: 09.00–22.00
                        Friday–Saturday: 09.00–03.00
                        Sunday: 09.00–22.00

Outlines   from Absolute Press

A delightful collection of monographs detailing the loves and lives of some of the most prolific gay and lesbian creative artists of this century.
  Titles in the series:
  David Hockney
  Benjamin Britten
  Bessie Smith
  We are Michael Field
  Federico García Lorca
  Arthur Rimbaud
  k.d. lang
  Armistead Maupin
  Tallulah Bankhead

DENMARK
OASIS
SAUNA

SUN BEDS
2 SAUNAS
WHIRLPOOL
REST ROOMS
COFFEE SHOP
STEAM ROOM
SWIMMING POOL
QUALIFIED MASSEURS

Denmark Oasis Sauna
75 - 76 Grand Parade
Brighton BN2 2JA
Tel: 01273 689966

Opening Hours
Sunday - Thursday 12am - 10pm
Friday - Saturday 12am - 4am

Admission charges £8
Food available Refreshments
Facilities Includes sauna, steam room, private and communal rest rooms.

Intimate little sauna situated in the heart of the gay village. Always clean and tidy offering a pass-out facility enabling you to call back on the same day if there is nothing in that takes your fancy. Updated details regarding this sauna were unavailable. Please phone for further details.

Unit One Sauna
St Margarets Place
High Street
Rottingdean
Brighton
BN2 7HA   Telephone 01273 307 253

Nearest train station Brighton Central (catch 27 or 27A bus from here)
Car parking Public car park nearby
A–Z ref. P37/3F
Nearest landmark The Windmill

Membership details None required
Opening hours   Monday–Sunday: 12.00–22.30

**the
ultimate
GAY
guide**

Tell us what you think

Ultimate Guides
PO Box 64
Manchester
M7 4NZ

email
ugg@ic24.net

(or you can use the form at
the back of this book)

The Friendly Place to be

**UNIT ONE
SAUNA**

ROTTINGDEAN, BRIGHTON
High Street, Seafront end
Open 11am - 11pm
7 days a week

Swimming pool
TV lounge
Sauna & Steam room
Rest rooms
Snacks
Home cooked meals
Massage: £10 half hour
              £18 one hour
Entrance: £10.50

Phone 01273 307 253

Admission charges   £10.50
Food available   Light snacks and refreshments
Facilities   Sauna cabin, steam room, swimming pool, massage area, TV lounge (smoking) and private rest rooms.

A clean and cruisy venue with a broad range of ages and types. Not much public action, guys tend to use the rest rooms. The sauna is situated on the sea front at Rottingdean (about three miles east of Brighton), close to Telescombe Cliffs, a notorious summer cruising area.

Cottage Health Club

19 West Street
Old Market
Bristol
BS2 DDF   Telephone 0117 903 0622
                E-mail chclub@aol.com

Nearest train station   Bristol Templemeads
Car parking   Private car park after 17.00/limited street parking
A–Z ref.   P66/3B
Nearest landmark   Evening News roundabout (turning right from Templemeads)

Membership details   As the Cottage is a private members club, it is a requirement to produce positive identification for membership on first visit (no details are either recorded or kept). Membership card issued
Opening hours   Monday–Tuesday: 16.00–02.00
                        Wednesday–Thursday: 13.00–02.00
                        Friday–Saturday: 13.00–04.00
                        Sunday: 13.00–23.00
Admission charges   £10
                        £7.50 Concessions (positive identification required – benefit book, etc.)
                        Admission price includes tea/coffee/soft drinks and light snacks
                        £70 Gold card membership: unlimited use for two months (limited supply)
                        Refund of 2.50 for toll bridge users – customers from Wales – proof required
                        Discount to members of Sailors, London/Heroes, Stourbridge
Food available   No, but complimentary refreshments and light snacks available
Facilities   Ground floor: Sauna, showers, lockers, TV lounge (smoking – this is the No Sex Zone). First floor: Toilets, dark room, 20 private rest rooms, video lounge. Second floor: Chill-out area. Surprise room (. . . by telling you would spoil the fun!). Loads of dark nooks and crannies to explore as well as darkened corridors and little rooms.

The Cottage is a cruisy venue for men to meet men. With The Downs vicinity becoming more of a no-go area, this place is a much more worthwhile alternative, in more ways than one. Having said that, there is a ' no sex zone' on the ground floor where you can relax, read the papers, have a drink (non-alcoholic) and/or chat. (This room is to be extended shortly.) Extremely well-managed, friendly and welcoming – so much so that it is almost guaranteed that you will return.

First Tuesday of the month is a private function: Different Strokes, for leather, rubber, uniform and WS enthusiasts. Open from 20.00 to 06.00. Admission is £15 (first visit includes membership) and £10 thereafter. (For further details please phone the venue direct.) This venue should appeal to the man who does not venture out (for whatever reason) on to the gay scene. It is safe and discreet and more importantly there is no attitude. Being a licensed and regulated venue ensures that all the authorities are satisfied with the premises and there will be no reason for them to enter.

Nero's Roman Spa

Whitelegge Street
Bury
BL8   Telephone 0161 764 2576

Nearest train station Bury, Bolton Street (taxi required from here)
Car parking Ample street parking (advise side-streets)
A–Z ref. P27/1H
Nearest landmark Citroën garage on Tottington Road

Membership details £4 on first admission/renewed every year for £3
(Key tag issued with your membership number – must be produced)

Opening hours	Monday–Friday: 12.00–24.00
	Saturday: 12.00–03.00
	Sunday: 12.00–24.00
Admission charges	£10
	Price on application concessions (proof required)

Facilities Ground floor: Reception area leading to the clean and well laid out changing rooms/toilets. Door leads into the wet area, a huge room designed to look like a Roman spa. Three communal showers, loads of seating dotted around, MTV playing on a series of monitors, large purpose-built Jacuzzi, large cold plunge pool (more like a small swimming pool), massage/aromatherapy room (fixed times/appointments required). Three doors at the far side of the room, the first is the very large steam room (probably the largest), the second is the sauna cabin and the third is the entrance to the stairway to the first floor. The stairway is a facility in itself, darkened rooms and areas leading off even before you reach the stairs. Very well laid out sauna over two large levels and particularly popular with married and bi men due to its location away from the city centre. First floor: At the top of these stairs you will come to the private rest rooms (approximately ten) all with controllable lighting and door locks. Here is entrance to the cinema with seating showing gay films continuously. Through the cinema is the entrance to 'The Maze', a series of darkened corridors leading to . . . (?) The corridors are narrow, enabling you to squeeeeeeze past the man of your dreams. Returning back to the entrance to the rest rooms you will be in the area set aside for reading, chatting, etc. Sunbed facilities are here (stand up fast-tan cabin, for which you will need to obtain token from reception). At the end of this area is the stairway leading down to the changing rooms (making it an ideal place to cruise around without having to backtrack on yourself). Also on the first floor is the excellent restaurant/snack bar serving a wide range of value-for-money home cooked food. The TV room (smoking) is comfortable and homely.

★ **over 11,000 members** ★

NERO'S
ROMAN SPA

The Norths First Purpose Built Roman Sauna For Gay Gentlemen
All housed in a secure private building with a relaxed and friendly atmosphere

Continually Copied But Not Bettered As Yet!

A warm friendly atmosphere where you are part of the club, happy and lively staff, good, warm and exciting friends where a wonderful time is guaranteed.

Also:

The Most Comprehensive Facilities In Britain

1 20 Man Scandinavian Pine Sauna
2 25 Man Prague Steam Room
3 Dive-in Plunge Pool
4 15 Man, 12 Hydrotherapy Jet Jacuzzi
5 Robert Craig Therapy Centre
6 Splash Showers, Security Lockers
7 MTV Screen Entertainment
8 Full Restaurant Facilities
9 TV Lounge
10 Promenade Lounge
11 Full Circular Turbo Sun Bed
12 Darkened Lounge
13 Darkened Corridors Leading To ...
14 Black Hole
15 Ten Private Rest Rooms
16 Cinema
17 The Maze (The Only One Of Its Kind)
18 The Shop
19 Thirty Day Club (Visit Us For £5 A Go)
20 Bunty (Say No More)

No wonder we are still the most comprehensive sauna club in Britain and most definitely the best value for money.

Phone for details:

0161 764 2576

**NOW OPEN 12 HOURS DAILY.
12 NOON TO 12 MIDNIGHT.
SATURDAYS 'TIL LATE.**

Nero's holds many party nights throughout the year which are always advertised well in advance in the gay press. On occasional Sundays (one of the busiest days, with a regular attendance of over 150 punters) there is a stripper to entertain you (usually about 19.00). Whitelegge Street is off Tottington Road (B6213) Look out for the Citroen garage and turn on to Whitelegge Street, The entrance is down a small alleyway (A small sign on the wall points to 'Nero's'). As it is a residential area, try your best not to park in front of anyone's house. It is advisable to park in one of the many side-streets (not outside anyone's house) and walk the short distance to the sauna.

Greenhouse Health Club
Willenhall Road
Darlaston
West Midlands
WS10 8JG   Telephone 0121 568 6126
                 Website http://www.gay-sauna.com

Nearest train station Walsall or Wolverhampton
Car parking Secure and secluded car parking for 70 cars at venue/street parking
A–Z ref. P32/2B
Nearest landmark Ikea (Junction 9/M6)

Membership details Free: card issued on first visit with membership number (no personal details are recorded or kept)
Opening hours   Monday–Thursday: 10.00–02.00
                         Friday–Saturday: 10.00–08.00 (all night)
                         Sunday: 12.00–08.00 (all night)
Admission charges £10 at all times
Food available Large selection of hot and cold snacks, refreshments
Facilities (Due to open on 28 May 1999. I received an outline prior to this on what the proposed layout and facilities will be.) Ground floor: Reception leading to the changing rooms (270+ lockers) vanity area, public phone box (one of the old fashioned red ones), dining area and cigarette machine. Basement: Dedicated to 'relaxing'. Large communal rest room and private rest rooms. There are two flights of stairs, one at either side of the room in order that you can quite easily cruise through without everyone thinking you're gagging for it. First floor: Houses the multi-gym and further toilet facilities and the huge swimming pool, built with a waterfall. Through the waterfall is a 'cave' which houses the Jacuzzi (sounds fab!). By the pool there will be a semi enclosed massage area, a further Jacuzzi (enclosed) the steam room and more shower facilities. Second floor: Sauna cabin, larger steam room with a dividing 'wall' in order to create two separate steamy areas. Also on this floor will be a shower area, cinema room and two lounges (one smoking, the other non-smoking), two sunbed rooms and even more rest areas (private and communal). Third floor: Totally secluded roof garden (summer).

Checkout the website for up to date details or phone the number above. As with all Greenhouse venues, the staff are exceptionally friendly and will do their utmost to ensure your visit is pleasant and enjoyable.

The Denmark Sauna

84–86 Denmark Villas
Hove
East Sussex
BN3 3TJ   Telephone 01273 723 733

Nearest train station Hove
Car parking Plenty of side-street parking
A–Z ref. P27/3H
Nearest landmark Hove Station

Membership details None required
Opening hours   Monday–Sunday: 12.00–22.00
Admission charges   £11
                                £90 Season tickets (pre-paid) for ten sessions
Food available Excellent range of chilled (not frozen) food available. Cold
cabinet. Hot and cold drinks available
Facilities Coffee shop incorporating TV room, changing area with large
spacious lockers, shower area and hand basin (razors and shampoos available at
reception). Opposite the showers is the steam room, which has eucalyptus
essence pumping into the steam. The T-shaped sauna cabin is the next facility
down the corridor, then the rest seating area and massage room. Down another
corridor are the private rest rooms each having a Hollywood diva's nameplate
in case you get lost! At the end of the corridor is the Jacuzzi room, which
houses a large Jacuzzi that can hold up to 12 people quite comfortably.

The layout of the Denmark consists of a series of corridors (which in itself should
be rated as a top class facility). There is soft lighting throughout (very flattering)
and relaxing music playing constantly. The Denmark has five resident masseurs
(massage £20 per hour/£12 per half-hour). Aromatherapy and sports therapy
being included. Advance booking for these services is advised. Although this is a
gay sauna it does attract a welcome proportion of bi and straight(!) men. There
are occasional overnight parties held here. Keep an eye on the gay press for
details, or alternatively, phone for dates.

Blue Corner Sauna

43 High Street
Hull
HU1 1PT   Telephone 01482 620 775

Nearest train station Hull
Car parking Limited street parking
A–Z ref. P26/D3
Nearest landmark The Black Boy Pub (Blue Corner is situated opposite the pub
behind the wrought-iron railings)

Membership details Free membership; no personal details required
Opening hours   Sunday–Thursday: 13.00–23.00
                                Friday: 13.00–02.00
                                Saturday: 13.00–06.00 (all night)
Admission charges   £7 at all times
                                £5 concessions (UB40/NUS/benefits/etc.): positive
                                identification required

Food available Extensive menu available plus hot and cold drinks
Facilities First floor: From the reception entrance turn right up the stairs to the changing room. From here, after exploring all the nooks and crannies, you will come to the shower area and toilets. The passage opens out to the large cruisy seating area with access to the five private rest rooms and one large communal rest room and galleried TV and video area (non-smoking) Make your way back down to the reception . . . for the Ground floor: Turn left for the sunbeds, through the gloriously busy dark passage and on to the cafe; smoking and non-smoking areas are available. Heading through the cafe you will come to the wet area: the 12-man sauna cabin is on the right as are and the simply huge 20-man steam room and Jacuzzi.

Hull's first sauna exclusively for gay and bi men opened in December 1998 and has already proved to be a total success. Occupying a picturesque old warehouse taking in three levels and refurbished to an extremely high standard. The stylish cafe area, split into two, to accommodate the smokers and non-smokers is situated with the vantage point of being able to see all the comings and goings of the wet area. The Blue Corner in Hull, is the sister venue to the popular Blue Corner in Newcastle (see separate listing) and with venues like this you can rest assured that there will be more to come. The staff here are friendly and welcoming. If it is your first visit and wish to be shown around then ask at the desk. Absolutely nothing is too much trouble for them. Brilliant!

Rainbows Sauna
374 Anlaby Road
Hull
HU3   Telephone 01482 504 981

Nearest train station Hull
Car parking Public car park close by/off-road parking
Nearest landmark Hull Infirmary (two minutes by car over flyover)

Membership details Free membership on first visit
Opening hours   Monday–Thursday: 11.00–23.00
                       Friday–Saturday: 11.00–11.00 (all night)
                       Sunday: 11.00–23.00
Admission charges   £10
                       £7 for people18–24 years of age (positive identification required)
                       Concessions may be available for UB40/NUS/UK Bears, etc.
Food available Full service gourmet restaurant. Weekly complimentary salad bar (Fully licensed bar – to be confirmed)
Facilities A very large Finnish sauna, a very large Finnish steam room, Jacuzzi, 25 dark and cruisy rest rooms on two floors, two TV lounges with 53 inch TVs, bar (smoking) and restaurant (smoking and non-smoking) upstairs, cinema room and a very large play room!

At the time of going to print this top-notch venue was still heavily under construction and promises to be one of the best sauna complexes in the North of England. Application for an alcohol licence has been put forward making it only the second gay sauna complex in the country to be granted one (there seems to be little doubt that it will be refused). With 6,500 square feet of space spread out over two floors (2,500 feet devoted to communal and private rest rooms) it looks set to become a market leader. Gay-owned and run. Shortly after opening there will be planned theme evenings. For example: Leather nights, Bears nights, Stripper evenings and Movie nights all designed to give the gay person a welcome alternative to the pubs and clubs and a safer option to cruising. July 1999 will see the opening of a hair salon and massage parlour with additional facilities continuously being added in order to make your visit as enjoyable as possible. Keep an eye on the gay press for further details.

Spartan Mantalk

72 Bayswater Road
Harehills
Leeds
West Yorkshire
L58 5NW   Telephone 0113 248 7757

Nearest train station Leeds (and then a bus to St James' University Hospital)
Car parking Side-streets (not outside anyone's house)
A–Z ref. P46/4B
Nearest landmark Garage on Harehills Road (corner of Bayswater Road). The sauna is also situated behind St James' University Hospital

Membership details None required
Opening hours   24 hours every day of the year (except Christmas Day and
                                      New Years Day)
Admission charges   £10 At all times
                                      Free pass-out facility valid for 24 hours
Food available Yes, and good value for money and refreshments too
Facilities Ground floor: Entrance/reception area, changing area with small private lockers. TV room (smoking) and (the very popular) darkened communal video lounge. Additional toilet facility situated along the corridor. A slight staircase leads you to . . . the Lower ground floor: Here you will find the Jacuzzi and toilets. A few more steps lead to the shower area, steam room (completely tiled and comfortable) and sauna cabin.

Spartan Mantalk has been in operation for over four years and is continuously going from strength to strength. There are ten private rest rooms with locks for privacy as well as a large darkened communal rest room with soft porn video films playing constantly. There is a doorbell for gaining entry to the sauna. You have to wait until the door is opened for you.

The Dolphin Sauna

129 Mount Road
Wallasey
Liverpool
L45 9JS   Telephone 0151 630 1516

Nearest train station New Brighton
Car parking Limited street parking (not outside anyone's house)
A–Z ref. P41/1D
Nearest landmark Victoria Hotel (telephone box outside if you need to phone)

Membership details None required
Opening hours   Sunday–Saturday: 14.00–21.30
Admission charges   £9
                                      £3 Sunbed hire

SPARTAN MANTALK
sauna
'Going from strength to strength'

The steamiest, friendliest venue in Leeds, open 24 hours a day, seven days a week.

Come and enjoy

continuous films

private and communal rest rooms

refreshments

communal video lounge

steam sauna jacuzzi

and

by the time you read this, we are confident we will have our drinks licence

**Bayswater Road, Harehills
Leeds L58 5NW**

0113 245 7757

Food available Good selection of hot and cold snacks and refreshments too
Facilities Ground floor: Reception area, coffee bar, toilet and locker rooms.
First floor: Jacuzzi, sauna cabin, showers, toilet and steam room. Second floor:
television lounge, sunbed room, three private rest rooms, relaxation area.

Very clean (absolutely spotless) venue situated in a small shopping precinct.
Well laid out wet area with a delightful sunken Jacuzzi. Mixed age range. The
only gay sauna in Liverpool, means that the catchment area is huge (The nearest
gay sauna to this is Nero's in Bury). They have had people from all five continents
and from 35 different countries (not personally, I'm talking visitors). The
Dolphin is a very friendly sauna, a place to socialise as well as to . . . erm . . . and
all will be made welcome. Finding Mount Road may be a little tricky without the
use of an A–Z. If you do get stuck, telephone the number above and they will be
more than happy to direct you.

The Greenhouse Health Club

23 Crawley Road
Luton
Bedfordshire   Telephone 01582 487 701
                 Website http://www.gay-sauna.com

Nearest train station Luton (five minutes walk)
Car parking Street parking in addition to monitored council car park at rear
Nearest landmark Kennings Garage (opposite)

Membership details None required
Opening hours   Monday–Thursday: 11.00–02.00
                     Friday: 11.00–06.00
                     Saturday: 12.00–08.00
                     Sunday: 12.00–24.00
Admission charges £10 at all times
                     Identification will need to be shown if you look under 18
Food available Full range of hot and cold snacks. Refreshments
Facilities Ground floor: Reception area and locker room (150+ lockers) leading
to dining area and food bar. Small rest room, shower area and large Jacuzzi set
in 'cave' surroundings incorporating a dark room. First floor: two lounges (one
smoking, the other non-smoking), large sauna cabin and large steam room.
Second floor: Dark rooms and rest areas. Third floor: Hotel only (accessed by
lift).

Very spacious premises with passageways galore and plenty of secluded
facilities. This venue provides scope to cruise around the premises without really
having to backtrack on yourself. Every last Sunday in the month is the 'Bears
Picnic', always packed and pulling in all the big boys and their admirers from as
far afield as London. The Greenhouse chain operates saunas in Newport,
Barnsley and Darlaston. Their advertising policy includes the mainstream press
so you can be guaranteed plenty of hunks and boys that do not frequent the gay
scene. The staff (in all Greenhouse establishments) are always friendly and
accommodating and will do their utmost to see that your visit is enjoyable. Hotel
accommodation available on the fourth floor, telephone for rates and availability.
Checkout the listings in this guide for other Greenhouse venues in addition to
their website.

Apollo Sauna

18 Tariff Street
Manchester
M1   Telephone 0161 236 9999/0161 236 1000
            E-mail ApolloGaySauna@hotmail.com

Nearest train station Piccadilly (two minute walk)
Car parking Plenty of on-street parking
A–Z ref. P87/4F
Nearest landmark Piccadilly Station or Foo Foos Palace, Dale Street (Tariff Street is opposite)

Membership details £4 yearly membership required. Positive identification is not required although you will be asked to sign a form stating that you know the house rules and promise to abide by them – fair enough
Opening hours   24 hours, 7 days a week
Admission charges   £10
                        £8 NUS/UB40/club and pub staff (positive identification required)
Food available Light snacks, hot meals and refreshments available in the Cafe Bar
Facilities Includes 30-man sauna cabin, Jacuzzi, executive rest rooms, video room, TV lounge, cruising lounge (this area includes a dance floor and will be used for various theme nights through the year i.e. leather nights, boot camp nights, stripper nights, bears night, army and navy and under-25s only night)

Another new sauna to open just before this goes to print and yet again I do not have any firm details to pass on to you. However, I have been given the proposed layout and facilities as a guide to what promises to be another great asset to the gay Manchester scene. Situated right slap-bang in the middle of the notorious cruising area, Apollo must surely receive the award for 'best marketing strategy'. Far enough out of the gay village to be accessible to even the most apprehensive male, yet close enough to stagger to after a good night's clubbing. On arrival at the sauna you will have to ring the security buzzer to be allowed entry. Remember that the outside door will have to be closed before the internal door is opened (for our own safety). The door is monitored by CCTV so they will know when you have entered. *Note*: With the Ducie Street cruising area becoming more of a thoroughfare for the straight clubs, it is worth bearing in mind that there is now a safer (and more productive) alternative than The Canal (see 'Cruising' listings). The owners of The Apollo have made it perfectly clear that the sauna will become a focal point of the gay community offering more than just the basics. Keep an eye out for the flyers that will be advertising frequent party nights.

Eurosauna

202 Hill Lane
Higher Blakeley
Manchester
M9 6RG   Telephone 0161 740 5152

Nearest train station Piccadilly (taxi to here £4.50-ish)
Car parking Park at bottom of road near Victoria Avenue
A–Z ref. P61/5F+6F
Nearest landmark Barclays Bank on Victoria Avenue

Membership details Not compulsory although membership at £20 per year offers reduced admission

Opening hours   Monday–Sunday: 13.00–21.00

Admission charges £7 Members/£8 non-members

£7.00 Concessions (proof required)

Food available Light snacks and refreshments

Facilities Ground floor: Entrance hall leading to changing rooms (separate cubicles). Large steam room, two large shower areas, cold plunge pool and large sauna cabin, non-smoking lounge area, wash room and toilets. First floor: Reception area, kitchen, TV Lounge (smoking), two communal rest rooms, toilet facility, four private rest rooms and video room.

Long established gent's gay sauna (established 1973). Entrance to Eurosauna is by the side of the launderette on Hill Lane close to The Lion and Lamb public house. Popular during the daytime with a varied age group. Loads of dark corners to explore . . .

H20 Zone

36–38 Sackville Street
Manchester
M1   Telephone 0161 236 3876

Nearest train station Piccadilly

Car parking NCP, Bloom Street (closes 18.30 approx.). Ample street parking in the evening

A–Z ref. P87/5E

Nearest landmark Chorlton Street Bus Station

Membership details Not required although priority memberships are available for reduced admission charges

Opening hours   Monday–Thursday: 12.00–23.00 (last entry 22.00)

Friday–Saturday: 14.00–08.00 (last entry 04.00)

Sunday: 14.00–24.00 (last entry 21.00)

Admission charges £10 Monday–Saturday

£9 Sunday

Food available Light snacks and refreshments in separate cafe area

Facilities Includes sauna cabin, Jacuzzi, shower area, steam room, solariums, video lounge, rest rooms and cafe.

Right slap-bang in the middle of the gay village, opened in March 1998. Situated above Clone Zone on Sackville Street, this is a clean, friendly and stylish venue.

Stallions Sauna

153 Upper Chorlton Road
Whalley Range
Manchester
M16 7SH   Telephone 0161 860 729

Nearest train station Piccadilly (taxi required from here)

Car parking Car park at venue/street parking

A–Z ref. P100/5A

Membership details Annual membership fee £2 payable on first visit
VIP Membership available for £20 (details at reception)

Opening hours	Monday–Thursday: 12.00–23.00
	Friday–Saturday: 12.00–23.00 (closed till midnight for cleaning)
	Friday–Saturday: 24.00–07.00 (all-nighters)
	Sunday: 12.00–23.00
Admission charges	£9 Members
	Concessions available (NUS/UB40: identification required)
	£5 Hotel guests
	Half price to all-nighter if in during the evening

Facilities Includes steam room, sauna, Jacuzzi, rest rooms and TV lounge (smoking).

Situated underneath the Carlton House Hotel, approximately two miles out of the city centre.
For further details please telephone the venue direct.

Zeus

71 Ratcliffe Gate
Mansfield
Nottingham   Telephone 01623 422 257

Nearest train station Mansfield (ten minute walk)
Car parking Ample on street parking
Nearest landmark Mansfield Brewery

Membership details Free – card issued at venue
Opening hours   Monday–Sunday: 11.00–20.00
Admission charges £6
Food available Coffee bar serving light refreshments and snacks
Facilities Ground floor: Reception leading through to the cafe lounge area, changing rooms and Jacuzzi. First floor: Steam room, two sauna cabins, three individual sunbed rooms and showers. Second floor: Communal rest areas divided into private sections.

At the time of going to print this venue was still under construction and final details still have to be decided so the description is offered only as a guideline. Situated in a safe and discreet commercial area of the town.

Blue Corner Sauna

164B Heaton Park Road
Heaton
Newcastle upon Tyne
NE6 5AD   Telephone 0191 240 0122

Nearest train station Newcastle upon Tyne (Central)
Car parking Unrestricted street parking
A–Z ref. P44/5C

Nearest landmark Heaton Public Library

Membership details £2 on first visit included in the admission charge
Opening hours   Monday–Saturday: 11:00–22.00
                         Sunday: 13.00–20.00
Admission charges   First visit: £10/subsequent visits: £8
                         Concessions: before 18.00 (UB40/NUS: photo identification
                         required)
Food available Large selection of hot and cold snacks and refreshments too
Facilities Includes two shower areas, large steam room and large sauna cabin.
In addition to the restaurant there are two television lounges, one lavishly
furnished in Victorian style showing terrestrial TV (smoking), the other
showing videos (non-smoking). There are numerous nooks and crannies and
discreet areas to wander around and 'explore', as well as three private rest
rooms and one large communal relaxation lounge.

Extremely clean and well-maintained men-only sauna situated half a mile from
Newcastle's city centre in a secure private building. The friendly, welcoming
staff are totally attitude-free towards everything and will ensure that your visit
to the Blue Corner will be an enjoyable one. As this is Newcastle's only gay sauna
it does tend to get quite busy on weekend afternoons. The age range is across the
board so there is someone here for everyone! Check out the listing for Blue Corner
in Hull.

Pennine Sauna

96 Rochdale Road
Shaw
Oldham
Lancashire   Telephone 01706 842 000

Nearest train station Shaw and Crompton
Car parking Private car park
A–Z ref. P35/6F
Nearest landmark Warburtons Bakery

Membership details None required
Opening hours   Monday: 13.00–21.00
                         Wednesday: 12.00–21.00
                         Saturday: 13.00–18.00
                         Sunday: 13.00–21.00
Admission charges £8 (subject to review in 1999)
Food available Excellent home cooked food available and refreshments too

Pennine Sauna is a discreet venue for gay and bi men on the above four days
only. Very popular during the daytime (particularly Wednesday and Saturday).
Has all the usual facilities associated with a gay sauna. Further details can be
obtained by telephoning the sauna direct. Come off at Junction 21 on the M62
and take the A663 (Shaw) through to the B6194 (Rochdale Road). The sauna is
situated close to the Warburtons Bakery.

Tropics Sauna

2 Marketway
Portsmouth
Hampshire
PO1   Telephone 01705 296 100

Nearest train station Portsmouth and Southsea
Car parking Either pay and display (close by) or Office World car park (free)
A–Z ref. P23/2F
Nearest landmark Office World

Membership details None required
Opening hours   Monday–Saturday: 12.00–22.00
                       Sunday: Closed
                       Last admission: 21.00
Admission charges £8.50
Food available Light snacks and refreshments available
Facilities Ground floor: Reception area, sunbed and showers, changing room, TV lounge (smoking – this is the only part of the venue where smoking is allowed). First floor: two sauna cabins, steam room, showers and toilet facilities. Second floor: Showers, toilet facility and large rest area. This subtly lit room is partitioned at intervals, giving a modicum of privacy. Bath robes are available if required.

Tropics is a compact, friendly sauna spread out over three floors, situated in the city centre of Portsmouth. Directions to 'pay and display' car park: from the M27 turn on to the M275 into Portsmouth and follow it to the end. At the roundabout, take the first left and then turn right into the small car park. From here it's a short walk. Walk down the main road (this is the road that you would have taken if you had gone straight at the roundabout) At the next roundabout turn right and Tropics is on your right, in the parade of shops just around the bend. Alternatively, park up in The Office World car park across the road from the sauna.

Essex Sauna and Steam

239 High Road
Chadwell Heath
Romford
Essex   Telephone 0181 597 9610

Nearest train station Chadwell Heath
Car parking Side-street parking
A–Z ref. P37/6F
Nearest landmark Tolgate public house (opposite)

Membership details Enquire at venue
Opening hours   Monday–Friday: 11.00–23.00
                       Saturday: 11.00–Late
                       Sunday: 12.00–23.00
Admission charges £9/£7 before 14.00
                     Friday and Saturday after 19.00: two admissions for £14
Food available No, but free refreshments available
Facilities Ground floor: TV room (smoking) sauna cabin, steam room and showers. First floor: Toilets and rest areas (smoking allowed in rest areas).

This friendly and compact gay sauna is situated on the main road.

The Bronx Sauna

208 Saville Street East
Sheffield
S4   Telephone 0114 261 7510

Nearest train station Sheffield (five minutes)
Car parking Secure enclosed private car park/ample street parking
A–Z ref. P87/5H (on the A6109)
Nearest landmark There isn't one, though it is extremely easy to find: Junction 34 off the M1 (five minutes from motorway); one and a half miles from Meadowhall

Membership details £2 (to be confirmed) Private Members Club (correct identification required to issue card). Personal details will not be recorded nor kept

Opening hours   Monday–Thursday: 12.00–24.00
                         Friday: 12.00–24.00 (1st Friday of the month is an all-nighter)
                         Saturday: 12.00–08.00 (all night)
                         Sunday: 09.00–24.00
                         (First Friday of the month will include Bears Club – open to all)
Admission charges   £10 at all times
                         Concessions (to be confirmed – phone for details)
Food available Hot and cold meals and snacks and refreshments too
Facilities (proposed layout) Ground floor: Reception leads through to the locker rooms. TV lounge and comfortable bistro restaurant (top class food will feature heavily). The original 'cottage' is being kept as a facility 'to be used' (obviously revamped and lit accordingly). Jacuzzi here too. First floor: Huge 23-man, 'double', specially built sauna cabin (divided so as to allow one side hot and the other side bearable without having to gasp for breath!). Large communal rest room and approximately eight private rest rooms. Fully tiled (including seating) steam room, communal shower block with vanity units (just like being in the army!). There is also a huge basement area, plans for which are not yet available but you can rest assured that they will be . . . erm . . . appropriate.

At the time of going to press this venue was still heavily under major construction. The extensive outline of the proposed facilities that I was given points to what will be one of the best saunas north of Watford. The building itself dates back to 1863, and what was once the biggest pub in Sheffield (The Bronx –

208 SAVILE ST EAST
SHEFFIELD S4 7UQ
0114.2780383/2872888

SPONSORED BY DRAINER BAR-CELONA   MENS-BAR
                                         Attercliffe gay zone

hence the name) will now be another outstanding addition to the Sheffield Scene. The Bronx is situated in the commercial area of Sheffield, which means that it is 100% discreet, far enough away from the gay scene and bright lights to encourage even the most 'apprehensive' male. There will be no disguising the fact that this venue will be 100% cruisy, and advertised as an indoor cruising ground. The myriad of corridors and hidey-holes will be utilised to their fullest extent . . . so don't say that you weren't warned! The enthusiasm of the owners to provide a safe, hygienic and welcoming environment to their customers is indescribable and in all probability this venue will undoubtedly become the new generation of sauna for gay and bi men.

Heat Sauna and Steam

27–29 London Road (corner of Mill Street)
Stockport
Lancashire
SK7   Telephone 0161 483 6102
             E-mail heatsauna@hotmail.com

Nearest train station Hazel Grove (five minutes)
Car parking Ample street parking/private car park available about 50 yards from the venue
A–Z ref. P144/2D (Mill Street not actually on page)
Nearest landmark George and Dragon pub on Stockport Road/Buxton Road – Mill Street is 20 yards on the left (Manchester to Stockport direction)

Membership details Heat is a private members sauna, so membership is required. There is a £3 joining fee at the venue: a membership card will then be issued. Membership should be renewed every January
Opening hours   Monday–Sunday: 12.00–late (about 23.00)
                      As this sauna was not even open at the time of going to print the opening hours may change, particularly over the weekends
Admission charges £10 at all times
Food available Sandwiches, light snacks and refreshments
Facilities Ground floor: Reception area and changing rooms leading to the gymnasium and wet area, which comprises of Jacuzzi, wet lounge (?), 30-man sauna, 20-man steam room and two fast-tan vertical sun cabins. There are also two TV lounges (one smoking and the other non-smoking). First floor: Consists of a large cruising lounge and approximately eight private rest rooms.

Heat is yet another new gay sauna, with a planned opening date of April 1999. Details at this time are still sketchy, particularly the opening hours. Spread out over two floors Heat takes up 4,500 square feet of space. Further details and directions can be obtained by phoning the number above.

Heroes Health Club

4 Lower High Street
Stourbridge
West Midlands   Telephone 01384 442 030

Nearest train station Stourbridge
Car parking Street parking
A–Z ref. P83/2F
Nearest landmark Giles Hill Church

Membership details Enquire by phone
Opening hours   Monday–Thursday: 12.00–23.00
                      Friday–Saturday: 12.00–02.00
                      Sunday: 12.00–23.00
Admission charges   £10/£3 discount if you book in before 18.00
                      Concessions: on application (UB40/income support:
                      identification required)
                      £45 Gold Card application
                      £1 Pass-outs
Food available Light snacks and refreshments
Facilities Includes large sauna, steam room, whirlpool, Jacuzzi, rest rooms,
coffee shop, fast-tan sunbed, snack bar and smoking/non-smoking TV rooms.

Party night is every second Friday of the month (telephone to confirm details).
Heroes is exclusively for gay and bi men.

The Boiler Room

Ocean House Hotel
Hunsdon Road
Torquay
Devon
TQ1 1QB   Telephone 01803 296 538
               Website http://www.oceanhouse.co.uk

Nearest train station Torquay
Car parking Ample parking space at venue

Membership details None required
Opening hours   Thursday–Sunday: 18.00–23.00
Admission charges   £7
                      Free to residents of the hotel
Facilities Terrace: Swimming pool (outside) and gardens. Lower floor: Steam
room, showers and TV room (smoking). First floor: Bar restaurant.

The steam bath is part of this luxurious, exclusively gay hotel. It is popular with
the locals and residents of the hotel attracting the younger age group, of which
the hotel caters for. The facilities associated with a custom-built sauna are
limited, although The Boiler Room can rightly boast the largest steam room in
Devon. Details of the hotel accommodation can be accessed through the website
or by telephoning the above number.

Woodbine Villa Sauna

Fore Street
Grampound
Truro
Cornwall
TR2 4QP   Telephone 01726 882 005

Nearest train station St Austell
Car parking On-site
Nearest landmark Town Hall

Membership details None required
Opening hours   Wednesday & Sunday: 18.00–22.00
Admission charges £5
Food available Refreshments
Facilities Ground floor: Sauna and shower area, TV and video(!) room (non-smoking). First floor: Open-plan communal rest room (room split by the staircase).

A compact gay sauna attached to a small exclusively gay guest-house, yet is also open to non-residents. Because of the location and the complete lack of localised gay facilities, this venue, though limited, offers the gay male a welcome chance to meet up in a relaxed and friendly atmosphere. The outside of the property offers no visible clue of the nature of the building so it is advisable to phone beforehand for precise location. Mention that you saw the listing in this guide. Open on the above two days only, it does tend to be popular with people from all of the surrounding areas (including Devon) as well as the locals. The Woodbine Villa is an exclusively gay guest-house in this beautiful part of the world. For details of accommodation please phone the above number.

SCOTLAND

No. Eighteen Sauna

18 Albert Place
Edinburgh
EH7 5HN   Telephone 0131 553 3222

Nearest train station Waverley (ten minute walk)
Car parking Adequate parking around the venue, front and rear
A–Z ref. P15/1J
Nearest landmark Edinburgh Playhouse (five minute walk)

Membership details Free membership
Opening hours   Monday–Saturday: 12.00–22.00
                       Sunday: 14.00–22.00
Admission charges £8
                     £5 Concessions (proof required)
Food available Refreshments
Facilities Ground floor: Reception, changing area, TV lounge (smoking) and private rest-rooms. Basement: Huge sauna cabin (at least 15-man), large steam room (12–14), Jacuzzi, communal rest room (complimentary lighting!) and private rest rooms.

This exclusively gay sauna is situated close to Central Edinburgh and within the 'Gay Triangle'. If you are stuck for precise travel directions, telephone the helpful staff who will be only too happy to oblige (I think everyone who works here is called Graham). For those who are not in the know, Albert Place is situated at the top of Leith Walk, on the right hand side.

Centurion Health Club and Sauna

19 Dixon Street
Glasgow
Scotland   Telephone 0141 248 4485

Nearest train station Glasgow Central
Nearest tube St Enoch Square
Car parking Ample around venue
A–Z ref. P83/5F
Nearest landmark Glass Pyramid/St Enoch Square

Membership details Free membership/loyalty card scheme (see below)
Opening hours   Monday–Friday: 12.00–22.00
                         Saturday: 12.00–07.00 (all-nighter)
                         (Last admission on a Saturday night is 02.00)
                         Sunday: 12.00–22.00
Admission charges   Monday–Friday: £8
                         Saturday: £10
                         Sunday: £6

Food available Free soup at all times. Refreshments and snacks too
Facilities Large, well-equipped gym (multi-gym and free weights, etc.). Use of
the gym is included in the admission price. Sunbed facilities, two sauna cabins,
steam room and Jacuzzi. Television lounge (smoking) and video lounge (non-
smoking). There are a number of video monitors throughout the building (even
in the changing room and corridors). There is ample rest room space (private
and communal) and the corridors could be . . . erm . . . well, you know what I
mean.

The Centurion is a large single-storey building ideally located, overlooking St
Enoch square in the centre of Glasgow. On Saturday the venue is open all day and
night. If you go in during the day you are allowed a free pass-out (bearing in
mind that last admission to the sauna is 02.00) In addition, for those with the
stamina to make it through the night there is a free breakfast on Sunday morning.
Pass-outs during the week will incur a £2 re-admission fee.
The Centurion also operates a 'loyalty card' scheme, whereby you will be issued
with a card which is stamped on each visit. After four visits the fifth one costs £5.

W A L E S

Locker Room

50 Charles Street
Cardiff
South Wales
CF1   Telephone 01222 220 388

Nearest train station Cardiff Central
Car parking Limited street parking/multi-storey car park at bottom of street
A–Z ref. P30/3B
Nearest landmark The side of Marks and Spencers

Membership details £2 annual membership, paid on first visit or £1 for day
membership (card will be issued). You should bring the card with you on all
subsequent visits
Opening hours   Monday–Friday: 13.00–23.00

	Saturday: 13.00–08.00 (all night)

Admission charges   £11 first visit (includes £2 annual membership) and £9 per subsequent visit or £9 plus £1 day membership
Special weekly and monthly rates available (enquire at reception)

Food available Hot and cold food, snacks and refreshments

Facilities Ground floor: Reception through to the comfortable cafe area and the changing rooms. Continuing through is the wet area with the sauna, steam room and Jacuzzi. First floor: Video lounge (non-smoking) and TV lounge (smoking). Second floor: A whole floor devoted to relaxation, either by yourself or 'communally'.

Conveniently situated next to the Exit Bar in Cardiff town centre. The Locker Room is a large, clean and luxurious gay sauna. Extremely busy at weekends. Afternoons tend to get the business crowd in. The venue is immaculately kept with ample seating dotted around.

Greenhouse Sauna

24 Church Street
Newport
Gwent   Telephone 01633 221 172
                 Website http://www.gay-sauna.com

Nearest train station Newport
Car parking On premises (patrolled)
A–Z ref. P63/3G
Nearest landmark Suspension bridge by docks

Membership details £1 membership on first visit: card issued (no personal details are either recorded or kept)

Opening hours   Monday–Thursday: 13.00–23.00
                      Friday: 12.00–02.00
                      Saturday: 12.00 -08.00 (all night)
                      Sunday: 13.00–23.00

Admission charges £9 plus £1 membership on first visit

Food available Hot and cold snacks available and refreshments too

Facilities Ground floor: Reception leads through to changing rooms. Snack bar and dining room, large shower facility, toilets, Jacuzzi, steam room, and sunbed room. First floor: Sauna, showers, toilets, 2 TV lounges (smoking and non-smoking). Second floor: Private and communal rest rooms.

As with all Greenhouse saunas you will not be disappointed. Plenty of dark and cruisy passages along with ample communal and private rest space. Checkout the website.

Jack's Sauna

Beach Road
Penmaenmawr
Gwynedd
LL36 6AY   Telephone 01492 622 878/0800 074 0873 (Freephone)

Nearest train station Penmaenmawr
Car parking On premises (secure and floodlit)

Nearest landmark Penmaenmawr Station (two minute walk – phone from here)

Membership details None required, although membership facilities are available (enquire at reception)

Opening hours   Monday–Sunday: 12.30–22.30

Admission charges   £6 Members/£8 non-members (£4 each subsequent visit in same week)

Concessions available: please ask or phone for further details

Food available Food served all day

Facilities Ground floor: Reception and entrance, changing rooms, newly refurbished relaxation lounge including TV room (smoking), private screened sun terrace (open subject to weather), sauna cabin, showers, steam room, large Jacuzzi and toilet facilities. There are also additional private rest rooms and a large, subtly lit video lounge. First floor: Walk in fast-tan sun room and Submarine(!).

Jack's Sauna is part of The Pennant Hall Hotel, an exclusively gay hotel complex. Sauna guests are welcome to use both the hotel *á la carte* restaurant and licensed bar and can return to the sauna afterwards at no extra cost. Non-residents are welcome to use the sauna facilities at any time. The sauna has a separate entrance. Because of the lack of gay venues in this part of North Wales (the nearest club being at St Asaph – and that's fortnightly) Jack's Sauna is popular with the locals as well as visitors from the surrounding areas. Located on the North Wales Llandudno to Bangor coast the hotel can offer accommodation, although booking is advised during the summer months (see 'Accommodation' listings). Jack's Sauna will be undergoing extensive refurbishment and improvement during the summer of 1999. Therefore there may be alterations to the layout and admission prices.

the ultimate guide to

Cruising Grounds

Introduction

In 1967, the decriminalisation of homosexuals meant that gay and bisexual men no longer had the need to frequent cruising areas in order to have sex or to meet other like-minded males. Then there was the upsurge of gay pubs and clubs, particularly in towns and cities, and the need to resort to cottages and cruising grounds *should* have been quite unnecessary. However, as we know, this has not been the case. Cruising grounds have become even more popular and widespread, much to the annoyance of the police force whose armoury of 'embarrassment factor' has diminished considerably. There is little, if any, stigma felt by the men who do go cruising, looking upon it as yet another outlet for picking up other men just for sex' sake.

The cruising ground is to some extent still populated by the (closeted) married man whom, for some reason or another, cannot bear to publicly 'out' himself by going in to a gay bar or club, thus admitting to himself that he *might* be gay. The cruising ground offers him complete anonymity to fulfil his sexual frustrations. Some men, particularly in rural areas, do not have the transport or economic means to get to the big urban cities and towns and use the cruising ground as their 'local'.

Whatever the reasons, many men choose cruising as a viable way of meeting other men, whether for casual sex or, in the hope that they will meet a prospective long term partner (although this option is highly unlikely). Cruising can be exiting as well as dangerous, and the excitement is one of the reasons that many men are drawn back time and again to the cruising ground. There is something about it. Being opportunistic, you never know who will be turning up. There may be occasions when, for one reason or another, no one will be there that takes your fancy. Yet on another occasion, you may be spoilt for choice!

The kind of men you get are usually very attractive ones; they are often married or have girlfriends, so you do not have to worry about things becoming complicated. The downside is that these men who do not frequent 'the scene' have little or virtually no access to safer health information which means that they may take uninformed risks with their health.

Policing of cruising grounds is (apparently) 'low priority'. This does not alter the fact that the police do make arrests and are usually helped with an admission from the defendant. It is not illegal to be walking through a park, or any other area for that matter, late at night, despite the fact that the area is a well-known cruising ground. It is a well-known fact that there can be undercover policemen patrolling the cruising area, although, thankfully, this is becoming rare.

If you choose to have sex in an exhibitionistic way, then the chances of you being caught (with your trousers down, so to speak) are greatly increased. It is always best to go to a spot where there are absolutely no onlookers, and where the risk of you being caught is reduced.

Soliciting for sex (paid or otherwise) and having sex in a public place is illegal. The police have a duty to investigate all complaints from the public, which will result in regular patrols of the cruising area, and men convicted of 'victimless' public sex offences may have their name included in the sex offenders register along with paedophiles. It is best to avoid any unwelcome visits by the police by curtailing your activities to areas where the public will not 'happen upon you'.

There are three golden rules that you must always adhere to if you are unfortunate enough to be caught by the police:

Admit nothing, no matter what the police say they have seen or what they accuse you of.

Say nothing, even though they will try to get you to lose your temper by name-calling, etc., and . . .

If arrested, always (without fail) ask for a solicitor to represent you at the station and inform LLGS and/or GALOP.

There is more on the subject of policing cruising grounds in the sections that follow.

It is worth mentioning at this stage that the activity of cruising is an extremely contentious issue, not only with the straight community but also with some members of the gay community. However the latter does seem to be more tolerant of the activity, believing that 'lifestyle choice' should not be dictated or morally judged by anyone and for any reason. All the same, you should have the decency to respect other people's feelings on the issue and thus not provoke hostile reaction by openly engaging in 'mutual affection' when there is the slightest possibility that any member of the public could chance upon you. It is advisable at some of the more 'open' cruising areas (such as parks) that the practice of picking up and taking away, to a more secluded area, be used.

The subsequent listings are by no means exhaustive of the cruising grounds in the country. However, they are by far the most comprehensive listings ever yet to be published, in any literature. Again, I request that additions, retractions and amendments should be forwarded to the address at the front of this book.

Finally, it is well worth remembering that cruising, by it's very nature may well be dangerous. As stated time and again in this guide, you must always be on your guard, be particularly aware of your surroundings and remember above all, if you feel that you are in danger, you probably are.

Notice of Disclaimer

I am obliged to inform you that 'soliciting for sex' whether paid for, or otherwise, is illegal. The publishers, contributors and myself cannot be held responsible for any action whatsoever brought against you or any acquaintance of yours. Neither can we be held responsible for any incident caused to you or any acquaintance of yours from any use of the listings. All listings regarding cruising areas are for *informative purposes only*.

Safety First

What odds would Ladbrokes give you on a wager that the police would be in a cruising ground just as a gay man was being assaulted? I say the odds would be greater than Turkey winning the Eurovision Song Contest! I'm not saying that the police would not be present – on the contrary they would be – but they would be there with different intentions. Their argument is that cruising is a crime and that their job is to ensure that it does not happen. They will not mention however, that cruising is a 'victimless' crime, nor that whilst they are skulking around cruising grounds, hoping to catch us 'at it' – employing surveillance equipment and video-equipped cars for the cause – they are further under-staffing a force fighting serious crimes such as burglary, grief-riding and mugging.

Bearing this in mind, it is up to you to take responsibility for your own safety. The actual number of *reported* physical assaults on gay men in cruising grounds is surprisingly low, considering the number of gay men on the cruising circuit. The reporting press highlight the serious incidents, with undertones that the victim asked for it. The police will say that although the incident was regrettable, it wouldn't have happened had the victim adhered to the law.

It is a plain fact that cruising (like prostitution) does go on and will continue to do so, despite the fact that gay bars and clubs are opening at a phenomenal rate.

So, what can you do to protect yourself? Firstly, don't ask for trouble. Cruising grounds are, by nature of their public locations, used by the public! Always be aware of whom you are approaching. Just because someone is walking through a cruising ground it doesn't necessarily mean that they are there for the same reason that you are. If you are not sure, I recommend that you follow the person in question at a safe distance. You will know soon enough if he is just passing through, and whether he does or doesn't want you to follow him. If he makes it plain by totally ignoring you, then take it that he is not interested in you and move on to the next one. Don't labour the point thinking that he doesn't know what he's missing, and if you hang around him for long enough then he'll change his mind . . . Get real – accept the fact that you are not his type and give him space.

I believe that you should not go cruising with your mates (or to saunas for that matter). Not only is it intimidating to others, wondering as to whether you are a group of lads out for trouble, but it also stops anyone approaching you or someone with whom you are with. Another downside is that you are obliged to stay with your mates and your cruising activities are seriously curtailed.

The following is a list of *dos* and *don'ts* which, if followed, will help you get the most out of your nocturnal activities;

Never take your wallet to a cruising ground. Leave it in your car, with a friend or better still, leave it at home. If you are going to a bar or club beforehand then take only enough ready cash to get you through the evening. If you are planning to take a taxi home then only carry enough for this purpose. Do not keep cash in your back pocket; put it in an inside pocket or the fob pocket in your jeans. This way you will know if someone is trying to relieve you of your cash as well as your bodily fluids.

Always be aware of your surroundings and the people around you. It is well-known that in group sessions, a couple of lads can be working together. Whilst one is lavishing attention on you, the other is going through your trouser pockets.

On a one-to-one basis there are actually quite a few tell-tale signs to watch out for, to check if your new found friend is all that he purports to be. While he is touching you, probably telling you what a good build you are, etc., he is actually trying to work out whether you are worth robbing or not. On the same theme, whilst you have got your trousers around your ankles and he is (pretending) to lavish attention around your genitalia, his hands are actually rummaging through your trouser pockets without you knowing it. After he has got what he is after (which is completely different to what you are after) he will make his excuses and leave. Should you ever think 'Blimey, that was quick!' check your pockets to see if anything is missing. However, if you had taken note of the above paragraph you would not be missing anything.

Always tell someone that you are going cruising. Personally, I do not think that there is anything wrong with cruising, although I know people who do, and they are quite closeted about it. I tell most people where I go and which areas I usually hang out. This ensures that if anything should happen, the police will have a starting point.

Do not carry a knife or other weapon. If you are searched for any reason, or, you threaten to use it, it will be *you* who will be in *serious* trouble. In addition it may even be used on you.

Be aware of your surroundings. If you are new to an area, it is preferable to drive around in your car for the first hour or so familiarising yourself with all the exits in – and out – of the area. Make a mental note of where people are going, where they are gathering, etc.

Find out if there are any straight bars and clubs in the area that may result in straights walking through the area after closing time. Look up. Are there any infra red cameras guarding the warehouses and buildings commonly associated with cruising areas?

Report any incident to the police. This may sound alien to a lot of people, but it has to be done. If, however, reporting an incident to the police would be impossible for you to do, then telephone the Gay Switchboard and report the incident to them (in confidence). They will in turn report it to the police on your behalf. It would be nice to think that when difficult situations occur, you would be able to rely on the assistance of your fellow cruisers; sadly, this will not be the case. Believe it or not, you are out there on your own. I hope that things will change in the future but until then do not rely on anyone else's assistance.

Be extra vigilant: if you go to a secluded area with someone with whom you have doubts, it may be a trap. It may be better not to go at all.

Never remove *all* of your clothing. It is impossible that anyone will ever ask this of you. If they do, then alarm bells should start ringing.

A common procedure of prior warning being adopted is for car cruisers to beep their horn twice – their car horn that is – if they see anything untoward happening, or possibly about to happen. For example, if the police are about to enter a secluded area, the sound of the car horn will give the occupants a little bit of warning to 'get themselves together'. It may be argued that pranksters may 'cry wolf' but in the absence of a foolproof procedure, the above is the best that we have.

All the above paints an extremely bleak picture of cruising activities. This is indeed intentional. The point of it is to show you what could, and at times, does happen *if you are not careful*!

You and the Law
A 'run-in' with the police can be a frightening and nerve-racking experience, especially if you are gay or bisexual, and even more so if the 'run-in' is on a notorious cruising ground. The gay, lesbian and bisexual anti-violence and police monitoring group GALOP has, since 1982, collected information on the treatment of London's gay and lesbian population by London's police. This information is used to inform and educate Londoners about current police practice and its effects on the gay and lesbian people of the city.

The information detailed below offers the basis of your rights confirmed as correct by GALOP as of January 1999.

If you are stopped in the street
The police can stop and search you and your vehicle without arresting you. They must tell you who they are and why they are doing this. It is well within your rights to ask for a written search record. In this situation: *Stay* calm. *Note* the officer's number (or ask for it, they must tell you). *Give* your correct name and address (the police can insist on this). *Do not* answer any leading questions. *Be polite* and remember to stay calm. *Ask* any bystanders to witness the event and/or to contact friends, family or solicitor.

If you are arrested

Ask the police 'why?' – they must tell you. *Give* your correct name and address. *Make* a note of the arresting officer's name and number, *until* you get to see a solicitor as recommended by the London Lesbian and Gay Switchboard (LLGS).

GALOP advise that you; *Do not* answer any police questions except for providing them with your correct name and address. *Do not* make or sign any police statement. *Do not* give consent to any police procedures (e.g. blood samples, identity parades). *Do not* plead guilty to any charge. *Do not* accept any kind of caution or warning (no matter how desirous it may seem at the time). The consequences of a caution or warning need to be affirmed by an approved solicitor (not the police).

In the first instance, you must ask to notify LLGS that you have been arrested, by phoning: 0171 837 7324 or GALOP: 0171 704 2040. GALOP and the LLGS hold referral lists of solicitors who specialise in gay related offences.

Remember that legal advice at the police station is free at all times. Exercise your rights – ask for a solicitor. Asking for a solicitor will not make you look guilty and it is essential to have somebody on your side who knows the law. Make sure that you also phone one other person to tell them where you are. This is your right also.

You can volunteer to go to the police station but you cannot be detained there without being arrested. Your rights are detailed in PACE police codes of practice. You have the right to consult this code throughout your detention. If you are detained, ask for a copy; it will pass the time in the cell and will also inform you of your rights to food, drink and medical attention.

You can be held 'uncharged' for up to 24 hours (or sometimes 36 hours, however, this would be for an extremely serious offence). In exceptional circumstances, access to a lawyer/friends/family can be denied for up to 36 hours. Remember, if you have quite correctly chosen not to make a statement or answer any questions without the presence of a solicitor, the police will have substantially little cause to keep you detained for longer than necessary. Your detention must be reviewed within six hours and then every nine hours. By 36 hours you must be taken before a court. You have a right to a lawyer from now on and you can be detained after charge until the next court sitting.

When you are detained, you will be searched and your possessions will be listed. Ask to keep your watch, pen and paper in order that your detention can be recorded. This request can rightly be refused. The police may intimately search (without your consent) your mouth, nose, ears, anus, vagina for 'Class A' drugs or dangerous items using 'reasonable force' if necessary. This search will be carried out normally by a doctor or nurse. If you are concerned that the search is not being conducted correctly, do speak to your solicitor, but be careful about resisting the search physically as you could end up being charged with assaulting the person searching you. Intimate bodily samples (e.g. blood or semen) can only be taken with your written consent. Do not give this without first consulting your solicitor. Bodily samples can only be taken by a registered doctor or nurse.

You may be photographed but force must not be used.

Most cases regarding gross indecency, or whatever, are proven only by your own admission without a solicitor being present. You will probably be told by Mr Nice Policeman that if you co-operate with the police and make a statement then the whole thing will be easier for you. They will prey on your embarrassment, make remarks that the incident will be reported in the papers, that all your work colleagues will find out, etc. The fact of the matter is that it will be easier for them to prosecute you and trawl you through the courts should you be stupid enough to admit to anything without a solicitor being present.

Immediately after your release, write down everything that has happened. This may be useful as evidence. Please call the GALOP Shoutline on 0171 704 2040. Although it has a Greater London remit they will accept calls and offer assistance nation-wide. As is the case with most switchboards, you will find that they will constantly be engaged. Keep trying. Remember: GALOP's Shoutline promises you confidentiality. They can offer you support and referrals. *They are not the police.*

You have a wealth of information, advice and support, specifically set up in order to help you in situations such as this. Use them. The police, (God love 'em) will do all in their power to deter you from doing so. They will make (unwritten) promises, 'advise' you and so forth. It is in your own interest to follow the guidelines above.

In order to understand how the law stands with regard to cruisers or, as the case may be, a person innocently walking through a cruising ground, it is worth bearing in mind the following points of (absurd) law:

Buggery and Gross Indecency
These are the two main 'homosexual offences'. Buggery means anal intercourse (not necessarily with emissions). Both partners can be prosecuted. Gross indecency is not defined and is a vague, arbitrary

concept. Judges will usually tell a jury to use their common sense in determining what 'gross indecency' is. Most courts consider that acts of mutual masturbation are 'grossly indecent', and you will have an almost impossible task persuading them otherwise.

There are three conditions that make buggery and gross indecency legal. These are: both men must be over 18, the sexual activity must be private, and both partners must consent to the activity.

Both men must be over 18. Where one or both are under this age then there can only be a prosecution by the Director of Public Prosecutions (DPP). The police cannot bring a prosecution themselves, although this does not prevent men in this situation being arrested, charged, held in custody (if only overnight) and then enduring the agonising wait to see if they will be prosecuted.

The sexual activity must be carried out in private. This is extremely narrowly defined. It is not private where more than two persons are present. Again, it is not private if it takes place in a lavatory that can be used by the public, even if there are *only* two persons inside and the door is locked. In other cases it will depend on the circumstances and the court's view of whether the act was private or not. For instance, two men in a lonely wood or a dark lane may be considered 'in private' depending on all the circumstances (for instance the lighting and the likelihood of a third person arriving on the scene). It is important to realise that though it is a homosexual activity in public that is considered a crime, men can be, and usually are convicted on the evidence of one police officer alone, even though no member of the public saw or complained of what was happening.

Both men must consent. Buggery without the other man's consent does have a heavier maximum sentence and if there is no buggery, the charge of 'indecent assault' (rather than the weaker one of 'gross indecency') would be brought.

Soliciting

It is an offence for a man 'persistently to solicit or importune in a public place for an immoral purpose'. The maximum penalty is two years. This section was based on an old law, the purpose of which was not to convict male homosexuals but rather to get at prostitutes, touts and pimps. Nowadays it is used exclusively against male homosexuals. It is appalling to note that it has been held specifically *not* to apply to male kerb-crawlers who try to pick up women (*Crook v. Edmunson*, 1966)

Solicit and importune mean the same thing. According to one or more of the leading decisions (*Dale v. Smith*, 1967) 'persistently' seems to mean more than one invitation to one person, or a number of invitations to different people. This decision also shows the slender evidence needed to convict someone. The judge said, '. . . that the fact the accused man had walked up to groups of youths and said "hello" was a piece of evidence that could be used against him'. As for the charge of 'indecent behaviour', it is not necessary to show that a member of the public had been annoyed or offended or even that they were aware that they were being solicited (*DPP v. Rogers*, 1953). The courts usually convict on police evidence alone.

Brothels
It is an offence to own or manage a brothel for men. Judging from the decisions in heterosexual cases, it would seem that sexual inter-course in itself is enough to make a place into a brothel even though no prostitution is involved and even though the owner of the building receives no money. For instance, the owner of a café/dance hall was convicted of managing a brothel just on the grounds that heterosexual couples went there to have sex. It is because of cases such as this, for example, that owners of men's saunas get prosecuted for managing brothels even though there is no actual 'trade' or prostitution. Theoretically, though this is very unlikely, even the owner of a private house could be prosecuted. However, for the prosecution even to begin proving such a case, they would have to show that more than one male homosexual was being visited by men, as, in law, a brothel does not apply to a situation where one woman or one man receives a number of men. It will be of interest to note, that as a man cannot be a prostitute 'in law' they are often charged with associate offences such as 'obstruction of the highway', which carries a fine. It is also an offence:

To procure a man to have sex with a third man.

For someone to live on the earnings of a male prostitute.

For a brothel to be kept and for a landlord/landlady/tenant to allow premises to be used as a brothel.

The above (edited and updated) text was reprinted by kind permission of the Manchester Law Centre.

In preparation for the next edition, I am interested in receiving personal case histories regarding matters of police intervention in cruisers' activities. All correspondence will be kept completely confidential and no personal details will be held on any kind of retrieval system. It is hoped that these previous cases may help others who might find themselves in a similar situation. Write in confidence to the address given in the introduction to this book.

As a final note, local by-laws will vary from county to county. Some counties may tolerate cruising whilst others will have zero tolerance preferring to utilise under-funded police resources, policing victimless crimes (but providing a 100% success rate) and leaving the more serious incidents undetected.

The above text is written purely as a guide and is not deemed to be the final word of the law. Should you find yourself in need of sympathetic legal representation you should phone your local switchboard or GALOP for a solicitor who specialises in homosexual cases.

About GALOP

What is GALOP?
GALOP is a voluntary sector, anti-violence and police monitoring community project for gay men, lesbians and bisexuals.

GALOP knows that gay men, lesbians and bisexuals are often the targets of homophobic/lesbian-hating violence. They know that some members of our communities are also subjected to other hate crimes such as racism and women hating. They believe: 'Hate crimes affect our freedom. We have the right to feel safe. We have the right to protection'

GALOP recognises that gay men, lesbians and bisexuals have, historically, had a difficult relationship with the police. They believe that all communities should receive a fair and non-discriminatory service from the police.

What do GALOP do?
Their core service is their helpline, Shoutline. They also lobby, influence policy, liaise with statutory agencies, outreach to other gay/lesbian/bisexual groups and provide training for the police and local authorities.

How can GALOP help you?
Their Shoutline can help you deal with any form of homophobic or lesbian-hating abuse such as verbal assault, physical assault,

domestic harassment or violence. 'The Shoutline is a non-judgmental service. We will not tell you what to do. We will discuss options with you and support whatever action you decide to take, if you want to take action at all. All calls are confidential.'

Their Shoutline can help you deal with any policing issue, including police harassment, homophobic-motivated arrest, custody and defence, policing of sexual offences and inadequate or unprofessional police assistance.

What does the Shoutline provide?

Free service.
   Confidential advice and emotional support.
   Legal information.
   Referrals to gay-/lesbian-friendly solicitors.
   Referrals to gay-/lesbian-friendly police officers.
   Advocacy with agencies such as housing and the police.
   You can ask to speak to a lesbian or gay man when you call.

   Telephone
   Shoutline 0171 704 2040 (always keep this number handy)
   (Administration line) 0171 704 6767
   (Minicom) 0171 704 3111

Use the administration number to make a donation; to request pertinent literature (it is best to write for literature enclosing an SAE and donation – whatever you can afford – to the address that follows); to become a member of GALOP and/or to request details of their training courses. Do not use this number for Shoutline services.

Remember, as with all gay, lesbian and bisexual voluntary services it is not only vital for the success of the organisation, but also courteous, to enclose a donation of whatever you can afford, should you find yourself in a position requiring their help. Write to:

> GALOP
> Unit 2G Leroy House
> 436 Essex Road
> London
> N1 3QP

And Finally . . .
Assertiveness is not something that comes easy to most people. However, it is a trait that you will have to become familiar with

when cruising. For example, should you be asked to do something that you are not keen to do then you must say so. You do not have to explain yourself to anyone, least of all a pick-up in a cruising ground. Just say that it's something you're not into, and anyone half-decent will accept it at that. You will also have to be assertive in the case of realising that you are not compatible with someone that you have just picked up. It's a bit embarrassing this one, but trust me, it does happen. Again, just be up-front and tell your partner that it's not working for you. It is appreciated that mistakes on the cruising circuit do happen, it's 'the nature of the beast' as they say. The point of all of this is: don't do anything that you do not want to do. If you are not happy with anything then say so.

On a final note, engaging in sex or heavy petting in a public place (e.g. a park) during the day, while there are families and children about, or, if a member of the public could chance upon you *is totally unacceptable*. There are listings in the following section that identify cruising areas located in what I would consider to be altogether inappropriate places, such as Earls Court Cemetery in London and Warriston Cemetery in Edinburgh, church grounds and so on. Cruising in such sensitive surroundings is bound to cause further hostile reactions from the general public towards gays, and it is advised that the use of these particular areas should cease and a more appropriate location found. In the summer of 1998, the Metropolitan Police started to use hand-held video cameras during the hours of daylight to deter (mostly gay) men from cruising. All of this came about because of the sheer number of complaints received by the police from the public and they were duty-bound to do something about it. Now that video cameras are used and the police are more often present on the cruising ground, we can all thank those selfish people who just couldn't be bothered to take their pick-up to a more secluded area. This policy is not just confined to London. On every cruising ground in the country there is a chance that a member of the public will be able to see what is going on. All it takes is a few complaints to the police, and the cruising ground will be targeted for closure. Go to somewhere a little more discreet and you will be able to enjoy your 'hobby' for a lot longer.

The listings that follow indicate the popularity of the cruising ground. Even so, they are not fully complete. I would welcome amendments, additions and (hopefully, not too many) detractions.

I have tried to identify each (known) location with the use of an A–Z reference. However, as most of the areas are outside the relevant town or city, they are not covered by A–Z guides (and are thus, without references). This also applies to particular parks or lay-bys, where the precise cruising area is unavailable. This said, the vast majority of listings are well identified by road numbers and names and, with the aid of a road map, should not prove too difficult to locate. At this point, I reiterate my request that more precise details be forwarded to me for all cruising areas throughout the country, in order to make this section of the guide the absolute authority.

All new sources will be verified prior to the next edition.

British Cruising Ground Listings

LONDON

Because of the sheer size of Greater London, the opportunity for the development of new cruising grounds is immense, particularly around the old disused warehouses situated on all parts of the Thames. If there are areas not listed or, indeed, not yet established then please write and let me know. Please bear in mind that the perfect site would be well away from residential areas and main road traffic and out of sight from any members of the public.

West Brompton Cemetry, Earls Court SW6
A–Z ref. P75/6K

Lots of outdoor cruising by the western wall where shrubbery and quite a few trees offer a degree of privacy. This site is used extensively throughout the day, however, the National Park police heavily patrol the area on foot and, at times, mount a sting operation. You probably don't need me to reiterate that this seems an entirely inappropriate ground to cruise. I'd advise you seek an alternative ground.

Brockwell Park SE24
A–Z ref. P94/7B

Detailed information required here please.

Wharfdale Road N1
A–Z ref. P61/2J

The area behind the Coleherne pub is popular but is mainly a place for rent boys.

Epping Forest E11
A–Z ref. P33/4H

Park in the car park on Snaresbrook Road (near the Crown Court) and take a wander around. Sound action most nights.

Hammersmith Towpath W6
A–Z ref. P74/5D

The towpath along the river between Hammersmith Bridge and Putney Bridge (P91/3G) is always busy after dark. Most of the cruising occurs at either the Hammersmith end near to the old Harrods furniture depository, or, at the Putney Bridge end just past the weir, where the path is no longer paved and the road ends.

Hampstead Heath NW3
A–Z ref. P44/3A

Between Hampstead and Golders Green tube stations. Outdoor cruising in the woods on the north side of the hill just below Jack Straws Castle (straight pub). The adjacent car park has direct access to the Heath (it is recommended that you do not park your car in the Jack Straws car park – find an alternative parking spot). Turn right at the bottom of the car park to get to where the action is. It is true that action can also be found during the daytime when the weather is warmer, although it is in the evenings after 11.00 which is still the busiest time. Bear in mind the warnings given regarding daytime cruising in public areas.

Heston Motorway Service Station, Hounslow
A–Z ref. P70/6B

The M4 between Junctions 2 and 3, near Heathrow Airport. Truck stop and car parks here with the main toilet area being busy, day and night. Eastbound facilities close around 22.00, however, the westbound facilities are open all night. Plenty of scope around the main doors close to the phone boxes. Particularly busy after 23.00.

Holland Walk W8
A–Z ref. P75/1H

A great late night cruising area in Central-West London. You will find it near Holland Park Underground Station. The walk is a short cut between Holland Park Avenue and Kensington High Street. It runs alongside Holland Park, between some very exclusive housing. It is a good place to meet guys coming home from a night out in Earls Court (after 23.00). You will find lots of cruising in the wooded areas behind the fencing. Caution advised.

Russell Square WC1
A–Z ref. P61/5J

The tube is busy seven nights a week (very busy!), usually, between 12.30–2.30. The garden area around the snack bar and the air-monitoring shack is where you should aim. On some nights the floodlights are switched on, so caution is advised. During the summer months the council starts to cut back the shrubbery, making privacy harder to find, but it can be found. Nearby Bloomsbury Square (P61/5J) and Queen Square (P61/4J) – although quieter – are also late evening local sex spots.

Streatham Common SW16
A–Z ref. P109/6K

By following the long footpath at the top of the common, make your way to the rookery, adjacent to the woods. Not much action during the day but heaving after dark, through to the early hours of the morning, any day of the week.

Tooting Bec Common SW16
A–Z ref. P109/2G

South London: nearest tube is Balham. Make your way to the area north of

Bedford Hill and west of the railway cutting. This area is extremely busy late in the evening and especially during the summer months.

Surrey Quays/Russia Dock SE16
A–Z ref. P80/2A

You will find action at night on the paths running beneath Stave Hill. The paths are at the bottom of this hill.

Croydon

Shirley Hills
A–Z ref. P135

Some daytime action (irregular), but lots more in the evenings, on the bottom car park and nearby woods. *Precise locations required – please write with details.*

Sunbury Lay-by/M3, Before J1

Lots of cars parked up along with lorries during the week. Sunday nights are also good. Leave London on the A316 towards the M3. There is a gantry just at the point where it becomes a proper motorway. After this gantry is a lay-by on the west-bound side (quite good for watching) but the best side is the London-bound lay-by. Leave at Junction 1, go round the roundabout and then just get back on the Central London-bound side. Pull in and wait. The area is well known to the police, but if you are careful, someone will know of a private place to go.

Richmond

Ham Common TW10
A–Z ref. P104/3D

This public park is very cruisy all year round, day and night, all ages. You need to follow the footpath into the woods to find other guys. Follow the sign to Ham House (National Trust) and park after the football pitches. Walk into the woods on your right. Discretion advised during the day.

Upper Norwood

Beaulieu Heights SE19
A–Z ref. P124/1E

Wooded park at Upper Norwood, behind the IBA Television mast. The toilet there is open 24 hours. The adjacent woods offer plenty of cover. This area can at times be quite busy. The toilet facility is best avoided although you are on a much safer bet if you use the Beaulieu Park cruising ground situated just around the corner going towards Norwood junction. You will find a small gate on the left; go through here and walk along the footpath, down the hill and then along the footpath to the cruisy woods at the end. Lots of action day and night.

Clapham Common SW4
A–Z ref. P93/5F

You'll find night-time cruising on the south-west side, especially after 23.00. *Caution: With the recent publicity in the papers, it may be best to leave this one out for a while.*

ENGLAND

Amersham

A413

A picnic site on the north side of the A413 dual carriageway, west of Amersham. This site is not one of the busiest places but well worth a look if you are passing. Evenings offer a nice shady place to hang around.

Arundel

Whiteways Picnic Area

This place is just outside the town, on the junction of the A29 and A284. There is a large wooded area with action happening throughout the day and into the evenings. There are toilet facilities where you are able to pick up and take away. Police at this site can be a problem so be warned; be discreet.

Aylesford

M20/J6 Cobtree Manor Country Park

Just off the M20 near the Travis Perkins depot, there is a park. You can park up at night and join the cruising that goes on in the nearby woods. Police are known to patrol the area.

Barnet

A1/South

From the M25/J23. Picnic areas east and west just before Mill Hill. *No detailed information on this area unfortunately.*

Bath

Sydney Gardens
A–Z ref. P106/2C

Near the railway cuttings. Best after dusk in the park area or later on, along the canal path. Beware; police patrols through the park at all times. Toilets are active throughout the day. Lots of action by the railway line at night.

M4/South/Junction 18/A46

Head towards Bath. 200-300 metres on the right, there is a rest area and car park with toilet block and adjoining woods. It is best to park in the car park and walk across the road to follow the path through the trees. Follow the well-trodden trails to enter the woodland and main cruising area. This has been a hot action spot for years. Fun throughout the day, hotting up from 20.00 onwards, especially during the summer months. If you are dubious about going to the woods on your first visit, the car park itself may hold some surprises!

Tog Hill Picnic Site

This is approximately three miles or so further on from the above site. Turn left off the A420, at the top of Tog Hill, and immediately left onto the picnic site. Yet another extremely busy site which is thoroughly recommended. Be very aware of police patrols late at night. Because of its close proximity to the site above, it makes for a perfect cruising circuit.

Beaconsfield

M40/North/A40

Leave the M40 at the Beaconsfield exit and go north to the A40. Turn right towards Gerrards Cross and take the first left to Jordans. Between here and the railway there are several parking places and a public footpath crossing the road into woodland on both sides. This site is busy every evening with car drivers going home from work, and at all times during the weekend. Weekday evenings can often be 'hit and miss'. *Note*: Care should be taken as this place is used by genuine dog walkers.

Birmingham

There are surely many more cruising areas in a city such as Birmingham. Even the ones listed are not covered in any great detail and further information would be appreciated on these.

Bull Ring: Manzoni Gardens
A–Z ref. P74/4A

This used to be a popular daytime cruising area however, during recent months, the area seems to have quietened down considerably. *Further information would be appreciated*.

Canal Bank

Rear of the canal side. *Again not much information regarding this area. More would be appreciated*.

Kennedy Gardens
A–Z ref. P74/3A

Situated close to Colmore Circus. *Not much information regarding this area. More would be appreciated*.

Kings Heath: Highbury Park
A–Z ref. P105/1H

Not much is known about this site although it may be worth mentioning. The action (apparently) takes place in the bushes just beneath Highbury House.

ENGLAND

Blackpool

North Pier
A–Z ref. P12/4A

Slightly further north from the North Pier is the Obelisk (war memorial). From here, follow the pathway going north (Middle Walk) that runs between the promenade and Lower Walk. It can be quite a distance (approximately one mile long) during which you will come to locations that will be used as a gathering area. Alternatively, there is Lower Walk, the pathway that runs along the beach, which offers more privacy and is the location to go when you meet someone on Middle Walk. Of course, being Blackpool, the busiest times are at weekend evenings and even more so during the summer months. The quality of talent is exceptional with an age range that goes across the board. In addition to Middle Walk and Lower Walk, it seems that Talbot Road (the main gay street) can prove successful in picking up too. There are a couple of late night take-aways which can give you a rather good excuse for 'hanging around'. Someone – without doubt – will ask you for the time or a light. *Note*: It is not recommended that you park your car near to the tram lines (on North Pier) but to use the many car parks and side streets surrounding the area.

St Annes Road
A–Z ref. P14/6A

The sand dunes near 'Starr Gate', opposite Pontins Holiday's chalets (summer months). The area used covers the car park and toilet facility on Clifton Drive North and ends at Starr Hills by the old people's home.

Bournemouth

Pier/Promenade
A–Z ref. P57/5H

Busy during the evening, especially during the summer months. Daytimes can hold a few surprises but even then, the availability of places to 'take away' to are limited. As it is out in the open you will just have to walk up and down either side of the Pier until you see someone that takes your fancy.

Meyrick Park (Central Drive)
A–Z ref. P57/3G

Near the Town Hall in the centre of the town there are two car parks: the first on the left is all gay and mainly young. The toilets have been demolished so now the action is in the woods after dark. I am led to believe that the car park to aim for is the one opposite the bowling green. The second car park on the left is hard to find. Look for a white 'single chain and post' fence on the right; the hidden entrance to the car park is 50 yards on the left. Not much gay action as yet although married couples occasionally seek single males here. There is some action in the car park adjoining the golf course after dark. Both car parks are about a quarter of a mile apart.

The Gardens (Queens Gardens)
A–Z ref. P57/3F

Access from Queens Road (just down from the Queens gay pub). Less activity over the last few years due to the radical pruning of shrubs in the area, and also substantiated reports of physical attacks. *If you have additional or contrary information regarding the above site, please write.*

Canford Cliffs
A–Z ref. P68/2C

The toilets, near to the library. It is very small and quiet but it has been known to happen. Look for parked cars outside with male occupants, they are likely to be there for the same reason. Plenty of places (especially during the summer) to take away to.

Bracknell

Englemere Pond

A nature reserve. This place has an extensive wooded area and is used in the afternoons, but mainly in the evening. The afternoon tends to have an awful lot of people (not, a lot of awful people!) walking their dogs, so do not *presume* anything. The car park seems to be the starting point with encouragement coming from others to follow them.

Bradford

Manningham Park

The area by the bowling green is popular during the day (especially during the summer months) – at least here you will have an excuse for sitting around. When you start to admire the pensioners playing bowls, you have been there far too long and it's time to move on.

Town Hall
A–Z ref. P58/4B

Cruisy during the evening. *Unfortunately there is not much information about this area. Further details would be appreciated.*

Lister Park
A–Z ref. P35/4D

Exact location in the park not known. The rather cruisy Rimmers Sauna might provide a more appropriate nearby venue for your activities.

Braunton
Braunton Burrows (summertime only)

Take the road from Braunton to Croyd and follow the signs to 'The Burrows' park in the Sandy Lane car park. Then follow the well-beaten path to the beach. Go past the large dune with the flagpole on the top and keep going in a straight line. When you get to the beach, instead of going on to it, turn left. Walk along the path at the top of the dunes for 300-400 yards and then turn back into the burrows. Lots of nude cruising with all ages of guys popping up out of the long grass. There are wardens, but the area is so large that they are not much of a threat. If you pick your spot correctly you will have plenty of warning. I believe that this location is open only between April and October. Mind you, it's worth waiting half of the year for, as the action is always there.

North Devon Link Road: A39 (Barnstaple and Bideford)

The rest area on the North Devon link road between Barnstaple and Bideford. This area was quite good until a couple of guys got busted a few years ago in a police raid. The area is slowly coming back into prominence, although the police still look into the toilets during the early evening now and again. The evening trade is still unsure and a visit is recommended if you are passing, but it's probably not worth making a special trip for.

Brighton

Dukes Mound
A–Z ref. P36/3A

The bushes situated by the marina at the end of Madeira Drive. You need to make your way to the bushes on the sand banks near to the official nudist beach. Lots of action at all times during the year but obviously, like most places, the summer months in particular. Late evenings are the best. The daytime hours, especially around teatime, can be worthwhile too.

Telscombe Cliffs (Saltdean)
A–Z ref. P38/4B

A few miles east of the town on the main coast road (A259) lies an unofficial nudist beach. Park your car at the top of the cliffs. Follow the path down to the beach and clamber over the rocks to reach the gay part of the beach. There is no access at high tide. You will find action in the caves (in the cliffs) Be very aware of tide times and ensure that someone else knows where you are going.

Angel Beach
A–Z ref. P28/5B

The beach promenade, directly west of the old West End Pier. Situated on the Brighton/Hove border, this place gets quite cruisy late on in the evening. More popular with the younger set after the clubs have closed. Caution is advised.

Eastbourne

Make your way to the open-air theatre and along the road above it. Police patrols take place, but it is very dark – so go with a pal. *Further information required for the above site.*

Bristol

The Downs
A–Z ref. P68/3B

Bristol's infamous cruising area. Situated on the promenade close to the observatory, under the suspension bridge on Clifton Downs. Mixed age range catering for all tastes and mostly attitude-free although care does need to be taken. You are strongly advised not to use the cruising ground before 20.00. Police patrols after that time will be extremely limited. The Cottage Sauna in

Bristol's Old Market (see 'Sauna' listing) would be the most viable alternative to using this place. You can get all that you require without any risk whatsoever. (Particularly good for married or bisexual men.)

Brogborough

M1/Junction 18

Brogborough picnic site – not the best ground in the country, although activity can still be found. The best time during the summer months is after 18.00. Winter sees activity after 20.00 (although you may have to hang around a while longer). Be aware of police patrols through the car park at varied intervals.

Budleigh Salterton

Budleigh Salterton Beach

Gay at far-right end. *Additional information required about this area.*

Cambridge

Jesus College
A–Z ref. P21/1D

Jesus Green, the big park behind the college, has to be one of the greatest spots in the country for daytime cruising (summer). During the daytime you should take your pick-ups elsewhere – indeed, this is perhaps the wisest course of action at all times. However, after dark there is cruising throughout the park and action can be found amongst the bushes, as well as the retaining wall behind the public swimming pool. Lots (*and lots*) of students and college-aged tourists from all over Europe.

Lammas Land
A–Z ref. P20/5C

As you pass Lammas Land on your left, and the road swings to your right, there is a small road which runs down sharp left (there is another straight ahead) down to a car park that serves as a recreation area. A wooded path runs from the back left-hand corner of the car park. Take this path; walk for approximately 30 metres and you will come to a raised part of the wood on your left. This is a very popular cruising spot with plenty of cover. Best times here are at lunchtimes and going-home-time. After dark, the action shifts across the river. Take the small footbridge near the front end of the car park and then turn left. Action can be found amongst the trees ahead of you, backing on to another bit of the river. During the summer months this place can still be going till 02.00 or even later. The cottage near to the car park is open only during the summer but should be avoided as there are too many families about. However, it does tend to see some action during the late evenings.

Caversham

Waitrose Car Park

A fairly decent site on the Thames starting with a cottage in Waitrose's car park, spreading to the grounds of the Boat House and into Christchurch Meadow where the real action can be found. There is also a second cottage in the middle of the playing fields. Obvious caution should be exercised around the car park vicinity.

Chatham

Great Lines

Wooded area overlooking the shopping centre with outdoor action during the daytime and early evening. Very busy during the summer.

Victoria Gardens

A small park. Used for take-aways. I would advise caution at this site. *Again, not much information available about this site.*

Cobham Woods

Take the A2 from London. About 30 miles out look out for the sign to Thong (there is also a sign for 'HOTEL'). As you come off the motorway take the very narrow road on the right (controlled by traffic lights) which effectively takes you over the top of the A2. Follow the winding lane. Car parking is at the end. Action is found in the woods and on the other side, (it will make sense when you get there). Always good.

Dartford River Crossing

Dartford River Crossing viewing area. Turn off the M25 immediately after the tollbooths going south, or immediately before the tollbooths going north. Cottage in the car park/picnic area in the middle of nowhere. Activity is in the cottage (though this is not advised) or in the adjacent woods, especially Saturday and Sunday. This area is going to be massive.

Chester

Broxton (just past Chester)

Located on the junction of the A41 (to Whitchurch) and the A534. The easiest and most straightforward route is by getting to the end of the M56 (Ellesmere Port) and following the A41 to Whitchurch. The area itself is a picnic area/lorry park with toilets open all night. Adjoining the picnic area is a small wood where most of the action takes place. Alternatively, it is not unknown for people to take a stroll around the lorry park or to use one of the many darkened corners around the car park (you are able to see quite clearly if anyone is approaching but they cannot see you). Remember, do not park your car in the lorry spaces. Weekdays are good between 21.00 and 01.00. Weekends between 21.00 and 03.00. Police activity is reported to be rare but not unknown.

Chester Railway Station
A–Z ref. P8/2A

Again, this is really a no-go area. A video camera is in operation 24 hours of the day monitoring the use of the toilet. Railway police have (allegedly) been known to entice people into the toilet; then arresting them.

The Walls
A–Z ref. P7/3H

There are several entrances to The Walls of Chester. Each entrance can be a good, viable and lucrative point to pick up, although in these cases you will not be too sure who is going to be around. Therefore, on your first visit it is advisable to make your way to Upper Northgate Street (opposite the Liverpool Arms) and enter The Walls from this side. There are two entrances here, one on either side of the road, it doesn't matter which one you use because you will be turning right. Keep walking for about 100 yards until you come to a complete right-angled turn, walk for about a further 30 yards or so and you will soon spot a collection of men taking a moonlit stroll around this (subtly lit) area. There is a wooden flight of stairs leading down to a secluded wooded area. Once you are familiar with this layout you will be able to park your car in the adjoining car park and be able to pop in and out as you please. Friday and Sunday nights seem to be the busiest times, however, I'm sure that you will be able to find something to take your fancy most nights.

(near) Dartmouth

Slapton Beach

Gay at far-left, cross the small cliff at the end for the private beach. All ages and plenty of action in the caves. *Further information required on this beach.*

Dorchester

Dorchester–Puddletown

On the A35 near Stinsford (heading away from Dorchester) there is a lay-by with toilets on your left. You may experience difficulty turning right if you are heading towards Dorchester. Most of the action takes place outside the cubicles or in the woods behind the lay-by.

Dover

Sea front

The sea front toilets situated about halfway between the eastern and western docks are closed at dusk. However, you may be able to pick up a bit of trade (usually truckers, etc.) by hanging around the benches and shelters.

Keston (Biggin Hill)

This is located in a picnic car park approximately one mile after Biggin Hill Airport (main terminal) heading towards Bromley. This area has its good days and its bad. The action takes place in a couple of secluded corners of the wood behind the cottage. Beware genuine picnickers on warm days.

Exeter

Halden Hill

At the top of Halden Hill. The road between the A380 and A38: there are two car parks where cruising occurs. There is plenty of woodland cover available. *Caution advised*: police surveillance was in operation at some time during summer 1997 and is probably on-going at regular intervals.

Ferndown

A31/Ringwood-Ferndown

Find this place on the A31, between Ringwood and Ferndown. Turn left at the roundabout, sign-posted Country Park. The toilets and car park are in use 24 hours a day but it's best in the evening after dark, till approximately 02.00. This area is also frequented by a few married couples looking for action with single males. Plenty of warning of cars approaching the car park.

Gloucester

A417

A 24 hour cottage, with parking and woods, opposite the A417 lay-by. Lots of action, day and night, especially up until 02.00. Take the A417 to Gloucester, pass The Highwayman pub and you will find it about one mile on your left. The A417 is quite a busy road and the area itself can get quite busy late on. There is a good mix of guys here.

Gravesend

A cruisy park: the A2 at Pepper Hill. Known locally as the 'Gravesend Lighthouse' because cars drive all around this service area at night. The toilets are now pretty much well-blown but there are woods behind, and a lot of guys in their cars. It is wise to stand out of your cars, smoking, drinking coffee or simply taking a stroll!

Guildford

Hindhead Common

The A3, ten miles south of Guildford and north of Hindhead village. Here there is a large picnic area (cafe and toilets). Truckers use this place as an overnight stop. During the day, there are genuine dog walkers using the area, so be careful not to presume anything.

Hastings

Bathing Pool

Checkout the area called the 'Bathing Pool' (locals will know it). Mostly active at night, though the Marina toilets are busy all day and night. Occasional police patrol.

Haydock

East Lancs. Road (Just off the M6)
A–Z ref.

Not so much a cruising ground but an ideal spot to take a rest from driving. This part of the East Lancs. Road consists of a series of lay-bys. The idea is that you park your car (leaving the sidelights on) and another car will pull up behind (or in front) of you. A couple of these lay-bys have shrubbery by the side of them where action will take place. It is well worth spending a couple of hours here on an evening even if it's just for a change of scenery. The best times are at weekends after 23.00 probably until 03.00. Weekdays are quiet, although if you hang out long enough something will come along.

Burtonwood Services (M62) Towards Liverpool

Toilets open 24 hours. A pretty good place for lorry drivers (before 23.00). The toilets are one of a dying breed where the insides of the cubicles are not tiled floor to ceiling (though by the time this book is in print, you will probably be staring at a Marley 6x6). Beware after midnight: the security guard will be on duty and will be patrolling the area. It's not such a worry. Try hanging around the telephone kiosks, and wait for someone to ask you for a light (or the time, or a . . .).

Hayton

Hayton Castle

From the M6/North/J43 take the A69 towards Newcastle. You will be directed towards a picnic area situated on a lay-by between Carlisle and Brampton. It is busy most of the day (though not all will be there for the same reason as you, so be careful). However, the best times to go are between 17.00 and 01.00 weekdays, and 21.00–03.00 weekends. The site is used by lorry drivers (mostly weekdays) who will use this area instead of the motorway service lorry park(!). The toilets here are open 24 hours. Most of the action takes place in and around the wooded area in addition to the quiet lanes nearby. Police activity is frequent. It is a well-known area to them and they can be quite intimidating *if you let them*. *Note*: If you are parked up and the police patrol car makes a visit, it is advisable not to leave before them. They will probably stop you on the road and do a spot check on your vehicle. Although there have been no reports of violence or intimidation in this area, the obligatory word of caution is suggested.

Huddersfield

Greenhead Park

Around the war memorial most evenings and nights.

Isle of Purbeck

Studland/Shell Bay

This beach is reported to be one of the very best. Very cruisy at the back of the nudist section, with plenty of action in the dunes and woods. The area is patrolled by National Trust wardens (easily spotted – they're the ones with walkie-talkies). The wardens can be a hassle, even to those who are genuinely into sun worship. Approach from the north by ferry (best on foot or bike because of the queue for cars), or south, from Corfe Castle and Studland Village. Park on the road where most cars are at the halfway point and walk along an obvious path through to the beach (about one mile). At the last moment, veer off to the left for about 200 metres. Now you can start exploring. This area is always busy especially at around teatime before everyone goes home.

Lancaster

Caton Village

East of Lancaster on the A683 (Junction 34 on the M6). Just outside Caton Village there are two picnic areas, (one either side). An isolated and usually quite safe area. Best after 21.00. The abundance of service areas on this stretch of the M6 makes this area a brilliant circuit during the week. The lack of truckers (if that's your bag) over the weekend somewhat minimises the availability of trade. However, if you do have the spare time it is well worth the trek.

Liverpool

Otterspool
A–Z ref. P110/1B

As you leave Albert Dock, turn right and keep going straight for as long as you can (go around the roundabouts obviously). Go past the Festival Park on your right, and past another park. You will then soon come to a sign that says 'Otterspool'. This place consists of a series of car parks (around six in all) with virtually no lighting whatsoever. The main ones of interest to you are car parks '3' and '4'. From here you can walk into the park and bushes where you'll find lots of activity. After car park '4' there is car park '5' (obviously). However, this one is set back and can easily be missed if you are just driving past. It is around this part that the action will take place. Best times to go are any times between 23.00 until 02.00 in the week, and 23.00 and 03.00 on weekends. Police activity (vehicular) happens now and again; they will move you on. It is best to move along before being told to and to return a little later on. The 'Dead End' sign at the far end of the road is in fact a barrier in the middle of the road and can quite easily be passed if you drive on the pavement. You are able to U-turn and re-enter this way. (Remember, driving on the pavement is illegal. Perhaps it may be best to re-enter the way you came in.) Despite this area being well out of the town centre, it can get extremely busy. The presence of parkland makes for an excellent cruising ground. I would recommend that you return to this area if your first visit proves unsuccessful.

Crosby Marine
A–Z ref. P16/3B

Located at the end of South Road. The cottage is quite busy at lunch times and early evenings. However, if it makes you feel more safe, try the Marine Gardens or Crescent Gardens next to the cottage. By all accounts this area gets quite busy.

Long Eaton

Forbes Hole Nature Reserve
A–Z ref. P65/2H

This nature reserve consists of about 10 acres of land with paths amongst mature trees and bushes. Action here of all kinds; after dark in the winter and at any time in the summer. You can take your pick-up over the main line railway to further heavily wooded areas beyond. From Sawley Railway Station, take the road that runs east next to the railway lines, and the park is on the left, just beyond the first bend in the road.

Maidenhead

M40/M4 Link Road

Make your way to the 'picnic area', just past the roundabout, before the Henley turn-off. You willl find a small wooded area, well used throughout the day, with interesting people, right through until the evening. This area is visited on occasions by patrol cars.

Manchester

Piccadilly Railway Station
A–Z ref. P87/5F

In the olden days this used to be a good place to cruise and to pick up, but not any more. The toilets are now covered by five closed circuit television cameras which *are* monitored. The first one watches you from behind as you enter the toilet, the second watches you from the front. There are two more cameras situated in the sink and cubicle areas, the fifth being above the urinals on the left-hand side. The railway police will not hesitate to make an issue out of cruisers' activities – so please be warned.

Cafe Hollywood (Phoenix Centre, Hart Street)
A–Z ref. P87/5E

Situated behind the Hollywood Showbar on Bloom Street/Princess Street, Cafe Hollywood was granted a 24 hour trading licence by Manchester City Council in liaison with the police. The reason being to substantially reduce the number of men using the canal as a cruising area after the pubs and clubs had closed, providing a safer alternative in the gay village itself. This does not mean that the two authorities condone the activity and any complaint received from the public will have to be investigated. It will be in your own interest to be discreet with your activity in order that this popular area can continue. Busiest times are, of course, after the pubs and clubs have closed, with the cafe usually being used as a starting place.

Manchester/Rochdale Canal
A–Z ref. P87/4E

Known locally as 'The Canal'. In actual fact it comprises of quite a large area, and only one part of this is actually by the canal. Like most areas, the busiest times are after midnight *any* day of the week. Police activity is contained to vehicular patrols during the week and the (once for show) foot patrol at the weekend. Police-gay relations in Manchester are extremely positive (although I can't say what would happen if you were unlucky enough to be caught in an uncompromising situation). The following list is the basis to all the areas around the canal. It is advisable, before doing anything, to familiarise yourself with the area. The canal comprises of five main areas.

1. The Canal

There are two entrances to the Canal area: The first is along the canal towpath starting where Canal Street, (the edge of the gay village) crosses with Minshull Street. There is a small gateway in the wall (opposite a small car park), walk down the ramp and follow the canal for as long as you can (about 200 yards) You will come to an undercover area, behind railings(!) which is usually the starting point of the evening. The lighting here is quite adequate and police activity is rare. (I am led to believe that foot patrols are made before 23.00 and are virtually non-existent after that time.) It is possible to pick up from here during the daylight hours although naturally, even more care is called for during these times. The railings area is split up into three parts. The first is the main entrance; for standing around and looking at what is coming in: a general pick-up area. The second and central part is an extremely dark passage generally used as a free-for-all, certainly not recommended for the faint of heart (beware pick-pockets too). The third and last part is a larger area where you can cruise to your heart's content. There's not many places down here for privacy (perhaps you don't want it!) but you can pick up and take away to more secluded areas off Ducie Street (see below). From here, go back to the railings entrance (Iron Gate) and turn right. Walk up the ramp until you come to the barrier (this paved area is also good for picking up) and turn a sharp right again, continuing up the ramp. You should now be at the Dale Street entrance.

2. Dale Street

The Dale Street entrance is used by people who have come in their cars (who hasn't?). Easy parking facilities around the area and the adjacent NCP Car Park allow for discreet comings and goings. Most people (including straights) use this area to park up and walk the short distance into the city centre. Dale Street is used by prostitutes, and the police will be patrolling this area in their vans constantly. Turn left from the canal entrance down to Ducie Street. This street is *the* main arena. If you come down by car it is advisable to park at one of the meters (obviously, you do not pay) and walk around. Alternatively walk up Ducie Street *away* from Piccadilly Station.

3. Ducie Street

On your right you will see a huge deserted warehouse, behind which are plenty of doorways, *but beware*: lots of police activity around this area, as the property belongs to British Rail. (There is also a rotating infra red camera on the roof of the BT building scanning this area constantly.) Across the road is an entrance to a small parkland area, (the council have recently cut down most of the shrubbery – you can gain access to the underneath of the bridge here). The road is an ideal place to hang around; passing trade will ensure that your evening will go with a bang. Continue over the bridge and cross the road towards . . .

4. Jutland Street

Hang around this area looking over the wall or quite simply walking about. This is an extremely good pick-up place. On the corner of Jutland Street, there is an entrance that, if you follow the walkway, will take you to a towpath *under* Jutland Street. This part is used as either a pick-up place or somewhere with scope for a modicum of privacy. Bear in mind that this walkway could be used by straights as a means of getting to the residential area a little further on. Get back on to Ducie Street. Across the road from Jutland Street, you will see a small wall next to a dark alleyway. By sitting on the wall you can encourage people to go down the alleyway. It's quite private around here and it is geared more towards straights looking for a little bit of adventure who may be put off from going down to the canal area. Back on to Ducie Street, continue walking up towards Ancoats (away from Piccadilly Station) and turn left at . . .

5. Peak Street/Tariff Street

If you have followed the road around correctly, you will have come to a quieter and more discreet part of the canal complex. The line of parked cars gives the game away. Around here is an abundance of places where, if privacy is what you want, then that's what you will get. *Warning*: should you go down to the Tariff Street canal there is an almighty drop into the water with no visible way to scramble back. Be sure you are with someone whom you feel safe with! *Note: Here too, the council have cut down the shrubbery. Although the lack of lighting still offers a scope of privacy, nothing down here can be seen from the main road without the use of a torch(!).* On subsequent visits to this area you will find that there are more than twice as many private areas to take your pick-ups to than those listed here. The above guide is more than enough to be starting with and in time you will no doubt learn about the others. On a final note; it seems that the council's way of reducing cruisers from this now very well established area is to keep cutting back shrubbery from locations away from the main road. This action is having a reverse effect of pushing cruisers onto the main road and further into the more residential areas of the town. *Note of warning: During the early part of summer 1998, an increase in the number of attacks on gay men was taking place in this normally attitude-free area. They were being caused by a small group of men who were after your money rather than the general, homophobic attacker. Prior to publishing, I was informed that the men responsible for these attacks were arrested by police, using surveillance techniques, and that the area's safety has now improved. I feel I should also point out that the police were able to operate this deployment due to the brave people who were willing to make detailed reports of the incidents. Congratulations to the police for taking them seriously.*

Marrow

Bisham Woods

From the A404, towards the M4. It is about six miles long from one motorway to the other. About midway, there is the Bisham roundabout, which signposts you off to the A308 Maidenhead. On the M4 side of this roundabout (on the left if heading towards the M4) there is a slip road marked as a picnic area. Turn in, park up and wander through the woods. This area is extremely busy during the summer months.

Alternative Circuits

Going north between the M4 and M40, leaving the M4 at junction 8/9; turn right on to the A40 at the Maidenhead Thicket Roundabout. Almost immediately, take a minor road to the left and a little way along there is a car park. Car drivers park here and walk along the footbridge into Maidenhead Thicket where there is plenty of cover. Quite busy at going–home–time.

Continue north along this minor road and re-join the main road you left at Maidenhead Thicket. A little further on there is a long lay-by with a picnic area behind the hedge. This area is worth stopping off at but don't spend time here.

Continue north to the next roundabout and you will be at Bisham Woods. *Note: Bisham Woods and the surrounding areas are quite well known as cruising areas. Further information is required in order to update this excellent circuit.*

Methley

M62/J30

Head towards Wakefield, take the first left and follow the road around until it passes under the motorway. Take the first left. Alongside the motorway is a lane. It is here in the evenings that some action will be taking place. It is not (yet) an extremely well-known place. Bushes along the walkway will provide some cover. Police activity will be in the form of patrols. Care and discretion recommended.

Newcastle

The Gardens
A–Z ref. P60/4B

Situated between the Quayside and Newcastle train station next to the Castle Keep and the high level bridge. This is a lightly wooded area. Cruising starts about lunch time until 15.00 and then from 17.00 until about 20.00. It starts up again at 22.00 until about 03.00. On the Gateshead side of the high level bridge you will find much the same, except cars are used. Any action that goes on is in the empty buildings. At the time of writing, the empty buildings were soon due to be demolished. *Note: extreme caution to be taken in this area. I would appreciate being updated on this area.*

Northampton

Bedford Road/Becketts Park
A–Z ref. P14/4D

Near the town centre, by the River Nene, all along the river path in the evening. There are two cottages, one near the town, the other about halfway down the river path. Occasional police activity here. The bushes near the second loo are a favourite place; also, the nature reserve over the bridge. Police cars patrol at night. Further down are the meadows. The parking area *should* be closed at night but most of the time it isn't. Cross the bridge and wander through the area. Again, police cars do visit this area.

A43 Northampton to Kettering

Long lay-bys about halfway between these two towns. They are well screened from the A43 and very good late at night with easy access to nearby fields. Police do tend to sniff about, but no reports of any arrests.

Norwich

A11

A lay–by with a cottage, in heavy woods, on the left-hand side of the A11 dual carriageway, about 10 miles out of Norwich. Not much during the day, however, the nights can be very busy. Police patrols are occasional. Rumour has it that an off-duty policeman walks his dog there hoping to catch someone at it . . . (Sad!)

Note: Norwich City Council have given permission to the police to install hidden miniature surveillance cameras in notorious cottages. Several prosecutions and convictions have followed. Be aware.

Nottingham

Normanshill Wood, Car Park

Known locally as 'Thieves Wood'. Take the A60 from Nottingham, past Nestead Abbey. At the Larch Farm junction turn left onto the B6020 towards Kirkby/Sutton in Ashfield. Take the second turning on the right. This road will sweep and bend to the left into the forest area. Normanshill Wood Car Park is up on the left. Pull into the car park and park up. Busy here all day and late nights as well. Plenty of travelling salesmen, local regulars and courting couples (usually evenings). Ample opportunities to cruise around the area. Plenty of trails in the wood, so it will be easy to find the hot spots. Police activity is contained to patrolling the car park. If they are seen entering the woods, cruisers in cars will beep their horn twice (*don't* rely on this though).

Peterborough

Nene Valley Picnic Area

Known as Wansford lorry park. From the A1 follow the sign for the A47 (Peterborough). Almost immediately, a sign indicates 'Picnic Area'. The entrance is easy to miss. You will come to a large car park with spaces for lorries, vans, etc. Here there is a toilet facility and absolutely tons of action, day and night, although, excluding lorry cabs, privacy will be hard to find. Police patrol the area on a regular basis and, on occasions, have been known to raid the toilet block. Care and discretion advised.

Stanley Recreation Ground
A–Z ref. P12/2A

Apparently, this area is quite active. *Unfortunately, I do not have current information regarding this site.*

Popham

M3/J7/A33

A lay-by, reachable by leaving Junction 7 off the M3 and following signs for the A33. After about two miles the road opens to a dual carriageway and on your left is a lay-by set back from the road. It gets quite busy during the daytime, right through into the evening. The general behaviour is to park your car, take a short stroll into the undergrowth and have fun. A good mix of clientele from young to old. There is not a great deal of tree cover although it is safe enough in the dark, but obviously a bit more risky during the day. As always, exercise caution and discretion.

Reading

Thameside Promenade

Park your car near to The Holiday Inn, in the Thameside car park. The toilet facility here can provide a meet but is considered too dangerous for anything more. It is better, and more safer, to take the short walk along the Thameside Promenade to the point where Cow Lane meets the prom. This can be a busy site at any time of the day but is especially so 18.00 onwards.

Rugby

M1/J18/A5

Various locations either side of the M1. The first is a former cottage by the motorway, which was the best in the Midlands but gradually died down to nothing after it was closed, was then later pulled down and the lay-bys ripped up for new development. The road has now been re-opened and initial signs are that it is starting again in new lay-bys which are much reduced in size. For the second, continue further north from the last location for about two miles by the radio mast in lay-bys. Additionally, there is the truck stop opposite and lanes leading to and from Lilbourne. The shower block in the truck stop is worth a look (not a guaranteed ground though).

Salisbury

A36 Southampton Road

Cottage and cruisy park at the A36 Southampton Road in addition to the car park opposite Salisbury College. Be aware that the car park is under video surveillance (but the cottage and park is not).

Shaftesbury

Shaftesbury–Sherborne

On the A30, three miles east of Henstridge (which is about halfway between Shaftesbury and Sherborne), there is a double road lay-by on the left-hand side as you go west. Action happens in the woods behind the furtherest bit of lay-by. Busy all afternoon and especially at going-home-time.

Sheerness

A249 Sheerness Road/Sittingbourne

From the M20/J7 follow the signs for Sheerness. Continue for four to five miles, keeping an eye out for a sign that says 'Parking 150 Yards' – this sign is easy to miss. The lay-by is long with thick woods on the left, rising steeply to fields beyond. Non-stop action with truckers, married types, all sorts. Police patrols at night (area is worth the hassle though). *Note*: This may be the same site as the one listed as Sittingbourne. The directions being; . . . known locally as Detling Hill lay-by, just past the Kent County Showground, there is a secluded pull in lay-by. A lot of action to be had in the woods there (and on the hillside) and further up in the fields behind. Take care after dark though, because it's a rabbit run of paths and dead ends. *Note: There has been recently publicised police activity in this area with them taking car numbers and recording them. The police activity is due to complaints from the public (apparently) so try to be more discreet in your activities. More detailed and precise description of this site required.*

Solihull

Coleshill: A446/South/M6
A–Z ref. P79/5E

Outdoor action in the woodland located next to the lay-by on the northbound A446 road, immediately south of its junction with the M6 Motorway. Action can be found at most times during the week. Care advised in this location but nothing too much to worry about.

Southampton

Southampton Common; North

Situated at the top of Hill Lane. Daytime action. The toilet is now boarded up but there is a huge amount of action in the woods over quite a large area. Mainly young to middle ages here.

Southampton Common; South

Near the county cricket ground, Cemetery Road. Night time action and easy parking. A large cruising area with plenty of action in the woods. Lads get younger as the evening progresses (apparently). There are many different ways out so it is advisable to familiarise yourself with this area before doing anything. *Note: I have been reliably informed that the police are taking more than a passing interest in the use of the south side of the common. This is due to the careless disposal of condoms, and the fact that this south side is used by families and children. The police have received more than a tolerable amount of complaints from the public. It is in your own interest therefore, to use the north of the common for your activities, to deter 'police interest'. You should dispose of 'rubbish' carefully and exercise caution and common-sense.*

Swindon

Cotswold Water Park

Situated on the A419 towards Cirencester. Travel from Swindon to Cirencester on this road and follow the signs for Ashton Keynes, looking for the sign for Cotswold Water Park. Hang around outside the area surrounding the toilets.

Tavistock

A30 towards Tavistock

Late night cruising area in the woods (near to Brentnor Church). Parking area, etc. Take the entrance off the A30 towards Tavistock; turn right at the junction and then left. Continue for a couple of miles until you see the sign for Chillaton. Turn left here and continue on until you arrive at the T-junction. Turn left again, through Chillaton, and continue for a couple of miles or so more until you see the sign for Brentnor Church. Locate the car park and park up. Not much cover here and not the most appropriate of areas either.

Tonbridge

Barnets Wood Picnic Site

The A21, heading for Hastings, just before Tonbridge: Barnets Wood Picnic Site. Activity in toilets and woods throughout the day . Closes early but I'm led to believe that the action carries on in the lay-by.

Torquay

Petit Tor Beach

This is the naturist beach in Torbay. Take a long walk down towards the sea; take a left at the bottom and continue down. On the beach, the gay area is to the left. There's plenty of action in the bushes and also amongst the rocks at the far end.

Wakefield

Clarence Park

This park is very cruisy most of the day and into the evening. The usual peak periods are lunch times and then 16.00–18.00. The large hill in the middle of the park, behind the bandstand in amongst the trees, is where you will find the action. You'll also find it by hanging around in close proximity to the toilet facility on the main road, where you can expect to be cruised quite easily.

Wells next to the Sea

Holkham Beach

This place can be very wild on a hot sunny weekend. Park at Queen Anne's Lane. Go down to the beach and turn left. Walk for miles, until you see a sign informing you that you are entering the nudist beach, and you are there. Contact is made in the sand dunes. The nearby woods offer privacy. Watch out for the wardens. They will call the police and will hold you until they arrive. They are apparently easy to spot, as they are the ones who are dressed.

Winchester

New Alresford

Travel from Winchester to New Alresford on the A31. Look for a long lay by about two miles from New Alresford. The toilets are now demolished but the area is still very busy throughout the day and quiet, but not dead, after dark. You'll find business men, lorry drivers and some locals. Follow the lay-by until the right-hand bend, passing the private house on the left (do not park close by here!), continue into the trees and park up. Lots of sitting in cars and occasional forays into nearby bushes by mainly older guys. One path leads down a long track to total seclusion: can be fun. Police pay regular visits.

Wisley Woods

M25/A3 Interchange

Some deep woodland running off a lay-by at the side of the A3. It's safe and very active after dusk on most days. To find your way in, enter the woods about 15 yards south of the footbridge over the A3. Bear left and you will meet the path from the footbridge. If you face along the main path into the woods away from the bridge, you will see that there is a hill climbing to your right. It is very cruisy at the top of this hill but to find the activity follow the path into the woods. It rounds the side of the hill and comes to a fairly obvious end, now swing left along the narrower path into the woods, but just before that is a clump of trees under which there is usually someone hanging around. Alternatively, cross the gravel track, bearing slightly to the left and you will find an area where all sorts is going on. Police do not appear to bother with this place. Apparently, a few years ago they used to ride through on their motorbikes until someone tied a piece of rope across the path and they haven't been back since (I would strongly advise against any such actions though). This place can, in places, be very dark so it is advisable to walk around during the daylight to familiarise yourself with the area. *Note*: You cannot reach the lay-by direct from the M25 or A3 as it is on the slope road leading on to the A3. Turn on to the roundabout at the M25/A3 interchange and take the exit for Guildford (A3) keeping to the near side lane. Keep your speed down, as finding a parking spot is tricky. Park in the lay-by immediately before, or after the footbridge. The lay-bys are busy so it may take a few attempts. Although the directions above sound complicated, once you are there you will find that they are precise rather than awkward, but well worth the hassle. *Please note: during the summer of 1998 there was a series of muggings in the Wisley/Ockham Common areas. Assaults were carried out by three young white men, one of whom was used as 'bait'. Information regarding these people should be forwarded to Ripley Police Station on 01483 531111 (or in confidence through your local switchboard).*

Wolverhampton

I'm sure there must be another half a dozen cruising areas in Wolverhampton and surrounding districts. I apologise for the lack of information but I have not been sent any other information apart than the one below.

West Park
A–Z ref. P29/1G

Cruising after dark on Park Road West. Stay away from the toilets.

Worsley

Worsley Wood
A–Z ref. P69/5G

Very popular during the summer months. This area is fast becoming an established site, along with Broxton, due to the closure of Junction 14 (picnic area) on the M56. Take the turn-off (J13/M62 North) and head towards Eccles. About 30 yards on your right you will come to a car park (sign-posted) adjoining the wood. Park up here and take a stroll around. This area is also popular with straight couples, some of whom are looking for a third party to join in their fun.

SCOTLAND

Dundee

Riverside Drive Truck Stop

Quite a bit of night-time action, especially along the track that leads up the side of the airport. It is wise to cruise this area in your car rather than on foot. There is also some action to be found around the sports pavilion opposite.

Dunfermline

Pittencrief Car Park

This area is a night-time hot spot (at times!). Again it is advisable to take the car, rather than walk. You can find action during the day in the park but it is worth saving it for the evenings. Exercise caution if you are cruising in the day however – there will be lots of people using the car park.

Edinburgh

Calton Hill
A–Z ref. P15/2J

Again, night-time activity. The Regent Terrace side is the area that you are after. Avoid the actual hill, as it can be a little bit dangerous.

Warriston Cemetery
A–Z ref. P8/6B

Not the most appropriate place for cruising activities and it is hoped that a more suitable location will be used. During the hours of daylight there are people walking their dogs and of course everyday visitors to the cemetery, making the area further unsuitable.

Fairlie

A78 Sea Front

The sea front toilets by the picnic area at night can be a hive of activity. It is advisable to park in the picnic area and walk along the sea front to take in some air. The toilets are open 24 hours although it is safer to cruise the sea front rather than cottage.

Glasgow

Queens Park
A–Z ref. P102/4C

Make your way to the Victoria Road side of the park using the entrance at the bottom of the road. Alternatively, you can access the area by using the Polockshaws Road entrance. Cruising goes on at the top of the park in the area behind the flagpole.

St Enochs Shopping Centre, Glasgow
A–Z ref. P83/5G

This place got so busy that they carried out successive clamp downs and now it is nothing to what it once was. There is now a security camera installed monitoring the toilet entrance.

Warnings: There are police cameras on the pole outside the toilets on the corner of St. Vincent Street/Buchannon Street, Glasgow. Although this is a notorious cottage you are advised to be aware that you are being watched.

Kelvingrove Park
A–Z ref.P82/1B

This park is as famous as Manchester Canal and Hampstead Heath put together, so, the obligatory warning of caution is hereby administered. For outsiders, the place to be heading for is the area opposite the university tower (after dark). The punters tend to be young and adventurous. *Note: Kelvin Way is a straight road that runs through the park, actually splitting it in two, and it is not rare to see the same car driving past twice, especially after it gets dark. Again it is extremely advisable to have a walk around the area during daylight in order to become familiar with escape routes as well as the spots where the action takes place.*

Kirkcaldy

Ravenscraig Park

Ravenscraig Park gets a lot of night-time action. It is best to park in the first car park and walk through the trees towards the sea. This area can be very dark so you must have your wits about you.

Motherwell

Strathclyde Country Park
A–Z ref. P142/1C

Can be good at times. There are lots of small car parks with lots going on in the bushes.

WALES

Abergele

Abergele Beach

Late in the evenings, straight couples meet up for a snog and a poke, whilst gay men cruise the area near to the public toilet block (who says we can't get along together?). The area gets quite active during the hot summer months, being used on the circuit along with Rhyl (see separate listing). What with the lack of gay facilities on the North Wales Coast and locals not willing to travel the distance to Manchester or Chester, the winter months can also prove to be quite fruitful.

Anglesey

Llanddwyn Beach

Access to the beach is easiest from Newborough on the west coast of Anglesey. Follow the signs to the beach and park up in the designated car park. When you get on to the beach, turn left and walk for about 15 minutes. The high dunes are the start of the cruising area. This area is particularly busy during the summer months. Anglesey attracts a lot of visitors, who stay in the many caravan parks surrounding the area.

Brecon

Pen Y Fan

Drive up the mountain road for about six-seven miles. Go past the big youth hostel on the left. Carry on for about 300 yards until you come to the National Park, Car Park. Park up here and you will find the action in the dense woods. This area is good either day or night. Police do patrol this area.

Cardiff

Bute Park
A–Z ref. P29/2H

Make your way to the area behind the Welsh College of Music and Drama. This is a busy, well-established 24 hour cruising area. *Precise details required.*

Cardiff Castle
A–Z ref. P29/3H

After 18.00 the main cruising ground is at least a half-hour's walk from anything remotely resembling civilisation. The best way to get there is to first find Cardiff Castle. This bit is easy as it is in the centre of Cardiff and all the roads in South Wales seem to lead to it. If you stand facing the main gates, you need to turn left and follow the road all the way down, keeping the castle grounds on your right. You will pass a lot of 'stone creatures' on the right and the Forte Posthouse Hotel on the left. You come to a bridge, which crosses the River Taff. Just on the other side of the bridge, on your right, is an entrance into the castle grounds. If you walk through this entrance and start up the side of the river, the first (and in the summer, the least active) cruising area is about 200 yards down this path. You'll find a few guys leaning against the railings and this is your starting point. From here, carry on along the path for about a mile (it is impossible to get a vehicle down here, so it's walking only I'm afraid). Eventually, you will come to a footbridge and if you cross this into the main castle grounds you'll find the main action.

Turning left after crossing the bridge will put you in the middle of the real heavy stuff, whilst a right turn will take you to the gentler cruising, and towards the area where the daytime cruising happens. In the daytime of course, you can enter by the main castle gates which will save you about 20 minutes of walking, but bear in mind that the grounds are heavily policed during the day.

Conwy

Rhyl Promenade

Make your way on to the promenade just past the car park situated between the fairground and the Sun Centre. In the season (March to September) the area is buzzing with guys from all parts of the country, either holidaying or just up for the evening for a change of scenery. There will be straight couples milling around up until about midnight and after that an increase in the gays till at least 03.00. Ages, because of the area and lack of gay pubs and clubs, will be wide-ranging. Off-season you will still be able to find action, as the locals from all the surrounding districts would otherwise have to travel to Chester for a decent night out.

Newport

The A449 heading north from the M4/J24 towards Raglan/Abergavenny. About two miles along there is a lorry park, picnic area and lay-by on the right. If you do have the time to drive along the dual carriageway to the opposite side you may find action there as well.

the ultimate guide to
Accommodation

Introduction

Following reports that some hotel and guest-house owners advertise themselves as 'gay- friendly' through the quieter off-season months and then, when demand for accommodation is at its peak during the high season, turn away that same gay custom, 'for fear of embarrassing other guests', the accommodation listings were compiled with all guest-houses complying to one or more of the following criteria:

a) Gay-owned and/or gay-run
b) Exclusively gay
c) Gay-friendly with a majority gay clientele and catering for straight friends of gays

I must apologise to those venues that fall within this criteria and yet have not been listed. There are inevitable constraints put upon any such guide in its first edition and to list every gay hotel/B&B across Britain is no small feat! If a venue is not listed then you should not imply that it was not suitable. If you know of any such venues then please contact me in order that this oversight can be rectified for subsequent reprints and/or the next edition.

Accommodation in Blackpool is not in short supply, therefore, only those establishments with a membership to BAGS (Blackpool Accommodation for Gays) are listed (with the exception of Trades, The Highlands and Mardis Gras — well-known and -respected establishments). BAGS was set up in order that the gay visitor should be made welcome by some of their own kind and thus keep the pink pound pink. Whislt not all BAGS establishments are exclusively gay, they are all gay-friendly and fall within the gay owned or -run criteria.

Please read through the notes below, defining some of the headings which follow in the listings:

Price guide
This relates to the price per person sharing a double/twin room, *en suite*, high season: usually the most expensive room available. In most cases there are standard rooms available at a lower cost. Nearly

all establishments offer a reduced rate for midweek stays. It is always worth mentioning *The Ultimate Gay Guide* as the source of your enquiry. Some establishments expressed an interest in offering a reduction to readers of this guide.

En suite
This means that the room has at least a shower and toilet facility. In most cases it refers to full *en suite* (bath, shower, WC and wash basin). Most of the rooms that do not have *en suite* facilities usually have a wash basin in the room.

Confirmation
If the booking for accommodation is made in advance, a request for your credit card details may be made, or alternatively a cheque for 10–50% of the booking. It is always best to ask about any cancellation fee or a charge for 'no show'. It is also a good idea to phone the establishment if you are due to arrive later than expected. In the high season, when demand for accommodation is at its greatest, the rooms may legitimately be re-let after 18.00, if you have not phoned to advise of a late arrival. Cancellation charges may apply if the room cannot be re-let, so always ensure you know the establishment's procedure regarding cancellation (one particular venue required 14 days!).

Licensed
This refers to whether or not a hotel or guest-house has a resident's licence, entitling them to serve alcoholic beverages. In the cases where a licence is not held, the owners were asked whether the guest could 'bring their own' and their responses are acknowledged to spare you sneaking vodka in under your coat when you don't have to. Venue owners who do have a resident's licence though, may not have their bar open at all hours. If this might be of concern to you, then establish the alternatives (if there are any) at the time of booking.

Exclusively gay
Gay refers to gay men *and* women unless stated otherwise. If venues accommodate lesbians or gay men *only* then it will say so.

It is worth reiterating that the following listings are only a guide. When making your booking, it is wise to confirm that the details you believe to be correct, are correct. For example, I was surprised to discover how many establishments are exclusively non- smoking. While this may be a benefit to non-smokers, it will no doubt be frustrating to those that do. If you have any special requirements, such as vegetarian or dietary needs, then make these clear at the time of booking. When booking you will also have to specify whether you want a double bed or twin beds.

Editor's Note

In preparation for the next edition of *The Ultimate Gay Guide*, I would be grateful for any kind of feedback regarding accommodation (listed or not listed) for the gay traveller; particularly those establishments that cater for lesbians and and the transgendered. I am aware that not all gay establishments are listed (a consequence of the pressing publication date) and again I offer my apologies with the promise that the situation will be remedied for the next edition.

Accommodation Services

@ Home Around The World
PO Box 19518
London
SW11 6WF   Telephone 0171 564 3739   Fax 0171 564 3739
Website http://www.homearoundtheworld.com
E-mail london@homearoundtheworld.com

A unique gay and lesbian home exchange agency with offices in London, Paris, San Francisco, New York and Sydney, connecting gay members from around the world. @ Home Around The World offers a refreshing alternative to holidaying in expensive, impersonal hotel accommodation and offers a variety of individual options to suit any gay traveller, reducing, if not eliminating the cost of accommodation. Gay-owned and – run, unlike other home exchange pro-grammes, members are part of a global network of gay and lesbian travellers; 'people like us' who value the security of dealing with a kindred spirit. They offer direct home exchanges and mutual hospitality; members provide free accommodation that is reciprocated at a later time, apartment rentals, hosting

LONDON ~ PARIS ~ SAN FRANCISCO ~ NEW YORK ~ SYDNEY

the international gay and lesbian
home exchange agency
… and more

Going on holiday and want to swap a house, share, or simply rent a room? ~ We can help you find the places you want to stay, the world you want to visit, and the people you want to meet. ~ Travelling for gay people has never been more affordable, so easy or so much fun!

for a colour brochure and information about
all our unique services contact :
@home around the world, PO Box 19518, London SW11 6WF
tel/fax: 0171 564 3739 email: london@homearoundtheworld.com

 IGLTA

for people
like us

exchanges ⁊ guests ⁊ hosts ⁊ discounts in gay shops gyms & saunas

www.homearoundtheworld.com

and renting a guest-room to paying guests, plus numerous other options. If the idea of having strangers at your home disturbs you, think a little longer; strangers only remain strangers until they become friends. The idea works because letters, e-mails, photographs and phone calls result in the building of friendships, so that by the time you are ready to make your exchange you have already established a relationship with them. The comprehensive and informative 28 page 'Guide To Successful Gay Home Exchanging' that comes as part of your membership pack shows you how.

Membership details There are two types of membership available: One is Directory Members, for those without Internet access, who will receive a directory of member listings, complete with photographs, updated twice a year. The other is On Line Members, who will receive a password allowing them to log on at any time and view up-to-the-minute listings of all accommodation available. On line members have the additional benefits of being able to view members' own home pages, and use the members 'Bulletin Board' where personal messages can be exchanged. All members can decide whether or not their personal contact information remains confidential. This is a superb package, especially when you consider the low pre- millennium fee on offer. Annual membership of this unique club is a nominal £39 and renewals become free, if you introduce new members during your first year. You can join on-line or, by contacting Ken Russell (no, not that one) at the above address requesting a full colour brochure with even more detailed information.

Accommodation Outlet

32 Old Compton Street
Soho
London
W1V 5PD   Telephone 0171 287 4244   Fax 0171 734 2249
               Website http://www.outlet.co.uk
               E-mail homes@outlet.co.uk

Opening hours Monday–Friday: 10.00–19.00
Saturday: 12.00–17.00

An intelligent and practical approach to home hunting and flat sharing, that has made Accommodation Outlet one of the largest and most successful lesbian and gay accommodation services in the UK. Accommodation Outlet knows that shared accommodation can be positive, supportive and fun when it works out and a nightmare when it doesn't. That's why they have created a unique computer matching system that enables them to iron out potential conflicts from the start. Not only do they get the whole picture of what each property has to offer, but also the people that live there, i.e. age, sex, hobbies and interests, 'quiet kittens' or 'party animals', etc. The computer wants to know who you are and what you want so that it can compile a unique list of suitable properties or potential new flatmates. The whole process takes their trained and experienced advisors just a few minutes, before showing you the different options available. They deal with over 250 properties per week and you are able to receive an update of new accommodation through the post, verbally over the phone, faxed on request, on printout at the office or through the website. A range of temporary holiday accommodation in London is also available. Cost for the above service is a nominal £10 per month.

British Accommodation Listings

LONDON

Aster House
3 Summer Place
London
SW7   Telephone 0171 581 5888   Fax 0171 584 4925

Nearest train station Victoria (tube from here)
Nearest tube South Kensington
Car parking Street parking (extremely difficult)
A–Z ref. P76/4B
Nearest landmark South Kensington Tube (one minute away)

Price guide £120 per double room
Room en suite Yes (all rooms)
Price includes breakfast Yes
Number of rooms 12
Check in time 13.00   *Check out time* 11.00
Confirmation required Credit card details/first night as deposit/14 day
cancellation requirement otherwise one night charge
Late keys Yes
Night porter No
Other facilities TV in all rooms/Tea and coffee making facilities/Mini fridge/
Hair-dryer
Close to clubs Taxi or tube required to Soho
Exclusively gay No, but gay-friendly. Not gay-owned or run . . . 'but no
problem'
Licensed No, but guests are welcome to bring their own
Other details Exclusively no-smoking establishment. Upmarket part of town
and central location.

Beaver Hotel
57–59 Philbeach Gardens
London
SW5   Telephone 0171 373 4553   Fax 0171 373 4555

Nearest train station Kensington Olympia
Nearest tube Earls Court
Car parking On-site facility for about 18 vehicles
A–Z ref. P75/5J
Nearest landmark Earls Court Exhibition Centre

Price guide £70 per double room
Room en suite Yes

Price includes breakfast Yes
Number of rooms 38 (standard rooms available)
Check in time As soon as room is ready   *Check out time* 12.00
Confirmation required Credit card details/same day bookings require prepayment
Late keys Yes
Night porter No
Other facilities Tea and coffee (complimentary) available in restaurant all day/ Direct dial telephone/TV in all rooms
Close to clubs Tube required to Soho and taxi back (about £8)
Exclusively gay No, but extremely gay-friendly. Used as an overspill from the Philbeach Hotel
Licensed Yes
Other details Pleasant, clean and very friendly hotel. Although not exclusively gay, it is very gay-friendly. Entire ground floor accommodation is non-smoking as is the TV lounge upstairs. Lift access to all floors.

Clone Zone Holiday Apartments

64 Old Compton Street
London
W1V 5TA   Telephone 0171 287 3530

Nearest train station Charing Cross (tube to Soho)
Nearest tube Piccadilly Circus
Car parking NCP close by
A–Z ref. P61/7H
Nearest landmark Shaftesbury Avenue

Price guide £75 per room
Room en suite Yes
Price includes breakfast No self-catering
Check in time 14.00   *Check out time* 12.00
Confirmation required Credit card details/first night's deposit
Late keys Yes
Night porter No
Other facilities Tea and coffee making facilities/TV in all rooms
Close to clubs Yes: situated in the heart of the gay village (you cannot get closer than this). Apartments situated above Clone Zone (completely private from shop).
Exclusively gay Yes
Licensed No, but guests are welcome (or expected) to bring their own
Other details There are a total of four modern accommodations, comprising three double bedded rooms with *en suite* shower rooms and a luxury penthouse flat with a fully fitted kitchen, *en suite* with bath, shower and a spacious lounge area. Check in at Clone Zone shop – 10% discount on Clone Zone products. Discount on stays of seven nights or more (phone for details). Clone Zone staff will be happy to advise on London places of interest.

MILLBANK INTERIORS

Professional & Reliable Builders

OFFICE
0171 582 6981

Mobile 24 HR
0860 333 153

Drawing upon 26 Years' experience of Commercial and Residential Building, Carpentry, Decorations, Electric's, Plumbing, Tiling, Plastering, Carpets, Glazing, Security, Refurbishment, Wooden Floors, Soft Furnishings and Design. Removal and Delivery Service. Small and Large Works Undertaken.
Excellent References Available.

"Reliable and courteous, the workmanship produced has been to a very high standard. No hesitation in recommending them"
Chief Executive, Prudential Insurance

"We congratulate Millbank for their work, professionalism and help"
Terrence Higgins Trust

"A gift to the gay community"
First Out Café

"Such excellence is no doubt in high demand"
Foundation Aids Counselling

"Our thanks and admiration for the quality and finish of the work undertaken"
Village and Yard Bars

"I would recommend them unreservedly, we are delighted with the finished results"
M.D. Harlech TV

"Without doubt one of the most efficient, skillful and trustworthy teams of professionals in this field"
Children with Aids Charity

"Efficient and professional service. We look forward to working with you again"
The Ku Bar

"Extremely pleasant to deal with. I'd certainly recommend you!"
Gay's The Word Bookshop

"Excellent work with a friendly crew. Highly recommended"
GAYtoZ

Employment enquiries from skilled Gay Tradesmen and women always welcome.
A 2% donation from all contracts will be made to HIV charities.
Createsmart LTD. trading as Millbank Interiors.
Free Consultation/ Estimates.

Halifax Hotel

65 Philbeach Gardens
Earls Court
London
SW5 9EE   Telephone 0171 373 4153

Nearest train station Kensington Olympia
Nearest tube Earls Court
Car parking Meters on road/NCP close by
A–Z ref. P75/5J
Nearest landmark Earls Court Exhibition Centre

Price guide £60 per double room
Room en suite Yes (shower facility in most rooms)
Price includes breakfast Yes
Number of rooms 15
Check in time As soon as room is ready   *Check out time* 11.00
Confirmation required Credit card details required/first night as deposit
Late keys Yes
Night porter No
Other facilities Shared toilet and shower facilities on each floor/TV and radio in all rooms
Close to clubs Central London easily accessible by tube (taxi back approximately £8)
Exclusively gay Yes: predominantly for gay men although women will certainly not be excluded and straight friends of gays are also welcome
Licensed No, but guests are welcome to bring their own
Other details Standard rooms available at approximately £45 per double room (shared facilities).

The New York Hotel

32 Philbeach Gardens
Earls Court
London
SW5 9EB   Telephone 0171 244 6884   Fax 0171 370 4961

Nearest train station Victoria
Nearest tube Earls Court
Car parking Public car park
A–Z ref. P75/5J
Nearest landmark Earls Court Exhibition Hall

Price guide £70–90 for double or twin room/£50–55 single/£90–110 triple
Room en suite Yes
Price includes breakfast Yes
Check in time As soon as room is ready   *Check out time* 12.00
Confirmation required Credit card details/same day booking requires prepayment/24 hour cancellation required otherwise first night charged
Late keys Yes
Night porter Yes – 24 hour reception
Other facilities Direct dial telephone/Laundry service/Hair-dryer/Iron and board/trouser press/Fridge/Cable TV/Tea and coffee making facilities/24 hour room service/Jacuzzi, sauna and showers/24 hour room service/Private garden

Close to clubs Yes: close to Bromptons and Colherne (tube to Soho/taxi back approximately £8)
Exclusively gay Yes, and for straight friends of gays
Licensed Yes, plus late bar at weekends
Other details Probably London's very best and most luxurious gay hotel. Voted 'Best Gay Hotel – 1997/1998' (*Out and About* – leading US magazine). All major credit cards accepted here and the staff are very friendly. The Hotel is located ideally for the many local gay bars, clubs, shops and activities in the Earls Court area. The hotel offers its visitors a unique and friendly atmosphere with many facilities including a relaxed luxury lounge, beautiful rear garden, Jacuzzi, sauna and shower area with licensed bar. The hotel is a three minute walk form Earls Court Underground Station and 10 to 15 minutes away from the West End and its theatres, gay pubs, clubs and restaurants and only five minutes away from Harrods. With these facilities on hand, nowhere is too far away.

Noel Coward Hotel

111 Ebury Street
Belgravia
London
SW1   Telephone 0171 730 2094   Fax 0171 730 8697
               E-mail sirncoward@aol.com

Nearest train station Victoria (tube required)
Nearest tube Sloane Square
Car parking NCP (discounted vouchers available from hotel)
A–Z ref. P76/4E
Nearest landmark Sloane Square

Price guide £70 per double room
Room en suite Yes
Price includes breakfast Yes
Check in time As soon as room is ready   *Check out time* 11.00
Confirmation required Credit card details required/same day booking requires prepayment
Late keys Yes
Night porter Yes
Other facilities TV in all rooms/Mini bars/Use of Olympic-sized swimming pool, sauna and steam/Bookings arranged for any West End shows/Tea and coffee making facilities
Close to clubs Tube/taxi required to Soho
Exclusively gay No, but extremely gay-friendly. Gay-owned and -run
Licensed Yes
Other details This hotel was the home of Noel Coward from 1917–30 and is now a private guest-house in the heart of Belgravia, formerly known as The Hesper Lewis Hotel. Five minutes from Victoria Station (Gatwick Express). Phone Mark or Edmund for further information.

Number Seven Guest-House

7 Josephine Avenue
Brixton
London
SW2 2JU   Telephone 0181 674 1880
                  Website http://www.no7.com
                  E-mail gb@no7.com

Nearest train station Brixton
Nearest tube Brixton (10 minute walk)
Car parking Free parking facilities
A–Z ref. P93/5K
Nearest landmark Carpet World on Brixton Hill

Price guide £95 per double room
Room en suite Yes (all rooms)
Price includes breakfast Yes
Check in time As soon as room is ready   *Check out time* 12.00
Confirmation required 50% deposit/credit card details/all bookings must be
confirmed in writing (phone for details)
Late keys Yes
Night porter No
Other facilities Tea and coffee making facilities/Direct dial telephone/Fridge/
Satellite TV in all rooms
Close to clubs Easily accessible by tube
Exclusively gay Yes, with straight friends of gays are welcome too
Licensed No, but guests are welcome to bring their own
Other details Visa, Access and American Express accepted. Minimum stay of
two nights over the weekend. No smoking in public areas.

The Philbeach Hotel

30–31 Philbeach Gardens
Earls Court
London
SW5 9EB   Telephone 0171 373 1244 (Hotel)/0171 835 1858 (Restaurant)
                  Fax 0171 373 0149

Nearest train station Kensington Olympia
Nearest tube Earls Court
Car parking Two parking spaces available at £14 per 24hours/NCP
A–Z ref. P75/5J
Nearest landmark Earls Court Exhibition Centre

Price guide £80 per double room
Room en suite Yes (shower facility)
Price includes breakfast Yes (continental)
Number of rooms 40
Check in time As soon as room is ready   *Check out time* 12.00
Confirmation required Credit card details/deposit by cheque
Late keys No
Night porter 24 hour reception
Other facilities Wilde About Oscar Restaurant (which is also open to non-
residents)/Tea and coffee making facilities/All rooms with telephone/Bar and
lounge

Close to clubs Easily accessible by tube (taxi back approximately £8)
Exclusively gay Yes, with straight friends of gays also welcome
Licensed Yes
Other details One of London's largest and friendliest gay hotels now in its 20th year. The Wilde About Oscar Restaurant ('Probably the best gay restaurant in London.' – *Time Out*) is open from 19.00–22.30, seven nights per week. For reservations, call the above number. Single rooms available from £45/triple rooms available at £75/budget rooms available at £35.

Russell Lodge

20–21 Little Russell Street
London
WC1   Telephone 0171 430 2489   Fax 0171 681 7604

Nearest train station Euston or Kings Cross
Nearest tube Russell Square or Holborn
Car parking Facility available at £16 for 24 hours
A–Z ref. P61/5J
Nearest landmark Russell Square

Price guide £69 per room
Room en suite Yes (standard rooms also available)
Price includes breakfast Yes
Check in time As soon as room is ready   *Check out time* 12.00

the ultimate GAY guide

Tell us what you think

Ultimate Guides
PO Box 64
Manchester
M7 4NZ

email
ugg@ic24.net

(or you can use the form at the back of this book)

The Philbeach Hotel

WHERE THERE'S ALWAYS MUCH MORE THAN MEETS THE EYE!

40 Bedrooms
24 Hour Reception
TV Lounge
Direct Dial Phones
Tea & Coffee Making Facilities

Appleby's Bar
5pm – Late
Happy Hour
Ideal for private functions

Wilde About Oscar
Garden Restaurant
Open 7 days a week, 6pm-11pm
Sunday Lunch, 1pm-4pm

30/31 Philbeach Gardens,
Earl's Court, London SW5 9EB
RESERVATIONS 0171 373 1244
F: 0171 244 0149
E: 10075.3112@compuserve.com

Confirmation required Credit card details/first night by cheque/same day booking requires prepayment. 24 hour cancellation required otherwise first night charged

Late keys Yes

Night porter No

Other facilities Cable TV in all rooms/Tea and coffee making facility in *en suite* rooms

Close to clubs Yes: close to Turnmills (for Melt)/tube to Soho

Exclusively gay Yes

Licensed No, but guests are welcome to bring their own

Other details Georgian style guest-house close to Covent Garden and Soho. Also available to rent on a long- or short-term basis is a luxurious private apartment, with two bedrooms, two bathrooms, kitchen, etc., near to Leicester Square Tube Station. For details make enquiries through Russell Lodge.

Waverley House Hotel

130 Southampton Row
London
WC1B 5AG   Telephone 0171 833 3691   Fax 0171 837 3485

Nearest train station Euston

Car parking NCP opposite

A–Z ref. P61/5J

Nearest landmark Russell Square

Price guide £100 per double room

Room en suite Yes

Price includes breakfast Yes

C.A. DAW & SON LTD

27 PALACE GATE LONDON W8 5LS
PROFESSIONAL PROPERTY MANAGERS

DO YOU LIVE IN
A BLOCK OF
FLATS IN
LONDON?

ARE YOU FED-UP
WITH YOUR
MANAGING
AGENTS?

WE HAVE BEEN IN THE BUSINESS FOR WELL OVER 100 YEARS
AND PRIDE OURSELVES ON BEING
A PROFESSIONAL AND EFFICIENT GAY-RUN COMPANY

FOR A FREE CONSULTATION AND QUOTATION
RING JEREMY LINDON ON 020-7584-1234
WE WILL BE HAPPY TO HELP

Number of rooms 108 (all *en suite*)
Check in time As soon as room is ready   *Check out time* 12.00
Confirmation required Credit card details/letter of confirmation
Late keys No
Night porter Yes
Other facilities Tea and coffee making facilities/Direct dial telephone/modem point/Fax in room (in and out)/TV (free in-house movies)
Close to clubs Yes: within ten minutes of Soho
Exclusively gay No, but extremely gay-friendly (see *Other details*)
Licensed Yes
Other details Not your average run-of-the-mill B&B, but part of a group of hotels (Aquarius). I have it on very good authority that this venue is extremely gay-friendly and runs a complete non-discriminatory policy.

The Woodlands

72 Honey Lane
Waltham Abbey
Essex
EN9 3BS   Telephone 01992 787 413   Fax 01992 650 618
                 Website http://www.woodlands72.freeserve.co.uk
                 E-mail alan@woodlands72.freeserve.co.uk

Nearest train station Waltham Cross (taxi required from here)
Nearest tube Loughton
Car parking Ample street parking

Price guide £24 per person
Room en suite No (one room with own shower)
Price includes breakfast Yes
Check in time As soon as rooms are ready   *Check out time* 12.00
Confirmation required First nights deposit on booking
Late keys Yes
Night porter No
Other facilities Tea and coffee making facilities in all rooms/TV in all rooms/ Standard rooms available at £19.50 per person
Close to clubs No
Exclusively gay Extremely gay-friendly. Gay-owned and -run
Licensed No, but guests are welcome to bring their own
Other details No smoking anywhere in the establishment. Comfortable bed and breakfast in a gay- owned Edwardian home. Though technically not a London venue, this place is only 35 minutes travel from Central London and three minutes from junction 26 of the M25 motorway. Situated in an ancient market town bordering beautiful countryside. Ideal for those wanting to be within easy reach of London and the Home Counties at a reasonable price. Phone Alan for further information and travel directions.

ENGLAND

The Lodge

Banwell Castle
Banwell
North Somerset
BS24 6NY   Telephone 01934 823 122

Nearest train station Weston-super-Mare
Car parking On-site facility
Nearest landmark Cheddar Gorge

Price guide £50 per double room
Room en suite All rooms are *en suite*
Price includes breakfast Yes
Number of rooms 5
Check in time After 12.00   *Check out time* 12.00 (Latest)
Confirmation required Credit card details may be required
Late keys Yes
Night porter No
Other facilities Tea and coffee making facilities/TV and video in rooms/Trouser press/Vegetarians catered for/The Keep Restaurant adjoins the premises for evening meals if required
Close to clubs No local clubs and bars, but Weston-super-Mare is about five miles away and Bristol is about a 20 minute drive
Exclusively gay Yes: gay men only
Licensed No
Other details The guest-house is situated five minutes from junction 21 off the M5. The famous Cheddar Gorge is situated about four miles away. Phone Chris for further details. Positive discount available.

Kennard Hotel

11 Henrietta Street
Bath
BA2 6LL   Telephone 01225 310 472   Fax 01225 460 054
                   E-mail kennard@dircon.co.uk Website http://www.kennard.co.uk

Nearest train station Bath Spa (10 minute walk)
Car parking On-street parking
A–Z ref. P106/2B
Nearest landmark Henrietta Park

Price guide £84–95 per room
Room en suite Yes
Price includes breakfast Yes
Number of rooms 13
Check in time 13.00   *Check out time* 11.00
Confirmation required Essential: credit card details required
Late keys Yes
Night porter No
Other facilities Tea and coffee making facilities/Satellite TV in all rooms/Direct dial telephones and modem point/Hair-dryer
Close to clubs Yes
Exclusively gay Extremely gay-friendly/gay men and women
Licensed No, but you are welcome to bring your own drink
Other details Situated in a quiet Georgian street within a few minutes of the city centre and pubs. All double rooms are *en suite* and the tariff includes a choice of full English breakfasts. It is the ideal location to enjoy the delights of the city. *Note*: This is a strictly no-smoking establishment. Visa and Access accepted. Phone Richard or Malcolm.

Clarence Hotel

13 St John Street
Bedford
MK42 0AH   Telephone   01234 352 781

Nearest train station Bedford (five minutes)
Car parking Large facility at venue
Nearest landmark Telecom House

Price guide £15 per person per night
Room en suite No, but bathroom close to rooms
Price includes breakfast No, but it does include an evening meal (if required)

The Fountain Inn

Wrentham Street
Birmingham
B5 6QL   Telephone   0121 622 1452   Fax   0121 622 5387

Nearest train station New Street (ten minutes)
Car parking Secure on-site parking
A–Z ref. P74/5A
Nearest landmark The Nightingale

Price guide £20 per person per night
Room en suite Yes
Price includes breakfast Yes, continental only
Check in time Any time, if room is ready   *Check out time* Midday
Confirmation required Credit card details generally required
Late keys Yes: 24 hour access
Night porter No
Other facilities Above gay bar (see listing)/Tea and coffee facilities in room/TV
in all rooms/Use of iron and board
Close to clubs Situated in the heart of Birmingham's gay village
Exclusively gay Yes: gay men and women
Licensed Yes: late bar
Other details A warm and friendly welcome guaranteed

Monument Gardens Guest-House

266 Monument Road
Edgbaston
Birmingham
B16 8XF   Telephone   0121 455 9459

Nearest train station New Street (taxi required from here)
Car parking On-site facility
A–Z ref. P73/4E
Nearest landmark B4124 is Monument Road, Ladywood

Price guide £40 double room
Room en suite Yes
Price includes breakfast Yes
Check in time As soon as room is ready   *Check out time* 11.00 (flexible)
Confirmation required Deposit required to confirm booking/same day booking
requires prepayment
Late keys Yes

Night porter No
Other facilities All rooms have double beds, even for single occupancy/Tea and coffee making facilities
Close to clubs Taxi/transport required to gay village (approximately £4)
Exclusively gay Extremely gay-friendly, with straight friends of gays welcome too. Gay-run too
Other details Large Georgian house with private garden for guests. Midweek and longer stay rates available.

Village Inn

152 Hurst Street
Birmingham
B5 6RY   Telephone 0121 622 4742   Fax 0121 622 4679

Nearest train station New Street
Car parking Side-street parking
A–Z ref. P74/4A

Nearest landmark Hippodrome Theatre

Price guide £20 per person per night
Room en suite Yes
Price includes breakfast Yes (continental)
Check in time After 13.00   *Check out time* 11.00
Confirmation required Yes: credit card details required
Late keys Yes. 24 hour private access
Night porter No
Other facilities Four poster deluxe room available (£45)/TV, satellite and video/ Continental breakfast served in your room/Tea and coffee making facilities
Close to clubs Yes: situated in the heart of the gay village
Exclusively gay Yes: gay men only
Licensed Yes: but no late bar after pub hours

Abbeyville

39 High Street
Blackpool
Lancashire
FY1 2BN   Telephone 01253 752 072

Nearest train station Blackpool North (two minutes)
Car parking Street parking/local car park at rear
A–Z ref. P12/3A

Nearest landmark Railway station

Price guide £14 per person
Room en suite No
Price includes breakfast Yes (full breakfast)
Number of rooms 7
Check in time As soon as room is ready   *Check out time* 11.00
Confirmation required Deposit required at booking/same day booking requires prepayment
Late keys Yes
Night porter No
Other facilities TV in all rooms/Tea and coffee making facilities/Sorry – no pets/Hair-dryer/iron and board on request

Close to clubs Yes: two minutes to Flamingo's/concessions to club available
Exclusively gay Extremely gay-friendly, with straight friends of gays are welcome too. Gay-owned and -run
Licensed No, but guests are welcome to bring their own
Other details Member of BAGS. A very friendly and relaxed venue. Contact Colin for further information.

Amalfi Hotel

19–21 Eaves Street
Blackpool
Lancashire
FY1   Telephone 01253 622 971/0378 893 532 (mobile)

Nearest train station Blackpool North
Car parking Street parking
A–Z ref. P12/2A
Nearest landmark North Pier (half a mile north, off Dickson Road which is approximately fifth on the right as you go along the prom past North Pier)

Price guide £14–18 per person
Room en suite No
Price includes breakfast Yes
Check in time As soon as room is ready   *Check out time* 10.00
Confirmation required Deposit required (usually 50%)/same day booking requires prepayment
Late keys Yes
Night porter No
Other facilities Pets welcome/Tea and coffee making facilities/TV in all rooms and TV lounge/Hair-dryer/iron and board on request
Close to clubs Ten minutes to Flamingo's and bars
Exclusively gay More or less: predominantly women guests (98%) with gay men and straight friends of gays accounting for the other 2%
Licensed No, but guests are welcome to bring their own
Other details No smoking in the TV lounge. A very friendly establishment and one of the most popular for women to stay in the North-West. Member of BAGS. Phone Marlene or Helen for further information.

Arendale Hotel

23 Gynn Avenue
Blackpool
Lancashire
FY1 2LD   Telephone 01253 351 044   Fax 01253 318 433

Nearest train station Blackpool North (five minutes)
Car parking On-street
A–Z ref. P12/1A
Nearest landmark Imperial Hotel/north of North Pier

Price guide £19 per person (twin beds – no double beds)
Room en suite Yes
Price includes breakfast Yes (big portions)
Check in time Anytime after 12.00   *Check out time* 10.00
Late keys No
Night porter Yes

Other facilities Vegetarians catered for/Tea and coffee facilities/TV in all rooms
Close to clubs Approximately five minute walk to Flamingo's and bars –
concessions to Flamingo's
Exclusively gay
No, but extremely gay-friendly and men and women are both welcome. The
hotel is gay-owned and -run
Licensed No, but guests are welcome to bring their own drink
*Other details*Dining room is non-smoking. Member of BAGS. Phone Keith or
Paul for further information.

Astoria Guest-House

50 Park Road
Blackpool
FY1   Telephone 01253 622 377

Nearest train station Blackpool North
Car parking On-site facility
A–Z ref. P12/4B
Nearest landmark Raikes Hill (off Church Street)

Price guide £17.50 per person
Room en suite Yes (5 rooms *en suite*)
Price includes breakfast Yes
Number of rooms 7 (2 rooms sleep 4)
Check in time From 14.00 (variable)   *Check out time* 10.30–11.00 (maximum)
Confirmation required Yes: credit card details required
Late keys Yes
Night porter No
Other facilities Tea and coffee making facilities in room/TV in all rooms/Use of
iron and board on request/Vegetarians catered for (state requirements as soon
as possible)/No smoking in lounge and dining room
Close to clubs Five minutes to Flamingo's and bars – concessions to club
available
Exclusively gay Extremely gay-friendly. Gay-owned and -run
Licensed No, but guests are welcome to bring their own drinks
Other details Most major credit cards accepted. Member of BAGS. Phone Peter
or John for further details.

The Belvedere Hotel

77 Dickson Road
Blackpool
Lancashire
FY1 2BX   Telephone 01253 624 733

Nearest train station Blackpool North
Car parking Street parking
A–Z ref. P12/3A
Nearest landmark North Pier (Dickson Road is off Talbot Road which is
approximately the second road on left)

Price guide £30 per double room
Room en suite Yes
Price includes breakfast Yes
Check in time As soon as room is ready   *Check out time* 11.00

Confirmation required Deposit or credit card details/same day booking requires prepayment
Late keys Yes
Night porter No
Other facilities Tea and coffee making facilities in all rooms/TV in all rooms/Hair-dryer
Close to clubs Flamingo's and bars two minutes away/club concessions available
Exclusively gay No, but extremely gay-friendly. Gay-owned and -run
Licensed Yes: late bar available at times
Other details Visa and Access accepted. Midweek and weekend break rates available. Member of BAGS. Phone Tony or Peter for details.

Casablanca Hotel
Newcome House
20 Bairstow Street
Blackpool
FY1   Telephone 01253 620 380

Nearest train station Blackpool North
Car parking Ample street parking
A–Z ref. P12/6A
Nearest landmark Close to Central Pier

Price guide £15 per person
Room en suite Yes
Price includes breakfast Yes – late breakfast available too
Check in time As soon as room is ready   *Check out time* 11.00 (very flexible)
Confirmation required Deposit required when booking/same day booking requires prepayment
Late keys Yes
Night porter No
Other facilities TV in all rooms/Tea and coffee making facilities
Close to clubs Yes: two minutes to Flamingo's and bars/concession to Flamingo's available
Exclusively gay Yes, with straight friends of gays welcome too. Gay-owned and -run
Licensed Yes
Other details Standard rooms available. Special rates for midweek breaks. Member of BAGS. Phone Dwayne for further information.

Coastings Hotel
62 Coronation Street
Blackpool
Lancashire
FY1 4PD   Telephone 01253 623 269

Nearest train station Blackpool North
Car parking Street parking
A–Z ref. P12/4A
Nearest landmark North Pier off Church Street

Price guide £15 per person

Room en suite Yes
Price includes breakfast Yes
Number of rooms 13
Check in time As soon as room is ready   *Check out time* 11.00
Confirmation required Deposit required/same day booking requires prepayment
Late keys Yes
Night porter No
Other facilities Tea and coffee making facilities in all rooms/Satellite TV in all rooms/Hair-dryer/iron and board on request
Close to clubs Yes: within two minutes of Flamingo's
Exclusively gay Extremely gay-friendly. Gay-owned and -run
Licensed Yes: late bar available at times
Other details Member of BAGS. Phone Wayne for further information.

Collins Hotel

9–11 Cocker Street
Blackpool
Lancashire
FY1 1SF   Telephone 01253 620 541

Nearest train station Blackpool North
Car parking On-street parking
A–Z ref. P12/3A
Nearest landmark North Pier (quarter of a mile north of Cocker Square – opposite toilet facility – and turn right into Cocker Street)

Price guide £15 per person (£10 weekdays)
Room en suite Yes
Price includes breakfast Yes
Number of rooms 26
Check in time 12.00   *Check out time* 11.00
Confirmation required Prepayment required on arrival
Late keys Yes
Night porter No
Other facilities Tea and coffee making facilities in room/TV in all rooms
Close to clubs Five minutes to Flamingo's and bars and concessions to Flamingo's
Exclusively gay Yes: men only. Gay-owned and -run
Licensed Yes: late bar available (enquire)
Other details Plenty of room to roam! (à la Trades). Midweek and weekend rates available. Member of BAGS. Phone Colin or David for further information.

Dudley House Hotel

27 Cocker Street
Blackpool
Lancashire
FY1   Telephone 01253 620 988

Nearest train station Blackpool North (two minutes)
Car Parking: Street parking
A–Z ref. P12/3A
Nearest landmark North Pier (after Metropole take first right)

Price guide £17 per person
Room en suite Available
Price includes breakfast Yes
Number of rooms 10 (7 rooms *en suite*)
Check in time As soon as room is available   *Check out time* 12.00
Confirmation required Deposit by cheque/credit card details/same day booking requires full prepayment
Late keys Yes
Night porter No
Other facilities Tea and coffee making facilities in rooms/TV lounge (TV facility not in rooms)
Close to clubs Flamingo's is about five minutes away – concession to Flamingo's available
Exclusively gay Extremely gay-friendly/Gay owned and -run/Straight friends of gays welcome
Licensed Yes: late bar available at times
Other details No smoking in dining room/smoking allowed in TV lounge. Member of BAGS. Phone Gary or John for further information.

Edward Hotel

27 Dickson Road
Blackpool
Lancashire
FY1 2AT   Telephone 01253 624 271

Nearest train station Blackpool North
Car parking Street parking
A–Z ref. P12/3A
Nearest landmark North Pier/Talbot Road

Price guide £15 per person
Room en suite Yes
Price includes breakfast Yes
Check in time 12.00   *Check out time* 11.00
Late keys Yes
Night porter No
Other facilities TV in all rooms/Tea and coffee making facilities in all rooms/ Vegetarians catered for (please give notice)
Close to clubs Yes: two minutes to Flamingo's and bars/concessions to club available
Exclusively gay Extremely gay and lesbian-friendly. Gay-owned and -run
Licensed Yes: late bar at weekends
Other details Hotel recently refurbished. Positive discount available. Member of BAGS. Phone Ian or Michael for further information.

The Hertford Hotel

18 Lord Street
Blackpool
Lancashire
FY1 2BE   Telephone 01253 622 793
                 E-mail Hertfordhotel@ceges.dircom.co.uk

Nearest train station Blackpool North

Car parking Street parking
A–Z ref. P12/3A
Nearest landmark Railway Station/Talbot Road

Price guide £19 per person
Room en suite Yes
Price includes breakfast Yes
Check in time As soon as room is ready   *Check out time* 10.00 (flexible)
Confirmation required Credit card details required/cheque/same day booking
requires prepayment
Late keys Yes
Night porter No
Other facilities TV in all rooms/Tea and coffee making facilities/Family rooms
available/Hair-dryer/iron and board on request
Close to clubs Yes: two minutes to Flamingo's and gay bars – concession to club
available
Exclusively gay No, but extremely gay-friendly. Gay-owned and -run
Licensed Yes: late bar available at times
Other details Credit cards accepted. Member of BAGS. Phone Chris or George
for further details.

High Bank Guest-House

46 Banks Street
Blackpool
Lancashire
FY1 2BE   Telephone 01253 294 797

Nearest train station Blackpool North (two minutes)
Car parking On-site private facility
A–Z ref. P12/3A
Nearest landmark Railway station

Price guide £12.50 per person
Room en suite No rooms are *en suite*
Price includes breakfast Yes
Number of rooms 8
Check in time 12.00   *Check out time* 11.00
Late keys Yes
Night porter No
Other facilities Tea and coffee making facilities in room/TV in all rooms
Close to clubs Two minutes to Flamingo's and bars/concessions to Flamingo's
Exclusively gay Extremely gay-friendly. Gay-owned and -run
Licensed No, but guests are welcome to bring their own drink
Other details Very clean and friendly. Member of BAGS. Phone Peter or Jerry
for further details.

The Highlands

46–54 High Street
Blackpool
Lancashire
FY1 2BN   Telephone 01253 752 264/01253 752 249   Fax 01253 294 598
                 Website http://www.gayhotel.netE-mail highlands@gayhotel.net

Nearest train station Blackpool North

Car parking Street parking
A–Z ref. P12/3A
Nearest landmark Railway station/Talbot Road

Price guide £45 per double room
Room en suite Yes
Price includes breakfast Yes
Number of rooms 32 (18 rooms *en suite*)
Check in time As soon as room is ready   *Check out time* 10.30
Confirmation required Deposit required/same day booking requires prepayment
Late keys Yes
Night porter No
Other facilities Pool table available/All rooms have TV and radio-alarm/Tea and coffee making facilities/Central heating
Close to clubs Yes: two minutes to all venues – concessions available to Flamingo's
Exclusively gay No, but extremely gay-friendly. Gay-owned and -run
Licensed Yes
Other details The Highland, being in the same group as Trade and Mardis Gras, will take in their overspill as well as catering for their own guests. Guests of The Highland are able to use the late bar at Trades over the weekend. Room-only rates available (full details on request).

Kingsmead Guest-House

58 Lord Street
Blackpool
Lancashire
FY1 2BJ   Telephone 01253 624 496   Fax 0870 055 3984
                   Website http://www.hotel.demon.co.ukE-mail
                   Kingsmead@hotel.demon.co.uk

Nearest train station Blackpool North
Car parking Street parking
A–Z ref. P12/3A
Nearest landmark Lord Street is behind High Street off Talbot Road

Price guide £15 per person
Room en suite No
Price includes breakfast Yes
Check in time 12.00   *Check out time* 11.00
Confirmation required Yes: credit card details required
Late keys Yes
Night porter No
Other facilities Fully qualified in-house masseur at reasonable rates/Tea and coffee making facilities in all rooms/TV lounge (no TV in rooms)
Close to clubs Flamingo's and bars two minutes away – concession to Flamingo's
Exclusively gay No, but about 90% of customers are gay. Gay-owned and -run (Bill is acting secretary of BAGS)
Licensed No, but guests are welcome to bring in their own drink
Other details Enquire about their popular Internet Weekends. Member of BAGS. Phone John or Bill for further information.

Lowen Guest-House

19 Carshalton Road
North Shore
Blackpool
Lancashire
FY1 2NR   Telephone 01253 626 608

Nearest train station Blackpool North (five minute walk)
Car parking Street parking
A–Z ref. P12/1A
Nearest landmark Derby Pool (close to venue)

Price guide £13 per person
Room en suite Yes
Price includes breakfast Yes
Number of rooms 6
Check in time As soon as room is available   *Check out time* 10.00 (flexible)
Confirmation required Deposit required/same day booking requires
prepayment
Late keys Yes
Night porter No
Other facilities Tea and coffee making facilities in room/TV in all rooms/Hair-
dryer/iron and board on request
Close to clubs Yes: five minutes to Flamingo's and bars – concession to
Flamingo's
Exclusively gay No, but extremely gay-friendly, with straight friends also
welcome. Gay-owned and -run
Licensed No, but guests are welcome to bring their own
Other details Member of BAGS. For further details contact Wendy or Lori.

Mardi Gras

41–43 Lord Street
Blackpool
Lancashire
FY1 2BD   Telephone 01253 751 087/01253 751 088   Fax 01253 294 598
               Website http://www.gayhotel.netE-mail mardisgras@gayhotel.net

Nearest train station Blackpool North
Car parking Street parking
A–Z ref. P12/3A
Nearest landmark North Pier (then via Talbot Road and Lord Street is behind
High Street)

Price guide £15–20 per person
Room en suite Yes
Price includes breakfast Yes
Number of rooms 21 (all *en suite*)
Check in time As soon as room is ready   *Check out time* 10.30
Confirmation required First night's deposit required/same day booking requires
prepayment
Late keys Yes
Night porter No
Other facilities Pool room/TV in all rooms/clock-radio/Tea and coffee making
facilities

Close to clubs Two minutes to Flamingo's and bars – concession to club
Exclusively gay No, but extremely gay-friendly. Straight friends of gays
welcome too. Gay-owned and -run
Licensed Yes and late bar at weekend
Other details Midweek and weekend rates available. Sister hotel to Trades and
the Highlands (see separate listings). Not a member of BAGS but a well-
established and respected hotel.

The Mount Hotel
30 Exchange Street
Blackpool
Lancashire
FY1 2BD   Telephone 01253 625 659

Nearest train station Blackpool North (one minute)
Car parking Street parking
A–Z ref. P12/3A
Nearest landmark Railway station

Price guide £14 per person
Room en suite No
Price includes breakfast Yes
Check in time As soon as room is ready   *Check out time* 11.00 (flexible)
Confirmation required Deposit required to confirm booking/no credit card
facility
Late keys Yes
Night porter No
Other facilities Tea and coffee making facilities in all rooms/TV lounge
(smoking)/rooms not equipped with TV
Close to clubs Yes: within minutes of all gay venues
Exclusively gay No, but extremely gay-friendly. Gay-owned and -run
Licensed Yes: late bar available
Other details Basic value-for-money accommodation. Member of BAGS. Phone
Tracy or Vanessa for further information.

New Nevada
23 Lord Street
Blackpool
Lancashire
FY1 2BD   Telephone 01253 290 700

Nearest train station Blackpool North
Car parking Street Parking
A–Z ref. P12/3A
Nearest landmark Railway Station

Price guide £14 per person
Room en suite Yes
Price includes breakfast Yes
Check in time As soon as room is available   *Check out time* 10.30
Confirmation required Full prepayment required
Late keys Yes
Night porter No
Other facilities TV in all rooms/Tea and coffee making facilities

Close to clubs Flamingo's and bars are a two minute walk away/concessions to
Flamingo's available
Exclusively gay Extremely gay-friendly/gay-owned and -run
Licensed Yes: late bar available at times
Other details Member of BAGS. Phone Tony or Lee for further information.

The New Bond Hotel

72 Lord Street
Blackpool
Lancashire
FY1 2OG   Telephone 01253 628 123

Nearest train station Blackpool North (two minutes)
Car parking Street parking
A–Z ref. P12/3A
Nearest landmark Railway station/Talbot Road

Price guide £15 per person
Room en suite Yes
Price includes breakfast Yes
Check in time As soon as room is ready   *Check out time* 10.00 (flexible)
Confirmation required Credit card details required
Late keys Yes
Night porter No
Other facilities Tea and coffee making facilities/TV in all rooms/Iron and board/
hair-dryer on request
Close to clubs Flamingo's and bars two minutes away–concessions to
Flamingo's and sauna
Exclusively gay No, but extremely gay-friendly, with straight friends of gays
welcome too. Gay-owned and -run
Licensed Yes
Other details No smoking in restaurant and part of lounge Member of BAGS
Telephone Seamus or Mike for further information.

The Newholme Hotel

77 Lords Street
Blackpool
Lancashire
FY1 2DG   Telephone 01253 625 059/07801 845 255 (James' mobile)/
                 0831 801 879 (Tracy's mobile)

Nearest train station Blackpool North
Car parking Street parking
A–Z ref. P12/3A
Nearest landmark Railway station/behind High Street

Price guide £16 per person
Room en suite No: shower facility in room (no WC)
Price includes breakfast Yes (09.00–10.30)
Check in time As soon as room is ready   *Check out time* Very flexible
Confirmation required Deposit required (usually 50%)/same day booking
requires prepayment
Late keys Yes
Night porter No

Other facilities Tea and coffee making facilities in room/TV in all rooms
Close to clubs Yes: two minutes to Flamingo's and bars–concessions to Flamingo's and sauna
Exclusively gay No, but extremely gay-friendly. Gay-owned and -run
Licensed Yes: late bar at times (details when booking)
Other details Very friendly establishment. No smoking in the dining room. Cheaper rates midweek and for longer stays (from £12 per person). Member of BAGS. Phone James or Tracy for further details.

The Primrose House Hotel
16 Lord Street
Blackpool
Lancashire
FY1 2BD   Telephone 01253 622 488

Nearest train station Blackpool North
Car parking Street parking
Nearest landmark Railway station/behind High Street
A–Z ref. P12/3A

Price guide £22 per person
Room en suite Yes
Price includes breakfast Yes
Number of rooms 10
Check in time As soon as room is ready   *Check out time* 12.00
Confirmation required Credit card details/same day booking requires prepayment
Late keys Yes
Night porter No
Other facilities Tea and coffee making facilities in all rooms/Remote control TV in all rooms/Hair-dryer/iron and board on request
Close to clubs Yes: all venues two minutes away–concessions to sauna and Flamingo's
Exclusively gay No, but extremely gay-friendly. Gay-owned and -run
Licensed Yes and late bar at weekends
Other details A little luxury in the heart of Blackpool's gay scene. Visa, Access and Switch accepted. Member of BAGS. Phone Steven for further information and ask about his internationally renowned pork sausage!

Raynor Guest-House
56 High Street
Blackpool
Lancashire
FY1 2BP   Telephone 01253 626 383

Nearest train station Blackpool North
Car parking Street parking
A–Z ref. P12/3A
Nearest landmark Railway station

Price guide £25 per double room
Room en suite No
Price includes breakfast Yes
Number of rooms 8

Check in time As soon as room is ready *Check out time* 10.00 (flexible)
Confirmation required Prepayment required
Late keys Yes
Night porter No
Other facilities Tea and coffee making facilities/TV in all rooms/radio-alarm
Close to clubs Yes: two minutes to Flamingo's and gay bars
Exclusively gay No, but extremely gay-friendly, with straight friends of gays
also welcome
Licensed No, but guests are welcome to bring their own
Other details Very friendly and relaxed atmosphere. Special rates available for
midweek breaks. Member of BAGS. Phone Ray or Norman for further details.

Renaissance Guest-House

268 Central Drive
Blackpool
Lancashire
FY1 5JB   Telephone 01253 400160
                 E-mail lynda@renaissance2.demon.co.uk

Nearest train station Blackpool North
Car parking Street parking
A–Z ref. P12/5A
Nearest landmark Go-Carting Centre is opposite

Price guide £15 per person per night
Room en suite No *en suite* rooms
Price includes breakfast Yes
Check in time As soon as room is ready *Check out time* 12.00 (very flexible)
Confirmation required First night as deposit/same day booking requires
prepayment
Late keys Yes
Night porter No
Other facilities TV in all rooms/Tea and coffee making facilities/Late breakfast
if required
Close to clubs Yes: five minute walk
Exclusively gay Extremely gay men- and women-friendly, with straight friends
of gays welcome too. Gay-owned and -run.
Licensed No, but guests are welcome to bring their own drink in
Other details Transvestites and transsexuals are particularly welcome and
catered for. The Renaissance is a very friendly place with a very open attitude.
Guests are made to feel at home with very few restrictions. Linda chairs the
TV/TS social group that meets twice a month. Phone for further details.
Member of BAGS. Phone Linda for further information.

Sandolin Guest-House

117 High Street
Blackpool
Lancashire
FY1 2DW   Telephone 01253 752 908

Nearest train station Blackpool North
Car parking Street parking/local car park
A–Z ref. P12/3A

Nearest landmark Railway station
Close to clubs Yes: within minutes of all gay venues–concessions to club available
Exclusively gay No, but extremely gay-friendly and both gay men and women are welcome. Gay-owned and -run
Other details Unfortunately, price guide details were unavailable at the time of going to press, however The Sandolin is a known member of BAGS so phone Ian or Malcolm for further details.

Sandylands Guest-House

47 Banks Street
Blackpool
Lancashire
FY1 2BH   Telephone 01253 294 670
                 Website http://www.sandylands.com

Nearest train station Blackpool North
Car parking Street parking/local car park
A–Z ref. P12/3A
Nearest landmark Railway station/off High Street

Price guide £12 per person
Room en suite No
Price includes breakfast Yes
Number of rooms 8
Check in time As soon as room is ready   *Check out time* 10.30
Confirmation required Deposit required/same day booking requires prepayment
Late keys Yes
Night porter No
Other facilities TV in all rooms/Tea and coffee making facilities/Separate ironing room
Close to clubs Two minutes to Flamingo's and bars
Exclusively gay No, but gay-friendly. Gay-owned and -run
Licensed No, but guests are welcome to bring their own
Other details Member of BAGS. Phone Kevin or Chris for further information.

The Sheron Hotel

21 Gynn Avenue
North Shore
Blackpool
Lancashire
FY1 2LD   Telephone 01253 354 614

Nearest train station Blackpool North (five minutes)
Car parking Street parking
A–Z ref. P12/1A
Nearest landmark Imperial Hotel/Gynn Square

Price guide £38 per room
Room en suite Yes
Price includes breakfast Yes
Number of rooms 8–standard and *en suite* rooms
Check in time As soon as room is ready   *Check out time* 10.00

Confirmation required Credit card details or deposit required/same day booking requires prepayment

Late keys Yes

Night porter No

*Other facilities*TV lounge (rooms are not equipped with TVs) Tea and coffee making facilities Vegetarians and dietary needs catered for

Close to clubs Yes: five minutes to Flamingo's and venues

Exclusively gay No, but extremely gay-friendly. Gay-owned and -run

Licensed No, but guests are welcome to bring their own

Other details All rooms are exclusively non-smoking, as is the dining room. Smoking is allowed in the TV lounge. Evening meals available with prior arrangement. Member of BAGS. Phone David or Stephen for further information.

Starlight Hotel

46 Dickson Road
Blackpool
FY1   Telephone 01253 622 810

Nearest train station Blackpool North

Car parking Street parking

A–Z ref. P12/3A

Nearest landmark Railway station/off Talbot Road

Price guide £17.50 per person

Room en suite Yes

Price includes breakfast Yes

Number of rooms 12 (standard rooms available too)

Check in time 12.00   *Check out time* 11.00

Confirmation required £10 deposit when booking/same day booking requires prepayment

Late keys Yes

Night porter No

Other facilities Tea and coffee making facilities/TV in all rooms/Direct dial telephone/Use of iron and board, etc., upon request

Close to clubs Yes. Two minutes from Flamingo's and bars

Exclusively gay No, but extremely gay-friendly, with straight friends of gays welcome too. Gay-owned and -run

Licensed Yes

Other details

Member of BAGS. Phone Ian and Roy for further information.

Sunnyside Hotel

16 Charles Street
Blackpool
Lancashire
FY1 3HD   Telephone 01253 622 983

Nearest train station Blackpool North

Car parking Street parking

A–Z ref. P12/4B

Nearest landmark Talbot Road-Cookson Street-Second on the left is Charles Street

Price guide £18 per person
Room en suite Yes (standard rooms available)
Price includes breakfast Yes
Check in time As soon as room is ready   *Check out time* 10.00
Confirmation required Deposit required (details at booking)/same day booking requires prepayment
Late keys Yes
Night porter No
Other facilities TV Lounge/Tea and coffee making facilities
Close to clubs Two minutes to Flamingo's and bars–concessions available
Exclusively gay No, but extremely gay-friendly. Gay-owned and -run
Licensed No, but guests are welcome to bring their own
Other details Established in 1988. Spotlessly clean. Cheaper rates for midweek and longer stays. Member of BAGS. Phone Bob for further information.

Trades Hotel

51–55 Lord Street
Blackpool
Lancashire
FY1 2BJ   Telephone 01253 294 812/01253 626 401   Fax 01253 294 598
                 Website http://www.gayhotel.netE-mail trades@gayhotel.net

Nearest train station Blackpool North
Car parking Street parking (ample)
A–Z ref. P12/3A
Nearest landmark Railway station/Lord Street is behind High Street

Price guide £50 per double room
Room en suite Yes
Price includes breakfast Yes
Number of rooms 32 (*en suite* and standard)
Check in time As soon as room is ready   *Check out time* 10.30–11.00
Confirmation required Credit card details/same day booking requires prepayment
Late keys Yes
Night porter No
Other facilities Pool room/TV in all rooms/Large dining area/Resident's free sauna and steam room open daily from 14.00/Tea and coffee facilities in all rooms
Close to clubs Yes: two minutes to Flamingo's and bars/concessions to club available
Exclusively gay Yes: exclusively for gay men only
Licensed Yes: late bar. Guests of residents welcome too
Other details Voted the 'North's Best Gay Hotel' by *Pink Paper* readers. Not a member of BAGS but the reputation of this establishment goes before it, what with the original 'room to roam' concept (. . . I've said too much as it is). Sister hotel to The Mardis Gras and The Highland (see separate listings).

Warwick Holiday Flats

39 Banks Street
Blackpool
Lancashire
FY1 2AR   Telephone 01253 623 787

Nearest train station Blackpool North (one minute)
Car parking Street parking
A–Z ref. P12/3A
Nearest landmark North Pier (Banks Street is approximately third right as you go north)

Price guide £10 per person (midweek)/£12 per person weekends
Room en suite Yes
Price includes breakfast Self-catering
Check in time As soon as apartment is ready   *Check out time* 10.00 (flexible)
Confirmation required Credit card details or deposit/same day booking requires prepayment
Late keys Yes
Night porter No
Other facilities Each flat has a separate kitchen with cooker, fridge and microwave. TV in all flats.
Close to clubs Yes: Flamingo's and bars two minutes away
Exclusively gay Extremely gay-friendly. Gay-owned and -run
Licensed No (bring your own)
Other details Warwick Flats offer more independence and more of a carefree break. Member of BAGS. Phone Martin or David.

Willowfield Guest-House

51 Banks Street
Blackpool
Lancashire
FY1 2BE   Telephone 01253 623 406

Nearest train station Blackpool North
Car parking Street parking/local car park
A–Z ref. P12/3A
Nearest landmark Railway station/off High Street

Price guide £12 per person
Room en suite No
Price includes breakfast Yes
Check in time As soon as room is ready   *Check out time* 10.30
Confirmation required Credit card details required/same day booking requires prepayment
Late keys Yes
Night porter No
Other facilities Tea and coffee making facilities/TV in all rooms/Hair-dryer/iron and board on request
Close to clubs Yes: two minutes to Flamingo's and gay bars/concession to club and sauna available
Exclusively gay Extremely gay-friendly, with straight friends of gays welcomed too. Gay-owned and -run

Licensed No, but guests are welcome to bring their own
Other details Longer stays enable lower room rates. Most credit cards accepted. Member of BAGS. Phone Jeff for further details.

The Bondi Hotel
43 St Michael's Road
Bournemouth
Dorset
BH2 5DP   Telephone   01202 554 893
                 E-mail   colin&malcolm@bondihotel.freeserve.co.uk

Nearest train station Bournemouth (one mile)
Car parking Street parking/local car parks
A–Z ref. P57/4G
Nearest landmark Triangle/approach from promenade (West Cliff)

Price guide £18 per person
Room en suite Yes (standard rooms also available)
Price includes breakfast Yes
Number of rooms 7 plus self-catering 2 bedroom apartment
Check in time As soon as room is ready   *Check out time* Before 10.30 (flexible)
Confirmation required Credit card details/same day booking requires prepayment
Late keys Yes
Night porter No
Other facilities TV in all rooms/Tea and coffee making facilities
Close to clubs Yes: two minutes to Triangle
Exclusively gay Yes; also welcoming straight friends of gays
Licensed No, but guests are welcome to bring their own
Other details Close to sea front (three minute walk)

The Chine Beach Hotel
14 Studland Road
Alum Chine
Bournemouth
Dorset
BH4 8JA   Telephone   01202 767 015   Fax 01202 761 218

Nearest train station Bournemouth
Car parking Local car park/on-site facility
A–Z ref. P57/6E
Nearest landmark Alum Chine

Price guide £25 per person
Room en suite Yes (standard rooms also available)
Price includes breakfast Yes
Number of rooms 25 *en suite*
Check in time As soon as room is ready   *Check out time* 11.00 (flexible)
Confirmation required Credit card details/deposit required to confirm room/ same day booking requires prepayment
Other facilities Satellite TV in all rooms/Swimming pool in grounds/Tea and coffee making facilities/TV in all rooms
Close to clubs Taxi/transport required
Exclusively gay Yes: for gay men and women

Licensed Yes
Other details Direct access onto The Chine from the hotel. Phone for further information

The Creffield

7 Cambridge Road
Bournemouth
Dorset
BH2 6AE   Telephone 01202 317 900

Nearest train station Bournemouth (one mile)
Car parking Secure on site facility
A–Z ref. P57/4F
Nearest landmark The Triangle

Price guide £48 double room
Room en suite Yes
Price includes breakfast Yes: late breakfasts available, served in the conservatory
Number of rooms 9 (all rooms *en suite*)
Check in time As soon as room is ready   *Check out time* 11.00
Confirmation required First night pre paid as deposit
Late keys Yes
Night porter No
Other facilities Hair-dryers/Large conservatory/TV in all rooms/Single rooms have double beds/The two largest rooms have four-poster beds/Tea and coffee making facilities
Close to clubs Two minute walk to all bars and clubs
Exclusively gay Yes, with straight friends of gays welcome too
Licensed Yes
Other details Phone Roger for further information.

The Orchard

15 Alumdale Road
Bournemouth
Dorset
BH4 8HX   Telephone 01202 767 767
                 Website http://www.orchardweb.co.uk/orchardE-mail
                 orchard@orchardweb.co.uk

Nearest train station Bournemouth or Branksome (taxi required)
Car parking Street parking
A–Z ref. P56/5D
Nearest landmark Herbert Hospital/off Alumhurst Road

Price guide £20 double room
Room en suite Yes
Price includes breakfast Yes
Number of rooms 10 (5 *en suite*; 5 with shared facilities)
Check in time As soon as room is ready   *Check out time* 12.00 (flexible)
Confirmation required First night prepaid
Late keys Yes
Night porter No
Other facilities TV in all rooms/Tea and coffee making facilities

Close to clubs Approximately a ten minute walk
Exclusively gay Yes, with straight friends of gays welcome too
Licensed Yes
Other details Possibly Bournemouth's longest established (over 21 years)
exclusively gay hotel. Located at the edge of Alum Chine, a beautiful wooded
valley that leads to the sea. Access and Visa accepted.

Alpha Lodge Hotel
19 New Steine
Brighton
BN2 1PD   Telephone 01273 609 632   Fax 01273 690 264

Nearest train station Brighton (taxi required from here)
Car parking Street parking
A–Z ref. P29/6F
Nearest landmark Palace Pier/off Marine Parade

Price guide £22 per person
Room en suite No (most rooms with shower facility)
Price includes breakfast Yes
Number of rooms 10 (all available as single–5 of which have double beds)
Check in time As soon as room is ready   *Check out time* 12.00
Confirmation required First nights charge as deposit/credit card details required
for weekend bookings
Late keys Yes
Night porter No
Other facilities Free steam room for residents only (Wednesday/Friday/
Saturday evenings)/TV, radio and intercom in all rooms/Tea and coffee making
facilities
Close to clubs Yes: approximately a five minute walk
Exclusively gay Yes: 98% gay men and 2% gay women. No straight friends of
gays, children or pets
Licensed No, but guests are welcome to bring their own (ice, soft drinks and
mixers are available 24hours a day)
Other details Probably Brighton's longest established (since 1980) exclusively
gay hotel, situated in a pleasant Regency square, overlooking the Victorian
Palace Pier. There are adequate public showers, toilets, a bathroom and a cosy
lounge with open fire and TV. There is a valuables safe available (free) for your
use and everything is geared to make your stay comfortable and relaxing. A
map of gay Brighton, a privilege card to gain entry into the gay clubs of
Brighton and welcoming drink on arrival are all provided as part of the basic
charge for the room. Visa, Access and American Express accepted. Phone
Derrick for further information.

Ashley Court Guest-House
33 Montpelier Road
Brighton
BN2 1PD   Telephone 01273 739 916

Nearest train station Brighton (five minute walk)
Car parking Street parking
A–Z ref. P28/5C
Nearest landmark West Pier

Price guide £42 per room
Room en suite Yes
Price includes breakfast Yes
Number of rooms 8 (all *en suite*)
Check in time As soon as room is ready   *Check out time* 12.00
Confirmation required Credit card details required/same day booking requires prepayment
Late keys Yes
Night porter No
Other facilities TV in all rooms/Tea and coffee making facilities/Shower facility in some rooms
Close to clubs Yes: five to ten minute walk
Exclusively gay No, but extremely gay-friendly. Gay-run
Licensed No, but guests are welcome to bring their own
Other details No smoking throughout the venue.

Avalon

7 Upper Rock Gardens
Brighton
BN2 1QE   Telephone 01273 692 344

Nearest train station Brighton
Car parking Street parking/local car parks
A–Z ref. P29/5F
Nearest landmark Palace Pier/off St James Street

Price guide £22 per person
Room en suite Yes
Price includes breakfast Yes
Number of rooms 8
Check in time As soon as room is ready   *Check out time* 11.00
Confirmation required Deposit required
Late keys Yes
Night porter No
Other facilities Vegetarians catered for/Late breakfasts/TV in all rooms/Sexy king-sized room for that special occasion/Romantic four-poster room/Tea and coffee making facilities
Close to clubs Yes: within ten minutes of venues
Exclusively gay Yes, with straight friends of gays also welcome
Other details Eight tastefully decorated rooms–clean, smart and friendly. Midweek and longer stay bargains available.

Bannings Guest-House

14 Upper Rock Gardens
Brighton
BN2 1QE   Telephone 01273 681 403

Nearest train station Brighton (ten minutes)
Car parking Street parking (vouchers available)
A–Z ref. P29/5F
Nearest landmark Palace Pier/access off Marine Parade (Rock Gardens)

Price guide £42
Room en suite Yes

Price includes breakfast Yes
Number of rooms 6 (some with shower facility)
Check in time As soon as room is ready   *Check out time* 11.30
Confirmation required Credit card details required/same day booking requires prepayment
Late keys Yes
Night porter No
Other facilities All rooms with shower/*en suite* available/Tea and coffee making facilities/TV and radio alarm in all rooms/Iron and board, etc. on request
Close to clubs Five to ten minutes to venues
Exclusively gay Yes: women particularly welcome. Women only at weekends
Licensed No, but guests are welcome to bring their own
Other details Clean and comfortable venue.

Barringtons Private Hotel

76 Grand Parade
Brighton
BN2 2JA   Telephone 01273 604 182

Nearest train station Brighton
Car parking Street parking/local car park
A–Z ref. P29/5E
Nearest landmark Palace Pier/Victoria Gardens

Price guide £25 per person
Room en suite No: shower and washbasin in room (shared WC)
Price includes breakfast Yes
Check in time As soon as room is ready   *Check out time* 11.00
Confirmation required Deposit required/same day booking requires prepayment
Late keys Yes
Night porter No
Other facilities Tea and coffee making facilities/TV in all rooms
Close to clubs Yes: within five minutes of gay venues
Exclusively gay Yes, with straight friends of gays also welcome
Licensed Yes

Catnaps Guest-House

21 Atlingworth Street
Brighton
BN2   Telephone 01273 685 193   Fax 01273 622 026

Nearest train station Brighton
Car parking Street Parking/car park opposite
A–Z ref. P29/6F
Nearest landmark Palace Pier

Price guide £36 twin/double room
Room en suite Shower
Price includes breakfast Yes
Check in time As soon as room is ready   *Check out time* 11.00
Confirmation required Phone on day to confirm arrival/same day booking requires prepayment

Late keys Yes
Night porter No
Other facilities Single rooms available £18 including breakfast./Tea and coffee on arrival/nominal charge thereafter
Close to clubs Yes: within minutes of gay venues
Exclusively gay Yes, with straight friends of gays welcome too
Licensed No, but guests are welcome to bring their own
Other details Aiming to provide good quality bed and breakfast in a friendly and relaxed atmosphere. No smoking in the dining room. No tea and coffee making facilities in the room. Phone Malcolm or Charles for further information.

Cowards Guest-House

12 Upper Rock Gardens
Brighton
BN2 1QE   Telephone 01273 692 677

Nearest train station Brighton (ten minutes)
Car parking Street parking (vouchers available)
A–Z ref. P29/5F
Nearest landmark Palace Pier/access off Marine Parade (Rock Gardens)

Price guide £55 per double room
Room en suite Yes
Price includes breakfast Yes
Number of rooms 8
Check in time As soon as room is ready   *Check out time* 11.00
Confirmation required Credit card details/same day booking requires prepayment
Late keys Yes
Night porter No
Other facilities Vegetarians catered for/Full en suite or showers/TV and radio alarms in all rooms/Tea and coffee making facilities/Late breakfasts
Close to clubs Five minutes to pubs and clubs/concessions to Revenge and Secrets
Exclusively gay Yes: for gay men only
Licensed No, but guests can bring their own
Other details Nice little courtyard opens up during the summer. Single rooms at £25 per night. Phone Gerry or Cyril for further details.

Craven Court Hotel

2 Atlingworth Street
Brighton
BN2 1PL   Telephone 01273 607 710   Fax 01273 628 739

Nearest train station Brighton (taxi required)
Car parking Street parking/local car park opposite
A–Z ref. P29/6F
Nearest landmark Palace Pier/off Marine Parade

Price guide £20 per person
Room en suite Yes
Price includes breakfast Yes
Check in time As soon as room is ready   *Check out time* 11.00

Confirmation required Deposit required/same day booking requires prepayment
Late keys Yes
Night porter No
Other facilities Most rooms en suite/TV in all rooms/Tea and coffee making facilities
Close to clubs Within five minutes of gay venues
Exclusively gay Yes, with straight friends of gays welcome too
Licensed Yes
Other details Special rates for midweek and weekends.

George IV Guest-House

34 Regency Square
Brighton
BN1 2FJ   Telephone 01273 321 196

Nearest train station Brighton (five minutes)
Car parking Street Parking/car park in square
A–Z ref. P28/5C
Nearest landmark West Pier

Price guide £50 double room
Room en suite Yes
Price includes breakfast Yes
Number of rooms 8 (all *en suite*)
Check in time As soon as rooms are ready   *Check out time* 11.30
Confirmation required Credit card details/same day booking requires prepayment
Late keys Yes
Night porter No
Other facilities Sea view, *en suite* rooms available/Tea and coffee making facilities/TV in all rooms/radio alarm/Direct dial telephones
Close to clubs Yes, within minutes of gay venues
Exclusively gay No. Extremely gay-friendly/gay owned
Licensed Yes. No late bar
Other details Lift available.

Gullivers Hotel

10 New Steine
Brighton
BN2 1PB   Telephone 01273 695 415   Fax 01273 622 663
                 E-mail GulliversH@aol.com

Nearest train station Brighton (ten minutes)
Car parking Street parking with vouchers (50p per hour)/Queens Park for free parking (ten minute walk)
A–Z ref. P29/6F
Nearest landmark Palace Pier

Price guide £52 per double room
Room en suite Yes
Price includes breakfast Yes (full, vegetarian or continental)
Number of rooms 8
Check in time Normally 14.00   *Check out time* 11.30

Confirmation required Credit card details held/cheque for first nights deposit
Late keys Yes
Night porter No
Other facilities Vegetarians catered for/Continental breakfast served in your
room/Tea and coffee making facilities/Direct dial telephone/Hair-dryer/iron
and board on request/Standard rooms available at £38
Close to clubs Yes
Exclusively gay No, but extremely gay-friendly. Women particularly welcome
Licensed No, but guests are welcome to bring their own
Other details Gullivers is a regency guest-house in a Brighton sea front square.
AA rated QQQ. Phone Sylvia or Jane for further information.

Hudsons

22 Devonshire Place
Brighton
BN2 1QA   Telephone 01273 683 642   Fax 01273 696 088
                 Website http://www.brighton.co.uk/hotels/hudsonsE-mail
                 hudsons@brighton.co.uk

Nearest train station Brighton (short taxi ride)
Car parking On-street parking
A–Z ref. P29/5F
Nearest landmark St James Street

Price guide £38–55 per room
Room en suite Yes (all rooms are equipped with showers)
Price includes breakfast Yes
Check in time As soon as room is ready after 12.00   *Check out time* 12.00 (no
later than)
Confirmation required Credit card details held/same day booking requires
prepayment
Late keys Yes
Night porter No
Other facilities Rooms fully en suite or shower only/Direct dial phones in each
room/TV and sofas in all rooms/Patio garden and sun deck/Vegetarians catered
for/Tea and coffee making facilities in all rooms
Close to clubs Yes: about two minutes to venues
Exclusively gay Yes
Licensed No, but guests are welcome to bring their own
Other details All rooms are extremely clean, well-maintained and decorated to
a high standard with Next™ furnishings. There are two exclusively non-
smoking rooms and there is no smoking in the dining room during breakfast.
Hudsons is awaiting a rating under the new BTA scheme and is quietly
optimistic that it will be rated as being amongst the best B&Bs in Britain.

Montpelier Hall Hotel

17 Montpelier Terrace
Brighton
BN1 3DF   Telephone 01273 203 599   Fax 01273 706 030

Nearest train station Brighton
Car parking On-site facility
A–Z ref. P28/4C

Nearest landmark Waitrose supermarket

Price guide £50 double room
Room en suite No
Price includes breakfast Yes
Number of rooms 7
Check in time As soon as room is ready after 12.00   *Check out time*
11.30–12.00 (no later than)
Confirmation required Credit card details/same day booking requires
prepayment
Late keys Yes
Night porter No
Other facilities Private walled garden/TV in all rooms/Tea and coffee making
facilities/Wash basin in all rooms/hair-dryer
Close to clubs Within easy walking distance
Exclusively gay No, but extremely gay-friendly, also welcoming straight
friends too. Gay-run also
Licensed No, but guests are welcome to bring their own
Other details Montpelier Hall is a beautiful Regency villa in the centre of
Brighton. Spacious rooms overlook the spectacular walled garden. Relax in the
grand drawing room and dine in the period dining room. Functions and parties
catered for too. The beautiful private garden is available for hire (blessings,
parties, etc.).

New Europe Hotel
31–32 Marine Parade
Brighton
BN2 1TR   Telephone 01273 624 462

Nearest train station Brighton (ten minute walk)
Car parking Street parking/local car park
A–Z ref. P29/6F
Nearest landmark Palace Pier

Price guide £50 per room (weekend rate)
Room en suite Yes
Price includes breakfast Yes
Check in time After 12.00 (when room is ready)   *Check out time* 12.00
Confirmation required Prepayment/credit cards not accepted
Late keys Yes
Night porter No
Other facilities Most rooms with sea view/Lift to all floors/Tea and coffee
making facilities/TV in all rooms
Close to clubs Situated in the heart of Brighton's gay village. Attached to
Legends Bar and Schwartz Bar (Schwartz Bar is Brighton's only strict dress code
bar, open Friday and Saturday 22.00–02.00)
Exclusively gay Yes: predominantly men but women welcome too
Licensed Yes: late bar open to residents and guests
Other details Midweek break rates available.

Portland House Hotel

55–56 Regency Square
Brighton
BN1 2FF   Telephone 01273 820 464

Nearest train station Brighton
Car parking Street Parking/local car park in square
A–Z ref. P28/5C
Nearest landmark West Pier

Price guide £50–85
Room en suite Yes
Price includes breakfast Yes
Number of rooms 24
Check in time As soon as room is ready   *Check out time* 11.00 (flexible)
Confirmation required Credit card details/same day booking requires prepayment
Late keys Yes (combination lock)
Night porter No
Other facilities Two balcony rooms available/Four-poster rooms available/Tea and coffee making facilities/Direct dial telephone/TV in all rooms
Close to clubs Yes: within walking distance
Exclusively gay No, but extremely gay-friendly. Gay men and women are welcome as well as straight friends of gays
Licensed Licence being applied for, but bring your own just in case
Other details Beautiful Grade 2 listed building.

Roland House

21 St George's Terrace
Brighton
BN2 1JJ   Telephone 01273 603 639

Nearest train station Brighton
Car parking Street parking
A–Z ref. P29/6G
Nearest landmark Behind Bristol Road/Bedford Street on Marine Parade

Price guide £20 per person
Room en suite Yes
Price includes breakfast Yes
Number of rooms 11
Check in time After 12.00   *Check out time* 10.30–11.00
Confirmation required Credit card details/same day booking requires prepayment
Late keys Yes
Night porter No
Other facilities TV in all rooms/radio alarm/Tea and coffee making facilities/ Wash basin in all rooms
Close to clubs Yes: within easy walking distance
Exclusively gay No, but extremely gay-friendly. Gay-run
Licensed No, but guests are welcome to bring their own
Other details No smoking in the dining room. Some bedrooms are exclusively non-smoking. Contact David for further information.

Shalimar Hotel

23 Broad Street
Brighton
BN2 1TJ   Telephone 01273 605 316 E-mail shalimar@dircon.co.uk

Nearest train station Brighton (ten minutes)
Car parking Street Parking
A–Z ref. P29/6E
Nearest landmark Palace Pier/Sealife Centre

Price guide £25 per person
Room en suite Yes
Price includes breakfast Yes
Number of rooms 6 (3 full *en suite*, 3 with shower)
Check in time As soon as room is ready   *Check out time* 11.00
Confirmation required Same day booking requires prepayment/otherwise deposit
Late keys Yes
Night porter No
Other facilities Tea and coffee making facilities/fridge/Hair-dryer/iron and board in room/Vegetarians catered for (notice required)/Some rooms with sea view
Close to clubs Yes: within easy walking distance
Exclusively gay No, but extremely gay-friendly
Licensed Yes and late bar sometimes available
Other details Some rooms exclusively non-smoking. No smoking in dining room.

The White House Hotel

6 Bedford Street
Brighton
BN2 1AN   Telephone 01273 626 266

Nearest train station Brighton (taxi required)
Car parking Street parking/local car park close by
A–Z ref. P29/6G
Nearest landmark Palace Pier/off Marine Parade

Price guide £20 per person
Room en suite Yes
Price includes breakfast Yes
Check in time As soon as room is ready   *Check out time* 11.00 (flexible)
Confirmation required Deposit required/same day booking requires prepayment
Late keys Yes
Night porter No
Other facilities Luxury four-poster and French room suites/Tea and coffee making facilities/TV in all rooms
Close to clubs Within five minutes of gay venues
Exclusively gay No, but extremely gay-friendly, with straight friends of gays welcome too
Other details A beautiful Regency house, offering high standards of friendly service. Only 150 metres from the sea front. Midweek and longer stay rates available. Phone Ant or Shane for further details.

Abbotswood Bristol

102 Abbotswood Gate
Yate
Bristol
BS37 4NF   Telephone 01454 324 324
                  E-mail headmanray@btinternet.com

Nearest train station Yate (taxi required)
Car parking Ample secure street parking
A–Z ref. P33/2F

Price guide £25 per double room
Room en suite No
Price includes breakfast Yes
Number of rooms 2 double rooms
Check in time As soon as room is ready   *Check out time* Flexible–early
mornings catered for
Confirmation required Strictly by pre-booking. Essential to phone in advance
Late keys Yes
Night porter No
Other facilities Courtesy car from railway station/Discounts for stays of three
nights or more/Local tours arranged for overseas visitors/TV and video in all
rooms
Close to clubs No: Yate is on the outskirts of Bristol
Exclusively gay Yes. Gay-owned
Other details Abbotswood caters more for the business man/truck driver/sales
rep who would prefer an early start, without having to be tied to regular
breakfast hours, etc. Not really suitable for the holiday makers. Phone Ray on
the above number for further information.

Maison George

10 Greville Road
Southville
Bristol
BS3 1LL   Telephone 0117 963 9416   Mobile: 0831 348 607

Nearest train station Bedminster (short taxi ride)
Car parking On-street parking
A–Z ref. P79/1D
Nearest landmark Off the B3120 (North Street)

Price guide £40 per room
Room en suite No
Price includes breakfast Yes
Check in time As soon as room is ready   *Check out time* 11.00 (at latest)
Confirmation required 50% deposit required/same day booking requires
prepayment
Late keys Yes
Night porter No
Other facilities Tea and coffee making facilities/TV in all rooms/radio alarm/
Complimentary toiletries in bathrooms
Close to clubs Transport required (over 1 mile away)
Exclusively gay No, but extremely gay-friendly. Maison George is gay-owned
and -run

Licensed No, but guests are welcome to bring their own
Other details Single rooms available at £20. Some rooms are exclusively non-smoking. Phone Dave or Steff for further details.

The Phoenix Inn
36 Andover Road
Cheltenham
Gloucestershire
GL50 2TS   Telephone 01242 529 417

Nearest train station Cheltenham
Car parking Ample street parking
A–Z ref. P15/1E
Nearest landmark Tivoli Centre

Price guide £17.50 per person per night
Room en suite No, although each room has a wash basin
Price includes breakfast Yes

The Bush Inn
16 The Hornet
Chichester
West Sussex
PO19 4JG   Telephone 01243 782 939

Nearest train station Chichester (three quarters of a mile)
Car parking On-site park (18 spaces)/NCP 180 metres
Nearest landmark Chichester Railway Station

Price guide £20 per person per night
Room en suite No, but bathroom close to rooms
Price includes breakfast No, but available at an additional charge

Yew Tree Cottage
Bradley Hill
Soudley
Gloucester
GL14 2UQ   Telephone 01594 824 823   Fax 01594 824 317

Nearest train station Lydney (five minutes)
Car parking On-site

Price guide £20 per person
Room en suite Yes
Price includes breakfast Yes
Check in time As soon as room is ready   *Check out time* 10.30
Late keys Yes
Night porter No
Other facilities Outdoor activities can be arranged/Tea and coffee making facilities/TV in all rooms
Close to clubs There are no local gay venues. Local pub–Travellers Rest at Stow
Exclusively gay No, but extremely gay-friendly. Gay-owned and -run
Licensed No, but guests are welcome to bring their own
Other details Yew Tree Cottage is situated in The Forest of Dean. All rooms are spacious and offer panoramic views of the forest and valley. Not the most ideal

spot for the disco queen; more of a secluded 'get away from it all with your boss' relaxing type of place with plenty of scope for outdoor pursuits: walking, biking, horse riding, etc.

Sherwood Hotel

15 Grosvenor Crescent
St Leonards on Sea
Hastings
TN38 0AA   Telephone 01424 433 331

Nearest train station St Leonards West (five minutes)
Car parking Street parking

Price guide £21.50 per person
Room en suite Room with shower
Price includes breakfast Yes
Check in time As soon as room is ready   *Check out time* 10.00
Confirmation required First night in advance as deposit
Late keys Yes
Night porter No
Other facilities
Some rooms with private shower and toilet/TV in all rooms/Tea and coffee making facilities/Two rooms with four-posters (that's beds, not 'Steps' posters)
Exclusively gay No, but gay-friendly. Gay owned and -run
Licensed Yes and late bar at times
Other details The Sherwood is a tastefully decorated Victorian guest-house, close to the sea front and established for over 12 years. The place to get away from it all with that someone special. No smoking in the dining room. Five minutes drive from the centre of Hastings. Access and Visa accepted. Pets welcome.

Feathers Hotel

119–125 Mount Pleasant
Liverpool
L3 5TF   Telephone 0151 709 9655

Nearest train station Liverpool Lime Street
Car parking Large lock-up garage (£5 per night)
A–Z ref. P67/3C
Nearest landmark Roman Catholic Cathedral

Price guide £65 per double room
Room en suite Yes
Price includes breakfast Yes (buffet breakfast)
Number of rooms 78
Check in time After 13.00   *Check out time* 11.00
Confirmation required Guarantee room by credit card/letter of confirmation. Phone to confirm if you expect to arrive late
Late keys No
Night porter Yes
Other facilities Tea and coffee making facilities/Satellite TV in all rooms/Hairdryer/Direct dial telephone
Close to clubs Yes: centrally situated
Exclusively gay No, but gay-friendly because of the location

Licensed Yes
Other details Not a gay hotel but I am assured that a non-discriminatory policy is in operation. The lack of gay establishments (as far as I am aware) in Liverpool leaves you with very little choice, however room prices are reasonable and facilities are well above average.

Parkfield Manor Hotel
34 Parkfield Road
Liverpool
L17 8UJ   Telephone 0151 726 9229

Nearest train station St Michael's Hamlet (five minutes)
Car parking Own facility
A–Z ref. P88/2A
Nearest landmark Princes Park

Price guide £40 per double room
Room en suite Yes
Price includes breakfast Yes
Number of rooms 14 (8 *en suite*)
Check in time As soon as room is ready   *Check out time* 12.00
Confirmation required Credit card details required/24 hours cancellation notice required
Late keys Yes
Night porter No
Other facilities TV in all rooms/Tea and coffee making facilities
Close to clubs No
Exclusively gay No, but extremely gay-friendly. Gay-owned and -run
Licensed No, but guests are welcome to bring their own
Other details Exclusively no-smoking establishment. Not ideally situated for the gay venues.

The Studio
52 Broad Street
Lyme Regis
Dorset
DT7 3QF   Telephone 01297 442 653   Fax 01297 442 616
                 Website http://www.travel-uk.net/thestudio

Nearest train station Axminster
Car parking On-site and street parking

Price guide £250–300 per week
Room en suite Apartment
Price includes breakfast Yes (continental)
Check in time N/A   *Check out time* N/A
Confirmation required Yes: deposit required (phone for further details)
Exclusively gay Yes: women guests only
Other details The Studio is a private apartment let on a weekly basis throughout June to August. It is let as a whole and can sleep up to six people. Guests travelling by train can be collected from the station. It is situated three minutes from the sea front and close to the fossiling beach. The facilities are as follows: huge kitchen, dining room with refectory table, sitting room, three double bedrooms and two bathrooms. You can find photos of the

accommodation at the above website. At all other times, it is let as bed and breakfast accommodation at £15 per person per night. There is no smoking in the bedrooms.

Carlton House Hotel

153 Upper Chorlton Road
Whalley Range
Manchester
M16 7SH   Telephone 0161 881 4635/0161 861 7653

Nearest train station Piccadilly (taxi required from here–approximately £4)
Car parking On-site facility
A–Z ref. P100/4B

Price guide £45 per double room
Room en suite Yes (standard rooms available)
Price includes breakfast Yes
Check in time As soon as room is ready   *Check out time* 11.30
Confirmation required Credit card details required/cheque deposit/same day booking requires prepayment
Late keys Yes
Night porter No
Other facilities Half price admission to Stallions Sauna (on premises)/Tea and coffee making facilities in room/TV in all rooms
Close to clubs Taxi required into town/well served by public transport
Exclusively gay Yes
Licensed Yes: late bar open for residents and guests
Other details Dining room is a no-smoking area. Phone David or Chris for further information. (See Sauna Listings for Stallions Sauna details.)

Clone Zone Apartments

37–39 Bloom Street
Manchester
M1 3LY   Telephone 0161 236 1398

Nearest train station Piccadilly (five minute walk)
Car parking Local NCP opposite/meters/side-street parking in the evening
A–Z ref. P87/5E
Nearest landmark Chorlton Street Bus Station)

Price guide 1–2 persons £35 per night (£65 two nights)/3–4 persons £45 (£80 two nights)
Room en suite No–shared shower room
Price includes breakfast No
Check in time As soon as apartment is ready   *Check out time* 12.00
Confirmation required Credit card details/cheque deposit
Late keys Yes
Night porter No
Other facilities 50% discount to H2O Sauna/10% discount in Clone Zone shop/Tea and coffee making facilities/TV in all rooms
Close to clubs Yes: situated in the heart of the gay village

Exclusively gay Yes, with straight friends of gays welcome too
Licensed No, but guests are welcome to bring their own
Other details Stylish luxury rooms with shared shower room. Double room or
up to four sharing (discounts). One room has a bed settee that will accommodate
an extra two people. Check in at Clone Zone shop on Sackville Street. Clone
Zone staff will be happy to advise on places of interest. Cheaper rates for
midweek and longer stays (phone for details).

Monroes Hotel and Bar

38 London Road
Piccadilly
Manchester   Telephone 0161 236 0564

Nearest train station Piccadilly (opposite)
Car parking Large car park on Whitworth Street (by Chains)
A–Z ref. P87/4F
Nearest landmark Piccadilly Station

Price guide £38 per double room
Room en suite No
Price includes breakfast Yes
Check in time As soon as room as ready   *Check out time* 11.00
Confirmation required Phone for requirements
Late keys Yes
Night porter No
Other facilities Tea and coffee making facilities/TV in all rooms
Close to clubs Yes: one minute to Chains and three minutes to gay village
Exclusively gay No, but extremely gay-friendly
Licensed Yes: Monroes (mixed) bar beneath hotel

The New Union Hotel

111 Princess Street/Canal Street
Manchester
M1 6JB   Telephone 0161 228 1492

Nearest train station Piccadilly
Car parking Local NCP/meters/ample free space in evenings on side-streets
A–Z ref. P87/5E
Nearest landmark Chorlton Street Bus Station

Price guide £45 per double or twin room/£40 single/£60 triple room
Room en suite Yes
Price includes breakfast Yes
Check in time As soon as room is ready   *Check out time* 12.00
Confirmation required Credit card details required/cheque deposit
Late keys Yes
Night porter No
Other facilities Tea and coffee making facilities/TV in all rooms
Close to clubs You can't get closer than this
Exclusively gay Yes
Licensed Yes
Other details Midweek and longer stay rates available. Advance booking is
recommended, particularly over the weekends as this venue does tend to get
booked up quite fast.

The Rembrandt Hotel

33 Sackville Street
Manchester
M1 3LZ   Telephone 0161 236 1311

Nearest train station Piccadilly (five minute walk)
Car parking Local NCP/meters/ample free parking in evenings on side-streets
A–Z ref. P87/5E
Nearest landmark Chorlton Street Bus Station

Price guide £45 per double room
Room en suite Yes (standard rooms available)
Price includes breakfast Yes
Check in time As soon as room is ready   *Check out time* 11.00
Confirmation required Credit card details required/same day booking requires prepayment
Late keys Yes
Night porter No
Other facilities Tea and coffee making facilities/TV in all rooms/Wash basins in all rooms
Close to clubs Yes: The Rembrandt is situated in the heart of the gay village
Exclusively gay Yes, with straight friends of gays also welcome
Licensed Yes, The Rembrandt is a gay bar (see Pubs and Clubs Listings)
Other details Very popular hotel situated right in the heart of Manchester's gay village. It is recommended that your booking is made well in advance as the hotel does to tend to fill up quickly, particularly at weekends.

Hodgkinsons Hotel

South Parade
Matlock Bath
Derbyshire
DE4 3NR   Telephone 01629 582 170   Fax 01629 584 891

Nearest train station Matlock Bath (two miles)
Car parking On-site facility

Price guide £60–90 per double room
Room en suite Yes
Price includes breakfast Yes
Number of rooms 7 (6 double and 1 single)
Check in time As soon as room is ready   *Check out time* 12.00 (latest)
Confirmation required Phone for requirements
Late keys Yes
Night porter No
Other facilities Tea and coffee making facilities/TV in all rooms/All rooms *en suite*/Vegetarians catered for (advance notice required)
Exclusively gay No, but extremely gay-friendly. Gay owned and -run
Licensed Yes
Other details Hodgkinson's is a small Georgian hotel with beautiful rooms, all *en suite*, serving excellent food. Restaurant is a no-smoking area. Near to Chatsworth, Haddon Hall, Keddleston and 30 miles from Alton Towers. Phone Malcolm or Nigel for further details.

Pear Tree House Hotel

Chapel Road
West Row
Mildenhall
Suffolk
IP28 8PA   Telephone 01638 711 112

Nearest train station Newmarket (eight miles)
Car parking On-site parking

Price guide £42 per double room
Room en suite Yes
Price includes breakfast Yes
Check in time After 12.00   *Check out time* 12.00 (no later than)
Confirmation required Deposit required
Late keys Yes
Night porter No
Other facilities TV in all rooms/Hair-dryer/Tea and coffee making facilities/
Discounts for longer stays
Exclusively gay No, but extremely gay-friendly. Gay-owned and -run
Licensed No, but guests are welcome to bring their own
Other details No smoking in the dining room and preferably not in the room.
Lounge available. The Pear Tree is a 240-year-old listed building, formerly The
Village Inn, with beautiful gardens open to guests. Standard double rooms at
£37 and standard singles available at £15. Evening meals available with prior
arrangement. 25 miles from Cambridge.

Pinkys @ Sands Ridge Hotel

Headland Road
Newquay
Cornwall
TR7 1HN   Telephone 01637 872 089

Nearest train station Newquay (ten minute walk)
Car parking Ample street parking
Nearest landmark Fistral Bench/golf course

Price guide £15 per person per night (normally £25 per person through week)
Room en suite Yes, when available
Price includes breakfast Yes
Sands Ridge Hotel is kept exclusively gay over the weekends and the
accommodation price includes free admission to Pinky's Club (see separate
'Club' listings). A room without breakfast is available at a reduced price.

The Lord Raglan

30 Bishopbridge Road
Norwich
NR1 4ET   Telephone 01603 623 304

Nearest train station Norwich (ten minutes)
Car parking Street Parking
Nearest landmark Norwich Cathedral

Price guide £45 per double room/£25 single
Room en suite Yes

Price includes breakfast Yes (continental)
Check in time As soon as room is ready   *Check out time* 11.00
Confirmation required Deposit required to hold room
Late keys Yes
Night porter No
Other facilities Private access/TV in rooms/Tea and coffee making facilities
Close to clubs Yes: B&B above gay venue and a five minute walk to the city
centre
Exclusively gay Yes, with straight friends of gays welcome too
Licensed Yes

Barkers Hotel

11 Seaview Terrace
St Ives
Cornwall
TR26 2DH   Telephone 01736 796 729

Nearest train station St Ives (three minutes)
Car parking Small on-site car park

Price guide £22 per person
Room en suite No
Price includes breakfast Yes
Check in time As soon as room is ready   *Check out time* 12.00 (flexible)
Confirmation required Phone beforehand for requirements
Late keys Yes
Night porter No
Other facilities Overlooking harbour/Three minutes to beaches/Tea and coffee
making facilities/TV Lounge (No TV in rooms)
Close to clubs No
Exclusively gay Yes
Licensed No, but guests welcome to bring their own
Other details Delightful Edwardian house overlooking the harbour. Home-
from-home kinda place—free and easy with minimal restrictions. Popular with
Londoners after a break away from the hustle and bustle of the City. Situated
close to the nudist beach.

Ryn Anneth

Southfield Place
St Ives
Cornwall
TR26 1RE   Telephone 01736 793 247

Nearest train station St Ives (eight minute walk)
Car parking Street parking/council car park close by (inexpensive)

Price guide £40 per double room
Room en suite Yes
Price includes breakfast Yes
Check in time As soon as room is ready   *Check out time* 11.00 (flexible)
Confirmation required Phone for requirements
Late keys Yes
Night porter No
Other facilities Tea and coffee making facilities in all rooms/TV in all rooms

Exclusively gay Yes
Licensed No, but guests are welcome to bring their own
Other details Smoking allowed but not encouraged. Five minutes to town centre and close to nudist beaches–Lelant is two miles away and Treen is a good car journey (20 miles) away. Phone Pete or Don for further information.

Longreach
1 Uplands Road
Saltford
Bath
BS31 3JQ   Telephone 01225 874 724/01225 355 720
                Website http://members.aol.com/lgreach/E-mail lgreach@aol.com

Nearest train station Bath Spa
Car parking Off-street parking facility
A–Z ref. P94/2A
Nearest landmark Saltford Golf Course

Price guide £20 per person
Room en suite Yes (standard rooms available)
Price includes breakfast Yes
Check in time As soon as room is available   *Check out time* 11.00
Confirmation required Deposit/no facility for credit cards
Late keys Yes
Night porter No
Other facilities Shared luxury bathroom/TV/radio alarm in all rooms/ Complimentary station pick-up/Wash hand basin in all rooms/Tea and coffee making facilities
Close to clubs Close to main bus route to Bath and Bristol
Exclusively gay Yes
Licensed No, but guests are welcome to bring their own
Other details Longreach B&B is just off the trunk road in Saltford, in sight of Bath and within easy reach of Bristol either by car or bus. The house is situated with fine views over the valley of the River Avon. There are two airy rooms, each with a wash hand basin, sharing a luxury bathroom with shower and spa bath and one *en suite* room with WC, shower and wash hand basin. Out of consideration for non-smokers it is requested that there is no smoking in the public areas of the house. Longreach is exceptionally friendly and welcoming and receives a lot of word-of-mouth business. Exclusively gay and ideally situated.

Interludes Hotel
32 Princess Street
Scarborough
North Yorkshire Telephone 01723 360 513   Fax 01723 368 597
                 Website http://www.interludes.mcmail.comE-mail
                 interludes@cwcom.net

Nearest train station Scarborough
Car parking Street parking (difficult in summer)/discounted NCP

Price guide £55 per double room
Room en suite Yes: shower or bath
Price includes breakfast Yes

Number of rooms 5 (4 full *en suite*)
Check in time As soon as room is ready   *Check out time* 10.30 (flexible)
Confirmation required Phone for requirements
Late keys Yes
Night porter No
Other facilities Sea view rooms available (four rooms)/Discounts on longer stays/TV and radio in all rooms/Hair-dryer/Tea and coffee making facilities/ Quality furnishings
Close to clubs There are no exclusive gay bars in Scarborough
Exclusively gay No, but extremely gay-friendly
Licensed Yes: for residents only (fine selection of wines available)
Other details
Interludes is a Grade 2 listed Georgian building. It is well placed in the heart of the old town conservation area, lying between castle and harbour. Evening meals are prepared to order and must be booked in advance. Vegetarian and dietary needs are catered for though advance notice is required. Midweek and weekend rates available. Interludes is an exclusively non-smoking establishment. Phone Ian or Bob for further details.

The Sunridge Hotel

Bleke Street
Shaftsbury
Dorset
SP7 8AW   Telephone 01747 853 130   Fax 01747 852 139

Nearest train station Gillingham (five miles)
Car parking On-site and street parking

Price guide £60–90 per room
Room en suite Yes (all rooms)
Price includes breakfast Yes
Check in time As soon as room is ready   *Check out time* 11.00 (flexible)
Confirmation required £10 non-refundable deposit/same day booking requires prepayment
Late keys Yes
Night porter No
Other facilities Luxury four-poster bedrooms available/Bar lounge/indoor heated pool/TV and radio in all rooms/Tea and coffee making facilities/Hair-dryer/trouser press
Exclusively gay No, but extremely gay-friendly. Gay-owned
Licensed Yes
Other details No smoking in the restaurant and in 80% of the rooms. The Sunridge is a Grade 2 listed building. Close to the town centre and 35 miles to Bournemouth. Phone Peter or Michael for further details.

Brockett House

1 Montgomery Road
Sheffield
S7 1LN   Telephone 0114 258 8952   Fax 0114 211 2868
                Website http://brocketthouse.hypermart.net
                E-mail brocketthouse@yahoo.com

Nearest train station Sheffield (five minutes)

Car parking Street parking
A–Z ref. P98/6C

Price guide £48 per double room
Room en suite Yes (standard rooms also available–£38)
Price includes breakfast Yes: choice of English, continental or vegetarian
Check in time As soon as room is available   *Check out time* 11.00
Confirmation required Phone for requirements
Late keys Yes
Night porter No
Other facilities TV and video in all rooms (videos available)/Hair-dryer/Tea and coffee making facilities
Close to clubs Ten minutes to Sheffield's gay village and five minutes from city centre and train station
Exclusively gay Yes
Licensed Yes
Other details Brockett House is an exclusively gay and lesbian guest-house situated in the leafy Victorian suburb of Nether Edge, only ten minutes from Sheffield's gay village. All rooms are spacious and elegantly decorated. All beds are either double or twin (most are king-sized). Reduced rates for stays of four nights or more. Friendly, relaxed and discreet venue. Exclusively non-smoking establishment.

The Rutland Arms

86 Brown Street
Sheffield
S1   Telephone 0114 272 9003

Nearest train station Sheffield (two minute walk)
Car parking Side of venue
A–Z ref. P99/3F
Nearest landmark New Centre for Popular Music (looks like four pickled onions gone mad)

Price guide £18.50 per person per night
Room en suite No–shower and wash basin in room with shared WC
Price includes breakfast Yes

Fairmount House Hotel

Herbert Road
Chelston
Torquay
TQ2 6RW   Telephone 01803 605 446

Nearest train station Torquay (half-mile)
Car parking On-site parking facility

Price guide £32 per person
Room en suite Yes (all rooms)
Price includes breakfast Yes
Check in time After 12.00   *Check out time* 11.00 (Flexible)
Confirmation required Credit card details required/cheque deposit

Late keys Yes
Night porter No
Other facilities Tea and coffee facilities in all rooms/TV in all rooms/Four-poster room available with nominal supplement
Exclusively gay No, but extremely gay-friendly. Gay-run
Licensed Yes
Other details No smoking is requested in all bedrooms and public areas. Peacefully situated near to Cockingham Country Park, but not far from gay venues. Fairmount House is in a class of its own. Exceptional standards of comfort and hospitality. Lovely gardens with balconies and sun terrace. A pleasant and enjoyable stay is ensured. Phone James or Clive for further information.

Homers Hotel

Warren Road
Torquay
TQ2 52T   Telephone 01803 213 456   Fax 01803 213 458

Nearest train station Torquay (five minutes)
Car parking On-site facility

Price guide £60 double room (with sea view)
Room en suite Yes
Price includes breakfast Yes
Number of rooms 14
Check in time As soon as room is ready   *Check out time* 11.00–12.00 (flexible)
Confirmation required 50% deposit required
Late keys Yes
Night porter No
Other facilities Cliff-top position/Vegetarians catered for/Tea and coffee making facilities/Direct dial telephone/Hair-dryers/Radio and TV in all rooms/Pets welcome
Close to clubs Yes
Exclusively gay No, but extremely gay-friendly. Gay-owned and -run
Licensed Yes
Other details Delightful Victorian establishment with panoramic views. Evening meals available if required. Restaurant and lounge are non-smoking areas. Special weekend rates available.

Ocean House Hotel

Hunsdon Road
Torquay
TQ1 1QB   Telephone 01803 296 538   Fax 01803 299 936
                 Website http://www.oceanhouse.co.uk
                 E-mail cshore@dircon.co.uk

Nearest train station Torquay (two miles)
Car parking On-site facility

Price guide £29.50 per person
Room en suite Yes
Price includes breakfast Yes
Number of rooms 14 (all *en suite*)
Check in time As soon as room is ready   *Check out time* 11.30
Confirmation required Credit card details required

Late keys Yes
Night porter No
Other facilities Swimming pool/Steam room/Sun bed/Tea and coffee making facilities/TV in all rooms
Close to clubs Five minutes to bars/concessions available
Exclusively gay Yes
Licensed Yes
Other details Established 1994. Midweek and weekend rates available. Open all year.

Palms Hotel

537 Babbacombe Road
Torquay
Devon
TQ1 1HQ   Telephone   01803 293 970

Nearest train station Torquay (taxi £2.20)
Car parking Own car park (limited spaces cannot be reserved)

Price guide £20 per person
Room en suite Yes
Price includes breakfast Yes
Number of rooms 10 (all *en suite*)
Check in time As soon as room is ready   *Check out time* 10.00 (very flexible)
Confirmation required Credit card details/£10 per person deposit
Late keys Yes
Night porter No
Other facilities Tea and coffee making facilities/TV in all rooms/Hair-dryer
Close to clubs Yes
Exclusively gay No, but extremely gay-friendly, welcoming straight friends of gays too. Gay-owned
Licensed Yes
Other details Excellent value-for-money accommodation with cheaper rates for longer stays. Very friendly and welcoming establishment with hosts Paul and Phil ensuring your stay will be enjoyable. Phone for further information

Rainbow Villa

24 Bridge Road
Torquay
TQ2 5BA   Telephone   01803 212 886

Nearest train station Torquay
Car parking Limited street parking/local car parks

Price guide £49 per double room
Room en suite Yes (standard rooms also available)
Price includes breakfast Yes
Check in time As soon as room is ready   *Check out time* 11.00
Confirmation required Credit card details/deposit required to hold room
Late keys Yes
Night porter No
Other facilities TV in all rooms/Hair-dryer/Breakfast served till 10.30/ continental till 12.00/Evening meals available and vegetarians catered for
Close to clubs Walking distance to gay venues

Exclusively gay Yes, with straight friends of gays welcome too. Gay-owned.
Other details Elegant gay-owned Victorian guest-house. Centrally located and
open all year. All bedrooms are exclusively non-smoking. Phone Tony for
further details.

Hedgefield House
Stella Road
Blaydon on Tyne
Tyne and Wear
NE21 4LR   Telephone 0191 413 7373/0958 304 942 (Mobile)

Nearest train station Blaydon/Newcastle
Car parking On-site for 20 cars
A–Z ref. P55/2E
Nearest landmark Hedgefield B6317

Price guide £30 per person/standard rooms available (£21 per person)
Room en suite Yes
Price includes breakfast Yes
Check in time As soon as room is ready   *Check out time* 11.00
Confirmation required Credit card details or £10 deposit to hold room
Late keys Yes
Night porter No
Other facilities Tea and coffee making facilities/TV in all rooms/Well-furnished
accommodation
Close to clubs Seven minutes from city centre/four minutes to Metro centre/
concessions to clubs and sauna
Exclusively gay Yes, with straight friends of gays also welcome
Licensed No, but guests are welcome to bring their own
Other details Fabulous friendly and welcoming Georgian mansion house in two
and a half acres of totally secluded wooded gardens. One mile from Gateshead
shopping centre. An ideal location for a luxury break. Visa and Access
accepted.

Holly Park House
1 Park Road
Windermere
Cumbria
LA23 2AW   Telephone 015394 42107   Fax 015394 48997
                  Website http://www.s-h-systems.co.uk/hotels/hollypk.html

Nearest train station Windermere (five minute walk)
Car parking On-site

Price guide £24 per person
Room en suite Yes (private bath or shower room)
Price includes breakfast Yes
Number of rooms 6 (including 1 family room)
Check in time As soon as room is ready   *Check out time* 11.00 (flexible)
Confirmation required Credit card details/deposit
Late keys Yes
Night porter No
Other facilities TV in all rooms/Tea and coffee making facilities/Midweek and
longer stay rates available

Exclusively gay No, but extremely gay-friendly. Gay-owned and -run
Licensed Yes
Other details Elegant stone-built guest-house (RAC–2 crowns/AA–QQQ).
Tastefully modernised and furnished to a high standard, offering spacious well-appointed *en suite* rooms for the discerning gay visitor who requires nothing but the best. Situated in a quiet area, only five minutes walk from the railway station and conveniently located for tours to famous beauty spots such as Grasmere or Hawkshead, and just one mile from Bowness and Lake Windermere itself. Your friendly and attentive hosts, Roger and James, aim to make your holiday or break as relaxed and as enjoyable as possible. Most major credit cards accepted. Phone above numbers for more information.

The Steam Packet

51 Stanley Street
Workington
Cumbria
CA14 2JG   Telephone 0190 062 186

Nearest train station Workington (500 yards)
Car parking Plenty: one on-site, the other across the road
Nearest landmark The Quayside

Price guide £15 per person per night
Room en suite No: all facilities are shared
Price includes breakfast Yes (room–without breakfast–available at £12.50 per person)

Astley House

123 Clifton
York
YO3 6BL   Telephone 01904 634 745   Fax 01904 621 327
              E-mail astley123@aol.com

Nearest train station York (short taxi drive required)
Car parking On-site facility
Nearest landmark Ten minutes from Minster

Price guide £25 per person
Room en suite Yes
Price includes breakfast Yes
Number of rooms 13 (12 doubles and 1 single)
Check in time As soon as room is ready   *Check out time* 10.00
Confirmation required First night as deposit (cheque)/no credit card facility
Late keys Yes
Night porter No
Other facilities Satellite TV in all rooms/Tea and coffee making facilities/Radio alarm clock/Hair-dryer/Direct dial telephone
Close to clubs Ten minutes to Bay Horse
Exclusively gay No, but gay-friendly
Licensed No, but guests are welcome to bring their own
Other details This venue used to be the exclusively gay Pauleda House Hotel. Now it is a non-discriminatory venue, welcoming all, irrespective of their sexuality. Midweek break rates available. Four-poster rooms available (approximately £30 per person). No smoking in public areas.

Bay Horse and Buddys Bar

54 Gillygate
York
YO3 7EO   Telephone 01904 627 679

Nearest train station York (one mile)
Car parking Car park at rear of venue
Nearest landmark Minster

Price guide £25 per person
Room en suite No
Price includes breakfast Yes
Number of rooms 3 letting bedrooms
Check in time As soon as room is ready   *Check out time* 11.00
Confirmation required 50% deposit required/balance by cheque or cash
Late keys Yes
Night porter No
Other facilities Satellite TV in all rooms/Tea and coffee making facilities
Close to clubs Bay Horse *is* the gay venue in York (how much closer do you want?)
Exclusively gay No, but extremely gay-friendly, welcoming straight friends of gays too
Licensed Yes, but no late bar (though drinks may be taken upstairs to your room)
Other details Requested that you do not smoke in the room (although ashtrays are provided). Family room available (sleeps four). Carol (landlady) is an exceptionally nice person who will do all that she can to ensure your stay is enjoyable. Checkout the pub listing for Bay Horse.

Bull Lodge

37 Bull Lane
Lawrence Street
York
YO1 3EN   Telephone 01904 415 522

Nearest train station York (one mile)
Car parking On-site (garage facility for bikes)

Price guide £20 per person
Room en suite Yes
Price includes breakfast Yes
Number of rooms 8 (3 rooms *en suite*)
Check in time As soon as room is ready   *Check out time* 10.30
Confirmation required Cheque deposit for first nights stay/credit card facility not available
Late keys Yes
Night porter No
Other facilities Tea and coffee making facilities/TV in all rooms/Hair-dryer/Radio-alarm clock/Direct dial telephone/Special rates for longer stays available
Close to clubs Yes: Bay Horse
Exclusively gay No, but gay-friendly and gay-run
Licensed No, but guests are welcome to bring their own
Other details One room available which is exclusively non-smoking. Annexe double room suitable for accompanied disabled (phone for details).

SCOTLAND

Albion Hotel
405–407 North Woodside Road
Glasgow
G20 6NN   Telephone 0141 339 8620   Fax 0141 334 8159

Nearest train station Glasgow Central (taxi required from here)
Nearest tube Kelvinbridge (one minute)
Car parking Street parking
A–Z ref. P62/6D
Nearest landmark Kelvinbridge Tube

Price guide £54 double or twin room/£43 single
Room en suite Yes
Price includes breakfast Yes (full Scottish or continental)
Check in time As soon as room is ready   *Check out time* 11.00
Confirmation required Credit card details or deposit
Late keys Yes
Night porter No
Other facilities TV in all rooms/Hair-dryer/trouser press/iron and board/Direct dial telephone/Tea and coffee making facilities
Close to clubs Requires transport (tube in and taxi back)
Exclusively gay No, but extremely gay-friendly. Neither gay-owned nor run
Licensed Yes: hotel bar is open from 18.00–22.00
Other details Situated in Glasgow's fashionable West End, the Albion is a small privately owned hotel which boasts 16 comfortably furnished *en suite* rooms. Five minute drive from the city centre and within walking distance of the underground and major bus routes.

WALES

Courtfield Hotel
101 Cathedral Road
Cardiff
CF1 9PH   Telephone 01222 227 701

Nearest train station Cardiff (ten minutes)
Car parking Street parking with no restrictions
A–Z ref. P29/2F
Nearest landmark Cathedral Road is the A4119

Price guide £55 per double room
Room en suite Yes
Price includes breakfast Yes
Number of rooms 14
Check in time As soon as room is ready   *Check out time* 10.30 (flexible)
Confirmation required Credit card details required
Late keys Yes
Night porter No
Other facilities Choice of bedrooms/TV in all rooms/direct dial telephone/Tea and coffee making facilities/Hair-dryer/iron and board on request
Close to clubs Yes: walking distance

Exclusively gay No, but extremely gay-friendly
Licensed Yes, but no late bar
Other details Popular hotel set in a fine conservation area close to Cardiff Castle and the city centre. Most major credit cards accepted. Single rooms available at £25 (standard) or £45 (*en suite*).

Pennant Hall Hotel

Beach Road
Penmaenmawr
North Wales
LL34 6AY   Telephone 0800 074 0873 (freephone)/01492 622 878   Fax
                  01492 622 875
                  E-mail pennanthall@virgin.net

Nearest train station Penmaenmawr (this is a request stop–hotel is opposite station). An alternative station is Llandudno Junction–a ten minute drive
Car parking Secure on-site facility

Price guide £48 per double room
Room en suite Yes
Price includes breakfast Yes
Check in time As soon as room is ready   *Check out time* 10.00 (flexible)
Confirmation required credit card details/deposit (£20)
Late keys Yes
Night porter No
Other facilities Bar and restaurant/Jack's Sauna attached–£6 charge for residents (see 'Sauna' listings)/All rooms are *en suite*/Tea and coffee making facilities/TV in all rooms/Four-poster rooms available
Close to clubs Yes: FAB in Chester (Friday nights) and to St Asaph's twice-a-month gay club night
Exclusively gay Yes, with straight friends of gays welcome also
Licensed Yes
Other details Rates reduce each extra night that you stay. Regularly organises commitment weekends where you are able to have your relationship blessed by a minister in a formal service. There are also Singles Weekends and Murder Mystery Weekend breaks organised (no arguing who's going to be Jessica Fletcher!) For details of all these events, phone the venue direct.

Pennant Hall

Beach Road, Penmaenmawr North Wales LL34 6AY
Freephone: 0800 074 0873 Email: pennant.hall@virgin.net

Exclusivley Lesbian & Gay Country Hotel

All rooms en-suite ★ Residents Lounge	***Jacks Sauna***
Licenced Bar & Restaurant	Newly Refurbished Suite ★ Steam Room
Freephone for special Offers and Brochure	Sauna ★ Private Rest Rooms
	Walk-in Sun Room
All facilities open to non-residents	Secluded Sun Terrace
Private Carpark	Large Jacuzzi & Submarine!!
Open All Year Round	Food Served All Day

the ultimate guide to
Media and Resources

Gay Press

There is a huge range of gay press available, more now than at any other time. Even if you live in the most rural parts of the country you are able to obtain the latest copies of all gay publications through subscription and they are (mostly) free at any gay and lesbian drop-in centre. Distribution of the free gay weekly press is usually on a Thursday to all gay venues nationwide including gay retail outlets, saunas and drop-in centres, and by Saturday, most of the copies have gone.

The following listings detail the availability and content of the most popular gay press available throughout the UK. I have excluded community newsletters, which are published on an ad hoc basis with both life-span and availability teetering on the edge of uncertainty. Finally, it is worth pointing out that the sight of discarded gay press in the streets is not only offensive to the general public but also to members of the gay community. Most contain images of an adult nature and could quite easily be picked up by children. Dispose of them carefully!

Attitude
(Editorial address)
Northern and Shell PLC
The Northern and Shell Tower
City Harbour
London
E14 9GL

Telephone 0171 308 5090   Fax 0171 308 5075   E-mail attitude@norshell.co.uk

Attitude
(Subscriptions address)
43 Mill Tower
Millharbour
London
E14 9TR

Telephone 0171 538 2546   E-mail subs@norshell.co.uk

Price £2.50 available from all leading newsagents/gay retail outlets/Virgin/ HMV

Frequency Monthly – usually at the beginning of the month
Subscriptions   £27 per year (UK)
                £40 per year (Europe)
                £57 per year (Rest of world)

Attitude=Where it's @ (affording the magazine its full title) is a full-colour glossy lifestyle magazine packed with the stuff that you should know but didn't know you needed to. Excellent fashion section, hard-hitting features, health bit and in-depth interviews too. A sort of cross between *Cosmopolitan* and *Gay Times*.

Axiom News

73 Collier Street
London
N1 9BE

Telephone 0171 833 3399   Fax 0171 837 2707

Price Axiom News is a free newspaper available in most gay venues/gay bookshops/gay adult shops *Axiom Magazine* is priced at £2 in gay retail outlets (WH Smith/John Menzies) or free at gay venues
Frequency Axiom News: Fortnightly Axiom Magazine: Monthly
Subscriptions   Axiom Magazine: £18 for 12 issues/£10 for 6 issues
                Axiom News: £14 for 13 issues/£24 for 26 issues
                Combined News and Magazine: £36 for 1 year
Make cheques payable to: Axiom Publishing Ltd. Correspondence sent out in plain envelope

Axiom News (Newspaper) covers news, current affairs, features, sports, recruitment and contacts. Absolutely tons of relevant information regarding the gay/bisexual lifestyle. A large proportion is devoted to new treatments regarding HIV and health promotion presented in a factual and easy-to-read manner. *Axiom Magazine* is a health and lifestyle magazine with excellent features on drug issues, scene reviews, loads of sex advice, music reviews, video games, film, theatre and the arts. Not forgetting, of course, advice on HIV treatments and other health matters. Subscription enquiries from abroad should be directed to the telephone number above.

Boyz

Cedar House
72 Holloway Road
London
N7 8NZ

Telephone 0171 296 6000 (Reception)/0171 296 6250
                (Advertising)/0171 296 6260 (Classifieds)/0171 296 6090
                (Subscriptions)   Fax 0171 296 0026   E-mail boyz@boyz.co.uk
                Website http://www.boyz.co.uk/chronos

Price Free in most gay venues/gay book shops and gay adult shops/gay drop in centres
Frequency Weekly – usually distributed on a Thursday
Subscriptions   £20 for 26 issues (London edition)

£39 for 52 issues (Boyz UK)

Make cheques and postal orders payable to Chronos Publishing

Credit cards are accepted for anyone wishing to set up a subscription by phone. Paper is sent in a plain envelope. Enquiries from abroad should be made to Subscriptions.

Sister paper to the *Pink Paper*, *Boyz* is the only officially audited magazine for gay men in Britain with an average combined circulation ('Nationwide' and 'London') of 55,000 weekly copies. There are two separate editions; one for London with a huge number of 'escort' ads and pages devoted to the London scene and the other; a Nationwide edition with scene reviews and information of venues outside London. A very light-hearted 'magazine' concept with great feature stories, loads of 'personal' ads and the full page Prowler Press pin-up in each edition – lovely.

Diva Magazine

Millivres Limited
Worldwide House
116–134 Bayham Street
London
NW1 0BA

Telephone 0171 284 0329/0171 267 0021 (Subscriptions – Monday–Friday: 10.00–18.00)   Fax 0171 284 0329   E-mail diva@gaytimes.co.uk

Price £2
Frequency Monthly (usually available from the 14th of each month)
Subscriptions   £24 for 12 issues
Subscriptions from abroad should telephone the above number
Make cheques or postal orders payable to Millivres Ltd. All correspondence sent under plain wrapper

Lesbian full-colour glossy lifestyle magazine published by Millivres (*Gay Times*). Available through subscription, gay bookstores and gay retail outlets and most leading newsagents such as WH Smiths, Menzies, Waterstone's and Books Etc. Contains loads of news items, books, music, arts and scene reviews, contact ads, top features, in-depth interviews and everything else pertaining to lesbian lifesyle.

DNA Magazine

DNA Publishing Ltd
PO Box 27717
London
E5 0YP

Telephone 0171 682 0832   Fax 0171 682 0830
E-mail dna.magazine@virgin.net   Website http://www.homoactive.co.uk/dna

Price £1 and available from Clone Zone/most gay retail outlets/some newsagents
Frequency Monthly (end of month)

Subsciptions: £13.95 for 12 issues
Make cheques and postal orders payable to DNA Publishing Ltd

Probably the most un-PC gay magazine available. They just don't give a fuck, but I (and probably all of their other readers) think it's one of the funniest and most irreverent 'fun' magazines around.

Fluid

Chronos Publishing
Cedar House
72 Holloway Road
London
N7 8NZ.

Telephone 0171 296 6000 (General enquiries)/0171 296 6250 (advertising)
        Fax 0171 296 0026 (General)/0171 700 1854 (advertising)
        E-mail editorial@fluid.co.uk

Price Free in all London gay venues £2 in selected gay venues nation-wide £2 in most gay retail outlets outside London
Frequency Monthly
Subscriptions   £10 for 6 issues
               £18 for 12 issues
Make cheques or postal orders payable to Chronos Publishing

Fluid is another new publication from Chronos Publishing (*Boyz*, *Pink Paper*, *Homosex*). Issue 1 has just hit the streets of London. A full-colour, glossy monthly magazine highlighting the best aspects of club life throughout the nation, although there is a London predominance throughout the first issue. This, however, will change, as the publication becomes available throughout the rest of the country. Featuring loads of top club reviews, crucial music releases, informative features, club charts and the latest products and tons (not literally) of photos; this mag looks set to be a winner.

Gay Scotland

17–23 Calton Road
Edinburgh
EH3 8DL

Telephone 031 557 2625/0131 556 3331   E-mail incoming@gayscotland.co.uk
            Website http://www.gayscotland.co.uk

Price Free in all gay outlets
Frequency Monthly (first Monday of the month)
Subscriptions   £12 per annum. Write to the above address making cheques or postal orders payable to Gay Scotland

Invaluable Scottish resource publication offering the most up-to-date information on gay life in Scotland and the North. Easily available to all gay, lesbian and bisexuals who do not have direct access to the scene. *Gay Scotland* is published on the first Monday of every month and is available throughout a wide range of outlets in Scotland and the North. It is a non-profit making organisation which is staffed by volunteers. The paper is distributed to over 228 outlets throughout the country ranging from commercial gay bars and clubs to gay-friendly theatres, community centres, bookshops, cafes, cinemas, libraries and art venues.

Gay Times

Millivres Limited
Ground Floor
Worldwide House
116–134 Bayham Street
London
NW1 0BA

Telephone 0171 482 2576 (Editorial, advertising and circulation)/0171 267 0021
(subscriptions and mail order)   Fax 0171 284 0329
E-mail edit@gaytimes.co.uk (editorial)/info@gaytimes.co.uk (advertising and subscriptions)   Website http://www.gaytimes.co.uk

Price £2.50
Frequency Monthly
Subscriptions   12 issues £28 or 24 issues £54 (United Kingdom only)
Most major credit cards accepted. For Europe and outside, phone above subscription number

Long running lifestyle and news magazine for the gay community. Has the latest news items concerning the gay community, top feature writers and top stories. Available from all leading newsagents, adult bookstores, gay bookshops or by subscription (posted in a non-transparent, bust-proof poly bag). Subscriptions to *Zipper* and *Vulcan*, two of Britain's most popular pin-up magazines, are also available through the above contact (they are also both available in selected newsagents). *Zipper* features the butch, brawny beefcake and *Vulcan*; the lithe, cheeky young lads. Both are full-colour throughout and packed with the best quality male nude photography. In addition, there are the regular outrageous readers' letters, fiction, book reviews, video reviews and the gay agony uncle and doctor. *Note*: There may be a discount available off the cover price by subscribing to them both (Usual cover price £4.99 each).

Gay to Z

41 Cooks Road
London
SE17 3NG

Telephone 0171 793 7450   Fax 0171 820 1366   E-mail s-coote@dircon.co.uk
Website http://www.gaytoz.co.uk

Price Free in most gay venues nationwide (various times throughout the year) and freely distributed at the London Mardi Gras and other national gay events £3 including postage and packing to above address
Frequency Annually
Make cheques and postal orders payable to Gay to Z Directories Limited

Gay to Z is a directory of gay businesses and gay-friendly business throughout the United Kingdom. Listing is free for a business name and telephone number and any extension on this will be charged. For further details telephone the above number.

Homosex
Chronos Publishing Limited
Cedar House
72 Holloway Road
London
N7 8NZ

Telephone 0171 296 6000 (All enquiries)/0171 296 6250
            (advertising)/0171 296 6260 (small ads)   Fax 0171 296 0026

Homosex (quick 'n' dirty gay reading) is the newest free magazine to hit the
streets of London (no plans to go nation-wide just yet – shame) produced by
those clever boys who bring you *Boyz*, *Fluid* and *Pink Paper*, and this one looks
set to become another winner. A5 in size, in excess of 50 pages and part colour, its
subject is simple – SEX! It is packed with things relating to front and back
bottoms. Stories about sex, real-life experiences about sex, sex toys and
accessories, sex groups, escorts selling sex (with pictures), sex lines and sex
news. At the time we went to print the first issue had just hit the streets and
unfortunately there were no subscription details available.

NOW (North Of Watford)
Walk 34
Middleton Road
Leeds
LS27 8BB

Telephone 08701 255 577/0113 238 8818 (Advertising)   Fax 08701 222 666
            Website http://www.nowmag.co.uk

Price Free in all gay venues north of Watford/gay retail outlets/drop-in centres
Frequency Monthly (usually distributed during the first week of the month)

NOW is a free glossy monthly magazine concentrating on the lighter side of gay
life outside of London. Loads of scene, music, internet reviews etc., as well as
in-depth interviews with whoever is hitting the headlines at the present time.
Re-issued after the sad demise of *APN* (All Points North) but with a totally
revamped and modern approach. Their 'no cocks' policy ensures that it can be
left lying around without your Great Aunt Fanny picking it up and having a
seizure.

Pink Paper
Chronos Publishing Limited
Cedar House
72 Holloway Road
London
N7 8NZ

Telephone 0171 296 6110 (Advertising)/0171 296 6210
            (Editorial)/0171 296 6260 (Classifieds)
            E-mail editorial@pinkpaper.co.uk

Price Free in all gay venues nationwide/gay retail shops, etc.
Frequency Weekly (usually distributed on a Thursday)

Well-established and probably the 'original' free gay paper, now with an average weekly circulation in excess of 56,000 copies. Recently revamped to include sections such as 'News' (always up-to-date and informative),'Virus' (HIV developments), 'Net' (Internet sites) 'Third Degree' (in-depth interview feature), 'Gear' (Fashion), plus a huge entertainment and arts section, letters page, book and music reviews, contact ads for men and women and a women's page reviewing the lesbian scene.

Positive Nation
Empower Publishing (HIV) Limited
250 Kennington Lane
London
SE11 5RD

Telephone 0171 564 2121/0171 564 2123 (Subscriptions)
          Fax 0171 564 2128   E-mail editor@positivenation.co.uk
          Website http://www.positivenation.co.uk

Price £2.20 or free at gay venues/gay retail outlets, etc.
Frequency Monthly
Subscriptions   Annual (10 issues)
                Personal UK: £15 or free if receiving invalidity/incapacity
                benefit (proof required)
                Personal Europe: £22.50
                Personal International: £32.50
                Charities and Voluntary UK: £35
                Statutory and Companies UK: £50

TURNAROUND
PUBLISHER SERVICES

With over 2,000 gay related titles, we are without doubt the largest trade distributor of gay and lesbian interest titles in the UK. Our recent catalogue features the best in lesbian and gay publishing from independent presses such as Bruno Gmünder and Alyson Publications, through to selected titles from international companies such as Penguin, Plume, St. Martin's Press, Virgin and Serpent's Tail.

Books can be obtained from retail outlets ranging from the major chain bookstores – W.H. Smiths, Waterstone's, Borders, Books Etc, to independent stores – Gay's The Word, Out!, Clone Zone, to key mail order companies – Gay Times Book Service, Male Image and Male Express.

Please contact us for a catalogue and details of our terms.
TURNAROUND PUBLISHER SERVICES
UNIT 3, OLYMPIA TRADING ESTATE
COBURG ROAD, LONDON, N22 6TZ
TEL: 020 8829 3000 FAX: 020 8881 5088
E-MAIL: sales@turnaround-uk.com

(All others to phone for details)

Positive Nation will not pass names and addresses onto any third party. All personal information will remain strictly confidential and subscriptions are posted in plain envelopes. An invoice for subscriptions will be sent with the first issue.

This is a free glossy (usually); well-produced, magazine for, as the name suggests, those with or affected by HIV/AIDS as well as everyone else, who should read it to keep abreast of current health related topics. The articles are informative, easy to read and interesting. Regular features include dietary advice and menu suggestions for positive people; additional articles and interviews; recruitment pages; dozens of small ads each month; a monthly gazette listing events, meetings, publications and services and a monthly directory listing of all HIV organisations in the UK. The on-line editions (past and present) can be viewed on the above server. The information in the on-line editions are not as comprehensive as the hard copy.

QX Magazine

Firststar
Second Floor
23 Denmark Street
London
WC2H 8NJ

Telephone 0171 379 7887   Fax 0171 379 7525   E-mail qxmag@dircon.co.uk
         Website http://www.qxmag.co.uk

Price Free in all gay outlets nationwide or by subscription
Frequency *QX International* is weekly (every Wednesday) for London and the South *QX Monthly* is nationwide once a month from all gay venues and gay retail outlets
Subscriptions   Phone above number for current price and details of subscriptions

QX is a free glossy publication that is eagerly awaited for, not only for the jam-packed London club/scene/music reviews, but for the personal contact ads (with photographs!). There is also a scaled down version of *QX International* on the above website. Checkout their Gallery website. Brilliant.

Scotsgay Magazine

PO Box 666
Edinburgh
EH7 5YW

Telephone 0131 539 0666   Fax 0131 539 2999   Website http://
         www.scotsgay.co.uk

Price £1 in newsagents and stores/free in all gay venues and retail outlets
Frequency Every two months. Usually distributed at the end of the 'even' months
Subscriptions   6 issues – (6 months) £6/overseas £12
                   12 issues – (1 years) £12/overseas 24

By subscribing for 6 months you will receive *Scotsgay* and *Inside Out* (three issues of each) through the post. Most major credit cards are accepted

Scotsgay was set up in December 1994 as a bi-monthly magazine for the lesbian, gay and bisexual community in Scotland. *Inside Out* is *Scotgay*'s 'scene' magazine (extremely up-to-date in their listings) and is issued free, as a separate magazine in the months that *Scotsgay* does not appear (namely the odd months). They are both also available in edited formats on the Internet (see above website address).

Bookshops

The shops listed here are those that hold an extensive range of gay and lesbian literature, including all of the national and regional gay press. Most shops will offer an ordering service for books that are not in stock and will be able to advise on the availability of certain books that fit into your field of interest. Most of the smaller shops act as an intermediary to gay resources, the majority having free information and contact sheets available as well as being an excellent source to find out more about the gay scene in your area. Nearly all have a well utilised notice-board advertising local services such as accommodation to let, flat sharing, gay groups in the area and so on. For people living in rural areas without the benefit of a specialised shop, you are able to order by telephone and know full-well that the person you are talking to will understand your needs and do their utmost to assist you. They will also be able to inform you about alternative choices that are in stock and any future releases that may be of interest. One quick look down the list will show that there are now very few 'specialised' shops. This is probably as an outcome of gay literature becoming acceptable in mainstream stores at the expense of the smaller establishment. The answer to this is quite simple – use it or lose it.

Blue Star
1 Victoria Street
York
YO23 1LZ   Telephone 01904 624 901
Opening hours   Tuesday–Saturday: 11.00–5.30

Situated off Nunnery Lane. Licensed adult shop with a good selection of gay books, magazines and videos.

Bookmark
83 Unthank Road
Norwich
NR2 2PE   Telephone 01603 762 855   Fax 01603 621 124

Opening hours   Monday–Friday: 09.30–17.30
                Saturday: 09.00–17.00

Independently gay-owned bookstore with a good selection of gay fiction and
non-fiction in addition to the usual free gay press and magazines.

Books Etc.
120 Charing Cross Road
London
WC2   Telephone 0171 379 6838

Books Etc.
163 Oxford Street
London
W1   Telephone 0171 734 8287

Books Etc.
26 James Street
Covent Garden
London
WC2   Telephone 0171 379 6947

Books Etc.
66 Victoria Streeet
London
SW1   Telephone 0171 931 0677

Books Etc.
16 Whiteley's Of Bayswater
London
W2   Telephone 0171 229 3865

Books Etc.
28 Broadway Shopping Centre
Hammersmith
London
W6   Telephone 0181 746 3912

Books Etc.
Level 2
Royal Festival Hall
South Bank Centre
London
SE1   Telephone 0171 620 0403

A large chain of bookshops with an above-average selection of gay and lesbian
literature. Phone for a copy of Out Etc., which lists current and available gay,
lesbian and associated titles (fiction and non-fiction).

Bookworm
25 St Johns Street
Bridgewater
Somerset   Telephone 01278 423 512

Stocks a reasonable selection of gay literature and magazines.

Compendium

234 Camden High Street
London
NW1   Telephone 0171 485 8944
Opening hours   Monday–Wednesday: 10.00–18.00
                       Thursday–Saturday: 10.00–19.00
                       Sunday: 12.00–18.00

Extensive gay and lesbian book section. Mail order service available too. Further enquiries should be made by phoning the above number.

Dillons Bookshops

Customer Order Department
82 Gower Street
London
WC1E   Telephone 0171 636 1577   Fax 0171 467 1690
                       Website http://www.dillons.co.uk

Subsidiary of Waterstone's and offering an equal amount of gay and lesbian literature but with its own mail order book service. Like Waterstone's, it has an extremely comprehensive on-line Internet book ordering service. You are able to search the entire catalogue using author, publisher, subject, ISBN, title or subject keywords to find the book that you want (or might want). Their secure server allows you to order as you browse, and pay for your goods by credit card. Alternatively, you can complete the order and telephone or post it through, paying by cheque or relating your credit card details over the telephone. In addition to this, Dillons also offer an out of print search to help you trace rare, second hand or out of print books (like 'Fly Fishing' by J.R. Hartley!). There is a £2 charge for this service (a three-book-search) but this is refundable against any subsequent purchase.For details on the service contact:
Out Of Print Book Search Service

Dillons University Bookshop

55–57 Sadler Street
Durham
DH1 3EJ   Telephone 0191 384 2095   Fax 0191 386 043
                       E-mail durham@dillons.eunet.co.uk

Frontline Books

255 Wilmslow Road
Rusholme
Manchester
M14 5LW   Telephone 0161 249 0202   Fax 0161 249 0203
Opening hours   Monday–Friday: 10.00–19.00
                       Saturday: 10.00–17.00

Probably one of the largest gay and radical bookshops in the North-West with an absolutely huge gay/bi/transgender/lesbian section as well as the free gay press and magazines. They also stock a range of cards, posters and T-shirts. The bottom line is; if it is gay related then you will be able to find it here. If you are not sure what you are looking for then the friendly and knowledgeable staff will be able to help you. They also offer a comprehensive mail order service if you are unable to visit the shop. Moved from Newton Street, Manchester in January 1999 to these larger premises.

Gay's The Word

66 Marchmount Street
London
WC1N 1AB   Telephone 0171 278 7654
Opening hours   Monday–Saturday: 10.00–18.00
                Sunday: 12.00–18.00
                Late opening on a Thursday

Well-established gay and lesbian bookshop stocking a wonderful selection of gay and lesbian literature – fiction, non-fiction, biography, coming out, travel, humour, erotica, cultural studies, history, TV/TS, relationships, crime, sex manuals, counselling and American imports. They are also stockists of a great selection of cards, magazines and videos. Good selection of secondhand books available in addition to the usual free gay press. Tea and coffee served in the back reading area. If you are unsure of what is available then ask the helpful and extremely friendly staff.

Green Leaf Bookshop

82 Colston Street
Bristol
BS1 5BB   Telephone 0117 921 1369
Opening hours   Monday–Friday: 09.30–17.30
                Saturday: 10.00–17.00

Huge range of lesbian and gay titles. The usual free gay press available.

In Other Words Limited

72 Mutley Plain
Plymouth
PL4 6LF   Telephone 01752 663 889
Opening hours   09.30–18.00
                10.00–17.30

Holds a large selection of gay and lesbian fiction and non-fiction books. Free gay press and magazines available.

Mushroom Bookshop

10 Heathcote Street
Nottingham
NG1 3AA   Telephone 0115 958 2506   Fax 0115 959 0971
Opening hours   Monday–Saturday: 10.00–18.00
                Sunday: Closed

Extensive range of gay and lesbian literature with the free gay press and magazines. Well-utilised noticeboard for all that's happening at the current time in Nottingham.

News From Nowhere Bookshop
96 Bold Street
Liverpool
L1 4HY   Telephone 0151 708 7270
Opening hours
Monday–Saturday: 09.30–17.45

Community bookshop with a large gay and lesbian section. Also stocks the current gay press and a well-utilised noticeboard with all the current scene information.

October Books
4 Onslow Road
Southampton
SO14 0JB   Telephone 01703 224 489
Opening hours   Monday–Saturday: 09.00–18.00

Huge selection of gay and lesbian fiction and non-fiction, in addition to academia, radical writing and poetry.

Out! Brighton
4–7 Dorset Street
Brighton
BN2 1WA   Telephone 01273 623 356
Opening hours   Monday–Thursday: 10.00–18.00
                 Friday–Saturday: 10.00–19.00
                 Sunday: 11.00–17.00

This store sells everything from books to magazines, as well as clothing and accessories, in addition to having the free gay press available.

Out Of The Blue
36 Broughton Street
Broughton
Edinburgh
EH3   Telephone 0131 478 7048   Fax 0131 478 7412
Opening hours   Monday–Sunday: 12.00–19.00

Situated in the basement of The Blue Moon Café. Not an exclusively gay 'adult' store but one which does stock a huge selection of magazines, erotic videos (Prowler, Zipper, Load and Pride), books (fiction and non-fiction), vests and T-shirts (Hom, T-Boy, Bond and Hanes), swimwear, cards and gifts. This, in addition to all those other little essentials that we just can't live without.No mail order service available unfortunately.

Read All About It
69 East Street
Brighton
BN1   Telephone 01273 205 824

Opening hours   Monday–Saturday: 09.30–19.00 Sunday: 12.00–18.00

A large selection of gay, lesbian and bisexual fiction and non-fiction titles in addition to the usual free gay press. Situated close to Brighton Pavilion.

Silver Moon
64–68 Charing Cross Road
London
WC2H 0BB   Telephone 0171 836 7906/0171 836 6848 (Mail order direct
                line)   Fax 0171 379 1018
                E-mail smwb@silvermoonbookshop.co.uk
Opening hours   Monday–Saturday: 09.30–19.30
                Thursday: 09.30–20.00
                Sunday: 12.00–18.00

Women's bookshop with a comprehensive mail order service. Phone or write for a free copy of their 'Silver Moon Quarterly' catalogue of goods.

Virgin Megastore
14–16 Oxford Street
London
W1   Telephone 0171 631 1234
Opening hours   Monday–Saturday: 09.30–20.00
                Sunday: 12.00–18.00

Apart from being one of the largest music stores around it also has an extremely comprehensive gay and lesbian book section. In addition to the London branch, most Virgin Megastores throughout the country do stock a good range of gay and lesbian titles.

Waterstone's
Mailing Service
4–5 Milsom Street
Bath
BA1 1DA   Telephone 01225 448 595   Fax 01225 444 732
                Website http://www.waterstones.co.uk

Waterstone's Booksearch
32–40 Calverley Road
Tunbridge Wells
Kent
TN1 2TD   Telephone01892 535 446   Fax 01892 535 517

Waterstone's are an extremely gay-friendly store. If you have access to the Internet, you will be able to browse at your leisure through their virtual bookstore at the website listed above. Search engines are fast, using a facility whereby you can conduct your own book search by subject, author, book title, publisher or ISBN number. There is also an on-line mail order 'shopping basket' facility using a secure server for credit card details. You will also be invited to join the Waterstone's Club, giving you the opportunity to browse through copies of the on-line version of W Magazine, the Waterstone's monthly guide to the best in books, authors and literary debate. If you do not have Internet access, all stores can usually obtain titles for you and hold them for your collection. Alternatively, phone the mail order department on the above number.

Gay Reading

The following books represent only a fraction of the gay literature available. The ones listed are intended to steer you towards reading further on the topics covered in this guide. There are also informative books relating to gay history. Most gay bookstores and mail order companies carry the complete range and, if they do not feature in stock, will no doubt be able to order it in for you. Prices are provided merely as an indication of what you can expect to pay and are based on recommended retail prices.

Family Secrets
Jean M. Baker (£9.99)
A refreshing and moving portrait of a mother's love for her two gay sons.

Ties That Bind
Guy Baldwin (£10.99)
An exploration of healthy safer sex, including S/M rubber and fetish.

Learning The Ropes
Race Bannon (£9.99)
A guide to the delights of safer S&M sex.

Leather Sex
Joseph W. Bean (£9.99)
A guide for the curious outsider and a manual for the serious participant.

Leather Sex: Questions And Answers
Joseph W. Bean (£11.99)
Questions and answers about leather sex and lifestyle.

Queen's Country
Paul Burston (£8.99)
Personal travel tales from around gay Britain.

Coming Out
Susie Byrne and Junior Larkins (£6.99)
A book for lesbians and gay men of all ages about coming out.
Entertainingly presented in question and answer formats.

Diesel Fuel
Pat Califia (£10.99)
Revealing Califia to be a poet of unusual power, this collection of
stunning, frank and powerful verse is not for the timid – leaving no
sexual stone unturned and clearing new ground for us all.

A Trouser-Wearing Character: The Life And Times Of Nancy Spain
Rose Collis (£25)
This fascinating biography reconstructs the life of one of Britain's
most extraordinary women.

Gay And Lesbian On Line
Jeff Dawson (£12.99)
Third edition of the guide to cyberspace, written from a queer
perspective.

The Five Lesbian Brothers' Guide To Life
(£9.99)
A raunchy reference book that will make all lesbians laugh.
Illustrated by Donna Evans, it is camp, subversive, lusty and side
splitting. Includes handy do's and don'ts and tips about seduction
and lifestyle. The Five Lesbian Brothers have written and starred in
four plays and have appeared on Broadway.

Awakening The Virgin
Edited by Nicole Foster (£8.99)
Collection of 30 short, erotic, true stories of lesbians seducing, or
being seduced by, virgin women.

Reflections Of A Rock Lobster
Aeron Fricke (£4.99)
New edition of the true classic about the American teenagers
attempts to take his boyfriend to the high school proms.

The Wild Good
Beatrix Gates (£13.99)
A vibrant multifaceted celebration of lesbian love within a vivid collection of photos, letters, poetry, fiction, memoirs and interviews. Divided into five sections, these 45 pieces describe the constellations that lesbians inhabit.

Gay Old Girls
Zsa Zsa Gerschick (£8.99)
A lively fascinating oral history of lesbians over the age of sixty, talking about their lives and loves. Illustrated throughout with black and white photographs from thirteen remarkable women's lives, often lived in secret.

Male Order
Barbara Gibson (£14.99)
Life stories from boys who sell sex.

What's Wrong With My Willy?
Ray Hamble (£5.95)
The Zipper doctor answers all those questions you would never dare to ask your GP.

The Day We Met
Edited by Jack Hart (£8.99)
The story of romantic first time encounters between gay men.

Gay Sex: A Manual For Men Who Love Men
Jack Hart (£12.99)
An invaluable guide with explicit drawings to sexual pleasure and good health.

My Biggest 'O'
Edited by Jack Hart (£7.99)
An engaging and erotic picture of the sexual tastes of gay men.

Gay Skins
Murray Healy (£13.99)

Authoritative and entertaining history of gay skins, with illustrations.

The Men With The Pink Triangle
Heinz Heger (£7.95)
This modern classic is one of the few first-hand accounts of life as a gay man in a concentration camp.

Coming Out To Parents
Mary V. Horhek

Reclaiming Your Life
Rick Isensee (£9.99)
A manual for the millennium on love and self-acceptance.

The Bent Lens
Claire Jackson and Peter Tapp (£19.95)
The complete guide to gay, lesbian and queer films currently available internationally, covering over 1,700 titles from 45 countries and spanning lesbian and gay film making from 1914 to the present day.

Dear Uncle Go
Peter A. Jackson (£11.99)
A study of male homosexuality in Thailand.

On The Safe Edge
Trevor Jacques (£14.99)
A pan-sexual book which answers questions a novice might have, as they begin to explore S&M play. Providing an understanding of how S&M play can be positive, safe and healthy.

One Teacher In Ten
Edited by Kevin Jennings (£8.99)
Gay and lesbian educators tell their story.

Sex Longing And Not Belonging
Badruddin Khan (£8.99)
An examination into the meaning of gay life within Muslim culture

Get On With It
Richard Laemer (£11.99)
A useful guide to getting on line in the gay community.

Queer Dharma
Edited by Winston Leyland (£13.99)
Thirty men integrate their sexuality and their spirituality by practising Buddhism.

Eyes Of Desire
Edited by Raymond Luczak (£7.95)
Lesbians and gay men who are deaf talk about their lives; discovering their sexual identities, overcoming barriers to communication and creating culture in a world that is often afraid of difference.

Together Forever
Andrew Marshall (£5.99)
A thoughtfully written and highly practical manual about the pleasures, problems and pitfalls of gay relationships.

PWA
Oscar Moore (£6.99)
Powerful and moving essays by the late *Guardian* columnist on his life with AIDS.

Butch/Femme
Edited by Sally Munt (£16.99)
Poetry, fiction, photographs and theory combine in this groundbreaking collection which addresses many different aspects of butch and femme identity.

Queer Kids
Robert E. Owens Jnr (£16.99)
A variety of fascinating kids tell their stories of coming out, survival, success and joy.

Out In The Workplace
Edited by Richard A. Rasi and Lourdes Rodriguez-Nogues
Series of essays by various people who have come out in their workplace (Legal implications apply to American Law).

The Master's Manual
Jack Rinella (£10.99)
A guide to S&M power, dominance and techniques.

Young, Gay And Proud
Edited by Don Romesburg (£4.99)

First published in 1980, this anthology of coming out experiences has been updated to take into account HIV and AIDS.

A–Z Of Gay Sex
Terry Sanderson (£9.95)
In this new erotic alphabet, Sanderson takes his readers on a quirky personal journey through the highways and byways of gay sex in an entertaining but informative way.

Assertively Gay
Terry Sanderson (£8.95)
New edition of *Gay Times*' mediawatch columnist offers practical advice on how to be more assertive in the latest of his self-help books.

How To Be A Happy Homosexual
Terry Sanderson (£6.95)
Fourth edition of this highly praised guide for gay men, full of practical and common-sense advice.

Making Gay Relationships Work
Terry Sanderson (£6.95)
A new and extensively revised edition of this handbook for male couples.

A Stranger In The Family
Terry Sanderson (£9.95)
A well-informed and practical handbook for parents whose child is gay or lesbian.

Living Well
Peter Shalit (£12.99)
An essential guide for gay men's health.

Gay Widowers
Edited by Michael Shernoff (£9.99)
Personal accounts of life after the death of a partner from AIDS.

Not Like Other Boys
Marlene Fanat Shyer and Christopher Shyer (£8.99)
Complimentary narratives by a mother and her son about her
awareness of, and his coming to terms with his gayness.

Outing Yourself
Michelangelo Signorile (£6.99)
14 steps towards the process (which may take a lifetime to achieve)
of outing yourself, with advice and exercises.

New Joy Of Gay Sex
Dr Charles Silverstein and Felice Picano (£16.95)
A new and completely revised edition of the legendary book on
gay sex and sensations.

My Mother's Last Dance
Honor Ford Smith (£7.99)
A powerful, moving and humorous collection of poems, which
celebrate the legacy of three generations of Caribbean women.

The Gay Kama Sutra
Colin Spencer (£14.99)
Beautifully illustrated in colour and black and white. This is a
coffee-table format update on the timeless Indian erotic classic.

Safer Sexy
Peter Tatchell (£14.99)
Explicit text and picture guide to safe gay sex.

Leatherfolk
Edited by Mark Thomson (£10.99)
Lively and likely to be contentious essays on leather lifestyles.

The Leatherman's Handbook
Larry Townsend (£9.99)
Twenty-fifth anniversary edition of this leather classic.

Viagra
Dr Susan C. Vaughan (£8.99)
A user-friendly and surprisingly entertaining guide to the much
hyped 'love drug'.

Good For You?
Tamsin Wilton (£12.99)

Essential information and advice on a wide range of lesbian and health issues, including tips on diet, exercise, sex and motherhood.

Out On Fraternity Row
Edited by Windmeyer and Freeman (£9.99)
Personal accounts of being gay on a college fraternity.

The Bear Book
Edited by Les Wright (£15.99)
Brings the bear out of his cave; this book says yes to beards, bellies and hairy chests and no to the dominant images of male beauty.

Bisexual Lives
Written by bisexuals about themselves.

Dear God, I'm Gay
Produced by a group of Ecumenical Christians.

Mail Order

In order to relieve any worries or concerns that you may have about mail order it is worth knowing the following:

The names and addresses received by reputable mail order companies are never disclosed to a third party or sold on (this is certainly true for the companies that are subsequently listed, unfortunately, I cannot speak for the many others). Only the relevant staff in each company's mail order department will have access to these details. They are usually held on a secure server.

It is worth bearing in mind that the name of the mail order company may appear on your credit card statement. For most of us this should not be a problem, however, if this might be a concern for you, it might be wise to check with the company as to what name will appear. If there remains a problem or worry then you should consider an alternative method of payment. Packaging will always be discreet and secure. The company's name will not be emblazoned over the front.

If receiving post or goods at home is a problem, then consider hiring a post-office box number. The minimun period for this service is one year and comes with an annual charge of approximately £52. You will be issued with an identification card which will initially be sent to your home address and no further contact by the post office will be made until your 'box' comes up for renewal. Mail and packages will be sent to the sorting office nearest to your home address. To set up this service contact: Royal Mail on 0345 740 740.

Ordering goods over the Internet is an ideal way of purchasing goods, however, there is always a concern that your credit card details 'could' be intercepted by a third party. Although this is virtually impossible (I have no proof to the contrary), should you have any doubts you are able to phone the mail order company direct and order your goods with credit card details over the phone.

Finally, always use 'established' mail order companies such as the ones listed here. This is not to say that companies listed in other publications are 'rogue dealers', it just makes common sense to deal with a company that has a reputation for service, longevity and an understanding of your needs.

All In Leather
PO Box 13
Battle
East Sussex
TN33 0WT   Telephone 01424 772 158

A mail order company well-established for over four years, specialising in custom-made restraint and dicipline equipment in leather and rubber, shoes and boots up to size (UK)13. Adult toys for boys and girls. Full photographic mail order catalogue costs £5 (refundable with first order). Fetish parties held monthly – for details of these phone the above number.

Bob's Rubberwear
37 Tenbury Close
London
E7 8AX   Telephone 0181 470 6635
Opening hours   09.00–21.00
                Personal callers by appointment only

'Rubber for men'. Fetish clothing for men only. Free mail order catalogue available on request.
Specialists in custom-made rubber clothing, sheeting and accessories.

Cardome 2000
47A St James Street
Brighton
BN1   Telephone 01273 692 916
Opening hours   Monday–Saturday: 09.30–17.30
                Sunday: 10.00–16.00 (high season only)

Card shop with adult section (entrance through 'Over 18' partition) stocking a wide range of gay, straight, TV/TS and lesbian magazines (with a good stock of American imports). Poppers available (reduced price for bulk purchase of 10+) plus adult cards and accessories. Mail order service available (no catalogue) – just telephone for requirements and they will be posted out to you. Payment details on request.

Clone Zone Limited

3rd Floor
Wellington House
Pollard Street East
Manchester
M40 7FS   Telephone 0800 783 7953 (Freephone)/0161 273 5246 (24 hour
               hotline)   Fax 0161 272 8410   E-mail mailord@clonezone.co.uk
               Website http://www.clonezone.co.uk

Mail order department of this well-established multi-million pound gay emporium. Everything you could possibly require from over 100 of their own original 'Flesh' clothing designs to magazines, books, videos, toys, underwear, leather, aromas, rubber, etc. Either write to the above address or phone the freephone number for a free copy of their mail order catalogue. There is also a secure on-line 'Home Shopping' catalogue at the above website. In addition to the comprehensive mail order service you will be welcomed at any of the Clone Zone stores at the following UK locations:

Clone Zone

64 Old Compton Street
Soho
London
W1   Telephone 0171 287 3530

Clone Zone

266 Old Brompton Road
Earls Court
London
SW5   Telephone 0171 373 0598

Clone Zone

84 Hurst Street
The Arcadian Centre
Birmingham
B5   Telephone 0121 666 6640

Clone Zone

3 The Strand
Blackpool
FY1   Telephone 01253 294 850

Clone Zone

35 Virginia Street
Glasgow
G1   Telephone 0141 248 2593

Clone Zone

36–38 Sackville Street
Manchester
M1   Telephone 0161 236 1398

Clone Zone

Flamingo's Nightclub (evenings only)
174–176 Talbot Road
Blackpool
FY1 3AZ

Cover Up

Department UGG
PO Box 40
Nuneaton
Warwickshire
CV10 0XB   Website http://www.coverup.co.uk

Black rubber industrial grade protective clothing, coats, jackets, overtrousers, souwesters, aprons, wellingtons, waders, chest waders, gasmasks, etc. Also available: total enclosure suits, firemans kit, construction gear and other specialist wear. Send an SAE to the above address for further details and a mail order catalogue.

Expectations
75 Great Eastern Street
London
EC2A 3HU   Telephone 0171 739 0292   Fax 0171 256 0910   Website http:// www.expectations.co.uk
Opening hours   Monday–Friday: 11.00–19.00
Saturday: 11.00–20.00
Sunday: 12.00–17.00

Specialising in leather, rubber, S&M equipment and sportswear. Expectations has built up a reputation for quality craftsmanship. The leather and rubber is handmade in their own workshop. A full repair, alteration and design service is available too. A comprehensive mail order service is available. Initial catalogue available at £8, which is deductable from your first order over £50. The catalogue is presented in a ring binder that enables you to add further pages as they are released and the fee covers you for all new release pages for a year. For overseas enquiries the catalogue will cost £10 (phone for further details). Tickets for most fetish parties and events can be purchased here.

Gay UK Mail Order
Department GUKUGG
Freepost LS5 930
LS27 8YY
Gay UK Mail Order
Walk 34
Middleton Road
Leeds
LS27 8BB   Telephone 0990 605 069 (24 hours)/08701 200 600
(Hotline)/0800 1382 425   Website http://www.mrgayuk.co.uk

Gay UK Mail Order produces a free up-to-date, 32 page colour catalogue every three months. It contains all the latest sexy gift ideas from the glossy, coffee-table male photography book to the one-handed horny read. Glossy magazines from America and the best on the British market. Toys to enhance most people's sex lives as well as the very popular, anatomically correct, Billy doll range. Underwear, rubberwear and leather harnesses are available together with a full range of novelties. Greetings cards, books and videos are added to regularly by an ever-growing list of fun products. Contact the above hotline for free mail order catalogue and information for 'Aromas Direct', special offers, etc. All major credit cards accepted.

The Gay Men's Press
(GMP Publishers)
PO Box 247
Swaffham
PE37 8PA
Central Books
99 Wallis Road
London
E9 5LN   Telephone 0181 986 4854   Fax 0181 533 5821
              Website http://www.gmppubs.co.uk   E-mail David@gmppubs.co.uk
              (general enquiries)/sales@gmppubs.co.uk (sales/mail order
              enquiries)

Make cheques and postal orders payable to GMP Publishers Ltd.
GMP is the oldest independent gay book publisher in the country. Established in 1979, they have been producing a quality range of gay fiction, general books. They are specialists in art and photography titles. Over 150 titles are currently available and further details and catalogues (including Aubrey Walters Editions) can be obtained by writing to the Central Books address. There is also an on-line catalogue and order form at the above website. A secure server can accept your credit card details. Alternatively, you are able to print out your order and then send them with credit card details/cheque/postal order GMP address. As a community publisher with a global outreach, they are always happy to receive submissions from new writers and artists. You are requested to send in a synopsis and sample extracts, either by e-mail or to the GMP address (SAE essential for return of document).

Honour
86 Lower Marsh
Waterloo
London
SE1 7AB   Telephone 0171 401 8220   E-mail mail@honour.co.uk
              Website http://www.honour.co.uk

Honour
27 Praed Street
Paddington
London
W2 1NJ   Telephone 0171 262 3600   E-mail mail@honour.co.uk
              Website http://www.honour.co.uk
Opening hours Monday–Friday:10.30–19.00
               Saturday: 11.30–17.00

The discerning enthusiast will take delight in their 'Bondage Attic', and the shoe lover in their 'Boot Corner'. Stocking the latest magazines from around the world in addition to their hand-picked video collection, combined with value and quality, have made Honour famous all over the world. From cocktail dresses to cock rings, their stores in London, in addition to their secure server on the

Internet, are packed with everything the kinky heart could desire. The Waterloo shop is two floors worth of coats, cloaks, boots, catsuits, shirts, skirts, lingerie, hosiery, straps, chaps, tops and crops. TV/TS particularly catered for with a large selection of boots and shoes to (UK) size 12. Honour is one of the fastest growing fetish companies in Europe. Their aim is to provide a completely confidential service for male and female clients, selling quality products at reasonable prices. This pledge is still brought to you today (ten years on) with even a wider range of products and services to its customers. Phone for mail order catalogue (it costs £5 which is refundable against your first order).

Laurence Corner

62–64 Hampstead Road
London
NW1 2NU   Telephone 0171 813 1010   Fax 0171 813 1413

Military fashion, action classics and surplus chic. Situated close to Warren Street and Euston, this store has probably the largest selection of government surplus anywhere. From uniforms to helmets, service shirts to army ties. This is not strictly a gay outlet although they do advertise in the gay press and understand the needs of the gay male. Free mail order catalogue on request.

Load Direct

Freepost NW6000
London
NW1 1YU   Telephone 0171 485 0237 (24 hour hotline)

Mail order only. Load produce some of the most erotic videos around with the cutest models and some of the raunchiest action (all R18) in addition to a selection of toys, magazines and books. Load videos are available from most gay mail order companies. Phone or write to the above for a catalogue and further information.

Male Image

PO Box 3821
London
N5 1UY   Telephone 0171 609 3427   E-mail books@bookworks.co.uk
            Website http://www.bookworks.co.uk

A mail order company with over one and a half thousand gay titles, from art to photography, fiction to memoirs, sexual politics to poetry and travel guides to self-help manuals. Male Image probably offers the widest selection of gay books and videos available by mail order. If you would like to request a free catalogue then phone the above number. Alternatively you can download the current and back issue catalogues at the above website.

Paradiso Bodyworks

41 Old Compton Street
London
W1V 5PN   Telephone 0171 287 2487   Fax 0181 348 9352
Opening hours   Monday–Sunday: 11.00–21.00

Large selection of fetish wear, S&M equipment, toys, lingerie and TV/TS clothing including footwear. Comprehensive mail order service available – phone for a catalogue.

Prowler Press

Male Express Limited
3 Broadbent Close
London
N6 5GG   Telephone 0800 454 566 (Freephone)/(International)
                +44 181 340 8644   Website http://www.prowler.co.uk (On-line shop with secure server)

Mail order company of Prowler Press; Europe's largest distributor of gay erotica. Free comprehensive catalogue available by phoning the above free number.

Prowler Soho

3–7 Brewer Street
Soho
London
W1R 3FN   Telephone 0171 734 4031   E-mail Miles@prowler.co.uk (store manager)

In addition to the extensive mail order catalogue and on-line secure server (see above). Prowler have a retail outlet which is a completely new kind of gay shopping experience. With huge windows, funky neon lighting and friendly staff who are just like you. Creating a guilt-free place to shop for all your needs in an environment every bit as stylish as you would find on Regent Street. The shop has at least five times more product than their nearest competitor and the enormous floor space allows them to stock the most comprehensive selection of products in each of their departments. Of course, whereas sex is the most important part of being gay – and they have enough magazines, toys and aromas to pep up the dullest sex life – they do also sell a huge amount of the latest fashion from big name designers and sell more books than any other shop in the West End. In addition to all of this they have an enviable selection of gifts, housewares and accessories. The shop is proud to carry the Prowler press ethos into the retail world and endeavor to bring you quality without fleecing you, so much so, that if you find a Prowler Soho product cheaper in another shop, then they will happily refund the difference.

Regulation

17A St Albans Place
Islington Green
London
N1 0NX   Telephone 0171 226 0665   Fax 0171 226 0658
                E-mail orderline@regulation-ltd.co.uk   Website http://www.regulation-ltd.co.uk
Opening hours   Monday–Saturday: 10.30–18.30
                Sunday: 12.00–17.00

'The art of control'. Located in North London, Regulation has on display over 2,000 items from full rubber suits and sleepsacks to leatherwear, in addition to a multitude of strapwork for all types of dungeon scenes. Always keen to answer the demands of their customers, they now have a range of inflatable equipment and vacuum equipment, as well as being the European distributor for Fetters bondage and restraint equipment. All of Regulation's leather and rubber gear is made in their own workshops adjoining the showroom They are currently working on a secure on-line Internet ordering system (shopping cart). Whilst they work on making the system as secure as possible, orders can be taken over the phone. Tickets to most fetish venues and one-off parties (i.e. Fist) are available from here. Comprehensive mail order sevice available. Phone for further information and details on how to receive their product catalogue.

Rob

24 Wells Street
London
W1P 3FG   Telephone 0171 735 7893   Fax 0171 637 4510
                 Website http://www.rob.nl   E-mail roblondon@rob.nl
Opening hours   Monday–Saturday: 10.30–18.30

The shop is situated by the Plaza shoping centre, north of Oxford Street, specialising in leather jackets, harnesses, rubber shirts, electro stimulation, tit wear, belts, leather hoods, whips, leather chaps, chasitity belts, leather restraints, rubber suits, leather gags, rubber shorts, boots caps, leather collars, leather posing pouches and accessories. In short: leather, rubber and twisted gear. Comprehensive mail order service available. Send for the catalogue which is in excess of 130 pages and costs £10 which is refundable on any first order of £75 or more. Phone the above number for further information.

Sh! Women's Exotic Emporium Limited

39 Coronet Street
London
N1 GHD   Telephone 0171 613 5458   Website http://www.sh-
                 womenstore.com
Opening hours   Monday–Saturday: 11.30–18.30
                 Thursday: 11.30–20.00

Exclusively women-only shop, selling a huge range of magazines, toys, restraint equipment, videos, books, hammocks, accessories, etc. Men are allowed in *only* if accompanied by a female. TV/TS both welcome and catered for. Most of the leather and rubber goods are manufactured by Sh! Tickets to most fetish parties and club nights can be purchased from here. A comprehensive mail order catalogue is available free of charge (A4 SAE appreciated).

ST Publishing

PO Box 2153
London
E7 0JZ   Telephone 0181 257 1753

CP/S&M/B&D. Stockists and publishers of *Sir* and *Houseboy* magazine. Also fully illustrated fetish mail order catalogue available. Write for further details.

Wish, Will and Pleasure

PO Box 3125
Brighton
BN1 6QW   Telephone 01273 550 883

Wish, Will and Pleasure is a new mail order company aimed at the lesbian
market. Products available include sex toys, accessories, harnesses, leather and
PVC goods, videos, cards and postcards, calendars, magnets and novelty goods.
Unique products include the range of 'toy tidies – boxes and bags to store your
sex toys in. From summer 1999, a range of books will also be available. A website
where products can be viewed and ordered is presently under development,
with a planned launch date of mid-1999. Wish, Will and Pleasure assures you
that all names and addresses held by them will only be used to mail customers
with and will not be passed on to any other organisation or individual for use. All
orders are sent with absolute discretion.

Zipperstore
283 Camden High Street
London
NW1 7BX   Telephone 0171 284 0537/0171 267 7665
                Fax 0171 428 0962   Website http://www.zipper.co.uk
Opening hours   Monday–Saturday: 10.00–18.00
                Sunday: 12.00–17.00

'The Biggest Little Sex Shop' for whatever you're into . . . located in the heart of
Camden town, adjacent to Camden Lock Market. Large, well-established (25
years), licenced gay and lesbian sex shop. Recently refurbished, the Zipperstore
is a haven for the gay shopper, carrying a huge range of sex toys, lubricants,
magazines, videos, books and CDs. They also carry a range of bondage gear from
the simple collar to full-body harness and lots of exciting restraints, including
fur-lined handcuffs and ankle cuffs. Their range of rubber clothing is quite
innovative, as is their stock of leather underwear, which is so soft and warm
you'd swear it was still breathing! For their current catalogue, write, phone or
visit them on their secure 'on-line' site to peruse their virtual Zipperstore.

Gay Hanky/Colour Codes

The hanky codes are not used much nowadays, which is a shame as it used to be a good way of breaking the ice and ensuring that you tag up with exactly the right sort of person. Perhaps someone could manufacture small, coloured enamel badges to take the place of the handkerchiefs. Colour codes are used extensively in the small personal ads as a means of attracting response from like-minded individuals, for example, instead of writing 'I would like to meet someone with whom I could piss on / be pissed on', all you need to do is write the word YELLOW, and save yourself about £3.60 in personal ad costs to boot.

The hanky should be placed in the back pocket of your jeans or trousers and inserted with just the tip sticking out (ooh-er). Bear in mind that the pocket the hanky is placed in (either left or right as viewed from the back) makes all the difference as to what you are 'advertising' your likes as, although at the end of the day, no matter which pocket the hanky is placed in, you will be attracting like for like and you can sort out the niggly details over a pint.

One final point: some colours have dual meanings (where the colour originated in America and was then adopted over here); these are both given and I have no easy remedy to sort out any ambiguities. Beware also the similarity of some colours; for example, if you swan around with a coral hanky in your right pocket expecting to suck a few toes and someone mistakes it for fuschia and whacks your arse when you bend down, you wont be best pleased will you? And to avoid a huge disappointment, ensure you know the difference between mustard and pale yellow in the right pocket!

WORN ON LEFT	HANKY COLOUR	WORN ON RIGHT
S&M top	BLACK	*S&M bottom*
Bondage Top	GREY	*Bondage Bottom*
Wants to be Sucked	LIGHT BLUE	*Wants to Suck*
Cop	MEDIUM BLUE	*Cop sucker*
Active	NAVY BLUE	*Passive*

Pilot/Flight Crew	AIR FORCE BLUE	*Likes Flyboys*
Sailor	LIGHT BLUE — WHITE STRIPE	*Wants Sailor*
Cock and Ball Torturer	TEAL BLUE	*Cock and Ball Torture Receiver*
Fist Fucker	RED	*Fist Receiver*
Enema Giver	MAROON	*Enema Receiver*
Two Handed Fister	DARK RED	*Two Handed Receiver*
Dildo Fucker	LIGHT PINK	*Dildo Receiver*
Tit Torturer	DARK PINK	*Tit Torture Receiver*
Into Navel Worship	MAUVE	*Navel Fetish*
Suck my Pits	MAGENTA	*Yes Please*
Piercer	PURPLE	*Piercee*
Likes TV/TS/Drag	LAVENDER (1)	*TV/TS/Drag*
Gay Curious/Bisexual	LAVENDER (2)	*Will Teach*
Piss/Watersports Giver	YELLOW	*Piss Receiver*
Spits	PALE YELLOW	*Spit Receiver*
Hung 8 Inches or More	MUSTARD	*Wants a Big One*
Two Looking for One	GOLD	*One Looking for Two*
Anything Top	ORANGE	*Anything Bottom*
Chubby	APRICOT	*Chubby Chaser*
Suck my Toes	CORAL	*Toe Sucker*
Spanker	FUSCHIA	*Spank Receiver*
Rent Boy	GREEN	*Wants to Buy*
Uniform Top	KHAKI (1)	*Uniform Bottom*
Has Uniform	KHAKI (2)	*Wants Uniform*
Rimmer	BEIGE	*Rimee*
Scat Top	BROWN	*Scat Bottom*
Uncut	BROWN LACE	*Likes Uncut*
Circumcised	BROWN SATIN	*Likes Circumcised*
Rubber Fetish Top	CHARCOAL	*Rubber Fetish Bottom*
Wears Suit	GREY FLANNEL	*Likes Suits*
Wants a Wank	WHITE	*Will Wank*
Safe Sex Top	BLACK & WHITE CHECK	*Safe Sex Bottom*
Shaver	RED & WHITE STRIPE	*Likes to be Shaved*
Hairy Bear	RED & BLACK STRIPE	*Likes Bears*
Likes White Bottom	WHITE LACE	*Likes White Top*
Likes Black Bottom	BLACK & WHITE STRIPE	*Likes Black Top*
Likes Brown Bottom	BROWN & WHITE STRIPE	*Likes Brown Top*

Likes Oriental Bottom	YELLOW & WHITE STRIPE	*Likes Oriental Top*
Likes White Suckers	LIGHT BLUE & WHITE DOTS	*Likes To Suck Whites*
Likes Black Suckers	LIGHT BLUE & BLACK DOTS	*Likes To Suck Blacks*
Likes Brown Suckers	LIGHT BLUE & BROWN DOTS	*Likes To Suck Brown*
Likes Oriental Suckers	LIGHT BLUE & YELLOW DOTS	*Likes To Suck Oriental*
Outside Sex Top	RED & WHITE GINGHAM (MOSQUITO NETTING ALSO)	*Outside Sex Bottom*
Outside Sex Top	MOSQUITO NETTING (RED & WHITE GINGHAM ALSO)	*Outside Sex Bottom*
Headmaster Role-Play	BROWN CORDUROY	*Student Role-Play*
Underwear Fetish	PAISLEY	*Likes Underwear*
Likes Muscleboy Bottom	GOLD LAME	*Likes Muscleboy Top*
Star Fucker	SILVER LAME	*Celebrity*
Has/Takes Videos	BLACK VELVET	*Will Perform*
Voyeur (Likes To Watch)	WHITE VELVET	*Will Put on a Show*
Has Tattoos	LEOPARD PRINT	*Likes Tattoos*
Smokes Cigars	CHAMOIS	*Likes Cigars*
Cuddler	TEDDY BEAR	*Likes a Cuddle*
Wears a Dirty Jockstrap	DIRTY JOCKSTRAP (SEE UNDERPANTS TOO)	*Sucks It clean*
'Yellow' Calvins	UNDERPANTS (SEE DIRTY JOCKSTRAP TOO)	*Sucks them Clean*
Has Drugs	RESEALABLE PLASTIC BAG	*Wants Drugs*
Stinks	KLEENEX TISSUE	*Sniffs*
Come Home with me	KEYS IN FRONT	*Has a Car*
Needs a Place to Stay	KEYS IN BACK	*Looking for a Ride*
Likes to Nibble	HOUNDS TOOTH	*Will be Bitten*
Skinhead Top	UNION JACK	*Skinhead Bottom*

New in Town	CALICO (UNBLEACHED)	*Tourists Welcome*
Sauna Top	TERRY TOWELLING	*Sauna Bottom*
Hosting an Orgy	WHITE/ MULTICOLOUR DOTS	*Looking for an Orgy*

Glossary Of Gay Slang And Sexual Terms

The following list is by no means complete, neither is it exhaustive in its interpretation. Some of the words listed below are Americanisms, listed because of their use in gay porno novels and skin-flick films. Fetish or 'hanky' codes (i.e. red, yellow, brown, etc.) and their descriptions are not listed here but are detailed in depth in the previous section. Personal advert codes are listed, however, it must be understood that these codes are not uniform in all publications for example; NS in one publication may mean non-smoker whilst in another it may mean non-scene, although most are now using the lower case follow up letter (NSm for non-smoker, NSc for non-scene, etc.) to avoid mistakes.

Ac/Dc *Bisexual*

Active *The Aggressive Sexual Partner*

Age of Consent *The Legal Age when you are allowed by law to have Sexual Relations*

Ala *All Letters Answered*

Alawp *All Letters Answered With Photograph*

Analingus *Licking, Penetration And Arousal of the Anus By the Tongue*

Angel *Man Who Pays For Sexual Favours*

Areola *The Dark Ring of Skin Surrounding the Nipple*

Around the World *The Act of Kissing the Entire Body As A Prelude To Sex*

Arthur *The Active Gay Partner (As Opposed To Martha, the Passive)*

Aquarium *Part of A Gay Venue Where Lesbians Tend To Congregate*

Aunty *An Ageing Gay Male*

Auto-Sadism *An Act Whereby One Inflicts Pain On Oneself*

Auxiliary Intercourse *Sexual Climax Achieved By Moving the Erect Penis Back And Forth in the Armpit*

B&D *Bondage And Domination*

Backscuttle *Perform Anal Intercourse*

Bag *The Scrotum*
Back Yard *The Anus*
Bare Back (Riding) *Sex Without A Condom*
Bathhouse *Sauna*
Bdsm (Generic) *Bondage/Discipline/Sado-Masochism*
Bear *Hairy And Usually Well-Built/Stocky Male*
Bestiality *Sex With Animals*
Beefcake *Hunky Male With Sex Appeal*
Bread Basket *The Bulge in A Male's Jeans, Trunks, Etc.*
Bisexual *Someone Who Is Sexually Attracted To Both Sexes*
Blind *An Uncircumcised Penis*
Blow *To Perform Oral Sex*
Blow Job *The Act of Oral Sex*
Blue Balls *Severe Need To Perform Sex*
Bnd *Boy Next Door*
Bottom *The Passive Partner in A Relationship (As Opposed To Top)*
Breeder *Heterosexual*
Bring off *Ejaculation in the Male*
Bronco *'Boy' Who Is Difficult To Restrain During Sex*
Brownie Queen *Passive Partner in Anal Intercourse*
Bugger *To Perform Anal Intercourse*
Buggery *The Act of Anal Intercourse*
Bull Dyke *Extremely Butch Lesbian*
Buns *The Buttocks*
Camp *Behave in An Effeminate Manner*
Candy Maker *A Woman or Man Who Masturbates A Male then Consumes the Ejaculated Semen*
Castration *To Render the Testicles Inoperable By Surgery*
Cbt *Cock And Ball Torture*
Cd *Cross-Dresser*
Change Your Luck *To Engage in A Gay Sex Act For the First Time*
Chaps *Crotchless (Usually Leather) Pants, Traditionally Worn By Cowboys To Protect their Jeans*
Cheat *To Be Unfaithful To Your Regular Sex Partner*
Chicken *A Young Attractive Male*
Chicken Hawk *Predatory Older Gay Male (Usually Mature)*
Circumcision *Removal of the Foreskin By Surgery*
Clap *Gonorrhoea or Other Venereal Disease*
Clone *Stereotype of the Gay Male Usually With Muir Cap, Leather Chaps And Moustache*
Closet *The 'Place' Where Gay People Are Said To Be Before they Come Out*

Closet Queen *A Gay Male Who Hides His Desires Towards Other Men*

Cock Ring *(Usually) A Band of Leather That Encircles the Penis And Scrotum Enabling You To Keep An Erection For Longer. It Is Also Used To Enhance Your Genitalia Through Clothing*

Cock Teaser *One Who Excites A Male Without Carrying On To Actual Sex*

Coitus *Sexual Intercourse*

Coitus Anno *Anal Intercourse*

Coitus Interuptus *Withdrawal of the Penis Prior To Ejaculation*

Come/Cum *To Achieve Sexual Orgasm/Semen*

Coming Out *Declaring/Confirming Your Sexuality*

Condom *Rubber Sheath Worn On the Penis*

Corona *Rim of Flesh That Forms the Base of the Head of the Penis*

Cottage *Public Convenience*

Cottaging *Using the Public Convenience For Sex/To Pick Up For Sex*

Crabs *Lice That Infect the Pubic Area of the Body*

Cruise *The Hunt For A Sex Partner*

Cs *Clean Shaven*

D&S *Dominance And Submission*

Daisy Chain *A Group Sex Activity in Which there Is A Linking of Several People By Oral And/Or Anal-Penis Connections*

Dental Dam *A Piece of Latex Placed Over the Anus Prior To Rimming To Prevent the Transmission of Disease*

Derriere *The Buttocks*

Diddle *To Perform Masturbation*

Dildo *An Artificial Penis*

Dinge Queen *Gay Man Who Prefers Black Sex Partners*

Dirt Box *The Anus*

Dog *An Unattractive Person*

Doggie Fashion *Sex Act Performed With the Passive Partner On Hands And Knees*

Dom *The Dominant Partner (As Opposed To Sub)*

Dominatrix *Woman Who Specialises in Sado Masochism*

Dose *Gonorrhoea or Other Venereal Disease*

Drag Queen *Male Who Dresses in Female Clothing (Usually A Stage Performer)*

Drag King *Female Who Dresses in Male Clothing (Predominantly A Stage Performer)*

Dry Fuck *Moving Against One Another Clothed*

Dyke *Lesbian (As Used By Lesbians – Derogatory Otherwise)*

Easy *A Person Who Needs Little Persuasion To Perform Sex*

Eat *To Perform Oral Sex*

Effeminate   *Description of Male Who Acts in A Feminine Manner*

Eunuch   *A Male Who Has Had His Testicles Removed*

Exhibitionist   *A Person Who Derives Sexual Pleasure By Displaying their Body To Others*

Faggot   *Gay Male (Derogatory)*

Fag Hag   *Woman Who Enjoys the Company of Gay Men*

Family Jewels   *Testicles*

Felching   *Consuming the Resultant Semen After Anal Sex*

Fellatio   *Stimulation of the Penis With the Mouth (Cocksucking)*

Fetish   *Any Object or Part of the Body Which Is Normally Considered Non-Sexual But Which Arouses Sexual Feelings (Rubber, Leather, Feet, Etc.)*

Fifth Wheel/Spare Wheel   *A Heterosexual in A Gay Group*

Fish   *Female*

Fisting   *Inserting A Whole Hand Into the Anus or Vagina*

Flagellation   *Whipping or Beating To Sexual Orgasm*

French   *To Perform Oral Sex*

Friend of Dorothy   *Gay Person*

Frottage   *Sexual Pleasure Derived From Rubbing Up Against Another Person*

Fruit   *Gay Male*

Full House   *Having More Than One Venereal Disease At the Same Time*

Gbf   *Gay Black Female*

Gbm   *Gay Black Male*

Gwf   *Gay White Female*

Gwm   *Gay White Male*

Gang Bang   *Group Sex/Where One Is Fucked Several Times By Many*

Gerbilling   *The Urban Myth Activity of Inserting A Gerbil or Other Small Rodent Into the Anus*

Get Your Rocks off   *Ejaculation*

Give Head   *To Perform Oral Sex*

Glory Hole   *An Opening Cut Into the Partition Separating Two Toilet Cubicles Through Which Oral Sex Can Be Performed*

Go Down On   *To Perform Oral Sex*

Golden Shower   *One Person Urinates On Another For Sexual Pleasure*

Goose   *To Press A Finger Into the Cleavage of the Backside*

Greek   *To Perform Anal Intercourse*

Handmade   *A Large Penis Usually Developed Through Masturbation*

Hermaphrodite   *Male or Female Who Has the Genatalia of the Opposite Sex (Either Whole or in Part)*

Heterosexual *One Who Desires Only Someone of the Opposite Sex*

Homophobe *Person Who Intensely Dislikes Homosexuals And/Or their Lifestyle*

Homosexual *One Who Desires Only Someone of the Same Sex*

Horny *Sexually Aroused/Passionate*

Horse Around *To Explore Sexually Without Engaging in Intercourse*

Hung *To Describe the Size of A Large Penis (I.E. Well-Hung)*

Hustler *Male Prostitute That Searches For Clients*

Impotent *Unable To Engage in Sexual Intercourse*

Incest *Sexual Relations Between Family Members*

Jack off/J.O. *To Masturbate*

J.O. Parties *Group Masturbation Parties*

Jail Bait *One Who Is Under the Legal Age of Consent*

Jerk off *To Masturbate*

John *One Who Financially Supports Another For Sexual Favours*

Kicks *Sexual Thrills*

Lace Curtains *The Foreskin*

Lavender *Pertaining To the Bisexual Lifestyle*

Lay *To Perform Sexual Intercourse*

Libido *Sexual Appetite*

Load *The Fluid From Ejaculation*

Lru (Generic) *Leather/Rubber/Uniform*

Lube *Lubricant*

Lunchbox *The Male Genitals*

Make Out *To Succeed Sexually*

Martha *The Passive Male Person (As Opposed To Arthur)*

Mary *An Effeminate Acting Male*

Masochism *Where Sexual Gratification Is Achieved By Pain*

Matinee *A Sex Session in the Afternoon*

Mba *Mutually Beneficial Arrangement*

Meat *The Penis*

Mons *Mound of Flesh Located Above the Vagina*

Muir Cap *Leather Peaked Cap With Chain Adornment (Popular With the Leather Clones of the 60S-70S)*

Narcissism *One Who Is Stimulated By their Own Body*

Nsm *Non-Smoker*

Old Dirt Road *Anal Intercourse (As in 'Going Up the Old Dirt Road')*

One Night Stand *A Sexual Affair Between Two or More People Who Will in All Probability Never See Each Other Again*

Orgasm *The Peak of Sexual Fulfilment*

Packet *The Bulge of A Male's Genitals*

Passive *The Receiver (As Opposed To Active)*

Pearl Diver *One Who Performs Oral Sex*

Pearl Necklace (To Give A) *To Ejaculate Over Your Partner's Chest/Face*

Pecker *The Penis*

Pederasty *Insertion of the Penis Into the Anus*

Peeping Tom *A Voyeur*

Perineum *The Area Between the Anus And the Testicles/Anus And Vagina*

Pick Up *Stranger Who Is Induced To Go Elsewhere For Sex (See Trade)*

Pink *Pertaining To the Gay Lifestyle*

Pink Pound *The Money Generated By the 'Gay Economy'*

Polari/Palari *'Gay Speak' Used in Order That Straights Could Not Understand What You Were On About, For Example: 'How Bona To Vada Your Eke (Nice To See You; Literally: How Good To See Your Face)*

Pt *Prick Teaser*

Pushover *Easily Persuaded To Engage in Sex*

Queen *An Effeminate Gay Man (Usually Mature)*

Queer *A Person Who Doesn't Identify As Being Heterosexual. It Used To Be A Derogatory Term, But Not So Much Nowadays*

Quickie *A Very Brief Sex Act*

Rim/Rimming *Using the Tongue To Stimulate the Anus*

Rubber *A Condom*

Sa/Sl *Straight Acting/Straight Looking (Used in Personal Ads To Denote 'Non-Camp' or 'Non-Effeminate')*

S&M / S/M *Sadism And Masochism/Sado-Masochism*

Sadism *Sexual Stimulation Associated With the Desire To Inflict Pain (Physical or Mental) On Another*

Sadomasochism *Both Sadism And Masochism Existing in the Same Person*

Safeword *The Code or Phrase Used in Any Sort of B&D/S&M Activity That Really Means 'Stop Now'*

Sea Food *A Sailor As A Sex Object*

Scat *Sex Involving Faeces*

Scene Queen *Gay Person Who Inhabits Gay Venues On A Regular Basis*

Size Queen *Someone Who Derides the Size of Another Mans Penis/ Someone Who Regards the Size of A Penis To Be An Important Facet of the Sexual Activity*

Sixty-Nine *Oral Sex Performed On Each Other Simultaneously*

Smegma *White Matter That Collects Under the Foreskin (Cheese)*

So *Significant Other*

Sodomy *Insertion of the Penis Into the Anus (Though the General Dictionary Definition Is 'Unnatural or Deviate Sexual Intercourse')*

Stallion *Male Who Possesses A Very Large Penis*

Straight *Heterosexual*

String of Pearls *Sperm On Upper Torso/Face*

Stud *A Male Who Is in Demand As A Sex Partner*

Sub *The Submissive Partner (As Opposed To Dom)*

Sugar Daddy *A Man Who Supports A Younger Person in Exchange For Sexual Favours*

Swinger *One Who Accepts Free Love Doctrine*

Swish/Swishy *A Male Who Behaves in An Effeminate Manner (Americanism For Camp)*

Switch Hitter *A Bisexual*

Tea Room *Public Convenience/Americanism For Cottage*

Third Sex *Homosexual*

Tom of Finland *Gay Artist Famous For His Black And White Images of Well-Endowed Men*

Top *The Active or Dominant Person in A Relationship (As Opposed To Bottom)*

Tourist *Closeted Gay Male (Usually Married) Who Irregularly Frequents the Gay Scene*

Trade *A Passive Male Prostitute Who Caters To Homosexuals/ General Usage For A Pick-Up*

Transvestite/Tv *An Individual Who Is Sexually or Emotionally Stimulated or Satisfied By Dressing in Clothing of the Opposite Sex*

Transsexual/Ts *A Person Who Has the Physical Characteristics of One Sex And the Psychological Characteristics of the Other*

Trick *A Sex Partner*

Turn A Trick *To Take On A Sex Partner For Money*

Ugg *Acronym For the Ultimate Gay Guide*

Uncut *An Uncircumcised Penis*

Urethra *The Duct That Runs From the Bladder To the Tip of the Penis*

Urolagnia *Sexual Pleasure Derived From Watching Another Drink Urine*

Vanilla Sex *Any Non-Kinky Sex Act/Very Tame Sex Act*

Voyeur *One Who Gains Sexual Satisfaction From Watching Others Undress or Engage in Sexual Acts*

Vulva *Collective Term Referring To A Woman's External Genitalia*

Watersports/W.S. *Sex Involving Urine or Urination*

W.E. *Well-Endowed/Large Penis*

Well-Hung *Well-Endowed/Large Penis*

X.X.W.E *Extremely Well-Endowed/Extra, Extra, Large Penis*

A-Z Reference Guide

The A-Z references have been used throughout this guide to further enhance the directional information for the establishments and areas listed. The majority of listings incorporate the A-Z reference. Those that don't (many of the cruising listings, for instance, which fall outside the boundaries of most A-Z guides) utilise the *nearest landmark* and *nearest train station* descriptives as a reference point. The list below then, details which cities and towns are covered by which guides. To find the reference for Walsall, for example, you would need to get your hands on the *Birmingham City Guide*.

Birmingham City Guide
Birmingham
Coventry
Darleston
Solihull
Stourbridge
Walsall
Wolverhampton

Blackpool Street Atlas
Blackpool
Lytham St Annes

Bournemouth Street Atlas
Bournemouth

Brighton & Worthing Street Atlas
Brighton
Hove
Rottingdean

Bristol & Bath City Guide
Bath
Bristol
Saltford

Cambridge Street Atlas
Cambridge

Cardiff & Newport Street Atlas
Cardiff

Cheltenham & Cloucester Street Atlas
Cheltenham

Chester Street Atlas
Chester

Derby Street Atlas
Derby

Edinburgh Street Atlas
Edinburgh

Exeter Street Atlas
Exeter

Glasgow City Guide
Glasgow
Motherwell

Hull Street Atlas
Hull

Kent Street Atlas
Chatham

Leeds & Bradford Street Atlas
Bradford
Leeds

Leicester Street Atlas
Leicester

Liverpool City Guide
Liverpool
Wallasey

London City Guide
London
Romford

Luton & Dunstable Street Atlas
Luton

Manchester City Guide
Ashton-under-Lyne
Bolton
Bury
Manchester
Oldham
Rochdale
Stockport
Worsley

**Newcastle upon Tyne
Street Atlas**
Blaydon on Tyne
Newcastle upon Tyne

Northampton Street Atlas
Northampton

Nottingham Street Atlas
Long Eaton

Norwich Street Atlas
Norwich

Oxford Street Atlas
Oxford

Peterborough Street Atlas
Peterborough

Plymouth Street Atlas
Plymouth

Sheffield Street Atlas
Barnsley
Chesterfield
Doncaster
Sheffield

Southampton Street Atlas
Southampton

Stoke-on-Trent Street Atlas
Hanley

Swansea Street Atlas
Swansea

Swindon Street Atlas
Swindon

Wakefield Street Atlas
Wakefield

A–Z by Establishment

A–Z by Town/City

Feedback Form

Ensure that the next edition of *The Ultimate Gay Guide* has everything you need–let me know your comments. The website will be operational from October 1999, with updated information and pages for you to post your comments to other readers. I need to know if there are establishments not listed that should be listed and I also need your feedback regarding those that are. Do you have any comments (praise, criticism, constructive alternatives) regarding these establishments? Have you an experience or case history that you wish to share? Your information could help others and absolute confidentiality is assured.

Website **http://www.absolutepress.demon.co.uk**

E-mail **ugg@ic24.net**

You can write too. Use this form or something bigger and send all correspondence to:

Ultimate Guides
PO Box 64
Manchester
M7 4NZ

Are there establishments not listed that should be?

Are there any sections that you would like to see included or enhanced in the next edition?

What do you think to the format of the guide?

Anything else?

Confidentiality assured. In all correspondence please state whether it is okay for you to receive a reply (replies cannot be guaranteed to all).

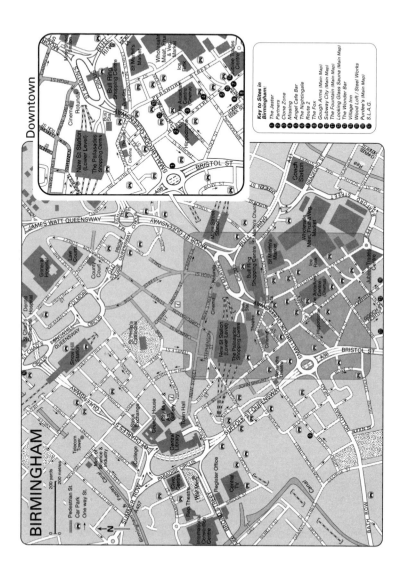

BIRMINGHAM

- Pedestrian St.
- Car Park
- One way St.
- K

200 yards
200 metres

N

Downtown

Key to Sites in Birmingham:

1. The Jester
2. Partners
3. Clone Zone
4. Missing
5. Angel Cafe Bar
6. The Nightingale
7. Route 2
8. The Fox
9. Gough Arms (Main Map)
10. Subway City (Main Map)
11. The Fountain (Main Map)
12. Looking Glass Sauna (Main Map)
13. Village Inn
14. The Wonder Bar
15. Wood Loft / Steel Works (Main Map)
16. Purdie's (Main Map)
17. S.L.A.G.

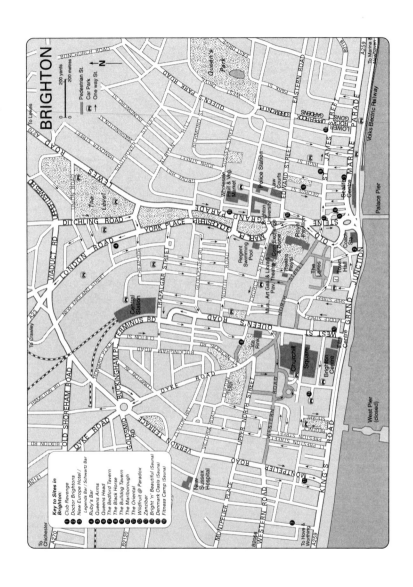

BRIGHTON

N

	0	200 yards
	0	200 metres

🅿 Pedestrian St.
🅿 Car Park
↑ One way St.

Key to Sites in Brighton:

1 Club Revenge
2 Doctor Brightons
3 New Europe Hotel /
  Legends Bar / Schwartz Bar
4 Ruby's Bar
5 Queens Arms
6 Queens Head
7 The Bedford Tavern
8 The Black Horse
9 The Bulldog Tavern
10 The Marlborough
11 The Oriental
12 Wildfruit @ Paradox
13 Zanzibar
14 Bright 'n' Beautiful (Sauna)
15 Denmark Oasis (Sauna)
16 Fitness Camp (Sauna)

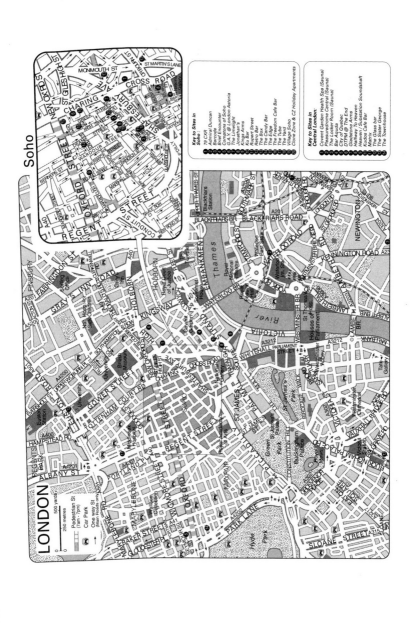

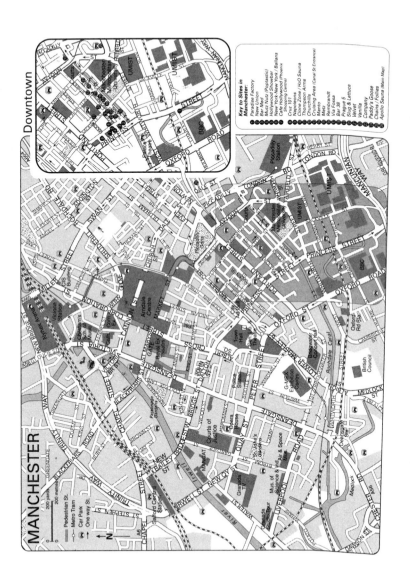

Downtown

MANCHESTER

Key to Sites in Manchester:

- Paradise Factory
- New Union
- Bar Med
- Mutz Nutz (Poptastic)
- Hollywood Showbar
- New York New York / Ballans
- Cafe Hollywood /Phoenix Shopping Centre)
- Cruz 101
- Napoleons
- Clone Zone / H2O Sauna
- Thompson Arms
- Churchills
- Cruising Area (Canal St Entrance)
- Manto
- Metz
- Rembrandt
- Via Fossa
- Bar 38
- Prague 5
- Slug & Lettuce
- Velvet
- Vanilla
- Company
- Paddy's Goose
- Chains / Follies
- Apollo Sauna (Main Map)

N

- - - Pedestrian St.
- - - Metro Tram
- P Car Park
- → One way St.

0 200 yards
0 200 metres